# Physiological Psychology

# THE DORSEY SERIES IN PSYCHOLOGY

EDITORIAL COMMITTEE

# Physiological Psychology

J. A. DEUTSCH
and
D. DEUTSCH
University of California, San Diego
La Jolla, California

With a chapter by I. P. Howard, University
of Durham, England, and a chapter by C. I.
Howarth, University of Nottingham, England.

1966

THE DORSEY PRESS · HOMEWOOD, ILLINOIS

First Printing, August, 1966

Library of Congress Catalog Card No. 66–24619

PRINTED IN THE UNITED STATES OF AMERICA

# PREFACE

Physiological psychology attempts to explain behavior in terms of underlying physiological mechanisms. Students interested in this area are either well-versed in biology, physiology, and anatomy or they are drawn to physiological psychology after a study of other branches of psychology. For the former class of students, introductory chapters on physiology can be dispensed with. On the other hand, students that have become interested in physiological psychology simply from a behavioral background are apt to become discouraged when they are faced with introductory chapters which seem unconnected with their interest. We have therefore planned the book so that the order of topics would maintain the student's original interest in psychology while allowing him to build on it when he, himself, sees the relevance. Accordingly, chapters on neurophysiology and anatomy have been placed at the end of the book, to be used by the student when his curiosity has been aroused by chapters in which lay his original interest.

J. A. DEUTSCH
D. DEUTSCH

La Jolla, California
*July, 1966*

# ACKNOWLEDGMENTS

Many friends have very kindly given their time to read and evaluate many of the chapters in this book. We thank especially Drs. Coons, Herberg, and Novin for their comments on the chapter, "Hunger and Thirst"; Dr. Whalen for his comments on the chapter, "Reproductive Behavior"; Drs. Chow, Howarth, McGaugh, and Morrell for their comments on the chapter on memory; Dr. Weinberger for his comments on the chapter, "Arousal, Sleep, and Attention"; Dr. Wenzel for her comments on the chapters on emotion; and Dr. Nowell Jones for his comments on the chapter, "Taste and Smell." The book as a whole was read by Dr. Eliot Stellar and Dr. H. F. Hunt. We are extremely grateful for their most helpful suggestions. One of us (J.A.D.) wrote the chapters, "Hunger and Thirst" (Ch. 1); "Reproductive Behavior" (Ch. 2); "Learning and Intracranial Self-stimulation" (Ch. 4); "The Physiological Bases of Memory and Learning" (Ch. 3); "Vision" (Ch. 11); and "Taste and Smell" (Ch. 12). The other (D.D.) wrote the chapters, "Arousal, Sleep, and Attention" (Ch. 5); "Emotion I" (Ch. 6); "Emotion II" (Ch. 7); "Peripheral Somesthetic Mechanisms" (Ch. 8); and "Central Pathways for the Skin Senses" (Ch. 9). The chapters, "Hearing" (Ch. 10) and "The Nervous System" (Ch. 15) were written jointly by the two of us.

We also wish to thank Dr. C. I. Howarth and Dr. I. P. Howard for their contributions to the book (Chapters 13 and 14). And we are grateful to Kenneth Rocklin, Jonathan Stone, and especially to Richard Kestenbaum for their help in compiling the references and illustrations.

# TABLE OF CONTENTS

# 1

# HUNGER AND THIRST

People and animals usually become hungry or thirsty when they have not had anything to eat or drink for some time. When food or water is then made available, they will usually not only consume the appropriate substances but also ingest them in the right amount. In this way they are able to maintain themselves in good health, and regulate their body weight within close limits. What is known of the mechanism which accomplishes the quantitative regulation of eating and drinking will be the subject of the first section of this chapter. In the second section we shall discuss the way in which qualitative regulation is carried out; that is, how in response to its bodily needs, an animal selects its diet from among the many substances in its environment.

We shall begin by considering how a shortage of food or water is translated by the body and the nervous system into the actions of eating or drinking.

## The Nature of the Initiating Physiological Change in Thirst

Though we usually drink when we are short of water, water loss in itself is not the immediate cause of drinking. Thirst may occur when there is no decrease in total body volume of water. For instance, an injection of hypertonic saline will produce a strong thirst. Further, depletion of water may occur under some circumstances without producing thirst. Darrow and Yannet (1935) report that dogs lacking in water and also salt-depleted showed no thirst. One interpretation of this finding is that salt depletion had lowered the effective concentration and consequently the osmotic pressure of the extracellular fluids. Therefore, there was no withdrawal of intracellular water, even though there had been a total water loss which under normal conditions would have been sufficient to withdraw water from inside the cells. An alternative hypothesis is that there has to be an increase in salt concentration in the whole body before thirst can occur.

However, Gilman (1937) made it clear that thirst is not merely a reflexion of the hypertonicity of the whole body system but that thirst is caused by the withdrawal of water from inside the body cells. He produced equal increments of osmotic pressure in dogs by injecting urea or sodium chloride. He found that drinking was greater after saline injections than after urea injections. It is known that urea passes easily through cell membranes whereas sodium chloride does not. As a result there would be very little alteration in the relative osmotic pressure gradient between the intra- and extracellular fluid after injecting urea, but a great deal of change in this gradient after injecting sodium chloride. Hence the sodium chloride would act to withdraw water from inside the body cells into the extracellular fluid until the osmotic pressures inside and outside the cell were more nearly equal.

This mechanism of the initiation of thirst has an interesting though paradoxical practical consequence. Dill (1938) reported that the loss of equal amounts of water through perspiration produced unequal amounts of thirst depending on whether this loss occurred in men who are acclimatized or unacclimatized to heat. Men that were unacclimatized felt less thirst after they had lost a given amount of water through perspiration than men who were acclimatized. The reason for this is that men who were not acclimatized lost more salt in an equal volume of sweat than men who were acclimatized. As a result there was more increase in extracellular osmotic pressure where more salt was retained per unit of water excreted as sweat (that is in the acclimatized man, whose sweat is less salty).

Further evidence for the osmometric theory of the genesis of thirst is provided by another experiment of Darrow and Yannet (1935). If thirst is the consequence of the effective osmotic pressure of extracellular fluids on the body cells, but not of total water loss, then relative dehydration of the extracellular fluids should not produce thirst provided that water is not withdrawn from inside cells. This was achieved by the intraperitoneal injection in dogs of 5 percent glucose. After this solution had made its way into the cells, the investigators withdrew an equivalent volume of fluid from each animal. As a result, though the tongue and mucous membranes of the mouth became dry, the animals did not display any signs of thirst. Sufficient water from the glucose solution had entered the body cells.

However, there is now some doubt whether a simple increase in extracellular osmotic pressure is the only cause of drinking. Fitzsimons (1961) found that simple decrease in fluid volume, such as that caused by bleeding, can also induce drinking. Experimenting with rats, Fitzsimons (1961) compared drinking induced by bleeding with that induced by an injection of sodium chloride. Onset of drinking was immediate in the chloride-treated group; in the other group there was no drinking in the first half hour. However the total amount of drinking during six hours was much smaller in the rats treated with sodium chloride. This would suggest that some further mediating change occurs when there is isotonic volume depletion.

There are other cases in which increased drinking does not follow the relation to be expected on the hypothesis that extracellular osmotic pressure is the cause of drinking. For instance, there is often overdrinking in animals that are salt-depleted (in contrast with Darrow and Yannet's findings). Such overdrinking occurs not at the onset of salt depletion but only after some time has elapsed, according to Holmes' (1960) summary of the evidence.

## The Nature of the Initiating Change in Hunger

The precise change, or changes, which act to initiate and maintain hunger have not been discovered. However a number of theories have been proposed, each with some evidence to support it. One of the reasons why changes occasioning hunger have been difficult to pinpoint is that most theories have assumed that hunger is due to the presence of a physiological state and satiation is due to its absence. However, as we shall see, satiation seems to occur before the removal of a state of bodily depletion. Therefore it seems that there are two factors involved in hunger: the first to initiate it, and the second to switch it off, independently of the continuance of the first. A further difficulty in deciding what changes produce hunger is that there are many different types of hunger, each mirroring deficiencies in various components of the diet. Each type of hunger will probably have its own special factors which act to start it and other factors which will signal that enough of a particular substance has been ingested.

Various theories of the physical changes producing hunger have been advanced. The three most prominent are the thermostatic theory of Brobeck, the glucostatic theory of Mayer, and the lipostatic theory of Kennedy.

### The Thermostatic Theory

Brobeck (1948) proposed that "animals eat to keep warm, and stop eating to prevent hyperthermia." It can be shown that body temperature rises after the ingestion of food, the amount of rise differing with various dietary constituents. This propensity to cause an increase in temperature is called the "specific dynamic action" of a food. In support of the hypothesis that eating is regulated by body temperature is the fact that eating is depressed by high temperatures and enhanced by low temperatures. Secondly, foods with a high specific dynamic action such as proteins have a high value in producing satiety but foods with a low specific dynamic action are not as effective in producing satiation.

Kennedy (1953) has objected to the thermostatic hypothesis since animals which are fed on a fat diet should become obese, which is not the case. Animals should also be food satiated by exercise, which raises body temperature by a far greater amount than does the ingestion of food.

An experiment which supports the thermostatic theory is reported by Andersson and Larsson (1961). They found that local cooling in the preoptic area and rostral hypothalamus induces eating in the satiated goat. On the other hand warming of the same area produces drinking and inhibits eating. Cooling also inhibits drinking. However, the shifts in temperature used to obtain these effects seem very large. Further, ablation of the area which causes alterations of intake with changes in temperature did not seem to cause abnormalities of food intake. The only result of the lesion was that the goat would eat at body temperatures at which normal goats will not eat and that the lesioned goat would not drink more at temperatures which elevate drinking in normal goats. Excessive eating would be expected on the thermostatic hypothesis. It is reasonable to conclude that temperature can affect eating and drinking in the normal animal, but that it is not the main or exclusive regulator of hunger.

### The Glucostatic Theory

Mayer (1953) has suggested that hunger occurs when glucose is unavailable for metabolic purposes and satiation supervenes when glucose is made available. One measure of the availability of glucose which has been suggested is the absolute level of glucose (Carlson, 1916) but this suggestion has been rejected (Mayer, 1955). Another purposed measure is the arteriovenous glucose difference. If there is no difference between the arterial and venous content of glucose, then no glucose is being taken up by the tissues en route between the arteries and the veins. The available glucose is therefore zero. If, on the other hand, there is a large difference, this must be due to the fact that glucose is being taken out by the tissues. Correlations between arteriovenous glucose differences and hunger have been demonstrated by Stunkard et al. (1955). Furthermore, Herberg (1960) has shown that minute injections of glucose into the ventricles of a rat depress food intake. Further discussion of this theory will be given when we consider factors producing satiation.

### The Lipostatic Theory

Kennedy (1953) has suggested that an animal is in some way sensitive to the overall fat stored in its body, perhaps through biochemical alterations which occur in the contents of its circulation as its fat depots enlarge. It is evident that some explanation must be given of the fact that an animal is capable of long-term regulation of its weight, which would be difficult to account for on the thermostatic or glucostatic theories. For instance, rats which have been artificially fattened, rapidly lose weight and

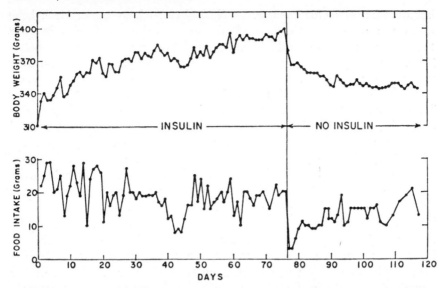

FIG. 1–1. A normal rat, made obese by insulin injections, allows its weight to return to a normal level when injections are discontinued. The top graph gives changes in weight, the lower graph, changes in food intake. (From Teitelbaum, P., *Excerpta Medica*, No. 47, 1962, p. 700.)

reach their previous size when allowed to regulate their own weight unhindered (Teitelbaum, 1962, Figure 1–1).

## The Locus of Action of Initiating Changes in Hunger and Thirst

### 1. *The Peripheral View*

In the preceding sections we have considered some of the facts and theories about the changes which produce hunger and thirst. We shall now inquire as to where these changes act, or are translated into neural activity. This again has been the subject of various theories. Historically the most important theories can be classified into two general hypotheses: the peripheral and the central. The peripheral theory holds that the initiating change acts on some peripheral organ or structure in such a way as to cause this organ to produce stimuli which are then relayed to the central nervous system. Thirst is, on this theory, explained as being due to dryness of the mouth and throat, and hunger as due to contractions of the stomach. It seems the proponents (Cannon, 1932; Carlson, 1916) of such theories sought to state what it was that we felt when we felt thirst or hunger. They sought to link the introspectible contents of consciousness to events in the afferent pathway conveying signals from peripheral structures. However, the question of what sensations we feel when we are thirsty is different from the question of how organisms regulate the amount they drink. This last question concerns us now. Psychologists, such as C. L. Hull, have taken the peripheral theory and attempted to make it a part of a behavioristic theory of food and water regulation, treating hunger contractions, for instance, as the origin of the stimuli which lead to eating responses in the animal.

Whether the peripheral theory is treated as a statement about our feelings or about our regulatory mechanisms, considerable evidence exists disproving it. Observations which seemed to support the theory attempted to show a correlation between subjective reports of hunger and the peripheral events thought to accompany these reports. For instance, Cannon and Washburn (1912) performed an experiment in which the amount of stomach contraction of a man was shown to correlate with subjective reports of hunger. The technique used to demonstrate this was interesting. A subject swallowed a balloon attached to a tube. When the balloon reached the stomach, it was inflated through the tube attached to it, and variations in the pressure on the balloon were recorded on a kymograph. The subject was asked simultaneously to signal when he felt hungry. The authors found that in general reports of hunger were accompanied by stomach contractions. However, Davis *et al.* (1959) have shown that this result was an artifact of the insertion of a balloon into an empty stomach. The stomach contractions reported during hunger were caused by the inflated balloon. Otherwise if the stomach was left empty while the subject was hungry there was less activity in the stomach than when the subject had eaten, and there was no correlation between any activity of the stomach and reports of hunger.

Further, it has been possible to obtain dissociations between the peripheral changes thought to cause hunger or thirst and the phenomena of successful and normal regulation of food or water intake, throwing strong doubt on the peripheral theory. For instance, it has been shown that the removal or absence of structures from which the peripheral impulses arise does not produce an absence of hunger, as might be expected on the peripheral theory. Sometimes it is necessary in human patients to intervene surgically by removing the stomach, or large parts of it. Yet such patients continue to display the usual symptoms of hunger. Wangensteen and Carlson (1931) report a case of this type (complete gastrectomy) in which the patient emphatically maintained that the sensation of hunger was unchanged after the operation. To make sure that the intestine had not begun to behave as the stomach did normally, a recording balloon was inserted into the intestine as in the experiment of Cannon and Washburn (quoted above). Contractions similar to those of the stomach were not apparent. Parallel results were obtained on animal subjects by Tsang (1938) and Bash (1939). Animals with their stomachs excised still showed hunger and appeared to be normally motivated for food. Secondly, intensification of the peripheral changes thought to be the basis of thirst has not produced the effects expected on the peripheral theory. Austin and

Steggerda (1936) and Steggerda (1941) report the case of a young man who apparently had a congenital absence of salivary glands. Consequently, the mucous membranes of his mouth were always dry. (There was however some mucinous secretion from other glands from under the tongue and inside the cheeks.) This man's fluid intake was measured over 18 days and compared with that of four normal subjects. His total water intake was no different, although he did take a small amount (about 60 cc.) of water nearly every hour to relieve the discomfort due to the dryness of his mouth. Zaus (1936) reported the case of a ten-year-old child with a similar abnormality where no excessive drinking was present. Therefore the prediction from the dry mouth or peripheral theory of thirst is not borne out.

Experiments on dogs with extirpated salivary glands have also been undertaken (Montgomery, 1931). No increase in average daily water intake was observed in these animals. Though the mucous membranes of the mouth remained moist due to secretions from other glands in the region of the mouth and throat, such secretions were much more viscid and it seems reasonable to suppose that the mouths of these dogs were drier than those of normal controls.

Many experiments have been performed which attempt to manipulate the peripheral state of the animal by pharmacological means. For instance, pilocarpine has been administered because it greatly promotes salivary flow. It was predicted on the peripheral theory that this should reduce drinking since the mouth should be less dry than normal. However, such experiments present a methodological difficulty since this drug also has various central actions which make its effect difficult to interpret. Montgomery (1931) showed that pilocarpine reduced water intake in dogs irrespective of whether they had their salivary glands removed or not. Thus the fact that pilocarpine increases salivary flow appears irrelevant.

In the light of the above evidence it seems that peripheral stimuli are better viewed as the concomitants rather than causes of the initiation of hunger and thirst.

## 2. The Central View

*Thirst.* A second view of the locus of action of physiological changes has been put forward. According to this view, the physiological changes initiating hunger and thirst act directly on circumscribed sites in the central nervous system. Recent experimental evidence lends strong support to such a view. Andersson and McCann (1955) showed that microinjections (0.003 to 0.01 cc.) of 2 to 3 percent sodium chloride into a circumscribed region of the hypothalamus of unanaesthetized goats induced drinking of water. Such drinking lasted from 2 to 5 minutes and began 30 to 60 seconds after the injection. Miller (1957) reported that injections of 0.15 cc. of 2 percent sodium chloride into the third ventricle of a cat produced drinking. An injection of isotonic saline in the same place produced no effect whereas a similar injection of distilled water actually reduced drinking. Miller (1961) reported that an injection of similarly small quantities of sodium chloride caused cats to perform a learned response of working for water and an injection of distilled water produced the reverse effect. Herberg (1962) obtained a similar result with rats. When rats were given a minute injection of hypertonic saline into a cannula implanted in the lateral ventricle, they almost immediately rushed towards the spout of the water bottle for a drink.

The very small amounts of hypertonic saline needed to produce drinking when injected either into the hypothalamus or into the ventricles suggest that there are structures in the hypothalamus highly sensitive to changes in osmotic pressure and that the stimulation of these structures is ultimately connected with the onset and maintenance of drinking behavior.

Electrical stimulation in such structures has also produced drinking. In a study by Andersson and McCann (1955), electrical stimulation initiated drinking within 10 to 30 seconds, and drinking stopped within 2 or 3 seconds after the current had been switched off. Overdrinking of up to 40 percent of body weight could be provoked. This mode of eliciting drinking did not lose its efficacy as swiftly as did microinjection. Greer (1955) also evoked drinking by electrical stimulation It has further been observed that drinking produced by stimulation of hypothalamic structures will extend to the ingestion of liquids which are normally distasteful to the animal, and that under such stimulation the animal will seek out sources of water which it has previously discovered. Further, if drinking is induced by stimulating an area containing structures which transform humoral changes into neural activity, then its destruction should lead to a cessation of drinking. Andersson and McCann (1955, 1956) have shown this to be the case. By electrolytically damaging the areas which upon stimulation produced thirst, a partial or complete loss of thirst was produced, with the degree of thirst depending upon the extent of the lesion.

It could be argued that in the foregoing experiments only the coordinated acts of drinking were induced or abolished, and that the structures in which drinking, as a reflexion of thirst, originated were not implicated. It should be stressed, however, that physiological stimuli were used which resembled those causing thirst (hypertonicity of extracellular fluids), and that animals sought out sources of water which they had previously discovered. Further evidence can be produced from the extirpation studies quoted above. Though dogs which had been operated on would not drink water, they readily drank such fluids as milk or broth when hungry. This shows that the motor act of drinking itself was preserved.

Clinical evidence suggests a similar central mechanism in man. For example, Kourilsky (1950) reported the case of a young woman with an arachnoid cyst in the hypothalamic region who suffered from excessive thirst. A sudden lowering of pressure, due to the incision of the cyst at operation, caused a sudden diminution of thirst which had been intense before and during the operation. Her water intake after the operation became normal.

Fisher and Coury (1962) were able to elicit drinking in rats by implants of carbachol (a cholinergic drug) in the septal region, anterior nucleus of the thalamus, the cingulate gyrus, and the lateral hypothalamus. Spread of the drug through the vascular or ventricular systems was not determined.

*Hunger.* Similar results have been obtained linking hunger to central structures as described above in the case of thirst. For instance Anand and his coworkers (1951, 1955, 1961) found that bilateral extirpation of the lateral region of the hypothalamus produced aphagia, i.e., a complete cessation of eating without any other apparent abnormality. Unilateral lesions had no effect on eating. Animals with bilateral lesions made no attempt to eat in the presence of food even though they were dying through lack of nourishment. Similar effects were later shown in cats and monkeys by Anand, Dua, and Shoenberg (1955). However, their effects are not as simple as was first thought. Animals with lesions of the lateral hypothalamus could, as Teitelbaum (1961) has shown, be nursed back so as to "escape" their loss of hunger and of thirst. Teitelbaum and Epstein (1962) have made a careful analysis of this recovery process. Adipsia may be the primary deficit in animals with these lesions. However, it seems that the lesions produced no simple loss of an urge to drink, but rather what seems like an actual aversion to rehydration. For instance, Williams and Teitelbaum (1959) found that animals with these lesions would not drink to avoid shock until the shock was made very strong. By using a technique showing that a normal rat can be taught to hydrate itself by pumping water directly into its own stomach, Epstein (1960) found that rats with lateral hypothalamic lesions did not learn this procedure, even though their learning ability was unimpaired. Further evidence that the lateral hypothalamus contains a mixture of pathways—some of them concerned with eating and drinking—has been reported by Grossman (1960). He found that by injecting minute amounts of carbachol (a cholinergic drug) into the lateral hypothalamus with an implanted hypodermic needle, drinking was produced; while similar injections of epinephrine or norepinephrine injected through the same needle produced increased eating. Studies by Miller (1965) using other pharmacological agents than those just mentioned, confirm the notion that an adrenergic system is involved in eating and that a cholinergic system produces drinking. It therefore appears that the pathways mediating eating and drinking have different transmitter substances.

Electrical, as well as biochemical, stimulation of the lateral hypothalamus can also produce marked increase in eating (Coons *et al.*, 1965,

Figure 1–2). To produce an effect, the electrical stimulation, in contrast
with lesions, need only be unilateral (Delgado and Anand, 1953; Anand
and Dua, 1955). Wyrwicka *et al.* (1959) have shown that food-getting
habits could be elicited with hunger induced by electrical stimulation.
They trained normally hungry goats to place their left foreleg on a food

FIG. 1–2. Bar-pressing for food, motivated by lateral hypothalamic
stimulation. Two bars were available, but only one produced a food reward.
The rats quickly learned to reverse their choice of a bar, depending on which
bar produced a reward. Except where the baseline is marked 100% to indicate
that every response was rewarded, the reinforcement was on a variable interval
fifteen second schedule. Each reversal of rewarded bar was preceded by extinction for rat I but not for rats II and III. (From Coons, E. E., *et al.*, *Science*, Vol. 150 No. 3701, December, 1965, p. 1321. Copyright 1965 by the
American Association for the Advancement of Science.)

tray to obtain a reward of oats. Even though the goats were satiated, the
same habit could then be evoked when lateral hypothalamic stimulation
was turned on. Such an evocation was not that of some automatism,
because when the reward of oats for the action was discontinued, the habit
dropped out as if extinction of the response had taken place, even though
electrical stimulation continued. The time course of such extinction of the
habit followed very closely the time course and characteristics of extinction
under normal conditions of hunger. When reward was again introduced,

goats stimulated in this way relearned after extinction had taken place. On the other hand, when the electrical stimulation was discontinued, disappearance of the learned response was very rapid, though reward was not withdrawn. Only one or two movements appeared after the discontinuation of stimulation.

Stimulation by the biochemical means normally responsible for hunger has not been performed, since the precise biochemical change or changes which give rise to hunger have not been established. Until such an effect of stimulation by microinjections in the lateral hypothalamus has been demonstrated, as in the case of thirst, an essential element will be lacking in the argument that the lateral hypothalamus is the structure translating into neural activity the biochemical change or changes that cause hunger. Though it seems extremely likely that the lateral region of the hypothalamus is the area where certain biochemical changes initiate eating and food-seeking behavior, it would be desirable to have all the kinds of evidence for this hypothesis as are available for the case of thirst. Otherwise it is possible that these structures merely involve the pathway from the structure initiating hunger, rather than the initiating locus itself.

Eating has been evoked by stimulation of other loci beside the lateral hypothalamus. Robinson and Mishkin (1962) experimented with rhesus monkeys and in a small percentage of the animals were able to evoke eating by stimulation from such areas as the anterior cingulate gyrus and the midline thalamus.

## Theories of the Regulation of Amount Eaten or Drunk

An important question to be considered is what kind of control system regulates eating or drinking. To answer such a question it is not of primary importance to know where the component parts of such a system reside or to what precise biochemical changes they respond. The important consideration in such a theoretical approach is the nature of the interrelations of the components of which the control system is made.

### The Simple Homeostat View

It has been a frequent and general assumption that eating or drinking continues as long as the change which induced this eating or drinking is in operation. The view that the activity of ingestion is coterminous with the change which evokes it can be called the simple homeostat view because it suggests a system of the same form as that which can be found in simple regulatory devices such as a thermostat. In this device, when the temperature of the environment falls below a certain point, a thermometer switches on a heater. As soon as the temperature rises above this point, the heat is again switched off. An analogous system can be proposed for eating and drinking: The onset of eating and drinking is controlled by a change in some body constituent (which has its parallel in a fall in temperature in the example of the thermostat) which at a certain point switches on the eating or drinking activity, via some structure which is sensitive to this change (paralleled by the thermometer). This activity then continues as long as the sensitive structure is being affected, and ceases as soon as the change which acted on the sensitive structure is reversed.

Such a scheme was suggested in essence by C. L. Hull. He assumed that when a drive (of which hunger and thirst are instances) acts on an organism, a physiological state generates afferent impulses (or stimuli), which in turn evoke relevant responses (e.g., eating in response to the drive stimuli of hunger). In time such responses reverse the change which evoked the stimuli, with the consequence that the organism stops eating. (Hull also believed that by the operation of other mechanisms the animal's overall behavior could be modified by learning.) Hull thought that the drive stimuli generated by a particular physiological deficit originated from peripheral structures. The drive stimuli of hunger were identified with afferent impulses from the stomach when it was contracting, and the drive stimuli of thirst were posited to be afferent impulses arising from a dry throat. Though this suggested peripheral locus of the origin of drive stimuli would doubtlessly be modified by Hull today since it is not essential to his theory, the character of his theory as a simple homeostat view would not be affected by this change.

Whether or not such a simple homeostat model is correct in the case of hunger and thirst can be determined by observations on the behavior of animals when they are eating or drinking. One test of the hypothesis is to see whether the change which initiates eating or drinking must be reversed before ingestion will stop.

## The Relation between the Initiating Change and Cessation of Ingestion

### Thirst

1. *Evidence from Preloads.*  Do animals stop drinking before the deficit which instigated their drinking is replenished? One method of finding out is to compare the time they normally take to drink with the time it takes for the physiological instigating change to be reversed. The time to reversal of such a change can be most directly assessed by placing water directly in the animal's stomach (or preloading). Then after various time intervals, water is offered to the animal to drink. If the time it takes to suppress drinking after a preload is longer than the time the animal normally spends in drinking the same amount, we can safely conclude that the normal inhibition of drinking is not due to the absorption of water by the system. Bellows (1939) has shown that a dog can drink just over 10 percent of its

body weight in 4 minutes, and that it takes 15 minutes after a preload of about 8 percent of body weight is placed directly into the dog's stomach before drinking is inhibited. This result indicates that drinking ceases long before the initiating change is reversed.

Towbin (1949), however, reported that drinking is considerably reduced after a preload of water even when drinking is allowed to occur just after such a preload. However, such immediate inhibition in Towbin's experiment was not due to water absorption or to a reversal of the initiating change, because he obtained similar results on immediate inhibition of drinking by injecting air into the stomach or by inflating a balloon in the stomach.

This conflict of evidence is probably due to the fact that Towbin's technique caused nausea due to stomach distention. Miller and Kessen (1954) have shown that rapid distention of the stomach, though it causes cessation of ingestion, can also be aversive. This is inconsistent with the notion that thirst is removed by the stomach distention procedure. In Miller and Kessen's experiment, rats were given a choice between two goal boxes in a T-maze. In one goal box a balloon was inflated in their stomachs. Though such an inflation of the balloon apparently satiated them, they learned to avoid the goal box in which the balloon was inflated. It seems that the rate of water injection is important; if it is too high, nausea will result.

On the other hand if water injection is too slow, especially in a small animal such as the rat where rate of absorption is high, such an experiment may run into another difficulty because there will be a reversal of the initiating change. Miller, Sampliner, and Woodrow (1957) obtained results which apparently showed the inhibitory nature of injecting water into the stomach of a rat, even though extreme care was taken not to inject water at a rate which might produce nausea. Water was injected through a chronically implanted stomach fistula at the rate of 1 cc. each 50 seconds, which is the rat's normal rate of drinking. All in all, 14 cc. of water were inserted into the stomach prior to the tests which consisted of bar-pressing for a reward of water and of ad libitum drinking from a graduated cylinder. An immediate and considerable inhibition of thirst occurred as a result of this preloading procedure.

However, in the case of such a small animal as the rat, where the surface area of the stomach is high in relation to its volume, the rate of dilution of body fluids is probably so high that it may have taken place almost entirely during the 12 minutes when water was being slowly injected. By monitoring changes in conductance (a measure of the concentration of body fluids) while a rat drinks, Novin (1962) was able to show a considerable diminution of body fluid tonicity within the first 12 minutes after drinking began. In summary, it appears that when the technique of preload is used in experiments on the shutoff of drinking, the results are not completely conclusive. The most likely evaluation of the evidence favors the view that absorption factors are not normally responsible for the cessation of drinking.

2. *Evidence from Use of Esophageal Fistulae.* Whether or not postingestional reversal of the initiating change stops drinking can also be determined by letting an animal drink while preventing water from reaching its stomach. This is achieved by transecting the esophagus so that as the animal drinks the water emerges from an aperture in its neck. This procedure of sham drinking was utilized by Bellows (1939), Adolph (1941), and Towbin (1949) in experiments on dogs. It seems clear from their results that the animal does not continue to drink until exhaustion supervenes, but stops when it has drunk an amount proportionate to its deficit, as calculated by the experimenter. This supports the idea that inhibition of drinking occurs through factors other than the reversal of the initiating deficit. However, one difficulty from this conclusion is that both Bellows and Towbin calculate that dogs will drink anywhere from 155 percent to 250 percent of their deficit before stopping for five minutes. Such figures are not necessarily accurate as it is difficult to know how much such dogs would have drunk without the esophageal fistula. Towbin, for instance, attempted to calculate the dogs' deficit in the following way. He assumed the deficit to be the least amount of water which when placed directly in the stomach produced an absence of drinking after it had been left in the stomach for an hour (a sufficient time for absorption). However it is known that a dog will only begin to drink when it has lost 0.4 percent of its body weight in water (Robinson and Adolph, 1943). So if Towbin inserted an amount of water into the stomach which would bring the deficit of water below the 0.4 percent mark, then the dog would not start drinking. However, if instead of inserting water into the stomach he had allowed the dog to drink, it would have drunk until its deficit of water was completely reversed. It seems therefore that this method of calculating the amount of water which the animal would have drunk under normal circumstances could produce a very considerable underestimate. Therefore, Towbin's figure of 250 percent overdrinking when the esophagus is transected is probably a considerable overestimate. Adolph's (1941) figures are more likely to be correct. He used deficit of body weight as an estimate of how much the dog with an esophageal fistula should drink, and on this basis, he found that the amount drunk was almost equal to such a deficit.

As can be seen, most of the conclusions concerning the causes of drinking cessation are based on somewhat circuitous arguments resulting from experiments employing techniques that are difficult to interpret. The technique of esophageal fistulation by transecting the esophagus may destroy some of the metering devices which are important in regulating drinking. Further, animals cannot eat their normal diet after such an operation, and in the author's experience, they are essentially sick animals. The technique of preloading the animal's stomach produces critical delays and so absorption of the preload, and it also complicates interpretation because stomach distention is abnormal.

3. *Evidence from Counterinjection.* In order to overcome such difficulties of intepretation, another type of approach was devised by Deutsch and Blumen (1962). One end of a tube was sewn into a rat's stomach and the other end was threaded under the skin, protruding between the ears. As the animal drinks, each lick actuates a pump electronically. This pump drives two syringes. One of these syringes delivers an amount of fluid to the rat's tongue. This amount of fluid is adjusted to be the same as that which the rat obtains by a single lick of a tube from which it normally obtains its water. The other syringe is connected to the tube going into the animal's stomach. This second syringe can be filled with saline of such a concentration as to produce isotonic saline when mixed in the animal's stomach with the water arriving from the other syringe via the mouth and then the esophagus. Only a small amount of the hypertonic solution need be injected if it is sufficiently concentrated. Therefore we can prevent an animal from deriving the normal physiological consequences received from drinking and tasting water, and the animal will in fact derive no short-term physiological reversal of the change which initiated drinking. On the other hand, outside the experimental situation the animal eats and drinks normally, remains healthy, and frequently gains weight. Using this method, one can study the effects of varying the taste of the fluid drunk while maintaining stomach tonicity, and one can also vary the stomach tonicity while maintaining taste factors. By determining the differences in the time course of drinking under these conditions, the relative importance of sensory and absorption factors in the slaking of normal thirst can be assessed.

Rats with a stomach tube inserted were tested under three conditions: (1) when they were tasting water and water was counterinjected into the stomach, (2) when they were tasting water and the hypertonic saline was counterinjected so that isotonic saline would result from the mixture in the stomach, and (3) when they were tasting hypotonic saline (0.6 percent saline) and the resulting mixture due to the counterinjection of hypertonic saline was again isotonic saline. The volume counterinjected in each of these three conditions was in the same proportion to the volume drunk in all three conditions.

The main results of the experiment are clear (see Figure 1–3). When the rat is tasting water, irrespective of what is arriving in its stomach, drinking stops after about 15 minutes (when the rat has been thirsty for 22 hours). Futhermore, as shown by the curves of intake over time, the time course of drinking is the same, irrespective of what is arriving in the rat's stomach when it is tasting water, over the period during which the rat makes up its normal deficit. However, if the normal physiological consequences do not follow, then the rat will resume drinking. On the other hand, a rat tasting 0.6 percent saline will exhibit a time course of drinking

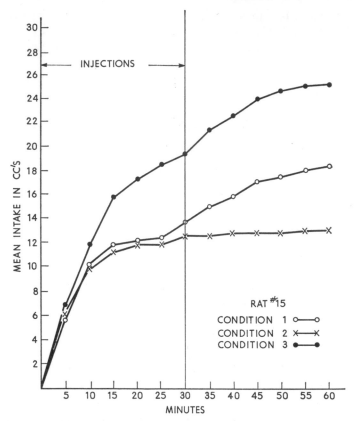

**FIG. 1–3.** Cumulative records at a rat drinking during counterinjection. The three conditions are explained in the text.

which is very different from that of a rat tasting water but receiving the same isotonic mixture in its stomach, showing again that taste factors are very important.

The experiments reviewed above bring out two points. First, it seems that placing water in the rat's stomach does not relieve thirst immediately but only after a period of time. This effect appears to work by reversing the change which initiates thirst. Second, there are factors which terminate drinking without the reversal of the initiating change which produces drinking. These factors seem to produce cessation of drinking in the normal case. Therefore, the simple homeostat theory of thirst cannot account for the data on drinking, though it does appear to contain a part of the truth when we consider the long-term effect of placing water in the stomach.

## Hunger

Experiments similar to those discussed have been carried out in the study of hunger but with different results. Food was placed directly in the stomach (Kohn, 1951; Berkun, Miller, and Kessen, 1952) and found to produce almost immediate satiation, even though explanations in terms of nausea can be excluded. Kohn (1951) measured the frequency of response in a Skinner box. He found that rate of lever-pressing in this apparatus declined after stomach injection of food. Berkun *et al.* (1952) measured the amount actually ingested by the rats after food had been placed in the stomach. There was a decrease in eating which could not be accounted for by a reversal of the physiological change which had initiated eating. It is unlikely that digestion of the inserted food could have taken place to a significant extent in the time allowed. Further, normal ingestion by mouth of the same amount of food as was injected directly into the stomach led to an even greater depression of eating, pointing to an effect of gustatory factors in satiation.

Smith and Duffy (1955) attempted to discover in more detail factors involved in this phenomenon of satiation through direct injection into the stomach. The question posed by Kohn's and Berkun, Miller, and Kessen's results was what aspects such as sheer bulk or nutritive properties of the injected substance produced satiation. Accordingly, Smith and Duffy trained rats in a Skinner box on an aperiodic reinforcement schedule to obtain food when they were hungry. After training was completed, they used a stomach tube to fill the rats' stomachs with various substances in order to determine the effect on the rate of subsequent bar-pressing.

Smith and Duffy's first experiment was similar to Kohn's. They injected three different substances—10 cc. of isotonic saline, 10 cc. of enriched milk, and 10 cc. of sugar solution (30 gms. of sugar to 70 cc. of water)—in a rat's stomach. They found that saline had little effect on the rate of bar-pressing whereas the milk and the sugar had a considerable effect. The number of bar presses in a 46-minute period before injection was 231, and this dropped to 37 bar presses after the sugar injection and 80 after the milk injection in the same period. In their second experiment they attempted to determine if simple indigestible bulk (which could not be assimilated as the saline could) would not account for their results on the basis of simple pressure effects. Accordingly, from a mixture of 40 gms. of kaoline (china clay) to 60 cc. water, they injected 10 cc., 7 cc., or 4 cc. into the rat's stomach. Smith and Duffy found that the kaolin injections into the stomach had no effect on response rate. However, in their third experiment they found that when the bulk was of a nutritive substance, it did have a depressive effect on the rate of responding. They found that with a 30 percent sucrose solution, the depressive effect on the rate of responding was "approximately linear with respect to quantity."

Though this experiment strongly suggests that hunger is decreased before restoration of the level of nutrients is achieved by the rat's digestive system, and though the factors responsible for this decrease are to a certain extent elucidated, the experiment is not completely satisfactory. After the intragastric injection, an average of seven and a half minutes elapsed before a rat was placed in the Skinner box. The test period was 46 minutes.

Therefore, digestive factors cannot be altogether excluded. It can, however, be said that the experiment does seem to establish the point that when nonnutrient bulk is injected slowly so as not to cause nausea, it does not have a satiating effect.

In view of the above experiments it can be strongly argued that cessation of eating is not due to a reversal of the change which acts on the central nervous system. Even given that digestion may have played some part in lessening subsequent food intake after the direct injection of food into the stomach, it is impossible to dispute the fact that normal ingestion by mouth of the same amounts of food led to an even greater depression of eating. This shows that there are satiating effects beyond any possible digestive factors.

Hull *et al.* (1951) have observed eating in a dog with an esophageal fistula. The dog used in this experiment weighed 10 kilos. before the operation. At the beginning of this experiment, this dog ate 8 kilos. of food, before stopping for five minutes. Even then cessation of eating was probably not due to normal satiation but to sheer exhaustion. It is reported that the dog showed "violent nervous shaking." Here as contrasted with the study of thirst, the effect of swallowing food when it does not reach the stomach does not seem to be strong enough to make the dog stop eating. Such an observation fits the simple homeostat view of ingestion well, but such a view is contradicted by the finding that the simple placing of food in the stomach inhibits eating before digestion can take place.

## The Afferent Inhibition View of Satiation

Another view has been elaborated by Deutsch (1953, 1960) and Stellar (1954). This theory resembles the simple homeostat model but adds an important complication. It will be recalled that in the simple homeostat model a physiological deficit excites a center which in turn produces activity. This activity reverses the change which excited the center and consequently switches itself off. In the system we are now considering, all this is assumed to be true, but another factor has been inserted. This factor consists of afferent activity originating in the receptors, and when the activity is conveyed to the excited center, it is rendered progressively less excitable by the initiating physiological change. In the case of drinking, it is hypothesized that such afferent activity is generated by taste receptors on the tongue that signal water, receptors in the throat that signal swallowing, and perhaps some receptors in the stomach. As the animal drinks, these receptors send back messages to the hypothalamic center activated in the thirst state and make the center gradually less excitable until the animal stops drinking. In this way drinking will usually cease before the physiological change which evoked the drinking is reversed as a result of advance information on how much has been drunk. On the other hand, insertion of water in the stomach can lead to a nonoccurrence of drinking if enough time is given for the water to reverse the change which would have initiated drinking had water been available. An analogous system is believed to operate in the case of eating, except that the main afferent message shutting off ingestion is considered probably to be generated by the upper gastrointestinal tract. Therefore placing food directly in the stomach has an inhibitory effect nor found with the introduction of water into the stomach in the study of thirst.

This system can be described as follows: A physiological change acts on a center. This center produces activity, which in turn produces afferent signals that desensitize the center in proportion to the number of signals received. Thus the center is rendered progressively less excitable by the initiating physiological change. In this way the cessation of an activity such as eating or drinking can be brought about in advance of the reversal of the physiological change which initiated these activities. On the other hand, such a reversal of the initiating change can also bring about a cessation, though this is never true in the ordinary situation because the signals generated by the activity, such as drinking, act in advance.

Therefore, in the ordinary case, the amount eaten or drunk will be a function first of the amount of excitation of the initiating central structure and second, it will be a function of the amount of signal fed back from the receptors to this center. Given a certain level of excitation in the center, the greater the amount of afferent stimulation per unit time, the more quickly the center will be rendered inexcitable. On the other hand, given a certain amount of afferent stimulation per unit time, the greater the excitement of the center generated by the physiological change, the longer the activity will last, because it will take a longer time for such a center to be desensitized.

## Diluted Water

It is possible to vary the number of afferent impulses derived from drinking simply by placing sodium chloride (common salt) in drinking water, as long as such a solution remains hypotonic. Zotterman (1956) made electrophysiological recordings from the chorda tympani nerve, which conveys afferent signals from the taste buds. He discovered that the same nerve fiber that is affected when a hypertonic solution of sodium chloride is placed on the tongue also responds to application of water. However such a fiber responds in an opposite way to these two substances. This fiber has a high and steady spontaneous or baseline rate of firing, presumably due to the normal salt content of the saliva. When a hypertonic sodium chloride solution is placed on the tongue there is an increase in the steady rate of firing of this nerve fiber. However, when water is placed on the tongue there is a decrease in the steady firing rate of the nerve fiber. Thus the presence of water is signaled by a fall in the amount of discharge in the fibers, which increase their firing when salt is present above the quantity normally found in saliva. When a small amount of salt is added to water—less than the amount present in the saliva—the solution continues to have the effect of decreasing the normal rate of firing in the fiber which signals the presence of water or of salt. However, such a decrease is not as large as that which is produced by pure water. Therefore, the effect of placing salt in water is to diminish the signal usually generated by the water. In some species, such as the rhesus monkey, there is a fiber which signals the presence of water by increases in rate of firing. However, in these animals the addition of salt to the water diminishes such an increase so that salt present in the water also diminishes its gustatory effect.

From this neurophysiological evidence it should be expected that when a small amount of salt is added to water, a more prolonged drinking of the slightly salty solution should result. Further, we should expect a progressive increase in the overdrinking of such salty solutions as the salt content of the water increases up to the level of the salt content already present in the saliva. The more salty the water up to this point of equality with the saliva the smaller the number of water messages generated by a given volume of fluid. When the salt content of the water applied to the tongue is greater than the salt content of the saliva, there will no longer be a depression of activity, and consequently, there will be no activity which can be interpreted as a signal of the presence of water. However, there will be an increase in activity in the water-salt fibers. This is the message for salt. Thus hypotonic saline will act on the taste receptors of the rat as if the solution were diluted water. On this basis, one might hypothesize that the animal will drink more of the hypotonic saline not because it prefers this solution but because more of the solution has to be drunk to have the same effect as a smaller volume of water.

The fact that rats will drink more hypotonic saline than water has been known for some time; therefore, this theoretical prediction seems to be confirmed. Furthermore, overdrinking of saline increases with the concentration of the solution up towards the point where it is isotonic. Overdrinking occurs even when water is freely available at the same time as the saline (Nelson, 1947; Bare, 1949; Young, 1949; Randoin et al.; 1950). Of course, it could be, as Mook (1963) points out, that more hypotonic saline is drunk because it is less efficient than water in reversing the physiological change which produces thirst; therefore, the effect which has been found might not be due to taste factors. However, Stellar and McCleary (1952) and Mook (1963), using animals with esophageal fistulae so that the ingested fluid did not reach the stomach, obtained essentially the same results. Here postingestinal factors were not operating. From Mook's results it seems that the peak in overdrinking of saline shifts somewhat to more dilute solutions of saline when nothing reaches the stomach. This would indicate that postingestional factors play a part in the situation when water was allowed to reach the stomach. Mook used a situation in which only one fluid was presented to the animal and only the total intake during one hour was measured. Results with such a procedure would reflect mainly the effects of the long-term reversal of the physiological change which produces thirst when the tasted fluid is allowed to reach the stomach. On the basis of taste factors, if the animal drank too little of a solution to produce reversal of the physiological change, this unreversed physiological change would shortly produce drinking again. Thus over a long period total intake of a fluid reflects its efficiency in reversing the physiological deficit which produces thirst. If on the other hand drinking occurs without any fluid entering the stomach, total "intake" should be grossly elevated, but the relative amount of intake of various solutions will reflect the influence of mouth factors alone. The afferent inhibition of drinking set up by drinking will occur more rapidly with some solutions than with others and last only a relatively brief time. As a result more drinking of less orally satiating solutions should occur.

A result which at first appears to be inconsistent with the diluted water hypothesis has been obtained by Mook (1963) using a variation of the fistulation technique quoted above. He transected the esophagus of rats in such a way that fluid drunk by the animal would drain out before reaching the stomach. However, each lick actuated a pump that would inject a predetermined amount of any fluid directly into the stomach through the lower end of the esophagus. When the animal was given different concentrations of saline to lick while no fluid was injected into the stomach, overdrinking of hypotonic saline occurred (as summarized above). However, if water was injected into the stomach while the rat licked different concentrations of saline, the rat drank the same amount of these as of water. On the basis of these results, Mook concluded that overdrinking of hypotonic saline is due to postingestional factors because it occurred only when saline reached the stomach, and did not appear when water only reached the stomach as a result of saline drinking. However, such a conclusion is contradicted by his own finding, quoted above, that overdrinking of saline did occur when nothing was allowed to reach the stomach. Here relative overdrinking of saline could not be due to postingestional factors (Figure 1-4).

As stated above, Mook measured only the total "intake" summed over a whole hour. Let us consider the discrepant case where the rat is "drinking" saline which escapes through the interrupted esophagus but receiving an equal volume of water in its stomach instead. If the rat initially "overdrinks" when it is licking saline, it will simply take more water into its stomach. After a while this will stop the rat from being thirsty by reversing the initiating physiological change. When the rat is no longer thirsty, there will be no further "drinking" during the hour if saline overdrinking is caused only by thirst. If the rat licks water instead of saline, there will be less "drinking" at the beginning (because the shutoff message is more efficient) with the consequence that the rat will take less water

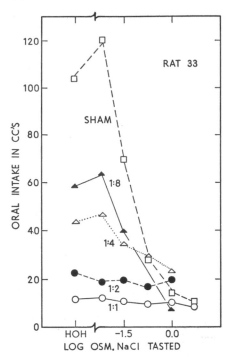

FIG. 1–4. Drinking of saline in Mook's animals as a function of concentration of saline which the rat tastes. The curve marked "sham" is obtained when the rat drinks saline, but nothing is allowed to reach the stomach. The curve marked 1:1 indicates the condition in which any volume of saline drunk (but not allowed to reach the stomach) is matched by the same volume of water injected directly into the stomach. The other curves are obtained when different ratios of saline drunk to water injected into the stomach are employed. The numbers on each curve indicate the ratio of water injected into the stomach to amount of saline drunk. (From Mook, D. G., *J. comp. physiol. Psych.*, 56, 1963, p. 656. By permission of American Psychological Association.)

into its stomach than when it is licking saline. In this case the rat will stay thirsty longer and continue to lick the water tube. All this adds up to saying again that thirst regulation over a period of an hour is bound to be governed by the cancellation of the initiating factor in thirst, i.e., rehydration. If on the other hand rehydration is not permitted, the relative amounts drunk will merely reflect the properties of the afferent shutoff message. Mook's results are therefore consistent with diluted water hypothesis and are in fact good evidence for it.

However, it might still be said that the evidence concerning the greater volume of saline drunk merely shows that the animal prefers saline to water. Indeed, it has usually been assumed that saline is overdrunk because of some preference for its taste. Rats have a preference for sugar solutions and will drink them in large amounts. To show that this argument is unlikely, Deutsch and Jones (1959, 1960) placed rats in a situation so that when they were thirsty they had to choose between equal volumes of water and hypotonic saline. If the rats preferred the taste of hypotonic saline, they should have learned to run to it; if, on the other hand, it appeared to the rats that the hypotonic saline was diluted water and therefore less thirst quenching, they should have learned to seek out the water. The rats learned to run to the water. This did not support the view that rats had a genuine preference for saline. On the other hand, this did support the view that saline is overdrunk because it is less satiating to a thirsty animal (Figures 1–5a and 1–5b).

FIG. 1–5a. This figure illustrates the relation of amount drunk of a solution in an ad libitum situation to its reward value when intake is limited. Saline produces fewer satiety signals per unit volume. A larger volume is drunk to produce satiety, and the same volume produces fewer satiety signals and so is less rewarding.

FIG. 1–5b. The graph shows increase of choice of water over 0.5 percent saline in a T-maze, as the rats learn. (From Deutsch, J. A., and Jones, A. D., *J. comp. physiol. Psych.* 53, 1960, p. 123. By permission of American Psychological Association.)

To test the view that there is a preference which accounts for the overdrinking even further, we (Deutsch and Jones) experimented with rats that had been satiated with water to see if they would learn to run to a reward of saline (0.2 percent and 0.8 percent) as one might expect if they liked the taste. After six days it was clear that the animals had no appetite for either solution. Although the average running time dropped from 82 seconds on the first day to 30 seconds on the sixth day, the whole reward of half a cc. was drunk on only four of the 90 trials. On one third of the trials the animals sniffed at the reward and probably took a lick and then left it alone. The rest of the time the rewards were completely ignored. It was therefore concluded that saline does not act as an incentive when the rat is not thirsty. So it appears that excessive drinking of saline is due to a smaller quantity of water signals from this liquid; which means that the rat has to drink more saline than water before the necessary number of signals arrive to switch off the thirst center.

By using a T-maze, limited amounts of water and saline as a reward, and some additional controls, Chiang and Wilson (1963) have confirmed the results obtained by Deutsch and Jones. Falk and Titlebaum (1963), on the other hand, found that when the animals used in their experiment were thirsty, there was no preference either for water or for saline. However, when they were not thirsty, there was a preference for saline; in fact, the animals would run for it.

Exploring this interesting discrepancy further, Deutsch and Wiener (unpublished) found that by using the strain of albino rat obtained from the same supplier as Falk and Titlebaum, they could obtain the same results only if the animals were maintained on a salt-deficient diet. That is, when placed in the T-maze, salt-deprived rats from the Charles River Laboratories chose saline and water equally when thirsty and they also ran to the saline when not thirsty. When placed in the T-maze, however, nonsalt-deprived rats from the same supplier preferred water but would not run for saline when they were not thirsty. In this respect the nonsalt-deprived rats resembled a parallel group of Long Evans hooded rats. However, a group of Long Evans rats maintained on a salt-deficient diet did not prefer water to saline when they were thirsty, although they would not run the maze when they were not thirsty. It appears therefore that Falk and Titlebaum's (1963) result was due to their use of a certain strain of rat kept accidentally on a salt-deficient diet. From observation in the laboratory it seemed that the strain of rat used by Falk and Titlebaum is particularly susceptible to salt deficiency. Therefore, in tests of the diluted water theory, it is particularly important to make sure that the animals being tested are not salt-depleted.

Chiang and Wilson (1963) reported a further discrepancy with the diluted water theory which has not yet been further investigated. Under ad libitum conditions, they measured the rat's frequency of drinking bouts from a bottle containing saline and a bottle containing water. It was found that rats would drink more frequently from the saline bottle than the water bottle. Such a result would not be predicted from the diluted water hypothesis which would predict a random and equal choice of the two bottles, although longer bouts on the saline bottle would be expected. The two-bottle ad libitum situation may be a very sensitive test for revealing slight salt craving. This may exist even with a diet which is perfectly compatible with growth. A more stringent test of the theory would be to see if overdrinking of saline still persists when animals are fed a diet richer in salt, even though choice of the saline bottle is random. With the use of a lesion, overdrinking of saline in the absence of saline deficiency can be dissociated from drinking of saline in response to a salt deficit. Wolf (1964) has shown that lesions in the dorsal part of the lateral area of the hypothalamus will abolish an increase of salt intake in response to treatment producing such an increase in normal animals. Therefore, lesioned animals seem unable to react behaviorally to salt deficiency. However, they show the same pattern of overdrinking the hypotonic saline as normal nondeprived controls. From this dissociation it would appear that normal overdrinking of saline and true salt preference due to salt deficiency are two different phenomena produced by different mechanisms. This supports the diluted water theory of saline overdrinking.

## Factors Switching Off Ingestive Activity

As was stated above, if water is placed in a thirsty dog's stomach, the dog will immediately drink approximately the same amount it would have drunk without this preload (Adolph, 1950). However, if the dog is forced to wait from 10–15 minutes, he will not drink (Bellows, 1939). This again is to be expected on the hypothesis which is being reviewed. A reversal of the change which initiates the activity takes place, even though such a reversal would never occur naturally because it would always have to be preceded by tasting and swallowing of water.

The evidence concerning hunger can be similarly examined in the light of this theory. In the case of hunger, it seems that the messages which shut off eating arise mainly in the upper end of the gastrointestinal tract (with a minor effect of taste messages on eating as shown by Kohn, 1951, and Berkun, Miller, and Kessen, 1952). If the stomach acts to generate such inhibitory afferent messages, then we can explain why placing food in the stomach, as in Kohn's or Smith and Duffy's experiment, should cause satiation of hunger. It can also be seen why a hungry dog with an esophageal fistula should not stop eating before physical exhaustion sets in. Since no food reaches the stomach, no afferent message is generated to switch off eating.

## The Message Causing Satiation

The message sent from the digestive tract to inhibit eating may well be biochemical in nature. Glucagon, a protein secreted by the α-cells in the pancreas, has been suggested as a possible factor. It has been found that injections of this substance will diminish hunger contractions and reports of hunger (Stunkard *et al.*, 1955) and will diminish the amount eaten (Schulman *et al.*, 1957). It has been thought that this substance acts by allowing glucose to be taken up by body cells, and that presumably glucagon also affects the central nervous structures (the ventromedial nucleus of the hypothalamus, see below p. 26) which may monitor the level of glucose being taken up. This view is based on the discovery (Van Itallie *et al.*, 1953; Stunkard and Wolff, 1954) that in man there is a correlation of satiety with a relatively large difference between arterial and venous blood. This signifies that glucose is being taken up by body cells as it passes from the arterial to the venous system. Hunger, on the other hand, never appears when the difference between the arterial and venous glucose is relatively large. Nevertheless, a small difference can be present without hunger occurring. Therefore, some other accompanying factors must be implicated in hunger.

It is tempting to suppose that glucagon which apparently produces satiety, does this by permitting body cells to take up glucose from the blood, and thus increase the arteriovenous difference in blood glucose. Unfortunately glucagon has various physiological effects. The particular effect necessary for this view has not been completely demonstrated, as is stressed by Behrens and Bromer (1958). It should also be mentioned that Herberg (1962) failed to find evidence for the action of glucagon when it was injected directly into the ventricles of the rat. Herberg found that no significant decrease in food intake resulted from such injection. However, he has reported reduction of food intake under some conditions of glucose injections into the ventricles (Herberg, 1960).

It is of course unlikely that there is a single satiating factor in hunger just as it is unlikely that there is a single initiating factor in hunger. There are many different hungers. For instance, an animal may be hungry for protein while it is satiated for carbohydrate. It appears that the satiating messages originate mainly from the upper gastrointestinal tract. Satiating messages do not seem to be neural because vagotomy (Grossman *et al.*, 1947) does not alter food intake significantly. It seems more probable that the shutoff messages are humoral. The upper gastrointestinal tract secretes a variety of hormones, such as pancreozymin, as a relatively differentiated response to the presence of various components of the diet. These are already known to act as messengers to promote the flow of the appropriate digestive juice ahead of such dietary components. The possibility that such hormones also exert a shutoff action on the central nervous system is at present being investigated by the authors.

## The Locus of Action of the Satiety Message

There is evidence that, whatever the message signaling for satiety may turn out to be, its locus of action is in or close to the ventromedial nucleus of the hypothalamus. The destruction of this region in rats produces overeating which leads to gross-obesity (Hetherington and Ranson, 1940, 1952; Brobeck *et al.*, 1943). (However, Reynolds [1963] has not found this to be the case.) Overeating has also been produced by a temporary block of the ventromedial nucleus through procaine injection (Epstein, 1960; Hoebel and Teitelbaum, 1962). Apart from their tendency to overeat, the rats seem physiologically normal (Teitelbaum, 1961). Rats with ventromedial lesions pass through two stages—the dynamic phase and the static phase. (1) Dynamic phase: Immediately after the operation the rats

FIG. 1–6. Rate of weight gain in rats with lesions of the ventromedial nucleus of the hypothalamus. Rat No. 3 is previously induced to become obese by insulin injections. Rat No. 4 starts from a normal weight. The rate of gain of weight in Rat No. 3 is also illustrated after it has been reduced after operation to its previous weight by being deprived of food. (From Teitelbaum, P., *Excerpta Medica*, No. 47, 1962, p. 700.)

displayed a wolfish appetite, sometimes even choking themselves by their frantic efforts to eat; however, if the animals are artificially fattened before the operation, this phase is correspondingly diminished (Figure 1–6). (2) Static phase: The rats enter this phase as their weight increase levels off. The overeating in this phase does not seem to be a result of greater hunger because when animals with ventromedial lesions have attained their final weight, though they overeat and maintain their body weight, they actually seem less hungry than normal animals on indices of hunger other than eating (Miller, Bailey, and Stevenson, 1950; Teitelbaum, 1957). For instance, if the task of obtaining food is at all strenuous or the food somewhat unpalatable, the ventromedial rat will tend to be more easily discouraged from obtaining or ingesting food than the normal rat. However, under conditions of normal availability of food, the hyperphagic rat will eat a larger meal (Teitelbaum, 1958). These results are to be expected if the path which normally inhibits eating via an advance message has been knocked out. The animal without its ventromedial nuclei would only stop eating when the change which had occasioned eating had been reversed. In fact the ventromedial animal has been converted into a simple homeostat as far as its food regulation is concerned. As a result, the animal overeats. This was predicted by the simple homeostat view. With larger meals, excess food is stored before it can all be used, resulting in obesity. The reason animals with ventromedial hypothalamic lesions actually seem less hungry though they eat more is, as Teitelbaum's (1957) work strongly suggests, the result of their obesity. These obese animals are not as strongly affected by food deprivation as are normal rats. Smaller hunger initiating changes may occur in an obese animal than in a normal animal when food deprivation conditions are equal.

There is also some likelihood that the reward value of eating is diminished in animals without the ventromedial hypothalamus. It seems (Teitelbaum, 1964) that a normal reward or feedback path is interrupted by lesions of the ventromedial nucleus of the hypothalamus. When normal rats are provided with a lever which they can press to cause delivery of a nutrient solution directly into their stomach, they will learn to press it rapidly and thus regulate their food intake within normal limits. However, rats with lesions of the ventromedial nucleus have great difficulty in learning to do this. Teitelbaum (1964) believes that some rats would even starve to death in this situation if they were not rescued. However, if a sweet taste is coupled with the intragastric injection, a lesioned animal will work hard enough at pressing the lever to become obese again.

It is also possible to produce lesions of the ventromedial nucleus of the hypothalamus by administration of gold thioglucose to mice. This substance tends to be selectively absorbed by the nuclei and destroys them by its toxic action. Such findings have been used to support the notion that the ventromedial nuclei are sensitive to the glucose level and so produce satiation when glucose enters them (Mayer and Marshall, 1956). On the other hand, Perry and Liebelt (1959) have shown that such injections also cause lesions in the fornix, hippocampus, preoptic area, and vagal nuclei, areas where the blood-brain barrier has greater permeability.

An experiment with many interesting possibilities in elucidating the role of the factors causing satiety was conducted by Hervey (1959). He used parabiotic rats (rats which have been made into artificial Siamese twins) so that substances present in one rat can diffuse slowly into the other rat. Hervey removed the ventromedial nuclei from one of the rats of such a pair. The lesioned rat became obese as would be expected. It also could be expected that the nutrients derived from the excessive eating by the lesioned rat would make its partner obese. However, the partner became very thin, which would seem to indicate that only the substance producing satiety had diffused from the lesioned partner (where it would be produced without effect by excessive eating).

Stimulation of the ventromedial nucleus produces a decrease in eating (Smith, 1956; Wyrwicka and Dobrzecka, 1960). However, Krasne (1962) showed that this may be due to the aversive effects of the stimulation, rather than a specific satiating effect. Further, cessation of stimulation of the nucleus is followed by eating. This is a rebound effect and is very powerful. However, it is interesting that the latency of the eating after stimulation has ceased may be several minutes.

## Electrical Recordings from the Hypothalamus

Anand (1961) and his collaborators have measured activity in the ventromedial and lateral regions of the hypothalamus by means of electrical recordings. They reported that during hyperglycemia there is an increase of activity in the ventromedial nucleus and some decrease of activity in the lateral region. Hypoglycemia produced the reverse picture.

## Interaction between Hunger and Thirst

Since most food is hypertonic, when an animal eats it also becomes thirsty. It has been shown (Cizek, 1959) that a dog's water intake decreases when available food is decreased and water intake increases when food intake increases. It seems therefore that a great deal of drinking occurs because eating has induced thirst. Similarly, it is a common observation that food intake drops sharply when water is not available. It seems as if thirst or its physiological cause in some way inhibits eating. (This is a useful arrangement because the consequences of the factors producing thirst damage the organism more rapidly than the consequences resulting from lack of food.) Consequently, the consumption of a hypertonic substance gradually ceases as thirst begins to be induced (Shuford, 1955). In separate tests, rats were given solutions of sucrose and glucose which were both equally preferred. The rats would stop drinking glucose earlier because glucose has a higher osmotic pressure. Experiments by McCleary (1953) and Schwartzbaum and Ward (1958) show that the osmotic pressure of substances placed in the stomach before ingestion of other substances is permitted, also influences the amount subsequently ingested. The reduction in subsequent ingestion is a function only of the osmotic pressure of the preload. It is unlikely that these experiments show, as has been suggested, that osmotic pressure produces normal satiation of hunger. Rather it seems that they illustrate the point made above, namely, that a thirsty animal will not make itself thirstier.

## The Stimuli Evoking Ingestion and Provoking Aversion

### The Unlearned Attractiveness of Certain Visual Stimuli Related to Feeding and Drinking

What leads animals to ingest some substances and to reject others? Though many preferences and aversions are learned, there is evidence that others are unlearned. Some of the unlearned gustatory preferences have already been discussed (pp. 19–25). Investigations have been carried out concerning the unlearned attractiveness of certain visual properties. For instance, Tinbergen and Perdeck (1950) demonstrated that the newly hatched herring gull chick would peck at objects resembling the beak of an adult herring gull. This chick is fed in the nest by its parent, and the sight of the adult beak is sufficient to evoke responses which are a part of the eating pattern. This responsiveness to stimuli which emanate from the adult beak is probably innate because it was found that these responses can be evoked most effectively by dummies of a normal adult beak. These dummies were far from exact copies of the adult beak, and in a certain sense were beak caricatures. Dummies which were much narrower than an adult beak and which had several adjacent, narrow bands of orange color at the base of the beak were superior to a natural beak. The adult herring gull has an orange patch near the base of its beak. Thus, by exaggerating some of the properties of the beak, a much more effective stimulus to pecking was found. If the herring gull chick had learned that the properties of the adult beak were attractive because it had been fed after seeing the beak, then we should have expected the natural beak to be the most attractive.

Rheingold and Hess (1957) obtained a similar result as Tinbergen and Perdeck when experimenting with the attractiveness of certain visual properties of water to newly hatched domestic chicks. In this experiment, factors of previous reward were more closely investigated. Rheingold and Hess attempted to isolate the cues which evoke a drinking behavior pattern in newly hatched chicks. Such a pattern is distinct from their pecking behavior. When the chick pecks, it begins with its beak pointed down and its head directly above the object it is attempting to ingest, and then it strikes with a quick motion downward, jerking its head up again at the end of the stroke. The drinking response is different in that the downward phase of the movement is slower and the beak is pushed forward when it touches the substance to be drunk, and then it is tilted up. The same stereotyped movement occurs even when a hard substance has evoked the response.

The subjects of Rheingold and Hess were three-day-old chicks which had never eaten or drunk. (Up to this age a chick can live on the internal yolk sac without undue detriment.) Each chick was placed in an experimental arrangement with six different substances placed around it in a semicircle. These substances were (a) tap water, (b) water colored blue to such an extent that it was no longer translucent, (c) water colored red, but still translucent, (d) a circle of polished aluminum, (e) mercury, and (f) a hard, translucent plastic which looked like water to the human eye. In order to eliminate learning, each chick was allowed to respond only once. The results showed that most of the chicks attempted to drink the mercury. Progressively fewer chose plastic, blue water, tap water, aluminum, and red water (in that order). Only a third as many chicks preferred tap water to mercury. After seven days the majority of these chicks—which had in the meantime been given experience with food and water—were given the same test again. Though they had received four days' experience with water and had been deprived of it for 12 hours, the relative number of chicks approaching the test stimuli was practically unchanged. Mercury again attracted the largest number and tap water the fourth largest. So it seems that mercury, as the artificial beak used by Tinbergen and Perdeck (see above), is more effective in evoking a particular response than the natural stimuli of water. Such stimuli have been termed "supernormal" by the ethologists. They have been demonstrated to exist in other contexts besides eating and drinking. For instance, it has been shown that the oyster catcher will attempt to incubate eggs larger than itself in preference to those in its own nest.

Thus the experiment of Rheingold and Hess shows convincingly that there are certain characteristics of substances which make animals attempt to ingest them without having had any previous process of learning. It further shows that when animals are placed among substances which were not present to the species during its evolution, such innate preferences may actually lead to the ingestion of useless or deleterious substances. Sometimes such substances may possess the characteristics of a supernormal stimulus, and therefore these useless or deleterious substances may be ingested in preference to the substance which is physiologically beneficial, because the useless substances in some way, and to a greater degree, possess the attractive characteristics of the beneficial substance.

Fantz (1957) performed a similar experiment on innate visually controlled food preferences in domestic chicks. He used different test objects of various shapes to see which the chicks peck at. Hess and Gogel (1954) had demonstrated such a preference in the case of colors. In his initial experiments, Fantz used newly hatched, one- to three-day-old domestic chicks which did not have any experience of food or water. They were tested in groups placed in various boxes. These boxes contained stimuli in the form of various small objects which were inedible. These could be pecked but not dislodged. The number of pecks at each object was recorded by means of the closure of an electric contact whenever a peck occurred. The results clearly show that the chicks pecked consistently more at round objects than at angular objects. Though the chicks order of preference for "edible" shape was maintained even after pecking which was unrewarded and also after feeding, it was possible to alter the preference, though not entirely, by giving the chicks food of an irregular, rather than a round, shape.

It seems clear therefore that when the chick hatches, it is already predisposed to ingest objects with certain preferred visual qualities. In the case of drinking, some of the properties of water such as a shiny and mobile surface seem attractive; in the case of eating, properties of food such as roundness (seeds and grain) evoke a pecking response. Such an arrangement has a clear biological usefulness because it increases the probability that in its ordinary environment a chick upon hatching will begin to drink or to peck at substances which are physiologically beneficial. It will therefore tend to eliminate some of the trial and error processes which would be necessary if the chick had to learn, without any initial built-in bias, what objects or substances were edible or drinkable.

## Stimuli Provoking Aversion

If it is useful for animals to be so constructed as to be attracted to certain kinds of objects or substances when they are hungry or thirsty, it is even more important that they should not ingest substances that are deleterious or harmful. Though it would be a handicap if a young chick were required to learn every characteristic of food objects in its environment, it would be an even greater danger to its life if it did not avoid certain properties of vision, taste, or smell. There are many substances in an animal's environment which would kill the animal or incapacitate it if they were ingested. Those individuals in a species which do not avoid harmful substances will not survive to reproduce. Therefore, there is a high selective pressure for a species where the mechanism for the avoidance of harmful substances is inborn. We should therefore on evolutionary grounds expect to find properties or qualities of substances which produce avoidance of a substance. In this way an animal is safeguarded against ingesting harmful substances which were present in the environment during the evolution of the species.

The problem of blocking certain behavior patterns in spite of the presence of the correct stimulating conditions must also be solved during other types of activity besides eating and drinking. For instance, many of the characteristics which evoke mating or copulatory reactions are present in individuals or even in objects, mating with whom is unlikely to lead to offspring. Through the process of natural selection, the properties of objects incapable of successful mating become repulsive to the animal, just as eating certain objects becomes aversive. By natural selection, individuals are selected with mechanisms which will block mating when certain characteristics are present, since these individuals are more likely to have progeny.

## Amygdalectomy and Aversive Function

Many of the behavioral abnormalities found by Klüver and Bucy (1939) to occur in monkeys following bilateral temporal lobectomy can also be produced by ablation of structures in the amygdaloid complex (see Chapter 6). Bilateral removal of this complex results in a whole set of symptoms. The animals become very tractable and tame (though exceptions have been noted), sexually indiscriminate (see also p. 59), and eat objects such as feces. Food selection is altered since the animals will now ingest such foods as meat or fish which they normally reject (Pribram and Bagshaw, 1953). Weiskrantz (personal communication) has established that such indiscriminate eating behavior is not the result of a sensory deficit in taste. Before their bilateral amygdalectomy, he trained rhesus monkeys on a two-bottle preference situation, in order to establish what concentration of saccharin these animals preferred. He used four different concentrations of saccharin in successive conditions. He also incorporated trials in which both bottles contained only water. At the same time as he carried out this saccharin solution preference test, he also carried out another experiment on the same animal to determine its absolute threshold for saccharin. He did this by rewarding some of the monkeys with a small piece of apple if they licked up 5 drops of saccharin and ignored the water from a container, the selection being made by taste. Other monkeys were rewarded with a piece of apple if they chose the water instead of the saccharin.

Weizkrantz repeated all of these tests after bilateral amygdalectomy. He found that the postoperative threshold for saccharin did not change. Trying to obtain a piece of apple, the animals could distinguish a weak solution of saccharin from water just as they could before the operation. However, preference for solutions of saccharin did change. The postoperative animals would drink the stronger concentrations of saccharin which they had tended to reject before amygdalectomy. (Saccharin tastes bitter in strong concentrations.) Behavior of the control operates (animals which had part of their striate cortex removed) did not appear to be significantly altered. Weiskrantz concluded that preference can be altered without any change in taste sensitivity, as measured by standard discrimination techniques. The results of this experiment also make it plausible to believe that a part of the system which leads the animal to reject certain substances has been removed. As has been argued, from general behavioral considerations it appears plausible that there are two systems which determine what an animal will treat as food. The first system leads an animal to select objects for food on the basis of certain qualities. The second system leads the animal to reject objects as being food because of certain other inherent qualities. We may suppose that the second system is damaged in bilateral amygdalectomy.

It is probable that the two systems are usually in balance; and depending on the strength of each system, selection takes its course. The hungrier an animal becomes, the stronger the attractive qualities of food become. As a result, aversive food which the animal would not ordinarily eat will be ingested because the animal is very hungry. Similarly, an animal that is nearly satiated will be more selective about its food than a hungry animal. Since animals with bilateral ablation of the amygdaloid complex are deficient in their aversion to food, they should eat more at each meal than normal control animals, especially if both groups are fed coarse diets. If the diet has fewer aversive properties, then the difference in preference of the two groups of animals should be decreased. In fact, animals without the amygdaloid complex become fatter than normal control animals.

Another line of evidence is obtained from ventromedial operates. Here the animal continues to eat, in spite of being in a very low hunger drive state. We should expect the operation of the aversive factor to be more clearly revealed in such an animal.

Teitelbaum (1955) has observed that the intake of ventromedial operates is very greatly affected by the sensory properties of their diet. Though these animals eat much more than normal animals, they are more fastidious and respond to a coarsening of the diet by decreasing their intake. Such observations on animals with lesions closely agrees with what would be expected of the mechanism as inferred above from behavioral and physiological data.

Some investigators have reported that lesions of the amygdaloid complex produce hypophagia. Green *et al.* (1957) found that damage to the anterior portion of the amygdala produced a decrease in eating, whereas lesions near the junction of the basal and lateral nuclei produced overeating. Koikegami *et al.* (1955) have also reported hypophagia or aphagia after lesions to the amygdala. It seems that this region is also involved in water intake as well as in food intake. Grossman and Grossman (1963) showed that small lesions in this area produced overdrinking as well as overeating. Further, chronic electrical stimulation reduced both food and water intake. This makes it probable that lesions which produce hypophagia have an irritative effect, since the effects of lesions and stimulation are in the same direction.

Influences on eating and drinking through chemical stimulation of the amygdala have been demonstrated by Grossman (1964). Reliable effects occur only if the animal is already hungry or thirsty. An adrenergic agent (norepinephrine) led to increased food motivation, while an adrenergic blocking agent (dibenzyline) led to a decrease of such motivation. A cholinergic agent (carbachol) greatly increased thirst motivation, while atropine (an anticholinergic agent) led to its decrease. As mentioned above (p. 9) similar pharmacological sensitivities occur in the hypothalamus. The fact that reliable effects can only be obtained while the animal is in a drive state further supports the view that the amygdala modulates eating or drinking rather than causes it. For instance increases or decreases of aversion to the quality of food being eaten would mainly become manifest only when the animal was eating.

Lesions of the frontal cortex have also been reported to produce hyperphagia (Richter and Hawkes, 1939; Langworth and Richter, 1939). The relation to ventromedial hypothalamic and amygdaloid hyperphagia is obscure at present.

## DIETARY SELECTION

So far hunger has been treated as if it were a unitary phenomenon. But hunger is in reality a name for a group of associated appetites. It is possible, for instance, for a rat to be satiated for carbohydrate and yet to be hungry for protein. When a rat is kept in a cage by the experimenter and supplied with a prepared compound rat cake, the rat does not have to select the components of its diet in order to maintain itself free of deficiency disease. On the other hand, an animal living in a free environment must select naturally occurring foods in such a way that dietary deficiency is avoided. Such an ability to select an adequate diet in a controlled setting has been demonstrated by Davis (1928) who worked with young children and by Richter (1942a) who worked with rats. In fact, rats allowed to make such a selection grow more rapidly than those fed on a standard laboratory diet (Richter, 1942b).

Because selection of diet by the animal normally results in maintenance of a healthy condition, it seems plausible to assume that the animal selects its diet on the basis of a physiological need. We would then expect that if the physiological need shifted, diet selection would show a corresponding alteration. Such is the case, for instance, in pregnancy. There is an increase in the intake of fat, protein, and minerals, but sugar intake in lowered. This corresponds to the requirements of the developing fetuses (Richter, 1942a). Dietary selection returns to normal after the young are weaned. Artificially induced deficits similarly lead to corrective selection. For instance, rats in which the pancreas has been removed decrease their intake of sugar to avoid diabetic symptoms but increase their intake of fat to maintain caloric intake (Richter and Schmidt, 1941). Also, after removal of the parathyroid gland, which has the consequence of increasing levels of phosphorus and decreasing levels of calcium, rats avoid phosphorus compounds and increase their calcium intake (Richter, 1939).

A species can adapt itself in relation to dietary requirements in various ways. It is possible to select individuals who have simple requirements concerning food sources. Thus a species may be selected which can live on a single food source, such as eucalyptus leaves in the case of Koala bears, or mulberry leaves in the case of silkworms. The silkworm, if it eats mulberry leaves, is supplied with all it needs for healthy development. In this way the animal has adapted so that, provided it eats enough of one particular foodstuff, it will not suffer dietary deficiency. The animal is somewhat like the laboratory rat in a cage. At the other extreme we may imagine an animal which evolved in an environment in which the combinations of basic food components were very unstable or random. Such an animal cannot adapt by choosing one kind of foodstuff sufficient for all its needs. It must be able to select its diet so that by varying the intake of different foodstuffs, the correct proportions of needed nutrients will be ingested.

Such an animal might, for instance, learn to detect the various constituents in food which it needs and then regulate its food intake according to the amount of these food components already ingested. A species of animal living in a capricious dietary environment cannot adapt by picking some naturally packaged combination of nutrients because no single package exists in the environment we have imagined. Such a species must recognize separately the various important dietary components.

However, usually the natural food environment of a species is such that the needed combinations or packages of nutrients are present. These nutrients have their own distinctive odors, tastes, and visual properties. Most animals consequently adapt in a manner somewhere between the two extremes outlined above. Many animals are equipped to select their diet from a variety of naturally occurring nutrient combinations in their environment so they can maintain themselves in good health. However, any one environment contains naturally occurring nutrient packages or combinations in which there are large sets of differing food components regularly associated in fixed proportions. On the whole, most animals only have an ability to recognize these packages and not their separate components.

Whether a species of animal has adapted by developing an ability to select naturally occurring combinations of nutrients, or to select a variety of foodstuffs, in either case the animal is innately attracted to the sight and taste of the substance as it occurs naturally. In many cases, it appears that animals have evolved in such a way that when they have a specific physiological nutrient deficit it is translated directly into a craving for a certain taste. Epstein and Stellar (1955) (see p. 39) showed that the appetite for salt occurred without learning when the salt deficiency occurred. Thus it is unlikely that tests in the laboratory can reflect the ability of a species to select an adequate diet in the food environment in which it evolved. Food substances offered to the animal in the laboratory may look, feel, taste, and smell unlike those found by the animal in its natural environment.

However, there are cases where animals can select foodstuffs on a basis which does not reflect built-in preferences. In such cases, animals may learn to ingest substances because of their beneficial after-effects. For instance, Harris et al. (1933) performed experiments on the ability of vitamin B deficient rats to discriminate between diets in which this vitamin was either present or absent. If the rats were not given a large choice of diets, after a short period of learning they were able to discriminate and eat the diet containing the vitamin. Having learned that one of the diets was beneficial, the rats would still continue to eat it when the vitamin was left out. Learning in this instance is dependent on the rapid relief of symptoms, since the beneficial after-effects of ingestion of this vitamin are rapid. When relief of symptoms is slow, as with vitamins A and D, learning does not take place. The same experiments carried out with animals deficient in vitamin A and vitamin D yielded negative results, i.e., the animals could not learn to select the right mixture to remedy their deficiency. It was concluded that the amelioration of the animals' condition was not rapid enough in these cases.

Scott and Verney (1947) showed that an appetite for the B complex of vitamins was acquired. If the food containing this vitamin was flavored with anise, animals deficient in B complex would learn to ingest the food with the anise taste instead of the plain food. If the vitamin was left out of the diet flavored with anise but added to the plain food instead, the rats would prefer to eat the plain food. In this way the experiment ruled out the possibility that the animals simply preferred food with a particular flavor and that their choice was independent of vitamin content.

Further, in a test which measured food intake over a three-week period, Scott and Quint (1946) have demonstrated that rats deficient in thiamine (vitamin $B_1$), riboflavin (vitamin $B_2$), and pyridoxine (vitamin $B_6$) will preferentially select foods containing these vitamins. Rats which were not deficient in these substances showed no such preferential selection. On the other hand, when pantothenate deficiency occurred, the rat found it difficult to learn what food to select. Scott and Quint found that an appetite for pantothenate cannot be developed unless the diet containing it is labeled with anise. However, even then some animals made the wrong choice.

It has been shown in the preceding examples that under some circumstances animals may learn to ingest diets which were at first preferentially neutral. Provided that the beneficial after-effects of ingestion are rapid enough and provided that there are not too many alternatives to confuse the animal, it will learn to eat what is good for it. However such a diet must not, on the other hand, be initially repulsive or aversive. As has been pointed out above (p. 32), an animal will avoid foods of certain tastes, smells, or other sensory properties because its ancestors did not consume such foods and survived to reproduce and transmit their "dislikes" to their progeny. Animals have many such aversions which often extend to substances which are beneficial or harmless. Human beings also find certain tastes repugnant. The bitterness of quinine, for instance, is extremely unpleasant. Rats, monkeys, and other animals also dislike quinine. Jukes (1938) found that even chickens avoided diets containing more than 0.03 percent quinine. They also avoided food containing more than 2 percent salt or 2 percent citric acid. Rats have been observed by Deuel and Movitt (1944) to dislike rancid flavors. Scott and Quint (1946) found that rats previously fed an unflavored diet avoided food with the taste of trimethylamine, which has a fishy flavor. Scott and Verney (1947) further found that rats disliked lactose, and Scott and Quint (1946) found that many more animals refused egg albumen in a mixed diet than other purified proteins such as casein, lactalbumen, and fibrin.

Since certain properties will produce a strong aversion in animals, it is not altogether surprising that when some animals are given certain choices of purified food components they would die rather than eat the evil-tasting and putrid-smelling beneficial substance offered to them. An experiment performed by Scott (1946) illustrates this point. He used six-week-old albino rats. In their cage there were four cups containing the following food components necessary for growth: sucrose, hydrogenated fat, casein, and a mixture of salts. Casein was liked by some rats and not liked by others. If they liked casein, they ate an average of 3 gm. per day and grew well. If they did not like it, they ate less than .01 gm. per day and died within a short time. That there was something unlearned about this dislike of casein is shown by a similarity in appetite which existed between rats who were littermates. This may be interpreted as a failure of the ability of rats to select a beneficial diet, as shown in a similar experiment by Pilgrim and Patton (1947). It should, however, be pointed out that purified casein has unattractive properties, at least to the human observer. It seems probable that in its natural environment an animal may avoid a substance with such properties as casein and increase its chances of survival.

Just as only in the laboratory are found beneficial substances which have a taste that usually belongs to poisons and therefore are avoided, so in the laboratory nonbeneficial substances are ingested because they share certain sensory properties with beneficial substances. Again, the normal association between the flavor of a substance and its after-effects which is found in the animal's natural environment may not be present in the laboratory. For example, Hausmann (1933) discovered that rats would drink large quantities of saccharin solution, which to the human tongue tastes sweet but which is of no nutritive value. A sweet taste is usually an indication of the presence of sugars, and is characteristic of ripe fruit or young vegetable shoots. Another interesting dissociation which can be demonstrated in the laboratory occurs in the case of diacetyl, a compound found in milk and which used with monobutyrin and butyric acid produces the flavor of butter. Deuel and Movitt (1944) found that diets to which this substance was added were preferred by rats. They conjectured that this may be manufactured by the lactating female to impart a characteristic taste to her milk. Though the milk itself has great nutritional importance, the dissociated flavoring material, diacetyl, possesses no physiological function as far as is known. It does not, for instance, act like a vitamin. So that, although it is nutritionally useful for a rat to ingest substances such as milk, which tastes of diacetyl, in its natural environment, the consumption of the flavoring material itself brings no benefit. It seems likely that an appetite for diacetyl may arise when the rat is short of some of the substances which in the normal environment are always associated with a diacetyl flavor.

A further point should be made concerning laboratory investigation of special appetites. The usual species employed in tests of dietary self-selection have been either domestic or laboratory strains of animals, such as chickens or albino rats. These strains of animals have not on the whole been selected for their ability to maintain a balanced diet. They have rather been selected for such characteristics as excessive egg laying or tameness. Such traits may be linked to inefficient food selection. That such hereditary considerations are of importance has been demonstrated by Scott (1946) who found that rats who are littermates tend to have similar appetites.

## Detailed Investigations of Special Appetites

One of the cases where it has been possible to demonstrate that an animal will make up a specific nutritional deficit is that involving sodium chloride (common salt). Richter (1942) demonstrated that when adrenal-ectomized rats, which lose sodium at a rapid rate (and so usually die in a few days if not provided with excess salt), are given access to salt, they will ingest enough 3 percent solution of salt to survive free of symptoms of salt deficiency. It has been suggested that adrenalectomized rats learn to ingest adequate amounts of salt because of the beneficial after-effects of the ingestion of salt, i.e. the animal learns to eat a substance that alleviates certain deficiency symptoms. Such an argument appears to be supported by the fact that such adrenalectomized animals increase their salt intake gradually after operation. However, Epstein and Stellar (1955) point out that this gradual increase in intake might, instead, reflect an increased need for sodium as progressively more of it is lost by the animal after its operation. To decide between the two hypotheses, they tested two groups of rats. The first was allowed access to a salt solution immediately after the operation and the second was only given access to it after a few days. They found that the first group did indeed increase its salt intake gradually. However when the second group was given the salt solution, it imme-diately consumed as much as the first group. This study demonstrates therefore that the increased appetite for salt in adrenalectomized rats is unlearned. A further experiment points to the same conclusion since it seems that rats cannot learn to ingest salt if they cannot taste it. Richter (1942) found that when he sectioned the nerves which convey messages from the taste receptors (glossopharyngeal, chorda tympani, and lingual), the animals which were salt deficient could no longer select the needed solution.

One may suggest that hunger for sodium chloride is regulated similarly to thirst. A deficit gives rise to excitation in cells which are specifically sensitive to such a deficit. This gives rise to ingestion, which produces afferent impulses. These afferent impulses, originating in the salt receptors, serve to desensitize the cells irritated by the initial deficit. Some evidence relating to the localization of the tissue sensitive to sodium deficit has been found. Wolf (1964) has shown that in rats bilateral lesions in the dorsal part of the lateral area of the hypothalamus produce a loss of reaction to sodium deficiency. Animals with such lesions do not increase their intake of salt after induced salt deficiency.

The appetite for sweet-tasting substances also appears to be a specific hunger, though the precise physiological deficit which occasions the appetite has not been identified. However it has been noted that during food deprivation, consumption of sweet-tasting nonnutritive solutions increases (Carper and Polliard, 1953). Moreover, it has been demonstrated that the afferent message regulates intake of sweet substances. Hagstrom and Pfaffmann (1959) have produced evidence that the amount of a sweet-tasting substance, such as fructose and sucrose, drunk in an ad libitum consumption situation correlated inversely with the amount of activity generated by "sweet" taste receptors in the chorda tympani. Hagstrom and Pfaffmann conclude that postingestional factors are responsible for this correlation because they assume that the amount ingested in the ad libitum situation is a direct measure of preference. However, these authors also found that the amount of activity in the chorda tympani was closely correlated with the reward value or preference of the substances when quantity drunk of various sweet-tasting substances was limited. This is the inverse of the ad libitum situation.

This result is comparable with the result found by Deutsch and Jones (1959, 1960) on the overdrinking and reward value of hypotonic saline, and it fits the diluted water hypothesis. On the basis of this hypothesis, we would expect ingestion to cease when a certain quantity of afferent messages have impinged on the center sensitive to physiological deficit. Two equal volumes of substances such as equiosmolar solutions of sucrose and fructose produce different amounts of a "sweet" signal in the afferent pathway. Then we would expect a greater consumption of the solution which produces a smaller amount of afferent signal because each unit volume will produce less desensitization of the initiating center. Therefore, on the basis of this hypothesis, the amount drunk in an ad libitum situation is not a measure of preference but a measure of the effectiveness of a substance in producing satiation. This hypothesis also regards the amount of a specific afferent message produced by an ingested substance as being directly proportional to its reward value. Therefore, if the same equiosmotic volumes of sucrose and fructose are ingested, the sucrose should be the more rewarding because it generates a larger number of afferent signals. So we should predict an inverse relation between the satiation value of substances and their reward. Such a finding, hitherto regarded as paradoxical, has also been obtained by Young and Greene (1953). These authors found that the animal preferred more concentrated sucrose solutions when it had to choose between various dilutions of sucrose in a situation where intake was restricted; however, more dilute solutions of sucrose were "preferred" (i.e., larger quantities consumed) when ad libitum drinking was permitted in another situation.

It seems that this appetite for sweet-tasting substances is inborn. De

Snoo (1937) studied twenty pregnant women suffering from polyhydramnios. This disorder is a painful swelling of the abdomen due to an excess of amniotic fluid in the uterus. He was able to show that this disorder was caused by a failure on the part of the fetus to drink amniotic fluid because for some reason or other the amniotic fluid in these patients did not taste sweet. When saccharin (a nonnutritive sweet-tasting substance) was injected, the painful swelling of the abdomen promptly went down. Methylene blue was injected to make sure that this was an effect of drinking on the part of the fetus and not some effect of the saccharin on secretion of amniotic fluid. De Snoo's hypothesis was corroborated when this harmless dye appeared in the mother's urine after, but not before, saccharin was injected. It seems that the fetus begins to drink when the taste of the amniotic fluid becomes sweet.

When given access to saccharin solution, rats will also ingest large quantities of it. Carper and Polliard (1953) found that an animal will consume large quantities of saccharin when it is hungry. As has been mentioned before, saccharin is nonnutritive. The evidence that saccharin is drunk by rats in spite of its nonnutritive value again lends support to the notion that it is an unlearned special hunger, as De Snoo's observation seems to indicate. However it should be mentioned that Smith and Capretta (1956) dissent from this view. They noted that animals used in experiments on saccharin ingestion could have been digesting food while they were allowed to drink the saccharin. Therefore, it is possible that the rats erroneously learned that the saccharin reduced their hunger, causing them to drink it in large quantities. Consequently an experiment was designed so that some of the rats were only given the saccharin solution after having been deprived of food for a long time. Other rats were allowed to drink soon after they had been fed. Smith and Capretta found that saccharin was treated as less rewarding by the group of rats which received the saccharin when they were hungry than by the control group which had been given the saccharin while the processes of digestion were still occurring. They therefore concluded that saccharin consumption is due to erroneous learning. However, other interpretations of this experiment are possible. Saccharin has various properties which might have produced such a result. The rate of absorption into the blood stream of hungry animals may have been much higher than in animals which had just eaten. It is known that an injection of saccharin produces a bitter taste in the mouth, whereas an injection of sucrose produces a sweet taste. (Saccharin in high concentrations in the mouth also tastes bitter.) In this way a high blood level of saccharin may have produced an unpleasant taste which was aversive to the animals. It would be interesting to repeat this experiment on rats with esophageal fistulae, or to use other sweet-tasting substances without the peculiar properties of saccharin.

# 2

# REPRODUCTIVE BEHAVIOR

## Behavioral Considerations

Courtship and copulation take many forms among the vertebrates. Since most of the physiological evidence quoted in this chapter is restricted to mammals—especially the rat and the cat—some account of the behavior of these two species will be given.

After the male rat has found an estrous female, he attempts to approach her. However she darts forward, fluttering her ears, and stops, repeating this behavior until the male mounts her. In response to this tactile stimulus she arches her back and raises and exposes the genitalia (lordosis). Having intromitted, the male dismounts and licks his own genitalia and then mounts again. The male intromits about twelve times before ejaculation occurs. Each intromission lasts about one third of a second and is separated from the previous one by an interval of 45 to 60 seconds.

The female cat shows pronounced and well-defined sexual responses which make it a convenient subject for study. Activities which precede mating include low vocalization, rubbing, rolling, and crouching accompanied by treading. This last kind of behavior consists of a lowering of the front part of the body, a raising of the pelvis, turning of the tail to one side, and a treading movement of the hind legs. In many cats, this action occurs quite spontaneously without any apparent external stimulus. In other cats, this behavior is induced either by a grasping of the neck by the male or simply by his presence or by stimulation of the genitalia. When genital stimulation or intromission by the male occurs, the female utters a loud cry, shriek, or growl. After coitus, the so-called after-reaction occurs, and this is somewhat variable. It usually consists of a "frantic rubbing, squirming, licking and rolling" (Ranson, 1940). This is accompanied, as is described below (p. 51), by electrical changes in parts of the hypothalamus. It is tempting to compare this reaction to orgasm in the human female.

It has been observed that the disposition of female cats to allow copulation varies. Some will permit only a very determined male to mate. It has also been claimed (Green *et al.*, 1957) that the female is affected by the location where she meets the male. She is much more receptive in strange territory than in her own cage. In the male cat, situational factors are similarly important. In contrast to the female, the male will copulate only in a place which he regards as his own territory and not in a strange place. In order to regard a place as his territory he must explore it to become familiar with it. When a female is introduced into his territory, he first behaves with great caution, and only after a prolonged period, does he seize the female by the neck and mount her. However, if on a subsequent occasion another cat is introduced into his territory he will mount it at once, regardless of its sex. On the other hand, he becomes quite wary if another cat is already in his territory when he appears, and he cautiously observes the other cat. It seems that the cat resembles the rabbit in this respect. The writer has observed that male rabbits in their own territory will attempt to mate with newly introduced males, until these bite and a fight develops. Homosexual mating is avoided here only through the noncompliance of the sex object and not through a discriminatory object choice of the initiating male.

## Hormonal Influence and Mating Behavior

As opposed to hunger, the biochemical changes which initiate sexual activity are well understood. In general, the occurrence of mating behavior is correlated with the presence of certain hormones. The androgens, secreted mainly by the male testes, are associated with masculine mating patterns. The estrogens, secreted by the female ovaries, are connected with female sexual behavior (see Chapter 10). This has been shown by observing behavior when these hormones are absent and also when they are present. For instance, fully developed mating behavior tends to occur after puberty, that is, after the gonads have become functional. Absence of the gonads and, therefore, the gonadal hormones tends to be correlated with an absence of mating activity, especially in females.

## Birds

### 1. *Castration*

In birds, castration reduces the frequency of elements of mating behavior, especially if the operation is performed prepuberally (Collias, 1950). The amount of such reduction varies greatly. In some male pigeons, copulatory behavior continues for as long as eight months after postpuberal castration (Carpenter, 1933). Observations of secondary sexual activities revealed increases in billing after castration (Carpenter, 1933a). In avian females, as contrasted with males, removal of the gonads leads to a complete cessation of all sexual activity.

## 2. *Hormone Administration in Immature Birds*

Noble and Zitrin (1942) have found that when male chicks were injected with testosterone propionate, they exhibited all the sexual behavior of the adult cock, such as crowing and a complete copulatory pattern. These authors also reported that when female chicks were given daily injections of estrogen since they were 15 days old, they squatted for treading males after about three weeks, thus prematurely showing the pattern typical of an adult hen. Boss (1943) induced sexual behavior in immature herring gulls by injecting testosterone. These experiments can be considered as evidence for two things: first, that sexual behavior occurs as a result of the presence of hormones; and second, that immature animals have a neural organization which is capable of producing sexual behavior, although this is not usually observed because of the absence of the relevant hormone.

# Mammals

## 1. *Castration before Puberty*

There is a very large diminution of sexual activity in mammalian males which have been castrated before puberty and in females whose ovaries have been removed prepuberally. Studies on this have been carried out on rats (Beach, 1942; Beach and Holtz, 1946), hamsters (Rosenblatt and Aronson, 1958, 1958a; and Warren and Aronson, 1957), guinea pigs (Sollenberger and Hamilton, 1939), and cats (Aronson, 1958). The example of a prepuberally castrated male chimpanzee (Clark, 1945) is often quoted to show that male sexual activity of primates is independent from the gonadal hormone. This chimpanzee was allegedly capable of vigorous sexual activity in adulthood. However, in reviewing this case, Rosenblatt and Aronson (1958a) drew attention to the fact that this animal was under hormone therapy, and that there is no published record showing that it ever copulated before administration of testosterone.

## 2. *Castration in Adulthood*

Many experimental observations have also been made on mammalian males castrated in adulthood. For instance, Stone (1927) reported that male rats castrated in adulthood lost their capacity to ejaculate before they failed to copulate. Forty-five percent of the castrates failed to copulate after two months. This percentage gradually increased with time. Thorek (1924) found that when male rhesus monkeys were castrated in adulthood, they made no mating attempts at the end of the sixth month after the operation. Other investigators have found a much greater length of persistence. Rosenblatt and Aronson (1958) reported that one of their castrated male cats intromitted four years after the operation. Many of their cats continued to make mating attempts, such as mounting, for years. However, considerable variability is found from one animal to another with regard to the persistence of mating activity after castration. Experience of mating prior to castration is an important factor here, as has been shown by Rosenblatt and Aronson (1958). They found that male cats with sexual experience before castration were more likely to exhibit the full mating pattern after castration than cats who have not had such experience.

### 3. Hormone Administration

Another line of evidence relating to the importance of hormones as initiating factors in sexual behavior comes from the effects of their administration. As in birds, sexual behavior can also be evoked in mammals through appropriate dosage with sex hormones. Beach (1948) reported cases of precocious sexual activity after giving mammals sex hormone treatment. Such results have been obtained in young male and female rats, mice, and dogs, but only weak results were obtained in guinea pigs (Gerall, 1958).

Injection of testosterone brings about sexual behavior in previously castrated males even when castration was performed before puberty. Such effects occur in all mammals. Stone reported that the return of sexual behavior in the rat after the injection of testosterone was the reverse order of its loss of sexual behavior following castration (Stone, 1939). For example, treatment with androgens results first in a return of copulatory behavior and later a return of ejaculation. Similar effects have been noted with estrogen injection in spayed females. Sexual receptivity occurs after estrogen injection in the female dog, cat, and rabbit. When an injection of progesterone in addition to a priming injection of estrogen is given to the rat, mouse, guinea pig, or hamster, sexual receptivity is increased. Similar effects are produced from various classes of normal animals that are not sexually active, such as senile animals and animals which have a seasonal quiescence of mating behavior. Minnick, Warden, and Arieti (1946), for example, restored copulatory activity in 28-month-old male rats. Beach (1948) reported a number of cases where various methods of manipulating the hormone level elicited mating behavior in animals which were out of season.

## Dependence of Mating on Sex Hormones

All the evidence available from animal studies suggests that females are completely dependent on gonadal hormones in their mating behavior (Beach, 1948). Evidence of any type of independence on gonadal hormones of mating activity is found only in prepuberally or postpuberally castrated males. It may be that the neural centers responsible for sexual behavior in the male are capable of residual activity without the biochemical stimulus normally supplied by sex hormones. On the other hand, it is also possible that in the male the neural centers which respond to hormonal influence are less specific in their sensitivity and consequently will continue to respond to a large range of biochemical factors after the gonads have been removed.

### THE LOCUS OF ACTION OF HORMONES: PERIPHERAL THEORIES

It has been believed that hormones produce mating behavior by their effect on peripheral bodily structures. In many ways this was a plausible idea. The presence of hormones does cause changes in peripheral structures. For example, during estrus, female monkeys develop conspicuous reddening and swelling of the skin around the genitalia. It was assumed that the stimulus which produced sexual behavior arose from the altered afferent messages arising from peripheral bodily structures. Such views are discussed and criticized by Lashley (1938). There is now considerable evidence against such peripheral theories since sex drive remains unimpaired by the removal or denervation of structures affected by sex hormones.

Ball (1934) demonstrated that female rats show normal patterns of mating behavior after the uterus and vagina have been removed. Bard (1935) obtained similar results in the female cat. Denervation of the sex organs of a cat (both the sensory fibers and the efferent sympathetic fibers) does not alter its mating behavior. In the male cat, desensitization of the genitalia by sectioning a part of the lower spinal cord still does not alter copulatory attempts (Root and Bard, 1947). Pauker (1948) found that ablation of the prostate and seminal vesicles in the hamster was without effect on mating behavior or on the rate of mating behavior disappearance after removal of the testes. Beach and Wilson (1963) have shown that ablation of the seminal vesicles does not change the mating behavior of the rat.

### THE CENTRAL LOCUS OF SENSITIVITY TO HORMONES

In the study of hunger and thirst, we have seen that there are structures in the hypothalamus which appear to translate biochemical factors into neural activity. The same is true in mating activity. Stimulation of restricted regions in the hypothalamus with minute quantities of hormone produces sexual activity (Fisher, 1956; Davidson and Sawyer, 1961). Restricted lesions in the hypothalamus abolish integrated mating behavior, even in the presence of adequate supplies of the appropriate hormone and the intactness of the development of genital structures and secondary sexual characteristics (Soulairac and Soulairac, 1956; Sawyer and Robinson, 1956). Such results will be more fully described in the next section when we consider central nervous structures which are critically involved in mating behavior.

## Evidence from Ablation Studies

In general, it may be said that two different effects may arise from lesions in the central nervous system both serving to abolish mating behavior; however, these effects have not always been distinguished. The effect of the first kind of lesions is to produce abolition of mating through gonadal atrophy in the following way.

Hypothalamic loci which are concerned with the regulation of the gonadotropic secretions of the anterior pituitary are destroyed (see p. 68) with the result that the gonads (testes or ovaries) become nonfunctional. Therefore the outcome of lesions of the first type is in effect the same as that of castration or of ovariectomy, because the supply of gonadal hormones is removed. This effect on mating behavior must be regarded as secondary, especially since mating behavior may be restored by the administration of the appropriate hormone. The effect of the second type of lesion is the complete abolition of spontaneous or integrated mating behavior even though no gonadal or genital atrophy results, and even in spite of the presence of adequate supplies of the appropriate hormone. Such lesions probably destroy the central nervous tissue which translates certain biochemical states into neural activity or the pathways leading from biochemically sensitive tissue. Consequently, the presence of hormones cannot be translated into the neural activity which produces mating behavior.

With this in mind let us now consider various ablation studies in detail. Soulairac and Soulairac (1956) found that two types of lesions served to abolish mating behavior in the male rat. The first type of lesion involves the medial and lateral mammillary nuclei. Reduction of copulatory behavior is sudden in animals with such lesions. In the presence of receptive females, male animals with such lesions show an undirected hyperactivity which often turns into aggressive behavior. Atrophy of the gonads and genitalia also results from these lesions. The second type of lesion consists of bilateral lesions of the preoptic area and of the suprachiasmatic nucleus. Mating behavior progressively decreases until it is completely abolished within 15 days after the operation. There is no atrophy of the testes or genitalia as a result of this type of lesion.

In male and female guinea pigs, lesions of the ventral portion of the anterior hypothalamus (between the optic chiasma and the stalk of the pituitary) eliminate mating behavior (Brookhart and Dey, 1941; Dey *et al.*, 1940). Injection of gonadal hormones does not evoke mating behavior in these guinea pigs (Brookhart *et al.*, 1940). Sawyer and Robinson (1956) produced lesions in the anterior hypothalamus of female cats. These lesions were produced rostral to the ventromedial nuclei and either medial

FIG. 2–1. Site of lesions in the female cat which interfere with reproductive behavior. A and B are anterior hypothalamic lesions which produce permanent anestrus which is not reversible by administration of estrogen. C is a lesion of the ventromedial hypothalamus, which induced ovarian atrophy. However mating behavior could be evoked by administration of estrogen. D, mammillary lesions with the same effect as in lesion illustrated in C. In E the reconstructions of the lesions are all projected on a midsagittal map: CA—anterior commissure; ch—optic chiasm; CP—posterior commissure; MI—massa intermedia; P—pons; IC—inferior colliculi; SC—superior colliculi; III—third ventricle; IV—fourth ventricle. (From Sawyer, C. H., *Handbook of Physiology*, 1960, p. 1232.)

to or within the area of the medial forebrain bundle. In most cases, such lesions result in a disappearance of estrous behavior in spite of estrogen administration. There is no ovarian regression, and ovulation can be induced by direct electrical stimulation of the ventromedial nucleus. Lesions of the ventromedial nucleus and destruction of the mammillary body or the premammillary region also result in anestrus. But such disappearance of estrus is due to ovarian regression, probably through a decline in the secretion of gonadotropic hormone by the anterior pituitary. Here mating behavior can be restored by administration of estrogen. (Figure 2–1.)

However, Sawyer (1957) found that in the female rabbit the site of lesion which produces anestrus without ovarian atrophy is in the mammillary region. Small bilateral lesions in this region led to an absence of estrous behavior, and this behavior could not be induced by administration of estrogen. The ovaries did not atrophy, and ovulation could be produced by stimulation of the hypophysis. However, ventral tuberal lesions involving the arcuate and the base of the ventromedial nuclei led to a failure of ovulation, and in some animals, such lesions led to ovarian atrophy. If a supply of estrogen was present, these animals would mate. From this evidence it seems that the release of ovulatory hormones by the pituitary is controlled by the basal tuberal area. On the other hand, the system involved in the initiation of mating activity appears to be in a different location in the cat than in the rabbit. In the cat this system is rostral to the basal tuberal area; in the rabbit it is caudal to the basal tuberal area. Nevertheless, there is a possibility that there are also effects on mating behavior in female rabbits when the anterior part of the hypothalamus is damaged. Sawyer reports that animals with damage in this area did not survive long enough to be tested. Experiments involving electrical recording from the anterior part of the hypothalamus (Green, 1954) suggest that this area is indeed involved (see below p. 51).

Different types of lesion effects have recently been obtained. Law and Meagher (1958) found in the rat that lesions of the midventral hypothalamus resulted in behavioral estrus without vaginal estrus. They found further that spayed female rats with such lesions also displayed behavioral estrus. Goy and Phoenix (1963) reported the latter condition in the guinea pig also after anterior ventral lesions of the hypothalamus. It remains to be determined whether or not such results are due to the destruction of some sexual inhibitory mechanism, or represent simply the irritative consequences of a lesion.

Evidence that mechanisms for both male and female behavior are present in females has been found by Hillarp et al. (1954). These workers made small bilateral lesions in the basal preoptic area of female rats. They found that within 20 to 30 minutes after awakening postoperatively from anesthesia, 18 animals (a small minority of their subjects) began to show male patterns of copulation directed indiscriminately at male or female animals. This behavior was continuously repeated for a few hours and then disappeared. It seems plausible to interpret this behavior as being due to an irritative effect of the lesion.

## Evidence from Local Hormonal Stimulation

Fisher (1956) has obtained further interesting evidence on hormone-sensitive loci within the hypothalamus. He used a technique similar to that which Andersson and coworkers used when studying thirst (see Chapter

1). This method involves the use of microinjections of substances thought to evoke certain behavior in order to determine the locus of their action on the nervous system. The substances are used in such minute quantities that their general effect after they have diffused would produce no noticeable reaction. Therefore if thirst or mating activity is produced by this method, it is likely that the excitatory substance has been injected very near the site of the cells which translate a particular biochemical state into specific behavior patterns. Fisher found that injections of 0.003 to 0.05 mg. of sodium testosterone sulfate (suspended in saline) in the region of the lateral preoptic area produced exaggerated sexual behavior. The elicited behavior often continued for more than 90 minutes following the injection. Though Fisher emphasized the possibility that causes other than hormonal may have produced this behavior, control injections of physiological saline, neural excitants, and electrical stimulation did not have the same effect in this experiment (but see p. 51).

However, male mating responses are not the only responses which have occurred after such treatment. Fisher describes responses such as nest building, retrieving, grooming litters of young, respiratory changes, diffuse hyperactivation, long-lasting exploratory-like behavior, repetitive localized muscular response, digging, leaping, and seizures. The effects of the hormone on the lateral preoptic region are therefore not clear-cut. It is possible that a high concentration of one hormone may excite centers which are maximally sensitive to other hormones.

Harris (1958) and Harris et al. (1958) reported that behavioral signs of estrus appeared when estrogen was placed into the hypothalamus of ovariectomized cats in quantities too small to be active if normally injected. Also, Kent and Liberman (1959) injected into the lateral ventricles of the brain doses of hormone which were too small to have any effects systemically. By this means they were able to provide further evidence of the central action of hormones on behavior. Having primed a castrated hamster with estrogen, they were able to produce behavioral estrus by an injection of progesterone into the ventricles.

Davidson and Sawyer (1961) used the technique of implanting estrogen-filled hypodermic needles into brain sites of rabbits, while Lisk (1962) used the same technique with rats. Again we see that it is possible to produce a state of behavioral receptivity by implants of estrogen in quantities too small to have an effect if normally injected. Using $C^{14}$-labeled estrogen for his implants in cats, Michael (1962) has shown that the spread of estrogen from the implant is very small (400–600 microns around the tip of the implant tube). Further, uptake of the hormone is restricted to a few cells, and there also seems to be a relation between the number of cells showing uptake of the estrogen around the implant and the behavioral effect of estrogen in promoting mating. This suggests that cells sensitive to the hormone are intermingled with cells having other functions.

## Evidence from Electrical Stimulation

Vaughn and Fisher (1962) in the rat have induced mounting, erection, and seminal emission as a part of coordinated sexual behavior by electrical stimulation in the anterior lateral hypothalamic area. MacLean and Ploog (1962) were able to produce erection in the squirrel monkey by stimulation in the septopreoptic area, septum, anterior and midline thalamic nuclei, hypothalamus, and cingulate gyrus. MacLean *et al.* (1962) obtained seminal discharge in the squirrel monkey by stimulating parts of the thalamus, especially from the parafascicular centromedian complex.

## Evidence from Recordings of Electrical Activity

Porter *et al.* (1957) have used electroencephalographic (EEG) recording from the hypothalamus during or after vaginal stimulation in the cat. Following copulation, the female cat exhibits a marked after-reaction that lasts for several minutes. During this after-reaction, bursts of high-amplitude EEG activity were observed in the medial forebrain bundle but never in the posterior hypothalamus. Such changes were seen only in the records of cats which were in estrus or to which estrogen had been administered.

Green (1954) obtained records of heightened electrical activity from the anterior hypothalamus of the female rabbit during sexual activity. He used the technique of chronic implantation of electrodes, which enabled him to record when the animals were unanaesthetised and unrestrained. As a result he was able to observe hypothalamic response during courtship and mating. Sawyer (1960) reported that he and Kawakami, using the same animal and a similar technique, have observed an after-reaction following copulation or vaginal stimulation. High-amplitude slow waves appear in the limbic cortical and hippocampal regions while the rabbit remains quiescent. The females in which this was observed had been treated with estrogen or a combination of progesterone and estrogen. In relation to studies using ablation techniques, a point of interest here is that this EEG after-reaction can be evoked by low-frequency electrical stimulation of the ventromedial region of the hypothalamus. Sawyer reports that neither vaginal nor hypothalamic stimulation evokes the EEG after-reaction when the female rabbit is anestrous.

### Transection Studies

*Spinal Copulatory Organization.* Many components of sexual activity can be demonstrated at the level of the spinal cord. It is possible in male animals to obtain erection of the penis and ejaculation through tactile stimulation following a supralumbar transection to the spinal cord. These responses may be obtained in spinal dog and spinal man. Sherrington (1900) noted that in the male dog, tactile stimulation following genital stimulation gives rise to movements which closely resemble those found during copulation. "These reflex movements suggest themselves as belonging to the act of copulation, and this suggestion is strengthened by failure to obtain similar movements on touching the analogous parts of the spinal bitch." This may be due to differences in peripheral morphological development which distinguishes the sexes.

*Hormones at the Spinal Level.* Do such neural mechanisms at the spinal level need sex hormones to render them functional? A study by Bromiley and Bard (1940) tends to rule out the notion that there are hormonal effects necessary for copulatory reflexes at the spinal level. These workers examined decapitated cats, both males and females in and out of estrus. They found that treading movements of the hindlegs and dorsal flexion of the pelvis occurred when the vulva or perineum of the female cat was gently rubbed. Also if one or the other side of the midline was touched, the tail moved to the opposite side and the pelvis turned towards the stimulated side. Such reactions occurred whether the females were fully in heat or fully anestrous; therefore, it appears that these lower neural systems are not themselves sensitive to hormonal influences in a way similar to certain portions of the hypothalamus, and that the lower neural systems operate well without such hormones. Such seems to be this independence that Bard (1940) states: "In fact one of the best examples of this spinal 'treading' was found in an animal which had been spayed thirty-nine months before and had never been treated with estrin; its genital tract was markedly atrophic." Dempsey and Rioch (1939) also found no change in spinal reflexes of the female guinea pig which could be ascribed to administration of estrogen and progesterone.

Bromiley and Bard stated that all the parts of the female copulatory reaction which they described in the female, they obtained in decapitate males. However, tail deflection was apparently less marked in males, and sometimes was even absent. Thus, in the tail deflection part of the female copulatory pattern of the cat, the spinal nervous mechanisms subserving tail deflection are insensitive to hormonal influence and are, to a large extent, common to both sexes.

Results on cats which are decerebrate (where only the medulla, pons, and lower mesencephalon are left intact) have been reported also by Bard and Bromiley (1940). In spite of the decerebrate rigidity found in such animals, an attitude suggestive of the feline estrual crouch can be elicited by stimulation of the vagina. Whether or not this response can be elicited does not depend on the hormonal condition of the animal. It can be in estrus or out of estrus.

*Components of Copulation.* The component reactions observed in copulation are produced by neural mechanisms other than those found in the hypothalamus, but these spinal mechanisms in the intact animal are a functional part of the system which is brought into activity when its hypothalamic component is hormonally stimulated. The responses which we have been considering are parts of the copulatory or end stage of sexual activity. However, mating behavior as elicited by hormones consists also of a large number of activities leading up to copulation. Many of these involve the detection and correct orientation towards a member of the opposite sex. Such activities presuppose a high degree of elaboration of afferent messages, especially those concerned with distance reception. In mammals, most of these activities are necessary for proper execution of the mating patterns of the male, while the female tends rather to provide a source of stimulation. It is therefore not surprising (as can be seen from Beach [1940, 1948] and Bard [1940]) that mating depends on cortical intactness to a greater degree in the male than in the female. Cortical ablation in the male cat may lead to the execution of copulatory movements before the animal has moved into the normal position for mating and therefore actual mating fails.

## BEHAVIORAL STUDIES AND THE NEURAL EXCITATORY POOL IN COPULATION

A set of studies on latencies to ejaculation in the rat suggest an interesting set of quantitative interactions to be explored at the neural level. As has been stated above (p. 42), the male rat intromits about twelve times before ejaculation occurs. Each intromission lasts about one third of a second and is separated from the previous one by an interval of 45 to 60 seconds. It has been found by Larsson (1956) and Rasmussen (quoted by Beach and Whalen, 1959b) that if this interval between intromissions is artificially lengthened by removing the female after the male has dismounted, the number of intromissions prior to ejaculation is decreased. This only occurs if the period between intromissions is increased up to three to five minutes. If the delay is increased up to 10 minutes, some males may not achieve ejaculation while other males will increase the number of intromissions before ejaculation.

Beach and Whalen interpreted these findings by saying that the stimulus of each intromission begins a process of excitation which rises for at least three minutes. Since this level of excitement must reach a certain threshold before ejaculation can occur, an enforced waiting period after each intromission will increase the excitatory store beyond the normal level. As a result, the excitatory level will reach an ejaculatory threshold after fewer intromissions. It could be suggested, as an alternative, that each intromission causes a swiftly occurring sensory change, such as adaptation, to occur to the receptors in the penis; this adaptation would cause withdrawal, and could gradually wear off after each withdrawal. Thus we can assume that only incoming stimulation is stored and added to the excitatory pool; and we can assume that a longer spacing of the intromissions will bring in more stimulation (or more of the correct kind of stimulation) with each intromission, since there is more time for adaptation to wear off between intromissions. It would not, according to this alternative hypothesis, be necessary to assume that the level of the excitatory pool increased spontaneously while the rat was inactive. If we assume, as in the previous explanation, that there is also a spontaneous decay of excitation in the excitatory pool, then we can account for the data that relates the interval between intromissions with the speed of ejaculation together with the fact of withdrawal itself.

In a further study of this problem, Beach and Whalen (1959) allowed male rats to intromit one, four, or seven times and then, after an imposed interval ranging from 75 to 120 minutes, they observed how many more times the rats would have to intromit before ejaculating. It appears from their results that the greater the number of initial intromissions, the smaller the number of additional intromissions needed to produce ejaculation when there are delays of at least 30 minutes following initial intromissions. In general, this study confirms the notion that in some way each intromission added to a pool of excitation that decays at a slow rate but increases with each successive intromission until the threshold for ejaculation is reached (providing delays between intromissions are not too long).

It has been observed that after the first ejaculation, the male rat will rest for about five minutes before he will begin to mate again. The second set of intromissions leading to ejaculation differs from the first set as follows: (1) the time between intromissions is less, and (2) fewer intromissions occur before ejaculation (e.g., Larsson, 1956; Beach and Jorden, 1956). This change continues in subsequent bouts of copulation in the series until mating ceases. Beach and Whalen (1959) found that the effect of the first ejaculation, that is, a reduction in time between intromissions, upon the subsequent copulatory bouts in the series lasted up to five hours. Similarly, the effect of the first ejaculation on the number of times intromission is necessary for a subsequent ejaculation was shown to persist for 90 minutes. During this time the number of intromissions necessary to produce an ejaculation was smaller than during the first set of intromissions leading to an ejaculation. The length of time between an ejaculation and a subsequent bout of intromissions also increases as a function of immediately preceding ejaculations. Such behavioral results are likely to be due to an interplay of ejaculatory mechanisms (which can function autonomously at the spinal level, at least in dog and man, see above p. 51) and other mechanisms higher in the nervous system.

## HORMONES VERSUS SEX OF ANIMAL AS DETERMINANTS OF BEHAVIOR

We have seen that the absence of hormones, male or female, tends to abolish sexual behavior. We may ask whether the type of behavior evoked depends on the specific hormone present, or on the sex of the recipient. To state it more concretely, will estrogen injected in a castrated male produce female mating behavior or male mating behavior? The safest generalization at present is that the behavior produced on administration of a hormone, whether it is androgen or an estrogen, is the behavior appropriate to the sex of the recipient. Castrated males will respond by exhibiting male behavior after the administration of estrogens. This has been shown in rats (Ball [1939] and Beach [1942]), in capons (Goodale, 1918), and in cats (Green *et al.*, 1957). However, it seems that the effectiveness of estrogens in producing this behavior is not strong. On the other hand there is only slight evidence that estrogens injected into castrated males may produce female behavior. The evidence on the injection of androgens into spayed females is complicated by the fact that a great deal of masculine behavior is manifested by normal females or by spayed females injected with estrogens. The evocation of female behavior by spayed females treated with androgens has been reported in rats by Beach (1942) and in cats by Green *et al.* (1957).

## SEXUAL DIFFERENTIATION

From the above evidence it seems that the effect of a hormone depends on the sex of the recipient or, more specifically, on the characteristics of the neural tissue which have been established by a process of differentiation at the fetal or neonatal stage. While it seems that in the adult the action of the hormone is merely to activate, it appears that it has a differentiating function while the organism is developing. In the mammal the presence of testosterone during fetal development (usually supplied by the immature fetal testes) leads to the development of male morphological characters. For instance, if testosterone is administered in utero to female fetuses, such as female rhesus monkeys (Young *et al.*, 1964), a penis and scrotum develop. On the other hand, in the castrated fetal male, there is a development of female sexual apparatus, presumably because testosterone is absent. Of profound importance to the student of behavior is the observation that a similar type of differentiation occurs in the central nervous system as well as in the peripheral sexual apparatus under the same hormonal fetal conditions. The presence of androgens during early stages of development produces an adult that will react to the presence of sex hormones by exhibiting male behavior. Such a behavioral effect has now been demonstrated in rats, guinea pigs, and rhesus monkeys (Young, *et al.*, 1964). It has also been possible to show that if males are castrated before the period of differentiation by testosterone, they will develop into adults that display feminine behavior when injected with estrogen and progesterone. In the rat such a demonstration is feasible. In this species, the period in which differentiation occurs appears to be postnatal rather than prenatal, and it ends about the tenth day after birth. It has been reported

(Young *et al.*, 1964) that when primed with female sex hormones, males castrated before they were five days old displayed a very large increase in feminine behavior compared to males castrated at or after the tenth day after birth. "On the one hand, females treated with androgen during the appropriate period show a regression or inhibition of feminine behavior and an accentuation of masculine behavioral traits. Males deprived of the principal source of endogenous androgen during a comparable period show accentuated feminine behavior and the absence of, or greatly diminished capacity for, masculine behavior" (Young *et al.*, 1964).

Of great interest also is the finding in the rhesus monkey that not only is sexual behavior altered but that social patterns characteristic of a particular sex are also reversed in a similar manner. Female monkeys treated with androgens during the stage of differentiation closely resemble males on such indices as facial threats or play patterns.

## The Genesis of Mating Behavior in Man

The conditions which can be brought about experimentally in rats, guinea pigs, and rhesus monkeys also occur as a result of disease or mishap in man. Individuals may be born with gonads (testes, ovaries) belonging to one sex but a genital morphology resembling the other sex in varying degrees. These are called pseudohermaphrodites. One class of pseudohermaphrodite possesses ovaries but a masculine external genital morphology. This is due to the presence of androgens during fetal development which may come about in various ways. For example, the mother may be given androgens or the orally active progestational compounds during her pregnancy for therapeutic reasons; or, in a condition known as congenital adrenal hyperplasia, the adrenal cortex of the fetus secretes excessive amounts of androgens. In a second class, the pseudohermaphrodite possesses testes, but a female external genital morphology. This may be caused by subnormal testicular function in the male fetus.

Such pseudohermaphrodites are generally reared as male or female depending on their external genital morphology. In later life they behave in the manner expected of the sex of their upbringing and not of their biological sex as determined by their possession of one or other type of gonad. Because of this conflict between biological sex and cultural or social sex, such cases have been quoted to support the argument that learning and not biologic sex determines sexual behavior (e.g., Hardy, 1964). Such an argument is, however, invalid. From the evidence in animals, we have seen that if hormones during fetal life produce a male type of genital morphology, they also result in male sexual behavior in later life, irrespective of the type of gonad present. Since a pseudohermaphrodite tends to be brought up according to the morphology of the genitalia, we would expect the same result on both the cultural and physiological view of the genesis of sexual behavior.

## THE EFFECTS OF EXPERIENCE ON MATING

In view of the fact that mating behavior tends to be dependent on the presence of certain hormones, we may ask whether the hormones evoke entire integrated sequences of behavior when they first stimulate the relevant parts of the nervous system or whether mating behavior is gradually perfected through experience. Species differences appear to be a factor governing the role of experience in mating.

Rats, both male and female, mate in the same way on the first occasion as on subsequent occasions; and so do some dogs and cats (Beach, 1958). However, Nissen (1953) reported that sexually naive chimpanzees need many periods of contact before they will mate. It is difficult to assess the importance of experience in the development of mating activity and other instinctive activity. Many assume that sexual activity is partially learnt. But it has not been made entirely clear what is meant by learning sexual activity. Is it learning in the sense of maze learning where the animal begins to manifest correct responses rather than incorrect responses? Or is it learning in the sense that a rat learns to eat in an originally unfamiliar place, where fear of strange surroundings had interfered with the feeding response?

There have been many studies on this problem. Hayward (1957) has shown that when immature male rats were trained to avoid females in heat, they would show inhibition of mating behavior when they became mature. Similarly, Rasmussen (1955) found that when male rats were given an electric shock whenever they attempted to mount females, they would later attempt to copulate with other males more frequently than with females. Also, Beach et al., (1956) were able to inhibit sexual responsiveness in male rats by subjecting them to electric shock every time they attempted to mate. These studies show that sexual behavior is similar to other types of behavior in that it is susceptible to interference effects. Particularly interesting are studies which have shown enhancement of sexual activity when as a result of learning one would expect the opposite to occur. Kagan and Beach (1953) reared immature male rats under two conditions: (1) one group of rats were periodically exposed to females, and (2) another group of rats were completely isolated from females. It was found that during testing the isolated group copulated more frequently than the group which had been given prepuberal contact. Kagan and Beach attributed this result to the interfering effects of previously learnt playful activity. These results show the importance of interfering behavior tendencies which may mask behavior patterns which are not learnt. However, in similar studies, Zimbardo (1958), who worked with the rat, obtained the opposite result as did Valenstein et al. (1955) who worked with the guinea pig.

Another experiment, with results at first sight paradoxical, has been reported by Beach and Fowler (1959). These authors subjected male rats in a particular environment to a series of painful electric shocks. They found that these rats later mated in this environment but that the number of intromissions to ejaculation was actually lower than in rats in a normal environment. As explanation for this behavior, these workers suggested that autonomic arousal due to fear of shock has a facilitatory effect on orgasm.

A series of experiments performed by Rabedeau and Whalen (1959) is especially pertinent to the idea that experience in mating leads to increased speed toward copulation mainly through elimination of competing responses. In their first experiment, they were able to show that male rats selected on the basis of their slowness to initiate coitus showed a very large decrement in latency to copulate as a result of copulatory experience. The results of this experiment could be explained in terms of an increase in arousability or learning to initiate copulation. However, in their second experiment of the series, Rabedeau and Whalen selected males who initiated coitus quickly. These rats were then divided into two groups. The first group were allowed to have sexual experience while the second group were not. To see if learning in terms of a higher "arousability" through experience had taken place, these workers castrated both groups of animals. This had the effect of lengthening latencies to coitus, presumably by lowering sex drive. Without such a procedure, latencies would have been so short for both groups that any effect of experience could not have been detected. However, in this second experiment, no significant difference due to prior experience could be found, although latencies to coitus were increased to a range where differences due to experience should have been detected.

It may be that a competing tendency has to wear off in rats which are slow to initiate coitus, whereas such a tendency is absent in animals which initiate coitus without delay, so that experience does not differentially remove a competing tendency.

In such species as the dog, cat, and rat, a sexually inexperienced female will mate and no learning is apparent in subsequent matings. However, Whalen (1963) has shown that sexually inexperienced female cats permit coitus more quickly after experience of intromission, thus showing a learning effect. From Whalen's description it seems that such learning was due to a lessening importance of conflicting aggressive tendencies. Whalen describes this as follows: ". . . Naive female cats would not readily mate in the laboratory even though they had been treated extensively with endogenous entrogen, and would assume the mating posture either spontaneously in the home cage or in response to perineal tapping by the investigator. When placed with a male, the naive queen would hiss and strike at the male when he approached. Usually this resistance by the female was rapidly overcome when the investigator held the female permitting the male to mount and achieve the initial intromission. Thereafter, mounting and intromission occurred without intervention."

## ABNORMALITIES OF SEXUAL BEHAVIOR AND BRAIN LESIONS

Kluver and Bucy (1939) noted that animals with their temporal lobes removed manifested, among other symptoms, "hypersexuality" (see Chapter 5). Schreiner and Kling (1956) demonstrated similar effects in the agouti, monkey, cat, and lynx, with more restricted lesions confined mainly to the amygdala and the overlying pyriform cortex. These effects appear mostly in the male and do not occur in the absence of sex hormones. Green et al. (1957) reported that the so-called hypersexual symptoms could be produced by lesions of the pyriform cortex alone, without damage to the neighboring amygdala. They found that male cats with such lesions differed from normal cats by copulating with other species, anesthetized animals, and kittens; by masturbating; and by indulging in sexual activities outside their own territory (Figure 2–2).

It might be argued that the effect of this lesion is irritative and that it simply acts to increase male copulatory tendencies in a similar way as the lesions inflicted on females by Hillarp et al. (1954). This argument is strengthened by the results of an experiment conducted by Green and co-workers where they inflicted similar lesions on female cats. After the operation a few of these cats began to show male sexual patterns, such as pouncing, mounting, neck grips, and genital sniffing. This behavior persisted in spite of vicious rebuffs by the animal being molested. That some abnormality of stimulation of the hypothalamus may have been occurring is indicated by the finding that one of these female cats ovulated spontaneously. In normal cats, ovulation only occurs as a consequence of mounting by a male through the intermediacy of the hypothalamic control of the anterior pituitary. However, Gastaut (1952) has reported that cats with rhinencephalic lesions show estrous behavior without accompanying changes in the reproductive organs. This finding is against the hypothesis of Schreiner and Kling that the "hypersexuality" observed in their male animals is due to an increase in sex hormones produced by the lesion. If this were true, then physiological signs of estrus should have been produced by such lesions in females. On the other hand, it is possible that differences in lesions were such that no direct comparison could be made. However, such findings do not exclude a direct irritative effect on mechanisms subserving sexual arousal in the hypothalamus.

On the other hand, it would be equally plausible to assign this disorder to causes similar to those responsible for indiscriminate eating due to lesions of the amygdala. In this case it was argued that an animal must avoid various properties possessed by certain substances which would be deleterious if ingested. The disruption of this mechanism was postulated as an explanation of the effects of amygdalectomy on feeding habits. Here it might similarly be argued that the occasions for copulation must also be delimited by attractions towards certain properties and repulsions from other properties. Copulation with "unsuitable" sexual partners could be interpreted as due to an absence of repulsion from them, rather than as an increase in their attractive properties.

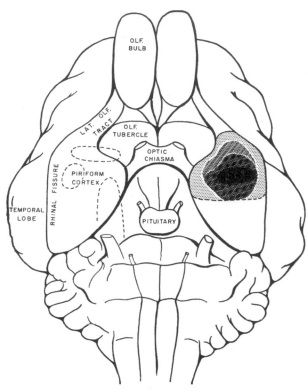

FIG. 2–2. Site of lesion which produces "hypersexuality" in cats. (Fig. 2, Green, J. D., Clemente, C. D., and DeGroot, J., *J. Comp. Neur.*, 108, 522.)

In support of this view is the finding that these animals also tend to show increased tameness. Fear and rage often seem to be absent. If these factors were absent it would be natural to expect copulatory attempts in an environment where these attempts would normally be inhibited by fear and on animals which would ordinarily evoke fear or aggression.

There have also been reports of human cases where similar areas of the brain have been excised, as in the animal studies quoted above, in attempts to ameliorate the condition of patients suffering from epilepsey or schizophrenia. Terzian and Dalle Ore (1955) reported the case of a young male epileptic with a bilateral removal of the anterior portion of the temporal lobes and the amygdaloid nucleus (similar to the lesions inflicted by Kluver and Bucy). This unfortunate man was reduced to a state bordering on imbecility, and he became docile and manageable in contrast to his previous dangerously violent tendencies. Beside other symptoms unrelated to sex, there appeared frequent masturbation, exhibitionistic, and some homosexual tendencies. However, with the exception of masturbation, these tendencies were only verbal in their expression. Sawa *et al.* (1954) reported the case of five male schizophrenics and one male epileptic with bilateral amygdalectomy. (This lesion appears to correspond to the area removed by Schreiner and Kling.) Though the patients were observed up to four months after the operations, there was found little accentuation of sexual behavior to speak of. "There was no such sexual response as a frequent erection of the penis as was reported in Kluver and Bucy's monkeys, the patients simply enjoyed talks on sexual topics to the nursing women, going no further than taking hands" (Sawa *et al.*, p. 326). Taken in the context of the patients' other symptoms, such behavior can hardly be taken to represent hypersexuality. However, in these cases it is difficult to be sure of the precise extent and location of the lesion.

## MATERNAL BEHAVIOR

Maternal behavior is a name for a set of behavior tendencies involved in care of the young. This may include such heterogeneous activities as nest building, retrieving of young, and feeding the young. In the cage-bred rat, maternal behavior consists of building a nest, cleaning the pups, nursing them, and retrieving them when they leave the nest. With the probable exception of retrieving such behavior is similar also for the caged domestic rabbit. However, when the same rabbit is released and permitted to live under seminatural conditions, a much larger repertoire of maternal activity is discovered. The pregnant female digs a tunnel that terminates in a spherical chamber. The tunnel is then sealed from the outside. Some time later the female gathers wisps of dry grass, opens up the nest again, and lines the base of the spherical chamber with the grass. She also plucks fur from her belly to lay on top of the grass. The entrance to the tunnel is again sealed. The female again enters the tunnel when the young are born. She nurses them once a day and seals up the entrance of the tunnel after every visit. When the female stops nursing, she makes a hole in the sealed entrance to the tunnel just large enough for the young to emerge. During the period of nursing the female keeps well away from the entrance of the tunnel. The sealing of the entrance is so well executed that it is almost impossible for the human eye to distinguish it from the surrounding earth. If one of the young is taken out of the nest and placed by the nursing female, there is no reaction besides sniffing. It is clear that retrieving has no place in the natural repertoire of this species of animal.

Thus maternal behavior is a complex of activities which differs from one species to another. Such behavior is evoked by an administration or withdrawal of hormones. A combination of hormones found in a pregnant female just before parturition is effective in producing maternal behavior. However, prolactin or lactogenic hormone secreted by the anterior pituitary is the most important of these hormones. Prolactin causes the development of the mammary glands and milk secretion. Estrogen, on the other hand, has been shown by Hain (1935) to inhibit maternal responses, even when the dose is too small to interrupt lactation. Injections of prolactin into virgin females and males also cause retrieving of the young. However, Leblond (1940) found that such activities will appear when these animals are simply exposed to young. Such cases could be analogous to the observation of Witschi (1935) who found that when a female pigeon saw another incubating female, this was sufficient to evoke secretion of lactogenic hormone by the pituitary, thus inducing the changes necessary for crop milk secretion.

The stimuli which evoke maternal behavior vary greatly even within one species. The writer has observed a rat which would repeatedly retrieve its own tail. It would leave the nest, see its tail, pick it up carefully between its teeth, and deposit it in the nest. Models of young rats possessing varying levels of crudity can also produce retrieving behavior. In general, however, it seems that the younger the pups, the greater the tendency for maternal behavior to be evoked (e.g. Wiesner, Sheard, 1933). This does not mean that occasionally even adult animals will not evoke maternal behavior. The writer has observed female ferrets (Putorius vulgaris) retrieving other adult female ferrets with great persistence and vigor.

The execution of maternal activities such as nest building and retrieving young depends to a large extent on exteroceptive cues. For instance, the young must normally be seen or heard squealing after they have left the nest before the mother will retrieve them. However, it seems that various sensory avenues are to some extent interchangeable in the rat. Wiesner and Sheard (1933) found that rats rendered anosmic and deaf still built nests and retrieved young. Somewhat similar findings have been reported by Beach and Jaynes (1956). These authors, however, found that blinding, rendering rats anosmic, and severing the sensory nerves to the snout at the same time completely destroyed maternal behavior. A combination of two of these handicaps produced serious impairment in the care of the young.

That sensory avenues are not always interchangeable for maternal behavior is shown by the behavior of the hen. If the hen can only see a distressed chick that manifests its distress clearly to a human observer and cannot hear it, then the hen takes no notice. However, the hen need only to hear the distress call of the chick and not see it for appropriate maternal action to take place.

A decrease in parental efficiency has also been reported by Beach (1937), Stone (1939), and Davis (1939) after extensive cortical lesions, the size of the lesion being reported as being more important than its placement. However, Stamm (1955) observed that removal of portions of the cingulate and retrosplenial cortex, comprising only about 16 percent of the cortex, impairs maternal behavior very seriously, whereas control lesions of a similar size elsewhere were without noticeable effect. Rosvold (1949) reported that in a rat, extended electroconvulsive shock during the last half of pregnancy abolishes nest building and care of the young. Though such a finding is not unexpected, an explanation of it is obscure.

## Nest Building

In a majority of instances, domestic rabbits that are permitted to live under seminatural conditions will work at nest building or burrowing only during pregnancy. In many other species, however, we find that some nest building or shelter construction takes place with no particular relation to the care of the young. However, there may be an enhancement of nest building during pregnancy as in the case of the laboratory rat (Kinder, 1927) and mouse (Koller, 1952, 1956). Koller (1952) also observed that administration of prolactin did not induce nest building in the mouse. It has been observed that hypophysectomy or thyroidectomy in rats leads to increased nest building (Richter, 1941). Such effects are probably due to the efforts of the animal to conserve heat, since there is a drop in the animal's temperature. Koller (1956) has induced increased nest building in mice by shaving their hair, and Kinder (1927) has increased nest building in rats by lowering room temperature. It seems that progesterone levels are important in regulating nest building. Koller (1952, 1956) has observed that administration of progesterone to male and female mice leads to an increase in nest building. However, administration of estrogens leads to a decrease in nest building in females but an increase in males. A relationship in the contrary direction exists in rabbits where it has been shown that removal of the corpus luteum during pregnancy leads to immediate nest-building behavior, including plucking of fur (Klein, 1952, (1956).

### THE ENDOCRINE SYSTEM

Because of the importance of glandular factors in instinctive activities, it is necessary to summarize the relevant information about the functioning of the endocrine glands. These glands secrete into the blood stream minute amounts of substances called hormones. They enter into and modify various biochemical processes in the body and thus exert their influence on various aspects of physiological functioning.

Many of the endocrine secretions directly affect the functioning of the nervous system. The secretions of the thyroid influence metabolism and the utilization of carbohydrates. In adulthood an absence of thyroid hormone can cause mental dulling and even psychotic symptoms (myxedematous madness). A congenital malfunction of this gland causes cretinism which manifests itself by extreme mental retardation and lack of growth.

Another organ secreting a hormone important in nervous function is the adrenal medulla. Epinephrine, which is secreted by the gland, has widespread effects that chiefly reinforce the sympathetic nervous system. It increases heart rate, induces more rapid blood clotting, increases sugar output by the liver, and in addition influences the central nervous system. It has been claimed that epinephrine acts directly on the reticular formation (Bonvallet *et al.*, 1954; Dell, 1958). EEG activation can be induced by the administration of epinephrine. Porter (1952) also reports EEG activation of the posterior hypothalamus in response to epinephrine. In this way secretion of epinephrine by the adrenal medulla might prolong and intensify arousal of the organism.

Other glands are important as regulators of the balance of various substances in the body. The beta cells of the pancreas secrete insulin which is necessary to maintain the level of sugar in the blood by promoting storage of sugar. A deficiency of insulin secretion, as in diabetes mellitus, causes an overproduction of glucose from internal and external sources, thus causing hyperglycemia. The alpha cells of the pancreas, on the other hand, produce glucagon which may promote glucose uptake (see p. 26).

Another gland that is useful in regulating levels of various substances in the blood is the parathyroid. This gland maintains calcium and phosphorus balance in the blood. Its removal causes loss of calcium and enhanced levels of phosphorus with consequent tetany. The potassium-sodium balance is maintained by hormones of the adrenal cortex. Among other symptoms, such as general muscular weakness, removal of the adrenal gland leads to rapid loss of sodium.

Of great importance from the behavioral point of view are the gonads. The male gonads secrete testosterone which causes development of the male physical characteristics. These physical characteristics vary from species to species. In man, these are the changes seen at puberty. There is growth of pubic hair, growth of facial hair, and increased hirsutism (though this varies from one genetic group to another), changes in the voice, development of the penis, and an increase in muscular development. On the other hand decrease in testosterone level, as in castration, causes changes on the surface and structure of the penis (Beach and Levinson, 1950). Ovarian hormones in the female influence physical development by causing changes in the genitalia and the appearance of secondary sexual characteristics. Ovarian secretions are for the greater part cyclic. These cycles are intimately connected with the activity of the anterior pituitary, which in turn is under the control of the hypothalamus.

## The Anterior Pituitary and Sex Hormones

The endocrine glands are controlled partly by the nervous system but mainly by chemical factors in the blood. Of these chemical factors, the most important comes from the anterior pituitary gland. This organ secretes a set of hormones that in turn stimulate many other endocrine glands to secrete their particular hormones. For instance the anterior pituitary secretes a luteinizing hormone that causes the development and maintenance of the interstitial cells of the testis and also affects the ovaries. The anterior pituitary also liberates follicle-stimulating hormone which causes the development of spermatozoa-producing tissue in the testis. The same hormone also causes the development of the ovary follicles. Under the influence of the luteinizing hormone from the pituitary, the testes produce their own hormones, called the androgens (testosterone, androstenodione). These in turn produce secondary sex characteristics and the behavioral tendencies of the male. Similarly, the female gonads (the ovaries) secrete hormones which produce female secondary sex characteristics in a complex cycle called the estrous cycle.

At the beginning of the estrous cycle, the follicles of the ovaries begin developing when the anterior pituitary secretes a follicle-stimulating hormone. As the immature follicle develops, it secretes estrogen. Estrogen then stimulates the anterior pituitary to produce the luteinizing hormone. The combination of the follicle-stimulating hormone and luteinizing hormone causes further development of the follicle, which thus secretes more estrogen. These large amounts of estrogen have two main effects: they alter the uterus and vagina (including their epithelium) and they change the ratio in which the pituitary secretes luteinizing and follicle-stimulating hormone. As a result more luteinizing and less follicle-stimulating hormone is secreted. As this occurs, the ovum is released by the rupture of the follicle (ovulation). After the ovum has left it, the ruptured follicle develops into the corpus luteum, continuing to secrete estrogen and also progesterone, a hormone which occurs in large quantities in pregnancy. These two hormones prepare the epithelium of the uterus for implantation of the ovum should fertilization of the ovum occur. If it does not, the corpus luteum regresses, and also the level of estrogen and progesterone. This drop in the level of these hormones causes the pituitary to secrete follicle-stimulating hormone again. This begins the next estrous cycle.

Parallel to these physiological changes there is a behavioral cycle of female receptivity, called heat, which occurs at the time of ovulation. In mammals with short estrous cycles, like rats and mice, progesterone is not secreted during the estrous cycle. It is, however, produced through the development of the corpus luteum if fertilization of the ovum, and then pregnancy occurs.

The outline of events occurring during the estrous cycle is basically similar in all spontaneously ovulating mammals. In the human case, however, the lining of the uterus is sloughed off, with resultant menstrual bleeding which should not be identified with heat or estrus in lower mammals. In most spontaneously ovulating mammals, copulation occurs only during the estrus or heat. However, as we ascend the phylogenetic scale from monkey to man, a progressive independence of intercourse with time of ovulation is observed. In some mammals, such as the rabbit, ovulation does not occur in spontaneous cycles but only after sexual excitement is produced in the female by a mounted male or by genital stimulation.

## Neural Influence on the Anterior Pituitary

It has been shown that the secretions of the anterior pituitary are of the greatest importance in regulating sexual functions. However, this structure is itself under the influence of neural factors. For instance, the estrous cycle has been described as if it were merely due to an interplay between the anterior pituitary and the ovary. However, it is known that in at least a part of this cycle the hypothalamus plays an indispensable role. Similar evidence for the importance of neural factors will be described as suggested first by behavioral evidence and then by physiological methods.

### Birds

Most birds are seasonal breeders. Gonadal development, which is under the control of the pituitary, and plumage changes, which may be under direct pituitary control or under indirect influence of the pituitary through the gonads, occur only at certain times in the year. Some birds adapt themselves immediately to a change of seasons when transported across the equator (Marshall, 1942). It has been shown that seasonal changes in light intensity stimulate pituitary gonadotropic activity in many species (Rowan, 1938). It seems that ovulation, which is under the control of the pituitary, occurs only during daylight in the domestic fowl (Warren and Scott, 1936). Artificial exclusion of light during the day and night lighting can lead to a reversal in the time of ovulation.

However, the dependence of endocrine changes on ambient illumination varies from one species to another. In the sparrow (Passer domesticus, Linnaeus), ovarian development is relatively unaffected by manipulation of the length of light to which this bird is exposed. Neural factors which emanate from nesting and mating activities seem to be important in bringing about the sparrow's ovarian development (Riley and Witschi, 1938). Darling (1938) has brought forward evidence that stimulation from other members of a flock may be a strong factor in bringing about the requisite endocrine development in the individual member of a flock. A good example of the importance of this type of stimulation occurs in the pigeon. A female pigeon in isolation does not ovulate. However, homosexual activity between two female pigeons causes both of them to lay eggs. Further, ovulation occurs if a female is simply placed within sight of a male pigeon, or another female, or even if she is supplied with a mirror so that the reflection of herself acts as the stimulus. Further, when the male pigeon sees an incubating female, a lactogenic hormone is secreted by the pituitary of the male pigeon, thus inducing the changes necessary for crop milk secretion (Witschi, 1935).

For any species of bird, the female generally lays a constant number of eggs in a clutch. It seems that the control of the number of eggs laid is through an inhibition of the ovulatory process (initiated by the pituitary) caused by stimulation produced by the eggs themselves after laying has occurred. If eggs are withdrawn as they are laid, laying continues (Witschi, 1935).

## Mammals

In mammals, neural factors also play an important role in regulating pituitary secretion. As in the case of birds, transporting mammals across the equator to the opposite hemisphere leads to a change in their breeding rhythm that corresponds with an alteration of the seasons. Such changes have been observed in sheep, deer, and many other species (Marshall, 1937). The reproductive rhythm of many common mammals is affected by variations in environmental lighting. Harris (1960) quotes as examples the mouse, rat, ferret, hedgehog, cotton-tailed rabbit, cat, raccoon, and goat. The influence of environmental lighting has been most extensively studied in the ferret (*Putorius vulgaris*). In the northern hemisphere, the female of this species does not exhibit estrous activity between September and February. However estrus can be induced by placing the animal in 16 hours of light per day during this period. It has been demonstrated (Harris, 1960) that this dependence of estrus on light exists because of a connection between the hypothalamus and the anterior pituitary gland.

In some mammals, ovulation itself is dependent not on a cycle but on some form of external stimulation (as was seen in some birds). Such is the case in the rabbit, ferret, cat, ground squirrel, and mink (Harris, 1960). Here ovulation depends on stimulation from a male or stimulation of parts of the genitalia, which then results in a gonadotropic discharge from the pars distalis of the anterior pituitary.

There is also a neural influence on other endocrines through the anterior pituitary. Selye (1950) has drawn attention to and summarized much of the work showing the effect of emotional stress on the adrenal cortex. Discharge of adrenal cortical hormone follows stress in many species such as the mouse, rat, rabbit, and human.

There is also evidence that the action of the thyroid is to some extent dependent on the nervous system. Emotional and physical stress lead to a lowered secretion of thyroid hormone (e.g., Brown-Grant *et al.*, 1954). It seems also that overactivity of the thyroid in Graves' disease follows upon emotional disturbance (e.g., Thompson and Blount, 1954). Therefore it is thought that the endocrine system is to a large extent controlled by the nervous system acting through the anterior pituitary.

## The Mechanism of Anterior Pituitary Control by the Hypothalamus

The behavioral evidence discussed above showing how sensory signals may modify the working of the endocrine system naturally leads us to the question as to how this control is exercised. Anatomically speaking, the anterior pituitary is close to the hypothalamus, joined to it by the hypophyseal stalk. The anterior lobe of the pituitary (also called the adenohypophysis) is subdivided into the pars distalis, pars tuberalis, and pars intermedia. The main secretory center is in the pars distalis.

It seems clear that messages from the hypothalamus excite the anterior pituitary to secrete gonadotrophic, adrenocorticotrophic, and thyrotrophic hormones. First, electrical stimulation of the hypothalamus releases these hormones from the pituitary. However, direct electrical stimulation of the anterior pituitary does not produce this effect (Harris, 1948). Second, transplantation of the anterior pituitary to other parts of the brain away from the hypothalamus causes absence of normal function by the transplant even though an adequate blood supply redevelops. Harris and Jacobsohn (1952) found that in such transplant cases there were no estrous cycles and that organs of reproduction suffered complete atrophy. Animals with a transplanted pituitary also showed marked atrophy of the adrenal cortex, though not to quite such a degree as when the pituitary was completely removed. Similar findings to these have been made concerning thyroid activity following a pituitary transplant.

However, the mode of control of the hypothalamus over the anterior pituitary is not by means of nervous pathways. It appears that the pars distalis is devoid of innervation by the hypothalamus. It seems instead that the anterior pituitary is stimulated to secretion by blood-borne chemical messages originating in the hypothalamus. The normal functioning of the anterior pituitary correlates well with the intactness of the blood supply passing from the hypothalamus and its state of regeneration after section of the hypophyseal stalk. Transplants of anterior pituitary tissue begin to function normally when their blood supply from the hypothalamus develops. It seems that there are cells in the hypothalamus (which have been called neurosecretory cells) that secrete substances capable of causing the anterior pituitary, in turn, to secrete hormones. These neurosecretory cells send out fibers that come into close proximity with blood vessels running into the anterior pituitary. It is thought that the secretion passes from these fibers of the neurosecretory cells into the circulatory system supplying the anterior pituitary, thus stimulating it to secrete, or inhibiting it from secreting.

## The Role of the Hypothalamus in Anterior Pituitary Control

As was stated above (p. 65) the anterior pituitary secretes luteinizing hormone and follicle-stimulating hormone besides other hormones. These secretions have a gonadotrophic effect in both sexes. In the female the release of these hormones is cyclic. In the male such a cycle as the estrous cycle is absent. It has been demonstrated that the pituitary itself is not sexually differentiated but that the cyclic character of its secretion in the female is imposed by the hypothalamus. A pituitary taken from a male rat and transplanted into the appropriate position in a female maintains a normal estrous cycle and pregnancy (Harris and Jacobsohn, 1952). If ovarian tissue is transplanted into a castrated male rat, follicular ripening occurs, but the cycle of phenomena described above (p. 65) is absent. This shows that it is not the presence of the ovary and its influence on the pituitary which causes the cycle.

It has also been shown by Harris and Jacobsohn (1952) that when pituitaries are taken from neonate rats and transplanted under the tuber cinereum of adult females that had been hypophysectomized, they produced an estrous cycle long before this cycle would have appeared in the original animal from which the pituitary had been taken. It therefore seems that the onset of puberty is also in some way produced by neural mechanisms. It has also been found that precocious puberty in young rats can be induced by hypothalamic lesions (Donovan and van der Werff ten Bosch, 1956). Such findings should be compared with clinical observations where precocious puberty occurs in cases of small hypothalamic tumors (Bauer, 1954). In these cases the location of the tumors is different. They are found in the region of the mammillary bodies. Further evidence that hypothalamic lesions affect pituitary function is provided by Sawyer and Robinson (1956) who reported genital atrophy and anestrus in female cats following lesions of the ventromedial nucleus, premammillary region, and the mammillary body. Similar findings have been reported on rabbits with tuberal lesions involving the arcuate and the base of the ventromedial nuclei (Sawyer, 1957).

The fact that this hypothalamic area is involved as a detector in the homeostatic regulation of hormone level is shown by the work of Lisk (1962) on the rat and by Davidson and Sawyer (1961) on the rabbit. Implants of estrogen in the basal tuberal-medial eminence region produces ovarian atrophy.

In guinea pigs and rats, lesions of the paraventricular nuclei behind the optic chiasma result in a state of permanent vaginal estrus. This effect seems to be due to the abolition of the rhythmic release of luteinizing hormone and the constant secretion of follicle-stimulating hormone. Such estrus is however correlated not with behavioral receptivity but with lack of receptivity instead. However, Greer (1953) found that if daily injections of small amounts of progesterone were given to these animals, the return of cyclical changes in the vagina followed. Caging with a male can also lead to an interruption of estrus in these animals. It should be noted in this regard that ovulation can be blocked in rats by exposing them to continuous illumination (Bunn and Everett, 1957).

Donovan and van der Werff ten Bosch (1956a) reported that estrus was brought on early in ferrets by the placement of lesions bilaterally behind the optic chiasma. A similar result has been obtained by these workers (1956) in bringing about precocious puberty in the rat.

Experiments involving direct electrical stimulation also confirm the view that signals from the hypothalamus control the activity of the anterior pituitary. Harris (1948) found that stimulation of the tuber cinereum for three minutes was sufficient to produce ovulation. On the other hand, if such stimulation was applied for as long as 7½ hours directly to the anterior pituitary, ovulation did not occur.

With regard to the thyrotropic and adrenocorticotrophic function of the pituitary, a certain amount of spontaneous secretion occurs even when the anterior pituitary is independent of the hypothalamus. This may be contrasted with the case of the gonadotrophic function of the anterior pituitary, which depends overwhelmingly on hypothalamic influence.

*The Feedback Mechanism Controlling Hormone Level.* Injection of adrenal cortical hormone in an intact animal leads to atrophy of the adrenal cortex. Administration of thiouracil, which lowers the effective level of thyroid hormone in the body, leads to an enlargement of the thyroid gland. Such phenomena, coupled with the fact that the level of testicular, thyroid, and adrenal cortical hormone stays constant, suggest the action of a feedback mechanism. Indeed it seems that the anterior pituitary increases its secretion of thyrotrophic hormone when the thyroid level falls. This has the effect of stimulating the growth of the thyroid and its secretion of the thyroid hormone. However, when the thyroid level rises, this has the effect of decreasing secretion of thyrotrophic hormone by the pituitary. When the thyroid level decreases below a certain point as a result of a decrease in the secretion of thyrotrophic hormone by the pituitary, the production of thyrotrophic hormone increases. Such an arrangement will evidently serve to keep the level of thyroid hormone stable around a certain point.

## The Nature of Hormone-Stabilizing Mechanism

As has been stated above, an excess of a certain hormone leads to a lessened output of this hormone by the appropriate gland as the trophic hormone output of the anterior pituitary, provoking this secretion, is cut down as a result. We may ask whether the excessive hormone acts directly on the pituitary thus causing a decrease by this organ of the relevant trophic hormone, or whether it acts on the hypothalamus which then cuts down its activation of the relevant part of the anterior pituitary. It seems that both mechanisms may be partly involved. It appears that the anterior pituitary can react directly to an excess of hormone by cutting down its output. For instance, in the case of the thyroid, von Euler and Holmgren (1956) reported that when extremely small doses of thyroxine were injected into the pituitary, the action of the thyroid gland was inhibited. On the other hand, an excess of hormone does not lead the hypothalamus to cut its activation of the thyrotrophic secretion of the pituitary. It was found by von Euler and Holmgren that injections of similar doses of thyroxine into the hypothalamus were without effect. However, a hormonal deficiency does not stimulate the pituitary itself to increase its output of the relevant hormone, or (to be entirely safe) does not do so in the absence of certain hypothalamic tissue. In a normal animal a partial excision of the thyroid gland or a unilateral adrenalectomy leads to a hypertrophy of the remaining glandular tissue. Similarly, administration of thiouracil, which diminishes the effective concentration of thyroid, leads to hypertrophy of the whole thyroid in an intact animal. However, in the rat, large anterior lesions of the hypothalamus prevent these compensatory responses of the thyroid (Greer, 1952).

Lesions in the region of the anterior median eminence have a similar effect in the case of the adrenal cortex. This has been demonstrated by Ganong and Hume (1954) on dogs and Fulford and McCann (1955) on rats. However, it was found in the dog that such lesions still led to adrenal atrophy following administration of exogenous sources of cortisone. This agrees with the view, stated above, that the pituitary itself responds to an increase in the relevant hormone by diminishing output of the matching trophic hormone, but that hypothalamic centers have to be intact if an increase of trophic hormone is to occur in response to a deficit of the matching hormone. The areas that on removal impair the ability of the pituitary to increase trophic hormone secretion in response to a deficit of hormone have been found upon electrical stimulation to provoke discharge of trophic hormones. Lesions of these regions also result in slow atrophy of the glands responsive to the trophic hormones. It seems from the above findings that the stabilizing mechanism operating in hormonal control is of some complexity. It is not completely understood.

# 3

# THE PHYSIOLOGICAL BASES OF
# MEMORY AND LEARNING

## THE NATURE OF THE PHYSICAL CHANGE IN LEARNING
## AND MEMORY

Though it is at present impossible to say what change occurs in the brain when a sensory event is registered in memory, there is both clinical and experimental evidence to indicate some properties of the change we are looking for. The passing of time makes interesting alterations in the stability of memory which presumably reflect the characteristics of the underlying physical change. Some of the more remarkable evidence comes from clinical cases of amnesia.

## AMNESIC PHENOMENA

Two main types of amnesia due to organic processes such as head injury or poisoning can be distinguished. The first is posttraumatic amnesia, or an inability to remember events which occurred after an accident. The second is retrograde amnesia, or an inability to recall happenings before an accident.

In the majority of accidents leading to amnesia, there is concussion. In this state there is a paralysis of cerebral function including motor, sensory, mental, and reflex manifestations. During the period of concussion there can be no registration of events in the environment and as a result there is a complete amnesia for events which occurred at this time. With the return of consciousness, mental functions gradually recover. It is the more complex functions which are the last to return. The period of recovery may vary from a few minutes to weeks.

During the period of recovery, memory is usually uniformly hazy. However, in a few cases there are reappearances of memory which will again disappear. Sometimes posttraumatic amnesia is delayed. That is,

72

everything at the time of the injury and some time after is clearly remembered but later there follows a period of confusion and amnesia. Such cases of posttraumatic amnesia are probably due to the delayed effects of injury such as hemorrhage. There are also cases in which paralysis of mental function does not occur during posttraumatic amnesia. There are cases of football players and boxers who continue to play or fight after a head injury and who later remember nothing of the game or fight that occurred after the injury. Such a state is similar to that of postepileptic automatism, where whole sequences of action may not be amenable to recall following a seizure. There are also cases when the patient on recovery will describe a "vision" which refers to something seen before the accident. However, the circumstances surrounding this isolated memory cannot be recalled.

The second type of amnesia of traumatic origin is found in cases of head injury, acute cerebral anoxia, after administration of electroconvulsive shock, and such accidents as carbon monoxide poisoning. This is retrograde amnesia. The memories which are lost in this type of amnesia cover the time period preceding the accident. It appears that it is always the period closest to the accident which is not remembered. That is, the gap in memory covers a continuous stretch of time, with one end of the time anchored to the accident. There is then a memory gap extending backwards, and this gap may shrink, with the memories most distant always returning first.

The period covered by such a gap is often very long, sometimes extending over years. For instance, during gradual recovery of consciousness a patient on being asked may give the current date as several years earlier and his age as correspondingly younger. In most cases, the posttraumatic gap in memory shrinks ultimately to a few minutes or seconds before the accident occurred. Russell and Nathan (1946) in their extensive review stress that recovery of memories in retrograde amnesia occurs not in order of importance but in order of time. It is the long past memories, however trivial they are, that are the first to return.

Another type of retrograde amnesia occurs in the Korsakoff psychosis. Such a psychosis is often the consequence of alcholism and is marked by a progressive loss of memory. Memory for progressively more remote events disappears until the patient may only remember childhood events. Memory for the events of the last few moments is preserved (Talland, 1965). Victor (1964) finds that the loss of memory in this syndrome is correlated with damage to the medial dorsal nuclei of the thalamus.

## THE RELATION OF RETROGRADE AMNESIA TO THE PHYSICAL CHANGE IN MEMORY

The symptoms of retrograde amnesia are so striking and paradoxical that we would expect them to tell us something important about the physical change responsible for memory. It is not older memories or less important memories, which introspectively seem fainter, that are selectively knocked out. On the contrary, the more recent memories are the most likely to disappear. This suggests that the physical change on which our capacity to remember rests becomes progressively more resistant to injury. It also suggests that a physical change is not laid down once and for all, but that it continues to consolidate so that it becomes more difficult to obliterate. The simplest way of accounting for this would be to assume that the physical change which was initiated during the act of registration continues to grow in magnitude. This would then explain the loss of more recent memories by assuming that the physical change initiated by the act of registration had not built up to a sufficient level to overcome obliterative effects imposed by injury or disease. Given a certain level of disruptive physical effects, we would expect all the memories laid down before a certain date to remain and all those registered after such a date to disappear.

However, it does not seem that the process can be quite so simple. The scheme suggested above ignores the fact that memories in retrograde amnesia do recover. If memories do return, then it seems that the changes underlying them must have remained in the interim but that they had somehow been inaccessible. It could be argued that the physical change on which memory rested had really diminished below a certain threshold of magnitude, this magnitude being necessary for the memory change to be accessible. During recovery such subliminal changes which were preserved could grow again until they exceeded the threshold of accessibility. This idea does not seem plausible because it implies an enormous range of subthreshold magnitudes of the memory change. Since less recent memories return first, we would have to assume that even though memories stretching say over five years were all inaccessible or below threshold, the relative amounts of past strengthening would still have to be preserved because otherwise an orderly return of the memories would not be possible. If a large number of discrete steps of consolidation can be preserved below threshold, it would imply that the normal mechanism of recall is very inefficient in utilizing a memory change. The preservation of a large number of informationally discrete steps below threshold implies that threshold could be much lower than it is.

Another way of accounting for the phenomena of retrograde amnesia which does not run into the above difficulties is as follows: We could assume that the change that subserves memory increases in some way with time but that it does not diminish during retrograde amnesia. Instead, as a result of injury or disease, another change occurs which makes it impossible to utilize a certain fixed amount of the memory change. If the accumulated memory change is large, a greater change due to injury or disease is necessary to counteract its normal function. Such a view would account both for the retrograde character of some amnesias—that is, the fact that the gap in memory extends back from the time of the injury—and also for the fact that recovery of memory is also possible. At present it is impossible to be sure whether such a view is the correct view. On the other hand, it seems highly plausible that some process of progressive strengthening or consolidation does in fact occur.

## EXPERIMENTS ON THE CONSOLIDATION OF THE MEMORY TRACE

Muller and Pilzecker (1900) and Hebb (1949) have suggested that a temporary perseveration of neural activity occurs after the reception of a sensory message and that during the time of this perseveration a permanent change gradually takes place. Thus the permanent change should be observed to consolidate during the temporary perseveration of neural activity. If this suggestion is correct, it should be possible to impair or even improve the process of learning by various types of treatment which might influence the temporary perseveration of neural activity after a learning trial. Such effects have indeed been found. It has been shown that learning can be impaired by the administration of electroconvulsive shock after a learning trial (Duncan, 1949; Thompson and Dean, 1955; Thomson et al., 1961). In this procedure a brief current is passed between the ears of the rat so that a convulsive seizure followed by unconsciousness occurs. By showing that the loss of memory also occurred when the current was applied to an animal under ether anesthesia and no seizure followed, McGaugh (1966) demonstrated that the loss of memory effect obtained was not due to the seizure caused by the electroconvulsive shock (ECS). Effects similar to that of ECS have been shown in the case of hypoxia (oxygen lack) (Thompson and Pryer, 1956) and when depressant drugs were administered (Leukel, 1957; Pearlman, et al., 1959). Cerf and Otis (1957) found that narcosis, produced by heating goldfish at various intervals after a learning trial, produced decrements in learning that were larger the closer the narcosis had been to the preceding trial. Such a temporal relation has also been demonstrated in the case of ECS. The closer the ECS to the end of a preceding learning trial, the severer the learning loss.

It has also been shown that the loss of memory effect cannot be attributed to possible punishing effects of electroconvulsive shock because the same shock applied across the hindlegs of rats under the same conditions produces no such decrement of learning (Duncan, 1949) except at the shortest interval used (20 seconds). (See also below p. 82.) Thomson et al. (1961) have demonstrated different effects of ECS on learning in rats that were descendants of the Tryon maze-bright strain and of the Tryon maze-dull strain. In the maze-dull strain, ECS produced a learning decrement after a much longer interval than that observed in the maze-bright strain. This evidence indicated to Thomson et al., that the process of consolidation takes a longer time in the Tryon maze-dull strain. Such results are of particular interest because it has been shown in McGaugh's laboratory (1961) that the maze-dull strain is only inferior to the maze-bright strain in learning mazes if the trials are massed. If the trials are spaced, the difference in learning rate between the two strains disappears. It is, of course, possible that such results are only coincidental. It could be argued that the maze-dull strain is in some way more sensitive to a given level of electric shock. Against this argument there is the finding of Woolley et al. (1960) that the maze-bright animals have lower thresholds in terms of current for seizures than the maze-dull rats, but such a finding is not conclusive because the threshold being measured is for seizure and not for effects on memory processes.

The results on shock administered after learning trials seem to indicate that there is no effect if the delay exceeds one hour. The performance of animals receiving shock after such a delay was not worse than that of controls not receiving shock. So it would seem from this evidence that the process of fixing or consolidating the change occurring in learning tapers off at around one hour.

Further evidence on the process of consolidation comes from the injection of anesthetic drugs administered to rats at various times after a learning trial. Working with a water maze, Leukel (1957) found some impairment in learning when thiopental was injected intraperitoneally one minute after each daily trial. However, if the injection was made 30 minutes after the end of each trial, no such effect was noted. Pearlman et al. (1961) have studied the effects of pentobarbital and ether administered at different intervals after the end of the learning trial. They trained rats to press a lever for a reward of water. After each animal had reached a certain criterion it received an electric shock through the lever. Administration of the drugs occurred after this single learning experience. An attempt was made to produce equal amounts of anesthesia in all groups. Retention tests were made 24 hours after learning. There was little or no effect if ether was administered at an interval of ten minutes after the learning trial; if administered ten seconds after the learning trial, the animals would press the lever at 30 percent of their initial rate; if administered five minutes after the learning trial, the rate would fall to 17 percent. Pentobarbital had a more profound and long-lasting effect. When pentobarbital was administered after a ten-second interval, the rate of lever-pressing was 76 percent of the previous rate, which means that memory of the shock was almost obliterated; when administered after a ten-minute interval, the rate of lever-pressing was only 23 percent of the previous level; and when administered after a 20-minute interval, memory of the shock was intact, as the rate of bar-pressing was only 1 percent of the previous level.

On the basis of their experimental findings, Coons and Miller (1960) have recently put forward an ingenious argument about the effects of ECS on the retention of a habit. They point out that the work demonstrating "loss of memory" for a given habit after ECS is vitiated by the fact that if the shock were felt, it would produce avoidance of a response which could be mistaken for amnesia. Accordingly, these workers used a somewhat complex design in which ECS, if felt, would facilitate learning. The results of their study support their contention. However, more recent results (Abt, *et al.*, 1961, using ether; McGaugh, 1961, using ECS; and Pearlman, *et al.*, 1961, using anesthetic drugs to produce amnesia) do not support Coons and Miller's findings. Abt *et al.* (1961) and McGaugh (1961) created a simpler situation by placing a rat on a small restrictive platform raised slightly above a much larger platform. Very shortly the rat stepped off the small platform and onto the larger platform where it obtained an electric shock. When these same animals were placed on the small platform a second time they stayed there when no amnesic agent had been applied. If an amnesic agent was applied immediately after the animal stepped off the small platform and the animal was then placed on the platform a second time, he would step off again. As in the studies already quoted, the effect of the amnesic agent diminished when application was postponed in relation to the crucial response. In this situation, the effects of ECS and shock to the feet should summate if the animal is avoiding the electroshock. The same argument could be applied to the more complex situation devised by Pearlman *et al.* (1961) when an animal "forgot" that it had been punished after pressing a lever. In each of these cases the amnesic agent, instead of increasing fear or avoidance, produced what is most plausibly interpreted as an amnesia. This conclusion is strengthened by the result of an experiment conducted by McGaugh and Madsen (1964). These investigators showed that rats did eventually learn to avoid a place when they were given ECS on successive occasions. However, such learning was slow compared with the learning of rats when the shock administered was of a lower intensity but was not strong enough to produce a convulsion. They further showed that when ECS was administered five seconds after the shock in amounts insufficient to produce a convulsion, it slowed down acquisition of avoidance learning of the place where such shocks were given. Supporting evidence has been reported by Quartermain, Paolino, and Miller (1965). Effects of ECS given after a longer time span have been reported by Hunt and Brady (1951), and a whole series of investigations designed to elucidate these effects has been reported by Hunt (1965). When a sound is used to signal impending unavoidable shock, the sound will suppress ongoing operant behavior, such as pressing a lever for water. This suppression of behavior caused by the sound can be eliminated by giving a rat a whole series of ECS treatments. Such treatments were applied four days after the end of training a rat to press a lever for a reward of water. The suppression of responding caused by the sound disappears for one or two weeks after the ECS treatments. The rat can be trained again during this period to reacquire the behavior. However, the loss of suppression of lever-pressing when the sound occurs is only temporary, and suppression reappears again spontaneously. Though this effect of the electroconvulsive shock looks like an amnesia in some respects, only the warning function of the sound seems forgotten. There is no amnesia for the lever-pressing habit for obtaining water. Other possible interpretations are discussed by Hunt (1965).

## DRUG FACILITATION OF LEARNING

Not only is it possible to impair learning by various procedures after a training trial, but apparently it is also possible to improve learning, as we might expect if the consolidation hypothesis is correct. In an impressive series of studies, McGaugh and co-workers have demonstrated that administration of various stimulant drugs, such as strychnine and picro-toxin, both before and after a training trial, increases the rate at which learning proceeds.

The evidence that learning can be improved with injections of stimulants after a training trial is of greater interest to us. Any effect of improved learning that is associated with injections which are given before the trial could be attributed to an increase of motivation, alertness, or some other such factor not necessarily connected with the process of storage per se. On the other hand, injection of a stimulant after the completion of a trial makes it much more likely that any observed improvement of learning is caused by the drug acting on some process set up by experience during the last preceding trial. Of course, it is possible that the drug's action persisted until the next batch of trials. However, McGaugh (1961) has shown that the closer the injection to the previous trial, the greater the improvement in performance on the succeeding trial. If the drug affected some process occurring during a learning trial and not one occurring immediately thereafter, then we should expect the opposite result; i.e., the further the injection from the previous day's trial, the greater the likely influence of the drugs on the succeeding day's test. So if we obtain less effect with an injection closer to the succeeding day's test than with one which is closer to the previous day's trials, we may conclude that the effect of the drug was on some process occurring and diminishing after a day's trial.

In their two strains of rats, McGaugh and co-workers (1963) have also found striking differences in the facilitative effects of drugs on learning. These differences can be compared with those they had previously found in reactions to ECS (see above p. 75). They used a newly synthesized compound (1757 I.S.) similar in effect, but not in structure, to strychnine. This was injected ten minutes before daily massed trials in a complex alley maze. They found that the descendants of the Tryon maze-dull animals which were injected with the drug showed a significant improvement over controls of the same strain which were not injected with this drug. On the other hand, no facilitation of learning was found in the descendants of the maze-bright animals. The number of errors made by the injected maze-bright animals was not lower than that of controls of the same strain which had not been injected with 1757 I.S. It is interesting that without the drug there was a large difference between maze-dull and maze-bright strains in the mean number of errors: the mean number of errors was 12.86 (S.D., 4.64) for the maze-bright strain as compared to 33.15 (S.D., 18.12) for the maze-dull strain. When we compare the two strains under the influence of the drug, we find that the mean number of errors for the maze-bright animals was 15.71 (S.D., 8.94) while that of the maze-dull was 17.33 (S.D., 10.30). In other words, when the drug is used, the difference

## TABLE 1

### Effect of Picrotoxin on Maze Learning

(M, Mean Number of Errors Made on Trials Two to Seven; S.D., Standard Deviation of Mean; N, Number of Animals)

| Strain | Control Group 0.9% Saline | | | Low-Dose 0.75 Mg./Kg. | | | Medium-Dose 1.0 Mg./Kg. | | | High-Dose 1.25 Mg./Kg. | | |
|---|---|---|---|---|---|---|---|---|---|---|---|---|
| | N | M | S.D. | N | M | S.D. | N | M | S.D. | N | M | S.D. |
| Maze-bright | 10 | 26.5 | 4.48 | 10 | 25.6 | 8.67 | 10 | 25.9 | 5.94 | 12 | 20.2 | 5.35 |
| Maze-dull | 10 | 22.2 | 2.99 | 10 | 16.6 | 9.41 | 11 | 14.5 | 7.28 | 11 | 13.8 | 4.57 |

between the strains under massed conditions of learning tends to disappear. As noted above, the learning ability of the maze-dull strain is inferior to the maze-bright strain only when the trials are massed.

If injections of a stimulant will abolish the difference between the maze-bright and maze-dull rats under massed conditions by leading to an improvement of the maze-dull rats, then we naturally might expect that the stimulant would cause the maze-dull rats to actually surpass the maze-bright rats under spaced conditions of learning. Breen and McGaugh (1963) found this to be true. In their study, the rats were given an injection of the stimulant picrotoxin after each day's trial (only one trial was given each day). Three different levels of dosage were used. As can be seen from Table 1, when under the drug's influence, the maze-dull rats were superior to the maze-bright animals.

It is tempting to assume, as McGaugh assumed, that the observed differences in the effects of ECS, stimulants, and distribution of practice of the maze-dull and maze-bright animals are caused by a difference in the consolidation rate of the neural trace. However, this view presents difficulties which further research may resolve. For instance, it is difficult to understand why the assumption that the stimulant increased the consolidation speed of a neural trace after each trial can be considered as an explanation for the fact that the maze-dull animals became as efficient as the maze-bright animals under massed conditions when a stimulant was administered. We would further have to assume that if a new process of consolidation was started before the previous process had finished, less of a neural trace would be laid down than if both processes of consolidation had gone on to completion. However, this would not explain why the drug-treated maze-dull animals made fewer errors than the treated or untreated maze-bright animals when the trials were spaced a day apart. In this case it seems that the postulated process of consolidation would reach an asymptote within 24 hours, even when the animals are untreated. (At least this is used as an argument concerning the consolidation hypothesis and to account for the lack of a difference between the maze-bright and maze-dull animals when the trials are widely spaced. It is argued that under these conditions the processes of consolidation do not overlap.) A speeding up of the processes of consolidation should therefore have no effect if the trials are widely spaced. If the overlap factor of consolidation is already minimal, a further speeding up of the consolidation process by drugs can hardly have an effect.

There may be no single explanation for the above experiments. Many factors unconnected with learning per se, such as a tendency to alternation or other biases, enter into the performance of a task, especially in a complex T-maze. These factors obscure the expression of learning as it is manifested in performance. The tendency toward spontaneous alternation decreases with time between trials; therefore, a greater tendency to alternate on the part of the maze-dull rats could make their performance worse when trials are closely spaced. Wide spacing of the trials greatly reduces this tendency, and consequently we should find, as is the case, that the difference in errors between the maze-bright and the maze-dull rats should diminish greatly. The maze-dull and maze-bright rats differ in many ways, many of them apparently unconnected with the qualities for which they were originally selected. For instance, it has been found in the writer's laboratory that there exist not only large differences in the amounts of saline and water drunk but also divergencies in the very manner of drinking. Thus, it is entirely possible that accidental correlations of drug sensitivity are confounding the results of the experiments in which different genetic strains are used.

However, such criticisms cannot be leveled at studies illustrating drug facilitation of learning in general. Westbrook and McGaugh (1964) have shown that such drug facilitation occurs during latent learning. It seems that learning is increased when rats in a complex maze are administered 1757 I.S. (a drug with a strychnine-like action) during a period of nonreward after each daily trial. When a food reward was introduced, injections were discontinued. However, the rats that had received the injections while unrewarded made significantly fewer errors than unin-jected controls when reward was introduced. (Figure 3–1) While interactions between hunger drive induced by previous injections and perform-

FIG. 3–1. Facilitation of latent learning when drug is injected only during period of unrewarded runs. NRC—non-rewarded controls, injected with saline only NRE—non-rewarded experimental animals injected with 1757IS after trials up to trial 5. RRE—rewarded experimental animals, injected with 1757IS after trials 1–5. RRC rewarded control animals injected with saline after each trial. Trials 6–10 all animals were treated in identical fashion— rewarded and injected with saline after each trial. (From McGaugh, J. L., in Kimble, D. P. [Ed.], *The Anatomy of Memory*. Palo Alto, Calif.: Science and Behavior Books, 1965.)

ance were not evaluated in this study, the design used is potentially a powerful one.

## RETROGRADE AMNESIA AND BRAIN LESIONS

Retrograde amnesia has been noted in patients whose medial temporal region is destroyed (Milner and Penfield, 1955; Scoville and Milner, 1957). Chow and Survis (1958) and Orbach and Fantz (1958) have shown that the retention of visual habits are less severely affected by temporal neocortical ablations when these habits have been overlearnt. While there probably is no strict comparability between the practice of a habit and the age of a memory, these experiments do suggest that the greater resistance of a memory to destructive influences might be caused by dissemination of the memory throughout the central nervous system as practice or time proceeds. Such an explanation is put forward by Chow and Survis (1958): "As the habit becomes well ingrained, the neural changes must involve or spread to more and more additional regions." However, an alternative explanation need not postulate such a spread, or an unequal destruction of the physical counterpart of the visual memory. One need only assume that irrelevant tendencies which obscure learning are ironed out during prolonged training so that if an equal amount of destruction of the memory trace for the visual memory is assumed, the overtrained habit would be less affected because there would be fewer irrelevant tendencies to compete with it than the undertrained habit. This alternative interpretation is supported by the finding of Chow and Survis (1958) that six out of the eight monkeys in their study retained a color discrimination which was taught as a pre-training problem and which was not overlearnt but was followed by overtraining on a different visual problem. However, this pre-training color discrimination was lost following ablation of the same cortical regions under identical conditions in monkeys to whom no subsequent visual overtraining was given before operation (Chow, 1952). Since the color problems were not overlearnt in this study, a spread due to practice cannot be postulated. On the other hand, irrelevant tendencies, which would interfere with the habit, could have been diminished by training on other discriminations. This was shown by Harlow (1959) in his studies on the acquisition of learning set.

## THE DURATION OF RETROGRADE AMNESIA

The evidence from retrograde amnesia in man suggests an entirely different time scale for the process of consolidation. The time scale for animals, as discussed in the studies above, was in terms of minutes or hours at the most, while the time scale for man is in terms of years or a lifetime. This may be due to the presence of two different processes or to a species difference. Whatever the answer, such observations make it difficult to interpret results of the animal studies. However, it has been shown in one study (Pearlman et al., 1961) that retrograde amnesia can be produced in rats which is measured in days; therefore the explanation in terms of a species difference is rendered less plausible. In this study (described above, p. 76), pentelenetetrazol (Metrazol) was used to induce seizures in a group of rats. One such seizure was induced four days after the single learning trials and produced almost as much amnesia as pentobarbital anesthesia given ten seconds after the trials. (The response level of the metrazol-treated group was 70 percent of their previous level, while that of the untreated controls was 1 percent of their previous level.) Apparently a metrazol-induced seizure was able to produce amnesia for an event which occurred four days before. It is possible that Metrazol may have been acting on a different process from that affected by pentobarbital and ether. A more plausible view is that Metrazol is simply a much more effective amnesic agent. When administered ten seconds after the learning trial, it produces complete amnesia. (Response is 100 percent, whereas it is 76 percent when pentobarbital is administered ten seconds after the trial.) Alternatively, it would be necessary to postulate that Metrazol severely affects both a short-term and a long-term process of consolidation.

With reference to the last alternative, it seems likely that there are two processes with different time scales present in memory: a short term and a long term, which may be distinguished on other grounds. For instance, it has long been known that if different lists of items are learnt correctly, i.e., to the same level of proficiency, by a subject on successive days, the number of items correctly recalled on each following day from the previous day's list decreases. This lessened efficiency of recall has been ascribed to an interference with the processes of recall of a list by the previous lists learnt. This is called "proactive inhibition." However, it has been shown (Deutsch and Mamakos, 1959) that the number of trials needed to reach a certain standard of recall decreases on each successive day. As a result there is a corresponding decrease in success of recall on the following day. It appears that practice can rapidly improve recall immediately after a list has been seen. Such practice does not improve recall of the same list 24 hours later. Such recall remains a function of the number of trials during which a list has been presented. If subjects are not trained to a given standard on the different successive lists on each day but the number of trials on each day is kept constant, recall on each successive day will show no decrement.

Another recent line of evidence is presented by Weiskrantz (1964). Monkeys with functionally disrupted frontal lobes were inferior to normal controls in performing easy discrimination tasks which required only a few trials to solve a given problem. There was no lag in learning difficult tasks for which training stretched over many days. Thus further evidence is furnished for the interpretation that in this case the frontal deficit is one of immediate memory, whereas long-term memory is unimpaired. Therefore, it appears that either memories can be laid down in the long-term store without going through the short-term store, or that memories first enter the short-term store where they are inaccessible before going to the long-term store.

Flexner, Flexner, and Stellar (1963) have been able to produce longer spans of retrograde amnesia in animals by the novel method of injecting puromycin directly into the brain substance. Puromycin is a drug which inhibits protein synthesis. Injections of the drug into the hippocampus, posterior neocortex, and entorhinal cortex of a mouse produced an amnesia for habits which were learned up to six days before. To produce an apparent amnesia for the same habit learned over six days before, injections of the drug had to be made over a larger area of the brain.

However, it may be that injections given over a wider area of the brain simply have a more confusing effect on the animal than those given to a more restricted area. Therefore, it is not necessary to postulate that after learning the memory trace somehow spreads with time until controls are made to evaluate the possibility of confusion.

Besides its action as a protein synthesis inhibitor, puromycin also has an effect on cholinesterase (Burkhalter, 1963). Cholinesterase prevents the accumulation of acetylcholine (a central and peripheral synaptic transmitter). When such accumulation occurs, transmission is paralyzed. Krech and Rosenzweig (1954) have suggested that the process of memory fixation is related to acetylcholine and they have measured cholinesterase concentrations in various strains of rats which lend support to this hypothesis. By feeding an anticholinesterase (systox) to rats, Russell (1956) was able to show some effect on rate of extinction of a learned habit.

With such considerations in mind, Deutsch et al. (1966) attempted to produce amnesia in rats by the direct injection of an anticholinesterase into the hippocampi. Rats were trained to escape from shock into the safe compartment of a Y-maze. After they reached the learning criterion, they were anesthetized with nembutal, placed in a stereotaxic instrument, and given a bilateral injection of DFP (diisopropylfluorophosphate) in the hippocampus. When the rats were tested in the y-maze 24 hours later, they demonstrated a partial loss of memory; however, when a similar group was tested five days later, memory of the habit returned. In a second part of the experiment, an attempt was made to discover what effect DFP would have on memories which had been in store for different lengths of time. Consequently, all the animals were not injected immediately after they had been trained. Injections were given to some of the animals after 3, 5, and 14 days, while other animals were injected immediately after they had learned the habit. All animals were tested 24 hours after the injection. Again there was a partial memory loss in animals injected immediately after they had learned the habit. However, the animals which learned the habit three days before injection showed no memory loss, their scores being identical with those of a control group. Up to this point, DFP caused a typical retrograde amnesia. But rats trained five days before operation again showed an impairment of memory, and those trained two weeks before the operation showed a complete loss of memory. The scores of this last group were virtually identical with the scores of a control group which were not trained but which were injected with DFP 24 hours before testing. The result cannot be due to normal forgetting because another control group showed that retention over a span of two weeks is practically perfect when there is no intervening treatment (Figure 3–2). The results show that as far as vulnerability to DFP is concerned, there are two definite stages. The first stage shows a diminishing vulnerability to the drug. After a memory is in store for three days, it is immune to interference

FIG. 3–2a. The first part of the diagram (days tested after injection) illustrates the return of memory after anticholinesterase induced amnesia. The interval between original learning and injection is kept constant, whereas the delay between injection and relearning is varied.

The second part of the diagram (days trained before injection) illustrates the number of trials to relearn when the interval between original learning and injection is varied while the delay between injection and relearning is kept constant at 24 hours. CTL-DFP, the number of trials taken to original learning by a group injected with DFP 24 hours before learning. CTL-PO, the score of a group trained 30 minutes before injection of peanut oil only. CTL-0, the score of a group retrained 15 days after original learning with no intervening treatment. (From Deutsch, J. A., et al., 1966, by permission of *Science*. Vol. 151, No. 3707, pp. 221 ff. Copyright 1966 by the American Association for the Advancement of Science.)

by DFP. This is in line with the findings on retrograde effects which are due to other treatments producing amnesia. Further, there is a recovery of memory which was subjected to treatment a short while after being stored. This return of memory is analagous to the observation of human traumatic amnesia and suggests that the process being impaired by the drug is one of retrieval or recollection rather than a loss of information laid down in the memory store. When memories have been in store for longer than three days a second stage appears. A different process supervenes which becomes more severely affected by the DFP treatment as time goes on. This may be

FIG. 3–2b. The results of a parallel experiment done with puromycin instead of DFP, except that relearning took place 5 days after injection (except at
P-21). P-CTL, the number of trials taken to original learning by a group
injected with puromycin 5 days before learning. Before this relearning, scores
were extremely high, making it impossible to evaluate degree of amnesia.
S-CTL, the score of a group trained 30 minutes before injection of saline only
and retested 5 days later. (Unpublished data, with Dahl H. and Leibowitz, SF.)

the counterpart of a long-term process of consolidation. After all, if there is
a long-term process of biochemical change, called consolidation, which
renders a memory less vulnerable to certain treatments, it is likely that it
will also make it more susceptible to certain other treatments.

Follow-up studies of this type of amnesia have shown that there is no
effect of injection of DFP one or two days after learning, as well as three
days after learning as already reported. Further, memory returns even after
injections 14 days after learning, when there is an initially complete
amnesia. Furthermore, a very similar pattern of amnesia emerges when
puromycin is injected instead of DFP. Also amnesia caused by injection
of puromycin 30 minutes after learning is not permanent and memory
returns completely. This suggests that the puromycin effect is in fact due
to an indirect reduction in cholinesterase activity.

## INTERPRETATION OF ANTICHOLINESTERASE-
## INDUCED AMNESIA

As mentioned above, an anticholinesterase drug reduces the activity of
acetylcholinesterase. Acetylcholinesterase destroys acetylcholine. An injection of an anticholinesterase therefore slows down the rate of destruction

of acetylcholine. A release of a sufficient quantity of acetylcholine on one side of the synapse indirectly causes the initiation of an action potential at the other side of the synapse and thus acetylcholine transmits a neural message across the synapse. This action as a synaptic transmitter may be affected in two main ways by the presence of an anticholinesterase. If the quality of transmitter is small, transmission may be improved. Inactivation of cholinesterase allows a larger build-up of acetylcholine at the synapse, as this transmitter is not destroyed as rapidly after being released. This enhanced buildup of transmitter in its turn results in the triggering of action potentials on the other side of the synapse where previously the buildup of transmitter would have been insufficient to do this. This boosting effect of anticholinesterase is made use of clinically in the treatment of myasthenia gravis, a disorder where muscular weakness is due to a decreased efficiency of transmission at the neuromuscular junction. Administration of anticholinesterase drugs improves transmission and so relieves the symptoms.

The second way in which anticholinesterase drugs may affect transmission is at synapses where the amount of acetylcholine released during transmission is high. Here decrease of destruction of acetylcholine will again lead to a build-up of this transmitter. However, when the level of acetylcholine at the synapse becomes too high, the synapse is blocked and no transmission occurs. Such a block is reversible and the synapse can again function normally when the excess of acetylcholine has subsided.

Deutsch (1966) has suggested an interpretation of anticholinesterase-induced amnesia based on the above pharmacological actions on the synapse. It will be recalled that (after an initial brief period) DFP produces no effect on memory from one to three days after learning. However, 5 days after learning injection of DFP produces considerable amnesia and complete amnesia at 14 days. Such amnesia is of a temporary nature. We may assume that memory is stored by alterations in the capacity of certain synapses to conduct and that such alterations take some time to become complete. When the amount of transmitter released is low, as it would be at the beginning of an increase in the conductivity of a synapse, its efficiency during transmission after an injection of anticholinesterase would be unimpaired, and should even be enhanced. However, as conductivity increases (or in other words, the amount of acetylcholine released during transmission increases) accumulation of transmitter due to the injected anticholinesterase reaches levels at which synaptic block occurs. On this theory then it looks as if there is initially a temporary store of transmitter which soon dissipates. After this there is a gradual growth of amount of acetylcholine released during transmission which makes transmission increasingly vulnerable to anticholinesterase-induced block.

This hypothesis is easily tested by repeating the experiment, but injecting an anticholinergic drug instead of an anticholinesterase. An anticholinergic reduces the effective level of acetylcholine (by competing with it for receptor sites on the synaptic membrane). The effect of injecting an anticholinergic such as scopolamine is to reduce the effectiveness of any level of acetylcholine released at the synapse. An injection of scopolamine, instead of DFP, should therefore have the opposite effect on memory. Scopolamine should produce amnesia when levels of acetylcholine during transmission are low and little or no memory loss if levels of acetylcholine are high. Low levels will be depressed by scopolamine below the threshold for triggering action potentials, whereas with high levels transmission will still occur. Therefore scopolamine was used instead of DFP in a parallel experiment (Deutsch and Rocklin). Groups were matched for initial learning scores. The group injected 30 minutes after learning had a relearning score (median trials to criterion) of 4.75, the group injected 1 day after learning, 16.5, the group injected 3 days after learning, 13, and the group injected 7 days after learning 4.25. The results are highly significant and the opposite in direction of those produced by DFP. This experiment therefore supports the hypothesis that the effective physiological basis of memory is a change in synaptic conductance, mediated by the capacity of the synapse to release transmitter. Once such a change has been initiated it seems to increase simply as a function of time, and this increase takes place even when no further training is given.

This last generalization, that an apparent increase in the level of transmitter occurs spontaneously with time after learning, gives rise to the question whether the level of transmitter at a given time after learning is dependent on the level of initial learning. It has been observed that better trained habits are more vulnerable to the effects of anticholinesterase than habits learned to a lower criterion (Deutsch and Lutzky) and so it is concluded that increased initial training leads to a higher level of transmitter at a later time. To support such a conclusion there is good evidence that a poorly learned habit is actually facilitated by the same dose of DFP as produces amnesia of the same habit if this habit is well learned (Deutsch and Lutzky; Deutsch and Stone). Rats actually remember a poorly learned habit 27 percent better after an injection of anticholinesterase than after an injection of only the vehicle (peanut oil). As was stated above, anticholinesterase facilitates transmission when effective levels of transmitter are low.

That transmitter levels seem to rise as a result of increased training has an interesting implication. It implies that the memory of repeated learning trials is stored at the same locus as an increase in the already present change responsible for storage. It could be imagined that repeated practice leads only to a reduplication in some other loci of the change already present in one locus. But if this was the case it is difficult to see why a better trained habit could be more sensitive to anticholinesterase disruption.

## THE NATURE OF THE PHYSIOLOGICAL
## CHANGE IN LEARNING

At present, the physiological change underlying learning is unknown. However, there have been recently discovered changes which are of suggestive significance. One of the most interesting changes has been reported by Morrell (1961). This came from his studies of "mirror" focus epileptiform discharge. It has often been clinically observed that a discharging focus in one hemisphere will set off a similar discharge in a corresponding area of the other hemisphere. Two stages of such a secondary or reflected discharge have been demonstrated. In the dependent stage such a spike discharge will only occur when the original focus discharges. Also, ablation of the original focus will abolish the discharge in the secondary region. In the independent stage the secondary region will discharge without such discharge activity in the primary region and the secondary region will continue to discharge even when the primary focus has been surgically removed. Morrell produced primary foci by applying ethyl chloride to a small area of the cortex. It was observed that the independent stage of the secondary contralateral epileptiform focus takes about 24 hours to several days to develop in the rabbit, four weeks to three months in the cat, and about eight weeks in the monkey. This stage appears to be permanent. Having been altered in its properties, the cortical region concerned retains this alteration. For instance, it was possible to isolate neuronally the region of the secondary discharge. Epileptiform discharge from this focus was abolished, as shown by EEG recording for several months. After this period the cortex was again exposed and it was possible to demonstrate that the isolated focus had retained its abnormal properties. Morrell states: "We believe this to be a crucial observation because it demonstrates that the mirror focus is a region which has not only 'learned' to behave in terms of paroxysmal discharge, but which 'remembers' this behavior even after months of inactivity. The isolation experiment has excluded reverberating impulses as the basis of the changed electrical behavior and makes it necessary to search for structural alterations." Such a search for structural alterations was in fact undertaken. A chemical alteration at the site of the focus was found. It appears that changes indicative of abnormally high concentrations of ribonucleic acid, or its intracellular state, occur in the cells at the site of the abnormally discharging focus.

A more direct attempt to measure learning changes in the biochemical constitution of selected parts of the nervous system has been made by Hyden and Egyhazy (1962, 1963) and Hyden and Pigon (1960). Rats learned to obtain food by traversing a kind of tightrope. An analysis was then made of the composition of RNA in the nuclei of Deiter's cells (in the first vestibular relay) and of the surrounding glial cells. Changes in the base composition of the RNA were found. However it is not clear that such changes were brought about by learning rather than by stimulation of the vestibular apparatus during climbing. It is true that there were "control" groups subjected to rotation but it does not seem that these animals experienced equivalent vestibular stimulation. A priori it seems unlikely that any skill of motor coordination the animal might have to learn in balancing would be represented by modifications in the almost peripheral vestibular apparatus.

Corning and John (1961) reported that tails of planaria regenerating in ribonuclease do not retain a conditioned response which is retained by tails regenerating in pond water. Since ribonuclease destroys RNA, it might be argued on the basis of this experiment that the RNA which supposedly stores the planarian memory had been dissolved by the ribonuclease. However, it is difficult to know how much of the so-called conditioned response to a paired light and shock represents simply a general sensitization (Jensen, 1965). Further, morphological anomalies were produced by the treatment with ribonuclease and these might interact with the rather complex factors governing the response of planaria to light recently discovered by Van Deventer and Ratner (1964).

Dingman and Sporn (1961) reported that when 8-azaguanine—a purine analog which can cause formation of nonfunctional RNA—is given to rats, it depresses to a small extent the learning of a new maze, though it does not affect the performance in obviously well-learned maze. Unfortunately, when compared with a well-established habit, new learning is very sensitive to all kinds of influence so that the result obtained is at best inconclusive (Singh, 1964).

A more convincing approach to the problem has been adopted by Gerard and co-workers (1963). When a unilateral brain lesion such as a cerebellar lesion is made, a postural asymmetry results. If the spinal cord is transected immediately after the brain lesion has been made, such an asymmetry disappears. However, such asymmetry persists if the transection of the spinal cord is delayed. Taking such a fixation of function as an analog of fixation in memory, it was possible to study the effect of pharmacological agents on the time before a postural asymmetry due to a lesion of the central nervous system would become irreversible in spite of the interruption of the spinal pathway. When 8-azaguanine is administered, it takes longer for the postural asymmetry caused by a cerebellar lesion to become irreversible, whereas another agent believed to increase RNA content of neurons, decreased the interval necessary for a postural asymmetry to become fixated. It remains for future research to determine the relation of this phenomenon to learning as it is normally conceived.

It has recently been claimed (Babich et al., 1965) that intraperitoneal injections into untrained rats of RNA extracted from the brains of trained rats transferred the training. However, in spite of many efforts by excellent investigators (e.g. Luttges *et al.*, 1966; Gross and Carey, 1965) it has been impossible to substantiate such claims. Further, it has been shown (Luttges *et al.*, 1966; Eist and Seal, 1965) that such RNA injected intraperitoneally reaches the brain in negligible quantity, if at all. However, even intracerebral injections of such RNA fail to produce transfer. In view of the very large number of attempts to produce transfer of training via injected RNA, it is not surprising simply on a statistical basis, that some "successes" have been obtained.

It can be seen from the above that a considerable amount of research has been devoted to an attempt to show that RNA is involved in the process of memory storage. These attempts have been inspired by the belief that RNA molecules are capable of carrying coded information in very large quantities, and because this large information carrying capacity of DNA and RNA is already used in the biological system in the mechanism of heredity transmission. The identification of RNA is made plausible by the further argument that a change in the excitability of a cell could not be permanent unless there was some change in the genetic information in the cell. All other cell constituents have a high rate of turnover, and there must be something which causes these constituents to remain different after learning. However, it seems that there are other possibilities which should not be forgotten. There are phenomena, such as the influx of melanin into the neurons of the nucleus niger in horses (Jung and Hassler, 1960), which suggest that the contents of a cell may be stably modified without any presumptive change in its genetic apparatus. It is also within the bounds of possibility to suppose that such a change of intracellular content might modify the excitability characteristics of the cell. If such suppositions are accepted, we need only postulate a sudden increase of permeability to a specific substance on the reception of a given signal to provide for an equally plausible learning substrate. It is easy to conceive that such a process would have the characteristics of high vulnerability at the outset, before permeation was complete, and that permeation could continue slowly over a long period of time to give the characteristics of long-term consolidation.

RNA is involved in protein synthesis, and as a result, differences in rate of stimulation on neurons are reflected in the RNA content of neurons as activity leads to increased protein turnover in cells transmitting impulses. For instance, decreased activity leads to a decrease in RNA in relatively inactive cells. It has been reported that there is a lowering of cytoplasmic RNA concentrations in the cells of the receptor and bipolar layers of the retina in animals which have been reared in the dark (Riesen, 1960; Rasch, *et al.*, 1959). Such a relation makes it very difficult to prove experimentally that RNA actually stores information in learning, rather than that it is, like water, simply necessary in any neural change or activity.

Besides the observations of Morrell (1961) on "mirror" foci described above, other possible related phenomena have been described which show moderately long-term effects of stimulation on the subsequent behavior of neural tissue. It has been found that there is a larger postsynaptic potential after a prolonged burst of high-frequency excitation at a synaptic region than before such stimulation took place. This phenomenon is called posttetanic potentiation, or PTP. Such an enhancement of responsiveness in motoneurons can be measured, sometimes up to a period of hours, when disuse has been produced at the synapse by sectioning the afferent fibers distal to their ganglia about 13 days previously. (Such a sectioning leads to depressed synaptic efficacy. [Eccles, 1961])

It appears unlikely that these phenomena form the change in learning. The changes described occur when one unit in the nervous system has excited another such unit, thus making excitation of the latter unit more likely. This would lead to a type of learning in which the organism would simply repeat what it had done previously, a type of learning not observed in animals.

Enhancement of single-unit firing in the central nervous system is reported by Olds and Olds (1961). These workers implanted electrodes on sites producing high frequencies of response as a result of electrical brain self-stimulation, namely, in the region of the medial forebrain bundle. Microelectrodes were then inserted into the brain. When slow repetitive discharges were picked up from single cells with the microelectrode, a pulse was inserted into the electrode in the medial forebrain bundle region at a fixed time after a discharge had occurred. It is reported that some cells, mainly in the subcortical regions, augmented their rate of firing in response to such stimulation. This suggests an analogy to learning by reward, an activity of a cell being rewarded instead of an act of the whole animal. Olds (personal communication) now believes that the result may have been influenced by a general enhancement of activity during anesthesia which occurs as a result of stimulation in the medial forebrain bundle. However, Chow (personal communication) suggests that during such a procedure, peripheral responses are being rewarded and that cerebral counterparts (causes or effects) of such peripheral responses are observed with the microelectrodes.

Other possibilities which have been canvassed as explanations for the physical change in learning have little basis in demonstrated alterations of neural function. Holt (1931) suggested that there was a growth change, leading to new connections in the nervous system during learning. Such growth does take place during embryonic development but there is no evidence that it takes place during learning. Hebb (1949) made a similar suggestion. He supposed that the connections (end-boutons) of one cell to another increase in number during excitation of one cell by the other, but there seems to be no good evidence for this.

Until very recently, the supposition that whether in learning or regeneration, growth could occur as a regular feature of the central nervous system did not seem very plausible. It had been observed that some central axons and dendrites could sprout, but that such cases were rare and no generality could be attached to the findings. However, recently, Rose and associates (1960) have produced interesting evidence with regard to the growth of nerve fibers in the cortex. These workers have been able selectively to destroy very narrow layers (about 100 to 200 $\mu$) below the surface of the cortex by bombardment with heavy subatomic particles. Such lesions are usually three to four millimeters wide. In such a lesion there is a destruction of nerve cells and fibers. However, a regrowth of nerve fibers from outside the lesion is seen (after seven weeks with moderate dosage) although nerve cells show no reappearance in the affected area. Similar observations have been reported by Purpura (1961). There is however no evidence that such growth is connected with learning. Also, such bombardment can cause excessive myelination of surviving fibers after a time, and this could be mistaken for regrowth.

One of the problems of investigating the physiological basis of learning has been our inability to pinpoint the locus of learning charge. However, Horridge (1965) discovered that leg posture could be learned by the ventral cord ganglia when the brain was absent in cockroaches, locusts, and similar large insects. Careful controls were undertaken to exclude possible factors other than associative learning. The relevant ganglion which did the learning contained only about 3,000 cells.

## INTEROCULAR TRANSFER AND STORAGE
## OF THE MEMORY TRACE

The bilateral symmetry of the nervous system offers interesting opportunities for its investigation. We may ask whether information which the animal has obtained through learning is stored in both hemispheres, whether it can be made available to a hemisphere even if at the time of learning this hemisphere received no direct sensory input, and so on. Most of the experiments on this subject involve the sectioning of the corpus callosum, a massive structure of nerve fibers which joins the two halves of the cortex. Studies of learning employing this technique were initiated by Bykoff (1924). This investigator taught a dog to expect food after a mechanical stimulus to the skin on one side of the animal. This causes the animal to salivate when the mechanical stimulus is applied. In the intact animal, salivation is produced without further training when the contralateral point on the skin is stimulated. However, in the animal with callosal section no such transfer was observed.

Beritoff and Chichinadze (1936, 1937) studied the problem of inter-hemispheric transfer in pigeons. There is complete crossover of visual fibers from one eye to the opposite hemisphere in the pigeon. Therefore information from one eye only travels to one hemisphere. These authors found that habits learned with one eye were not transferred when testing was done with the other eye. However, later studies by Levine (1945,

1952) and Siegel (1953) have shown that such transfer can occur. Since there is complete crossover of visual fibers, it seems that such transfer must be mediated at a fairly high neural level. The contradiction with the earlier Russian work has been explained as being caused by the use of different retinal loci. In the pigeon, transfer depends on the part of the visual field stimulated during training.

For the cat, monkey, and man, each hemisphere receives input from both retinae in such a way that each hemisphere has projected on it about half the visual field; therefore, training on only one eye means that both hemispheres are receiving messages from this eye. However, if the optic chiasma is cut in the sagittal plane, the animal becomes hemianopsic when either eye is shut, but has a complete visual field with both eyes open, except for nasal interference. The two hemispheres can then be trained separately by restricting vision to one eye only. Myers (1955) found that cats with such a section of the optic chiasma could transfer from one eye what they had learned with the other eye. Also Myers (1956) and Sperry et al. (1956) found that if the corpus callosum was sectioned in addition to the optic chiasma, no transfer of learning from one eye to the other occurred. However, Merkle and Sechzer (1960) found that this was not true for the simple task of brightness discrimination. Such a discrimination still transfers after a section of both the optic chiasm and the corpus callosum. Further, Sechzer (1964) has shown that after optic chiasm–corpus callosum section, interocular transfer of a horizontal-vertical discrimination resulted when shock avoidance was the motivation used and not food approach. Food approach had been used in all the studies of this problem.

It seems that the transfer found in the first study of Myers was carried from one hemisphere to the other by fibers in the corpus callosum. It has further been found that such interhemispheric transfer is contingent upon the intactness of a posterior portion of the corpus callosum. It appears from Myers' (1959) data that there is a considerable degree of functional equivalence between the various parts of the posterior portion of the corpus callosum. The intactness of any posterior part of the structure leads to interocular transfer after section of the chiasma. It seems that in different cats, entirely different parts of the posterior corpus callosum sufficed for transfer of the same visual discrimination problem. However, around two to three million callosal fibers were needed for successful transfer (though not all of these were visual fibers).

Such findings lead logically to other experiments. The lack of communication between the left and right hemispheres that is caused by callosal section apparently prevents the left hemisphere from utilizing information laid down in the right. On this theory we may ask whether this is because information is laid down in both hemispheres during normal learning at the time of training, or whether one hemisphere draws on information stored in the other during the time of testing. Work by Myers (1957), and

Sperry, Stamm, and Miner (1956), and Sperry (1958) would indicate that for some types of visual discrimination, storage appears to be bilateral, whereas it is unilateral for other more difficult visual discriminations. In tests with the contralateral eye, sectioning of the corpus callosum or removal of the cortex to which visual information passed during learning (prior to testing with the contralateral hemisphere) results in almost perfect retention. However, this has only been found true where the patterns to be discriminated are vertical and horizontal striations. For instance, where the patterns are small filled circles against larger unfilled wide ones, such transfer does not occur. The obvious conclusion which has been drawn is that there is carry-over of information from one hemisphere to the other during learning when the discrimination is simple, but no such carry-over when the discrimination is more complex. Whether this conclusion is correct will be decided by further investigation.

It has also been found that the animal with sectioned chiasma and callosum can learn diametrically opposed habits with no interference between the two habits (Myers, 1956; Sperry, 1958). Such results have been obtained with the monkey and the cat (Sperry, 1958; Trevarthen, 1960).

Work has also been undertaken on the transfer of somesthetic habits in animals with a section of the corpus callosum. As has been mentioned above, Bykoff (1924) found an absence of the usual transfer of a touch stimulus to the contralateral side. Stamm and Sperry (1957) found no transfer when cats with sectioned callosum had been trained to discriminate between two levers on the basis of touch. When the front paw on one side had been trained, there was no transfer to the other paw. Similar results have been obtained by Glickstein and Sperry (1960) and Ebner and Myers (1960) in the case of tactile object discrimination in monkeys, and by Myers and Henson (1960) who worked with chimpanzees.

Sperry (1959) has found a remarkable autonomy of function of the somesthetic cortex in cats, i.e., independence from the part of the cortex of the same hemisphere. The removal of most of the cortex on the same side together with callosal section did not affect the retention of learned somesthetic discriminations by the somesthetic cortical remnant, nor the speed of new learning. A similar autonomy has not been found for the visual cortex (Sperry et al., 1960).

It has been suggested that the transfer of learning of a pattern discrimination from one eye to the other depends on previous experience with some patterned light in the second eye. However this has been shown in a conclusive experiment not to be necessary (Meyers and McCleary, 1964).

Studies of interocular transfer in relation to memory have also been made with fish (Sperry and Clark, 1949; Schulte, 1957; McCleary, 1960). The study of this animal is of some interest because there is a complete crossover from a retina to the contralateral portion of the nervous system.

This means that each eye is represented separately and unilaterally. Further, since there is no neocortex, there is also no corpus callosum; there are, however, commisural fibers. Sperry and Clark (1949) and Schulte (1957) covered one eye of the fish which were then required to swim towards the correct one of two stimuli to obtain food. When the original eye used in the training was covered and the "naive" eye uncovered, transfer was evident, and the fish chose the correct stimuli for food. McCleary (1960) found interocular transfer in fish with a simple type of avoidance situation which used conditioned heart rate as an index. When a skeletal motor response of a simple nature was learned with one eye while the other eye was covered, no transfer occurred. However, when the naive eye was left uncovered during training though it could not see the training stimuli, transfer did occur. Covering an eye, however, did not prevent transfer if conditioned heart rate was used as an index. When a simple swimming escape response was required, failure of transfer occurred even if both eyes were covered with translucent blinders during training and also in the transfer tests. The stimulus was a thin beam of white light which was focused on one blinder during training and on the other blinder during transfer tests. The explanation of these findings is obscure.

A variant of the technique of collosal sectioning in the study of memory has been introduced by Bureš and Burešová (1960), using Leão's spreading depression. If a high concentration of a chemical agent such as potassium chloride is placed on the dura, a series of waves of depression is generated in the cortex with no recovery between them. In such a case, electroencephalographic activity may remain depressed for several hours. The production of such a depression in both hemispheres does not anesthetize an animal; the animal moves around much as usual. However, during the depression it does not manifest signs of previous learning.

A depression produced in one hemisphere does not spread to the other hemisphere, and this is what makes it a convenient tool in the study of interhemispheric transfer. Using this technique Bureš and Burešová trained rats in a simple avoidance habit. When the same hemisphere was depressed on the two successive days of learning, there was considerable saving in the retention of the habit on the second day. However, if one hemisphere was depressed on the first day and another hemisphere on the second day, there was no saving of learning on the second day. These authors suggest that the memory trace had remained localized in the hemisphere which had been involved in learning on the first day. On the second day this first hemisphere was inactivated so that the trace of the learning on the first day was unavailable to the animal. It follows from this reasoning that there was no transfer of a memory trace between the two hemispheres during the 24 hours or so during which they both functioned normally. Russell and Ochs (1961) reported that such inferred transfer occurs very quickly if the unilaterally learned habit is practised while both hemispheres are functioning.

It has been shown earlier in work on callosal sectioning that it is possible to train the two hemispheres separately in conflicting habits without any signs of interference. Bureš and Burešová (1960) were also able to show the coexistence of traces of conflicting habits in the two hemispheres, even when the callosum was intact. Animals were trained to escape by going to the left when one hemisphere was inactivated and to the right when the other was inactivated. On the second day they would choose to go either left or right depending on which hemisphere it was which was not activated. It was also observed that on recovery from spreading depression, memory traces of habits learned before the depression were left intact.

However, as in the work on callosal sectioning, complexities have appeared. Thompson (1964) reported that rats under bilateral spreading depression can learn a simple avoidance habit. Travis and Sparks (1963) obtained similar results using an escape habit. Further, Tapp (1962) found that the emotional components of a habit learned with the cortex normal transferred to the training situation when bilateral spreading depression was instituted. Also Bureš, Burešová, and Fifková (1964) reported partial transfer of a passive avoidance reaction from one hemisphere to the one inactivated by cortical spreading depression during training. The rat was given electric shock in one compartment of an apparatus while cortical spreading depression was applied to one hemisphere. The originally unaffected hemisphere was then placed under spreading depression while the affected one recovered and the amount of time spent by the rat in the compartment where it had been shocked was measured. Rats showed some retention of the avoidance habit when the hemisphere which was inactivated during training was now active and the other hemisphere active during learning was now depressed. This transfer occurred even in animals with a transected corpus callosum, showing that the memory trace could not have traveled from one hemisphere to the other via the corpus callosum. Further to exclude the possibility that the memory trace had somehow traveled from one hemisphere to the other, retention of the habit was demonstrated in rats where cortical spreading depression in the hemisphere used during training was evoked before the other hemisphere used in the retention test was allowed to recover. It looks, therefore, as if subcortical structures are somehow involved.

However, subcortical structures are not left unaltered by the application of spreading depression to the cortex. The activity of 90 percent of thalamic and hypothalamic units is severely depressed during cortical spreading depression, whereas the activity of over 60 percent of reticular units is increased.

Recent work suggests a completely different explanation of the experiments on interhemispheric transfer. This explanation is based on the old principle of generalization decrement. An instance of this was described by the seventeenth century philosopher, Locke: "It is of a young gentleman, who having learnt to dance, and that to a great perfection, there happen'd to stand an old trunk in the room where he learnt. The idea of this remarkable piece of household stuff had so mix'd itself with the turns and steps of all his dances, that though in that chamber he could dance excellently well, yet it was only while that trunk was there. . . ." Changes in apparently irrelevant aspects of the environment can lead to partial or complete disruption of a learned habit. It is probable that such changes can be brought about by physiological as well as by environmental manipulations. It may also be the case that in spreading depression, an

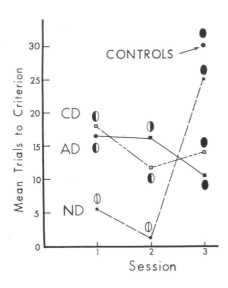

FIG. 3–3. Retention under spreading depression. Mean trials to reach criterion in each avoidance session. The control point represents the mean trials taken by each control group to reach criterion during the final session. The shading of the circles near each data point represents the depressed hemisphere or hemispheres. (Courtesy of Dr. Schneider.)

inability to switch hemispheres is not due to the fact that the memory resides in one hemisphere alone, but rather to the stimulus change brought about by a change of hemispheres.

The two hypotheses on interhemispheric transfer are clearly contrasted in the following experiment by Schneider (unpublished). Two groups of animals were trained in a shuttle box to avoid shock. One group (ND) was trained on two successive days with no spreading depression and then on the third day with both hemispheres depressed. The second group (CD and AD) was trained on the first day with one hemisphere depressed, on the second with the other hemisphere depressed, and on the third with both hemispheres depressed. According to the notion that memory is stored in a nondepressed hemisphere, we should expect no or equal savings on the third day of training in both groups when both hemispheres were depressed. On the other hand if transfer depends on the degree of stimulus change brought about by spreading depression, then the group trained under unilateral spreading depression would be expected to transfer much better to the condition of bilateral spreading depression than the group with no experience of spreading depression. This is shown in Figure 3–3.

In another experiment Schneider and Hamburg again used a shuttle box to train animals in an avoidance task. They investigated the notion that there is fast transfer from one hemisphere to the other when training occurred with both hemispheres undepressed, interposed between training with one and then the other hemisphere depressed as had apparently been shown (e.g., Russell and Ochs). With no training between the depression of one hemisphere and then the other, no transfer occurred, as has been

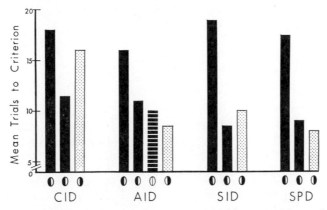

FIG. 3–4. Interhemispheric transfer. The mean number of trials-to-criterion (excluding the criterion trials) during each session; the first two sessions consisted of conditioning with the same hemisphere depressed (unilateral conditioning), the final session consisted of conditioning with the initially trained hemisphere depressed (contralateral retention). The third session in the AID group represents the number of trials required for 5 avoidance responses during the interdepression period. The shading represents the relationship between the depressed and the nondepressed hemispheres. Group CID received only unilateral training and contralateral test sessions. (Courtesy of Dr. Schneider.)

shown by other investigators (see Figure 3–4). With avoidance training under no depression interposed between training with one hemisphere depressed and then the other, transfer occurred between the situation where one hemisphere was depressed (group AID). However, the same transfer occurred in two other situations as in this last situation where avoidance training occurred between the two training sessions with unilateral depression on one cortical hemisphere in the first session and on the other hemisphere in the second session. These two situations are as follows: The rat is placed in the apparatus with both hemispheres undepressed between the two training sessions with unilateral depression and simply given nonavoidable shock in the shuttle box (group SID). This procedure produced transfer of avoidance responding between the condition where one hemisphere was depressed to the condition where the other was depressed. The results in the second situation are even more surprising on the memory trace transfer hypothesis. In the second situation, animals were given experience of the unavoidable shock with both hemispheres undepressed before any training with unilateral spreading depression (group SPD). Training with unilateral spreading depression was then begun, and the bilateral experience with shock led to no better learning rate than was obtained in initial learning with the other groups. Evidently the effect of the unavoidable shock had not been simply to facilitate learning under unilateral depression. When, however, the other hemisphere was now depressed with no training or treatment given between the session with one hemisphere depressed and then the other, perfect transfer occurred. This quite inconsistent with the notion that memory traces move from one hemisphere to the other to produce behavioral transfer of a habit learned under spreading depression. It is on the other hand again completely consistent with an explanation based on generalization decrement. The experience the animal had of the situation first with both hemispheres undepressed and then with unilateral depression enabled it to generalize better from this wider sample. So it appears that the memory engram remains as elusive as ever. It seems that we were not tracking the memory trace after all but indulging in a procedure analogous to moving Locke's "remarkable piece of household stuff."

## Electrophysiological Phenomena: Epileptiform Phenomena and Learning

We saw above that electrically and chemically induced convulsions produced memory disorders. Memory defects have also been observed in epileptic patients. These defects may be caused either by the seizures themselves, as in the case of the electrically induced seizure, or by the activity of the epileptogenic focus of abnormal activity alone. Such a focus can be demonstrated in the electroencephalogram as a steady discharging focus of abnormal activity. This is sharply localized, and it spreads to the surrounding tissue to produce a seizure only on occasions that may be months apart. In a series of interesting studies, Morrell (1956, 1957) has been able to shed light on the relation of these foci of abnormal activity to learning by using the technique of the alpha-block conditioning. When a visual stimulus is presented to a subject (for instance, a bright flash of light to a subject with his eyes shut), the eight to thirteen cycles per second alpha rhythm is not affected when a sound or touch of sufficiently low intensity impinges on the subject. However, if such a sound or touch is paired with the light stimulus, a normal subject will later show blocking of his alpha rhythm in response to the sound or touch alone. The number of paired presentations of sound or touch with light required in a normal subject varies from one to twenty trials. Morrell (1956) investigated the ability to form such alpha-block conditioned responses in patients with sharply localized temporal lobe spike foci. In such cases it is expected that the auditory system would be especially involved.

To obtain a measure of the selective impairment of auditory function, Morrell (1956) used not only auditory but also tactile stimuli. It was found that in these patients the capacity to form an alpha-block conditioned response to a tone was extremely impaired whereas learning to a tactile stimulus remained essentially normal. However, Morrell found no difference in these patients in the motor reaction time to touch and to tone stimuli. This finding may be related to that by Chow and Obrist (1954) in which production of an epileptogenic focus does not interfere with habits previously acquired.

In a similar study with monkeys, Morrell (1957) was again able to show that epileptic foci selectively impair the formation of an alpha-block conditioned response. Epileptic foci were experimentally created by the placement of aluminum hydroxide cream in selected locations in the central nervous system. This substance gives rise to chronically discharging seizure foci, resembling those of epileptic foci when electrographically recorded. Morrell was able to show that extreme impairment of learning occurred under these conditions. Animals with foci in the auditory cortex showed a deficit in conditioning to tone but not to touch. Those with foci in the postcentral leg area showed a deficit to touch but not to tone. Morrell (1957) was also able to show that if the paired stimuli were presented when a small and well-circumscribed focus was quiescent, alpha block which was conditioned to touch would appear. However, though such learning was well established, blocking to the conditioned stimulus (touch) would suddenly and completely disappear when a pairing of the stimuli occurred during a spike discharge. The unconditioned alpha block to light was, on the other hand, unaffected. Less than a minute later when the spike discharge subsided, the next trial with the touch stimulus produced an alpha block, showing that learning had remained intact. When the excisions of the discharging focus were unilateral, a marked improvement in the formation of an alpha-block conditioned response was evident. It seems, therefore, that if excision is unilateral, the abnormal discharge of a focus causes a greater deficit than the simple absence of the discharging tissue. The contralateral tissue can then presumably function without interference.

Other investigators (Kraft et al., 1960; Stamm and Pribram, 1960) have confirmed Morrell's observation that learning of a particular type is affected, depending on the site of the discharging focus. Kraft et al., for instance, found that monkeys with occipital implants of aluminum hydroxide cream showed impairment in learning visual discrimination tasks. However, no deficit was evident in their learning of an alternation task. Stamm and Pribram (1960) demonstrated a learning deficit for an alternation task when aluminum hydroxide cream was placed bilaterally on the frontal cortex. Though this learning deficit was very large, no detectable deficit was found in the retention of the same habit acquired preoperatively. These data should be contrasted with the findings of Chow (1961), who found that when a bilateral electrographic discharge was induced in their temporal cortices, monkeys had an inability to learn and retain visual habits. However, retention was not disturbed with bilateral hippocampal or occipital discharge.

## STEADY POTENTIAL SHIFTS AND LEARNING-LIKE PHENOMENA

Following the work of Rusinov (1953), Morrell (1961) demonstrated that after the application of low (2 to 10 $\mu$a) anodal constant current to a part of the motor cortex, phenomena resembling learning occurred. This constant current does not produce limb movement by itself. However, the limb movement that one would expect as a result of adequate stimulation of the motor area with other kinds of current was triggered as a result of a flash, sound, or touch. Even after the current has been switched off, such a movement can be produced by various stimuli for a period up to half an hour. The experiment was also conducted another way. A group of stimuli was selected, and all members of this group were repeated individually until habituation (as judged by the EEG record) to them occurred. Then one of these stimuli was chosen to be presented repeatedly while the constant anodal current was applied to the motor area of the cortex; this stimulus then elicited a limb movement and continued to do so even when the current was switched off. The other members of the group to which habituation had occurred and which had not been paired with the constant current did not elicit such a movement. However, other stimuli (to which habituation had not taken place and which were outside the previously selected group) elicited the limb movement for some time after the constant current had been switched off.

It seems that the steady current applied to the motor area renders it hyperexcitable and liable to be triggered by any disturbances. However, the process of habituation of a stimulus appears to attenuate the functional connection between the receiving area for this stimulus and the motor regions. The pairing of a habituated stimulus with the constant current application, however, results in a loss of this habituation, so that this stimulus becomes effective in eliciting the appropriate limb movement.

Another interesting phenomenon obtained in the same study concerns the application of the constant anodal current to the visual receiving area. Recordings were obtained from single neural units which responded to a single flash by a high-frequency burst of spikes. These units responded by a similar burst after each flash when such flashes were delivered at the rate of three per second. The effect of the constant current seemed to be that it would induce such a single unit to respond to a single flash delivered up to 20 minutes after the end of the three per second flicker by a series of bursts of spikes spaced at three per second (Figure 3–5). Morrell reported that no trace of such rhythmic activity was apparent in the record during this interval. These findings are evidence against the notion that reverberating circuits are necessary as short-term storage of information in the central nervous system.

Such grouping of single cell discharge has been observed by Jasper *et al.* (1960) with the monkey during low-frequency flicker and by Strumwasser and Rosenthal (1960) with the frog during intermittent direct-current stimulation of single neurons. However, these authors did not report

FIG. 3–5. Conditioning of a rhythmic burst response to a single flash in a single neuron in the visual cortex. Anodal polarization was applied to the visual receiving area. Single flash elicited a single burst in a quiescent (A) and in a randomly firing cell (B). Three per second stroboscopic stimulation (C) produced driving of unit discharge at frequency. A single flash (D) delivered 30 seconds after termination of the rhythmic stimulus resulted in repetitive unit discharge at about 3 per second. Unit potentials are seen in the upper channel of the oscilloscope; stimulus artifacts in the lower channel. Amplitude calibration: 2 millivolts. Time calibration: 500 milliseconds (A & B) and one second (C & D). (From Morrell, F., in Fields, W. S., and Abbot, W., 1963. Courtesy of Charles C. Thomas, Publisher, Springfield, Ill.)

storage of the pattern of stimulation during the time stimulation was absent. It may well be that the steady potential shifts induce, mimic, or produce some physiological changes to be found in the normal functioning of the central nervous system. Goldring and O'Leary (1957) have reported negative DC shifts of cortex when the midline thalamic reticular system is stimulated. Findings of a similar nature are also reported by Arduini (1958). Morrell (1961), coupling an auditory signal with stimulation of the midline thalamic reticular nuclei (which produce a negative DC shift), found that this shift would occur after thirty paired trials to a tone alone. Working with the rabbit, Morrell used low-frequency (four to five per second) unilateral stimulation of the centromedian nucleus. Such stimulation produced a negative DC shift in the central cortex on the same side as the stimulated area.

## ELECTRICAL ACTIVITY OF THE BRAIN AND ITS
## RELATION TO THE MEMORY TRACE

We shall now turn to a brief review of EEG phenomena in an effort to assess the possibility that the electrical events recorded by the electroencephalogram are used by the central nervous system as a signal in transmission or storage.

When a novel stimulus is presented to an animal, a desynchronization of its EEG rhythm occurs. The resting brain rhythms are replaced by low-voltage, fast electrical activity.

What does this measure of brain activity tell us about other behavior of the nervous system? Kogan (1960) measured thresholds of neural excitability during desynchronization. He found that the threshold for such excitability decreased in the primary sensory area to which the alerting sensory stimulus was relayed, but that it increased in other areas, though all showed EEG desynchronization. It has been shown by Ricci *et al.* (1957) that activity of individual units can be increased, decreased, or unaffected by desynchronization. Schlag (personal communication) has evidence that some of the above results are due to poor sampling inherent in the methods of microelectrode recording. Using larger electrodes he shows a good correlation between desynchronization and enhanced unit activity.

When a novel stimulus is repeatedly presented alone, a gradual decrease in the period of desynchronization occurs until it fails to develop altogether. Such a process is termed "habituation" and is selective and specific. A stimulus differing only slightly from that previously presented repeatedly will cause desynchronization (Sokolov, 1960; Sharpless and Jasper, 1956).

When habituation to a signal is complete, training is begun. The stimulus to which habituation has occurred is paired with some other stimulus which has either rewarding or punishing properties; arousal to the previously habituated stimulus tends to occur under such circumstances. Many papers (e.g., John and Killam, 1960; Morrell, 1960) describe the distribution of responses to a flickering light during conditioning. With avoidance conditioning there develops an enhancement of the response to the flicker in the reticular formation and the hippocampus. Later in training such an enhancement occurs in the nucleus ventralis anterior and structures of the visual system. However, it seems that when reward rather than punishment is introduced, the sequence of changes during learning is altered. These experiments raise the question whether we are observing in the EEG some signal which is identifiable with a short-term or long-term memory trace or its transmission; or whether instead we are observing other side effects of the learning situation. One example of such localized changes in EEG rhythms may be taken. High-frequency (40 cps.) activity in the amygdala arises during certain phases of learning. Gault and Leaton (1963) have recently shown that such discharges occur only when the animal sniffs. The EEG record is therefore a somewhat circuitous way of measuring olfactory exploration on the part of the animal.

The unlikelihood of identifying EEG rhythms as signals used by the central nervous system either in transmission or storage is increased by an excellent experiment by Chow (1960). He implanted electrodes in the inferior temporal cortex of the monkey and then required the animal to learn a discrimination which it is less able to perform without this part of the cortex. The animal was presented with visual patterns, the significance of which changed according to the frequency of the flicker in which they were displayed. No signs of this discontinuous stimulation appeared on the EEG record in the temporal area, even though it was an ingredient which had to be distinguished by the animal. The EEG changed in the temporal area only during the middle trials, being the same at the beginning and the end of learning. This is most plausibly interpreted by Chow as being caused by attentional factors. One might conclude as did Morrell (1961) that "the experiment of Chow serves to demonstrate that the material basis of the engram or durable memory trace is not likely to be revealed by the techniques of electrophysiology."

Various other EEG phenomena have been noted during conditioning. Slow waves appear when an animal is required to wait or to suppress a response. John, Leiman, and Sachs (1961) claimed that "inhibition of conditioned response is consistently accompanied by slow waves." However, they also reported that such slow waves also occur in relation to excitation as well as to inhibition, and there appeared to be no differences between the waves under these two circumstances.

It has also been noted by numerous workers (e.g., Morrell, 1957) that slow waves can be elicited by a steady tone, if this tone has been coupled with a flickering light. The experimental procedure used to show this was as follows. A pure tone of low intensity was presented to an animal repeatedly until it produced no alteration in the electroencephalographic record. At this point a low-frequency visual flicker was introduced at a fixed time after the beginning of the tone. The frequency of flicker was three to twelve per second and it produced "photic driving" of the EEG rhythm. By this we mean that an EEG rhythm of the same frequency as the light flicker could be observed from the visual cortex. After the few trials in which the tone and flicker were presented together, the tone alone began to produce a desynchronized EEG record in the same way that it did before habituation to the tone had taken place. This has been called stage I, and it may last from 15 to 60 trials depending on the animal. In stage II, when the tone was sounded and before presentation of the visual flicker, an EEG rhythm appeared, similar in frequency to that evoked by the flicker itself. This stage was brief (two to ten trials) and was soon replaced by stage III, which was a desynchronization localized to the visual cortex and which persisted, so that it may be regarded as the final stage. However, it is the frequency of the discharge in stage II after the tone is sounded and before the light appears that is of main interest here. It has been regarded by some workers as a neural memory trace of the flicker which the nervous system produces in order to compare an incoming frequency of flicker with those flicker frequencies which have already been presented. However, Morrell, Barlow, and Brazier (1960) reported two points of interest in relation to such a hypothesis. They found, contrary to general impression, that the shift in EEG frequency was not directly or linearly related to the shift in flash rate. For example, when one animal was first conditioned with a three per second flash, it developed a conditioned response at six per second. A second experiment, using a four per second flash resulted in a conditioned response at three per second. A third experiment using a six per second flash rate resulted in a response that was at or very close to six per second. These authors also examined the records from stage III with the help of a computer in order to see whether anything resembling the frequency of the flash appeared in the desynchronized record. When a large number of successive records were superimposed and the fluctuations for each moment of the record were averaged, random components tended to be ironed out which may have accidentally biased the single record in a positive or negative direction. The average record then emerged, and this should reveal any regularly repeating changes which are masked by random fluctuations on the individual records. Using this technique then to see whether the fluctuations of stage II persisted in stage III, Morrell *et al.* found evidence, which they considered unequivocal, that the rhythm of stage II disappears.

In view of these results, these investigators raised the possibility that the slow rhythms described in stage II represented the hippocampal arousal pattern which consists of slow waves and which occurs at a certain stage in the conditioning procedure described. It has been suggested by some that the occurrence of slow rhythms during stage II is a part of a memory storage mechanism. For instance, John *et al.* (1961) write: "A mechanism of this sort would appear to provide means for storage of a representation of a temporal sequence of events, lasting beyond the duration of the events themselves. Such a mechanism for internal representation of a past event seems, on logical basis, to be essential to enable an animal to perform two differentiated responses to two similar stimuli, either of which may be presented in a given experimental situation." This view is reminiscent of ancient theories of hearing in which it was considered that in order to recognize a sound it had to be compared with a similar sound stored in the ear. It is clear that such a mechanism is not essential on logical bases. It is merely a possible, though somewhat clumsy, mechanism. We can equally well suppose that there are arrangements of cells which are differentially set into activity by different incoming frequencies in a manner analogous to resonators. We do not, then, need to suppose that the occurrence of a frequency is stored by having a copy of it played by the nervous system. We only need to suppose that a record is kept of which "resonator" system has been activated by an incoming set of signals.

Whatever the theoretical possibilities are, the notion that the rhythms detected by the electroencephalogram carry information which is used by the nervous system has received experimental attention. Chow, Dement, and John (1957) used an avoidance task in which a cat had to jump from one compartment to another in order to avoid shock. The imminence of the shock was signaled by a flickering light. The light also produced an EEG wave at the frequency of the flicker, or photic driving, as it is called, which is usual in such a situation. In time the cat would jump from one compartment to another simply when the flicker occurred. After this phase of the experiment, a tone was sounded before the flickering stimulus, outside the avoidance situation. When animals had reached stage II in this procedure, that is, when the tone alone produced a low-frequency EEG rhythm similar to the photic driving, they were placed once again in the avoidance situation. The tone was sounded, and it produced the same EEG as the flicker. However, it did not produce any behavioral response. It does not therefore seem that the signal generated by flicker and picked up by the EEG electrodes is used by the nervous system itself as a signal.

# 4

# LEARNING AND INTRACRANIAL SELF-STIMULATION

## THE NATURE OF THE PROBLEM

In this chapter we shall be concerned with what is known about learning from the physiological point of view. A great deal is known from the descriptive or behavioral point of view about the adaptive changes which occur when an animal is repeatedly placed in the same situation. Such changes, or the capacity for such changes, are the property of some mechanism, or a set of mechanisms, to be found within the animal. It will be our task to consider what these mechanisms are.

Ideally, the discovery and description of such mechanisms appear simple. In order to discover the mechanism of learning we should observe the nervous system while learning is proceeding, much as we look at the works of a clock in order to discover how it keeps time, and this should tell us what the mechanism is which produces learning. Unfortunately, such a simple approach is not possible. The functional units of the nervous system are too small and numerous for us to be able to view their interactions simultaneously. We are, therefore, driven to less direct methods of discovering the mechanisms of learning. Since only certain kinds of observation are open to us, we must construct guesses about the kind of mechanism at work and then see what observations of the type available to us we should expect if such hypotheses were correct. Such observations might either be on the behavior of the intact organism, which are placed in the domain of experimental psychology, or on organisms where some interference, pharmacological or surgical, has occurred. These latter are collocated under the name of physiological psychology. The distinction that is here drawn between experimental and physiological psychology does not refer to a different theoretical purpose but simply to one of method or technique employed. The facts used as we attempt to frame hypotheses about the mechanisms which enable an animal to learn will be drawn both from studies on intact animals and those where physiological methods have been used. Both sets of data reflect the workings of the mechanism which in our hypotheses we attempt to discern. Both kinds of evidence can function as evidence for or against hypotheses about the mechanism which we could entertain.

## PROBLEMS ABOUT THE MECHANISM OF LEARNING

What is it about the nervous system that we are attempting to discover when we study learning? There are many questions which may be asked and which it will be useful to keep separate. We may wish to help engineers who are interested in constructing computers that display some of the advantageous features of biological learning systems. For instance, biological learning systems are capable of storing an enormous amount of information. Though this could be explained by the large number of components in biological systems, the speed with which stored information can be drawn upon by such systems (for instance, the speed with which we recognize) cannot be explained in such a way. On the contrary, the elements of which the nervous system is composed act very slowly in comparison to the vacuum tubes or transistors available to the engineer. The problem of storage and retrieval may be illustrated by the following example. Storage of signals on magnetic tape in very large quantities presents little problem. Long sequences of music, for instance, can be faithfully recorded. They can also be accurately reproduced, so that if we wish to know all that has been recorded in the machine we can ascertain this simply by playing back what has been recorded. However, we may not simply wish to know all that has been recorded. We may wish to know whether a given piece of music has already been recorded on the tape or not. In order to find this out we have to arrange for a comparison of all that has been recorded with the piece of music which may or may not have been recorded. The problem here is how to find this out quickly. In order to decide that the piece of music has not occurred before, it would be necessary to play through the whole of the tape on which recording had been made. If the process of recognition was carried out in this way, the time would rise with the amount already recorded. Such a process of "recognition" is clearly lengthy and inefficient. When we ourselves hear a melody, recognition is prompt. We do not have to search in series through all the tunes we have ever heard. An explanation of this property of fast access or retrieval will not lie in the speed of action of each component of the nervous system taken by itself, and consequently what it is made of. Rather the explanation of the speed with which stored information can be tapped will be found in the way in which the rather slow-acting components are arranged. That is, in animals and man the system of storage and retrieval is probably different from those found in man-made devices. If this is the case, the engineer will be able to build a system with properties similar to the nervous system out of components such as tubes or transistors available to him and so be able to construct more efficient machines. It is common to have the interconnections of the components, rather than their individual properties, determine the performance of the overall system. It is for this reason that it is possible to build a computer having the same repertoire out of physically quite different components, such as vacuum tubes or transistors. While the physical principles on which the basic units function are different, the interactions of these elements or basic units are kept the same.

On the other hand, we may be interested in determining the precise physical change which occurs in the nervous system when an animal learns. There is presumably some long-term alteration of a physical nature in the nervous system on which an animal's learning depends. Such a question is not directed at the explanation of learning in the same way as that concerning the learning system, which could be asked without an attempt at the physical specification of the parts composing the system. It is a question about the physical embodiment of an operation within the system. Even if we knew the precise physical change which occurred during learning, we could not, without a knowledge of the system within which it functions, predict the behavior of the organism when it learns. In the same way we cannot predict the storage performance of a computer merely by knowing that magnetization is the long-term change which occurs in the computer when it stores information. However, the answer to this question is important from another point of view. It would perhaps tell us why, for instance, cooling a biological system does not destroy learned habits or why more recent memories are affected after concussion while those of more distant events are left intact.

There is a third class of questions that we may wish to ask about learning and its relation to the nervous system. We may be interested to know what parts of the nervous system are necessary for learning to occur. This may be thought of as a question about the problems we discussed above; i.e., where in the nervous system the structures or neural organization subserving learning are to be found and where the physiological change necessary in learning is located. The answer to these questions would not of course enable us to understand behavior better than if we did not know where in the nervous system certain neural organizations were placed. Knowing the precise lesion which will produce aphasia still leaves us in ignorance of the mechanism of speech. However, though the answer to the question of places does not have direct implications for the understanding or explanation of behavior, it might in many instances be a prerequisite to the study of a system by direct neurophysiological means. A Martian invader might note that most cars in the United States are made in Detroit. But this tells him virtually nothing about how cars are made. However, it would direct his attention to Detroit if he wished to find out.

## THE LEARNING SYSTEM

There are in nature many instances of systems which alter their behavior on successive exposures to a situation. These may all to some extent be regarded as instances of learning systems. At one end are examples which only tenuously fit our notion of what we would consider to be learning. For instance, a pane of glass displays different behavior the second time a stone is thrown through it. At the other end and much nearer to what we would wish to call learning is the mechanism of acquired immunity. Here one exposure to a pathogenic organism can alter the reactions of the body in such a way that resistance specific to this pathogenic organism is built up when subsequent exposures take place.

Though there are many natural systems which display what we might wish to call learning, as psychologists we are interested in explaining changes in behavior. It is therefore necessary to consider whether suggested systems (or theories, as they can be called) tally in their properties with those exhibited by living organisms.

## Stimulus-Response Linkage as a Learning System

One of the most widely held views about learning is that it occurs as a result of the linkage of an afferent pathway in the nervous system (which conveys the stimulus) to an efferent pathway (activity which results in a response). There are differences in opinion among those who hold this general view about the precise conditions under which such a linkage occurs. What is common is the notion that the occurrence in close temporal contiguity of a stimulus and a response under certain conditions lead to a state of affairs in the nervous system such that on the next occasion the stimulus occurs, the afferent pathway down which it travels will be joined to the efferent pathway, so that the same response will occur again. On this view we should make at least two predictions about learning. The first is that learning of a habit should not occur without the execution of the responses involved in this habit. Stimuli must be followed by responses. Otherwise, no linkage between them can occur. The second prediction is that once a habit has been learnt, interference with the execution of the responses which occurred during the learning of the habit should lead to a disappearance of the habit. If a habit consists of a series of stimuli, each evoking a particular response, an abolition of the responses should lead to a disappearance of the habit.

There is a great deal of evidence against the first prediction that learning should not occur without the execution of responses involved in a habit. First, there is a group of experiments in which animals are conveyed through an environment by the experimenter and subsequently allowed to move through it themselves to see if they have learnt anything. Such an experiment was first suggested by Thorndike (1946), but it fell to Gleitman (1955) to be the first to perform it. In Gleitman's experiment the rats were drawn through an environment in a plexiglass car and given an electric shock in one particular place. This shock was then terminated in another place. The rats were subsequently released, and their avoidance of the place where they had been shocked was observed. The rats gave evidence of learning. They preferred the place where the shock was terminated to that where it was started.

McNamara, Long, and Wike (1956) adopted a similar procedure in a T-maze, rewarding their rats with food after a ride to one of the sides. They used two experimental groups of rats. One was carried through an elevated maze rich in external cues, the other through a maze where visual cues were considerably reduced. Two control groups were run through these same mazes, and their performance compared to that of the rats which were carried along. In the test trial when the experimental groups were allowed to run the maze, it was found that the group which had been carried in the environment rich in external cues had been equal or better in learning the maze. As was to be expected, however, the carried group in the maze where external cues were deficient was inferior to the control group. Dodwell and Bessant (1960) performed an experiment designed to ascertain whether learning without performance could occur in more complex tasks. These experimenters used a water maze with eight successive choice points. They used two groups of rats. The first group learnt to swim the maze for a reward of food. The second group was placed on a wooden trolley whose upper surface projected above the water. The rats in this group were then propelled through the maze on the trolley for ten trials and at the end of each trial rewarded with food in the goal box. After such treatment, this group was then made to swim the maze to see if there was any saving in the number of trials to criterion as compared with the group which had not been given the experience of being pushed through the alley. There was considerable saving due presumably to learning without performance. The mean number to criterion of trials for the trolley group was 5.6; for the swimmers only, it was 9.6.

These experiments suggest that what is learnt is not what response to make to what stimulus, but rather what stimulus follows what. Such a conclusion is supported by the type of experiment initially performed by Brogden (1939). Two stimuli, such as an auditory and a visual one, are repeatedly paired. One of these stimuli is conditioned to a response. It is then found that there is a tendency for the other member of the pair of stimuli to evoke that response without any further training.

A more direct way of observing the linkage of one stimulus to another is made possible by the technique of EEG measurement. It is possible to demonstrate by use of the EEG that a stimulus, say an auditory one, when it is paired with a visual stimulus, will produce in time the same EEG response as the visual stimulus. A light shone into a subject's eyes in the dark will cause the alpha rhythm to disappear while it is on. It was noted by Durup and Fessard (1935) and Loomis, *et al.* (1936) that alpha waves could be blocked not only by light stimuli but also by sounds when these sounds had been paired with the light. This type of learning is quite fast. For instance, Morrell and Jasper (1956) demonstrated such learning in eight monkeys in an average of about 11 trials. However, this phenomenon is somewhat irregular in its appearance. For instance, in a large study, Gastaut, *et al.* (1957), were able to obtain this "alpha block conditioned reflex" in only 60 percent of human subjects.

The second prediction concerns the disruption of a learnt habit if the responses made during the learning of the habit are disrupted or made impossible. Here also the stimulus-response linkage theory of learning fails to be substantiated. Once a habit has been learnt the animal can execute it using a wide variety of alternative means of responding. As Lashley (1930) states: "If we train an animal in a maze and observe carefully his subsequent errorless running, we find little identity of movement in successive trials. He gallops through in one trial, in another shuffles along, sniffing at the cover of the box. If we injure his cerebellum, he may roll through the maze. He follows the correct path with every variety of twist and posture, so that we cannot identify a single movement as characteristic of the habit" (Lashley and McCarthy, 1926). Lashley (1924) also reports a case of a cebus monkey trained on puzzle box problems. This animal had a lesion in the motor area of the right hemisphere. Consequently, the left arm was not used by the animal during training on the problem. Subsequently a similar lesion was placed in the left hemisphere. Now weakness and spasticity of the right arm led the animal to use its left arm, which by now had considerably recovered. This arm had not been used at all during training on the problem boxes.

This plasticity on the part of the nervous system does not accord with the stimulus-response linkage theory of learning. However, as any other theories advanced by psychologists to explain these phenomena were imprecise and smacked of mysticism, these phenomena of plasticity tended to be ignored or dismissed. As is often the case, the evidence became identified with the dubious theories which quoted it in support.

There is a set of experiments which at first sight appear to be relevant to the hypothesis under discussion. Many experiments have been performed which show that learning to respond to a conditioned stimulus can occur without the performance of such a response when the unconditioned stimulus is presented. For instance, Kellogg, *et al.* (1940) and Light and Gantt (1936) crushed the motor nerves leading to one of the legs of a dog. An avoidance conditioning procedure was then carried out. Though the appropriate response was impossible at the time of conditioning, the dog gave the appropriate response once the nerves had regenerated. Finch (1938) and Crisler (1930) carried out salivary conditioning while blocking salivation with atropine. However, when tests were made without atropine, it became clear that learning had taken place. In another study Harlow and Bromer (1942) produced motor paralysis in monkeys by applying a drug to the motor cortex. There was evidence that avoidance learning had occurred in spite of this paralysis.

Though these experiments are of interest in other contexts, they cannot be used as evidence to show that stimulus-response linkage is not the basis of learning. They are evidence against the view that a response as viewed by the observer is paired with a stimulus but not against the notion that events within the nervous system which normally evoke behavioral responses are linked to incoming messages. In the experiments quoted above it is not unreasonable to suppose that events within the nervous system were occurring to evoke the particular responses which appeared later, but that they were simply prevented from evoking their normal consequences.

## Cortical Stimulation and Learning

Connected with the techniques which show learning even when the response is prevented from occurring are experiments which circumvent the normal sensory channels and yet demonstrate learning. Loucks (1935, 1938) showed that direct electrical stimulation of the motor cortex could serve as a conditioned stimulus for forelimb flexion. Such conditioning occurred even when sensory messages resulting from the movement of the hind leg evoked by the cortical stimulation could be ruled out. This investigator also showed that direct electrical stimulation of the visual cortex could also serve as a conditioned stimulus. Doty, et al. (1956) have extended these findings, being especially careful to exclude any possible sources of artifact, such as the direct stimulation of the membranes surrounding the brain, the blood vessels, or similar effects. They trained cats to lift their paw to escape a shock. The signal for the shock was electrical stimulation applied to the cortex. Areas of the cortex where such stimulation was effective included a point on the frontal cortex and the marginal, postlateral, middle suprasylvian, middle, and posterior ectosylvian gyri.

Other workers have produced drive by the use of electrical stimulation applied directly to the nervous system, not only in cortical but also in subcortical structures. Delgado, et al. (1954) have found that electrical stimulation of thalamic, mesencephalic, and limbic structures in cats can produce learning to escape this stimulation. Stimulation in these loci produces similar behavior as occurs after peripherally applied electric shocks. In the procedure used, these workers sounded a tone or shone a flickering light as a warning. The cat could prevent electrical brain stimulation if it turned a wheel within five seconds of the warning. The cats learnt to do this after 16 to 92 trials. It is difficult to evaluate the significance of these findings. Even though we might agree that afferent pain pathways can be excluded, the experiments simply demonstrate that there are central areas which when directly stimulated produce similar effects to those produced by afferent pathways. Similar experiments are described and the significance discussed elsewhere in the book, especially Chapter 10.

Electrical stimulation of subcortical structures can not only have punishing effects, but can also lead to the repetition of the behavior which occurred just prior to the administration of the shock (Olds and Milner, 1954; Seward, *et al.* 1960). A rat can in this way be trained to press a lever or perform in a runway. The loci where such stimulation is effective are in the midline structures of the hypothalamus and rostral midbrain or in the limbic system. These experiments will be discussed more fully below (pp. 119–37). Behavior produced in this way shows interesting discrepancies with behavior rewarded under more normal conditions. Such discrepancies will best be understood when we consider the system which probably produces learning.

## What Information Is Stored in Learning?

According to the stimulus-response hypothesis the information that is stored in learning is what response should be evoked by a particular stimulus when this stimulus occurs. Such storage can be readily imagined to consist of a connection which is made between a receptor and a motor area. However, the likelihood is very small that it is information about the relation of a stimulus to a specific response which is stored in learning. Learning, as was shown above, can occur without the performance of a response. The response is not necessary during learning. (It is only necessary to enable us to verify that learning has taken place; without appropriate responses on some later occasion we could not observe that an organism had learnt.) Similarly, disruption of response mechanisms does not cause learning to disappear.

The following is the simplest assumption which emerges from the evidence we have considered. What is stored is information about the sequence of stimuli which the organism encounters. However, though this hypothesis appears in some ways to be obvious, there are difficulties if we attempt to use it to account for the organism's performance once it has learnt. On the stimulus-response view, it is easy to see how learning once it has occurred leads to performance. The occurrence of a stimulus will evoke that specific response to which the stimulus was linked during learning. On the stimulus linkage view, it is difficult to see how the occurrence of a stimulus produces any action at all. This is a real difficulty, but we must remember that the question we are here attempting to answer is not how is the information stored during learning utilized but rather what information is stored during learning. We shall now turn to the question of the utilization of the information laid down.

## How Is the Information Laid Down during Learning Utilized in Subsequent Performance?

If we agree that what is stored is the sequence of stimuli the animal encounters in the environment, then the question concerning the utilization of this information resolves itself into two parts. The first is: How can the occurrence of stimuli (whose sequential order has been stored) be translated into some useful or appropriate motor act? The second question is: How is the stimulus which is associated with motor activity selected? That is, why are some stimuli effective and not others?

We will consider the first question about the relation of the stored stimulus sequence and activity. It will be recalled that when we were examining the stimulus-response view of behavior we saw that an animal's overall performance was remarkably unaffected by interference with motor components. The animal can, it seems, run a maze correctly even when it is forced to make quite different component movements, for instance by cerebellar ablation. Similarly, the correct performance of an animal is extremely variable. It looks as if the animal can employ different means to achieve the same end. These observations lead us to suspect that the type of mechanism used is of a feedback type. Such mechanisms possess the flexibility of performance we observe. Take a very simple example of this type of mechanism built into a learning machine (Deutsch, 1954). A part of it is trolley with a conical beam of light thrown forward from it. The trolley has two wheels, each of which is separately driven by a reversible motor. There is near the trolley a set of light sensitive photocells which pass a signal when the light beam from the trolley impinges upon them. One of these light sensitive photocells is selected (by a separate mechanism) to pass a signal back to the trolley. When there is no signal relayed back to the trolley, one of the motors reverses. This has the result that the trolley turns round on its axis. As soon as the beam of light strikes the photocell, then the motor which has been reversing goes forward. As a consequence, the whole trolley moves forward, and so approaches the photocell. If the trolley starts in a wrong direction or does not run a straight course, as soon as its beam leaves the photocell the trolley will begin to rotate again. As soon as its beam strikes the cell again, the trolley goes forward and so gradually approaches the cell. The ability of the trolley to approximate to the cell persists even if the wheels do not drive forward at the same speed making the trolley as a whole move forward in a curve. Similarly, the placing of obstacles in the way of the trolley may alter the particular pattern of movements ("rotate," "go forward") but does not prevent final approximation of the trolley to the cell, provided success is possible at all in the face of the obstacles.

There are of course more complex and efficient steering or guidance systems than that outlined above. It is, nevertheless, an example of systems, where the external stimulus does not simply trigger a movement, which then runs its course independently (as in the stimulus-response paradigm). The external stimulus in such systems modifies the response as it is made. For instance, the external stimulus can act as a target, and any deviation from the course towards the target is taken and translated into a compensatory movement. Without entering into a prolonged discussion of the precise mechanisms by which this might be achieved in the animal, we shall assume that an external stimulus is "steered towards" through the action of a feedback system. The appropriate motor act into which the occurrence of a particular stimulus is translated is that of steering towards this stimulus.

## Motivation and Selection of Behavior Sequences

We now know that there are regions in the hypothalamus which contain cells monitoring various bodily states. Artificial stimulation of such cells produces activity of the same type as that which occurs in the animal when it is naturally motivated. Minute injections of hypertonic saline in the hypothalamus make the animal drink or perform tasks which it had learned to obtain water, and analogous experiments have shown that the same is true for eating or mating. Nevertheless the question still remains how such cells within the hypothalamus communicate with the rest of the nervous system so that lines of action are evoked which are appropriate to a particular motivated state or drive. For instance, Kendler (1946) has shown the following. A rat which is both hungry and thirsty is taught a maze shaped like a T. In the goal box at one end of the arm of the T there is water, and in the other end, food. On the critical trial the rat is made only hungry (or alternately only thirsty). It is found that the rat can choose the arm of the T which is appropriate to its motivational or drive state. A hungry rat chooses the food arm and a thirsty one will turn into the arm containing water, even though the water or the food cannot be detected at the choice point.

Now the most likely supposition to explain how one set of cells in the hypothalamus produces running towards one goal box when the animal is hungry is that such a set of cells sends messages to another set of cells within the brain, which in their turn direct the action of running towards a particular set of signals such as those which emanate from one of the alleys in the T-maze. Such messages we would naturally expect to travel down a particular set of fibers from one set of cells to the other. Such simple assumptions might help us to understand how when a particular motivational state such as hunger is present, the rat will perform one set of actions rather than another.

However, we still have the problem in our simple model of how the two sets of cells become connected. During the course of learning the animal seems to be able to connect the cells in the hypothalamus which signal when it is thirsty to at least two different sets of cells. The activity of these two sets produces different actions in the T-maze. (The same argument, of course, applies to the cells which signal when the animal is hungry.) There is, during learning the maze, a connection of one set of cells, rather than another, to the cells in the hypothalamus which signal thirst. Further, this connection is also an appropriate one to produce a particular outcome, such as the finding of water. That is, the thirst-signaling cells are connected to that set of cells which when active bring the animal towards cues at the end of that alley previously found to contain water and not the alley containing food.

Now how could such a selection take place? It looks as if the fibers leading from one set of cells to both other sets must already be there. Adult rats do not seem to be able to grow fibers in their central nervous system, and even if they could, the process of growth would have to be extraordinarily rapid. Some habits can be learned practically instantaneously. The problem, if we keep to our model, is to open a set of connections which are already there—to open one set of sluice gates rather than another in channels which have already been dug.

One way in which this might be done is as follows. We can imagine that as the animal runs towards a set of cues in the T-maze, signals impinge on one set of cells (those concerned with locomoting towards that set of cues), and not on the set of cells which is concerned with locomoting to another set of cues. Shortly after such signals impinge, the rat finds water. Other signals are then generated which in their turn impinge on the set of cells signaling thirst. In other words, the relevant set of cells receives a signal from the sense organs just before the thirst-signaling cells receive their own signal from the sense organs. We simply have to assume that two sets of cells receiving signals from the sense organs in close succession are connected together. As we speculated above, such a connection probably consists of making a preexisting connection functional. There must be some connection, and one that is already functional, between the two groups of cells in order for this change to take place. When these two groups of cells have received a message from the sense organs a message down this connection between the two groups will then open the other connection between them. This, as we have decided, carries signals when the animal becomes thirsty.

We now have a model in which groups of cells are joined by two kinds of connection. The first conveys messages from cells signaling bodily states of various kinds. Such connections may for convenience be called motivational connections. The second conveys messages which lead to the opening of motivational connections between groups of cells which have received messages from the parts of the sense organs connected to them in close succession. These we may call reinforcement pathways. Given such a model, we are now in a position to imagine in rather a general way what could be happening to the rats in Kendler's experiment. There is a host of other phenomena which have been uncovered by rat psychologists on the topics of motivation and reward and learning which can also be understood by a development of the notions described above. A learning machine devised on the above principles shows considerable simplicity (Deutsch, 1953, 1954, 1960). Such a hypothesis also enables us to analyze physiological manipulations of the central nervous system to produce learning. The hypothesis has been introduced to organize the facts concerning intracranial self-stimulation introduced in the next section.

## The Analogy between Reward and Electrical Stimulation in Certain Areas of the Central Nervous System

A discovery of Olds and Milner (1954) disclosed that electrical stimulation of certain subcortical centers can produce a repetition of the activity which just preceded the electrical stimulus. The characteristics of the behavior elicited by such stimulation, as will be seen below, correspond in some respects with behavior rewarded in a normal manner. However, there are also some striking differences between these two types of behavior. Such effects are produced chiefly by the stimulation of the medial forebrain bundle and connected pathways.

The electrical stimulation of these structures can be carried out through chronically implanted bipolar electrodes. These electrodes consist of two insulated silver wires (0.01 inches in diameter) 0.002 to 0.004 inches apart. These wires are mounted for a portion of their length in a plastic block, and this block is attached to the skull with small screws and dental cement. Only the cut cross section of the wires is free of insulation. Thus current can pass only through a rather small area. However, it is calculated that, due to the spread of current, an area 1 mm. in diameter is given a suprathreshold stimulus. A standard electrical stimulus which is used is alternating current stepped down from the mains. (This stimulus is therefore sinusoidal in shape and at a frequency of 60 cps.) Only a very small current is used for the purpose of stimulation. Standard levels range from 10 to 50 microamperes rms. The resistance of the bipolar electrodes to this current varies from 12,000 to 20,000 ohms. (It is also possible to stimulate through monopolar electrodes, with the indifferent electrode on the skull.)

The ends of the wires which protrude from the skull are connected to the source of stimulating current through some type of switch, which is usually placed under the animal's own control. The switch allows current to pass when a rat presses a lever and the rat so delivers an electrical stimulus to its own brain. Most of the switches used have a device which limits the temporal duration of the current, typically to half a second. In this way an animal is forced to repeat a bar press in order to maintain the electrical stimulation. It would be difficult to evaluate or compare the performance of rats which simply hold the bar down. By interrupting the current after a certain time we can obtain an estimate of the rate of responding as a function of various factors.

Most of the studies carried out on electrical brain stimulation have employed the technique of placing the rat in a box with a lever in it. The lever when touched delivers a current of short duration through implanted electrodes. The rate of bar-pressing is then recorded on a cumulative recorder. Such a technique is therefore superficially analogous to that employed in Skinnerian instrumental conditioning. In the basic situation of this kind an animal presses a lever and is rewarded for this lever press by a pellet of food dropping into a container through a chute. The animal then has to move to the container to collect the reward and back from the container to the reward in order to press the bar again. Animals find it difficult at the beginning of training to learn to move away from the food container once they have found food there. They have to learn that food is to be found in the container if and only if they have pressed the lever.

In the case where electrical brain stimulation serves as "reward," the "reward" is delivered as the animal presses the lever. It does not have to learn a conditional relation between two situations as in the case of instrumental responding for food. The situation is less like an instrumental response and more like a consummatory response, say, of drinking, where each tongue movement "delivers" the reward. This point may sound like a quibble but is nevertheless very important. Unless we know what type of normal behavior learning for brain stimulation most resembles, it is difficult to make any straightforward comparison or interpretation.

## Characteristics of Learning Produced by Electrical Brain Stimulation

When electrical stimulation is used as a "reward" the course of acquisition of a response is as gradual as it is in learning for a water or food reward. (See, for instance, Seward, Uyeda, and Olds, 1959.) When learning is complete, very high rates of lever-pressing occur. Rates of 7,000 per hour have been reported. In order to learn and perform, animals do not have to be in any drive state. They can be satiated for all their conceivable needs and yet they will keep on pressing the lever.

It has further been noted that bar-pressing under conditions of brain stimulation tends to continue until the animal is physically exhausted. In contrast, under ordinary conditions of reward, satiation occurs and so a rat's rate of responding slows down. If the intracranial stimulus is made sufficiently intense, rats will cross a more highly charged grid for an intracranial stimulus than for food when they are 24 hours hungry (Olds, 1958).

In spite of extreme persistence of responding while the shock supervenes on each response, a very rapid decrement of responding occurs when the current is switched off. This is very unlike the type of performance to be found in the instrumental conditioning situation for food, where there is often an initial increase in rate of responding with nonreward, gradually tapering off to a chance level. In the case of animals who learn through electrical stimulation, there is a sharp immediate decline.

This tendency quickly to "lose interest" in the lever once no more stimulation occurs appears to manifest itself again in other situations. It has been found by Sidman, et al. (1955) that animals will not learn to press the bar in situations where a brain stimulus is infrequent. For instance, the experimenter may arrange the apparatus in such a way that the animal obtains only one electrical stimulus for a great number of lever presses (the so-called fixed ratio schedule). Animals learn well under such a schedule when food or water are used as reinforcement, but not when an intracranial stimulus is the reinforcing agent. It seems likely that this difficulty is due to the very rapid "loss of interest" in bar-pressing once it is not followed by a brain stimulus. The animal may press for a short while after the brain stimulus has been turned off, but not a sufficient number of times to bridge the gap between one "rewarded" response and the next when the fixed ratio between "rewarded and nonrewarded" is high. However, Sidman et al. found that the fixed ratio performance of rats with certain electrode placements improved when they were hungry.

So far we have discussed the properties of brain stimulation as reward in an adapted Skinner box. There have also been efforts to have rats learn complex mazes with brain stimulation as a "reward," and this has been found difficult or impossible, with certain exceptions. Olds (1956) found that it was possible to train animals with electrode tips in the basomedial forebrain when the animals are running under 18 to 24 hours of food deprivation. (This is reminiscent of the results of Sidman, et al., quoted above, who found that hunger improved the fixed ratio performance of their animals.) As compared with rats running for a food reward in the same experiment, the electrically stimulated animals improved their performance in the maze very markedly during the 15 massed trials each day. However, there was a sharp decrement on the first trial of the next day. The rats seem to have lost interest in running until stimulation was applied next day. There was, however, a day-to-day improvement.

Seward, Uyeda, and Olds (1960) were also successful in teaching animals to perform in runway and grid crossing situations under conditions of both spaced and massed practice. Of the 17 animals, ten had electrode tips implanted in the ventromedial hypothalamus, six in the dorsolateral, and one in the medial thalamic nucleus. In contrast to the previous maze experiment by Olds (1956), these animals were deprived of neither food nor water. Animals received ten trials a day for 12 sessions. The interval between trials for the group receiving spaced training was 15 minutes. Again a sharp improvement occurred within one day's session for the massed group together with an overnight decrement in performance. These features are absent in the group for which the trials are spaced. In spite of the difference in rates of improvement within a day's trials and the sharp overnight decrement for the massed group, the rate of acquisition taking the first trials of each day only is comparable for both groups (Seward, personal communication).

There is another feature of learning for electrical brain stimulation which is different from learning for a food or water reward. Responding after extinction reappears quite suddenly at full strength when the current is again connected to the switch. There is no gradual warm-up period (Olds, 1955; Lilly, 1958).

## A HYPOTHESIS ABOUT INTRACRANIAL SELF-STIMULATION

As we reasoned above, groups of cells, sensitive to bodily deficits and hormones, are connected to other groups of cells, which underlie various actions, by two separate pathways. The first pathway, called a motivational pathway, conveys excitation from the cells sensitive to bodily deficits to the groups of cells underlying various actions. In this way, when a certain deficit arises and excites the cells sensitive to it, this deficit also indirectly excites other cells which then produce certain actions. However, the motivational pathways can only convey excitation between two groups of cells when a second pathway (called a reinforcement pathway) has passed a signal between the two groups of cells. The consequence of this is to make the motivational pathway between the two groups of cells functional.

We may assume that the electrode in intracranial self-stimulation stimulates both the reinforcement and motivational pathways between groups of cells. In this way a stimulus will not only render a motivational pathway functional by a stimulation of the reinforcement path but also send excitation down the same motivational pathway, thus causing a certain action to be executed. In this way an intracranial stimulus will provide not only the "reward" for the last action but also motivation for the next. Such induced motivation decays rapidly down to the level which was present in the motivational pathway before the electrical stimulus was applied. If we are stimulating a pathway which is normally excited when the animal is hungry, the level to which the induced drive will decay may be high if the animal is hungry, but low if it is satiated.

The facts we have already summarized agree well with the assumption that each brain stimulus excites a drive pathway, and that in the removal of such a stimulus such excitation decays. Such an assumption would explain why during massed training there is a very great improvement within a day's trials and a very large overnight decrement, whereas if trials are spaced there is no such improvement within a day's trials. It is easy to imagine that closely spaced brain shocks will summate, whereas if they are more widely spaced no such summation will take place. We can also see why rats did not perform in a situation such as Sidman's, when he spaced his shocks too far apart. The "drive" generated by one bar press would dissipate before the animal obtained the next "injection" of drive, with the consequence that it will stop bar pressing. We can also see why "relearning" after extinction should be so abrupt compared with normal relearning in such a situation. There has been no "unlearning" as in ordinary extinction but only a cessation of "drive." As a consequence when we "inject" drive again the learnt habit will reappear at full strength.

The assumptions about drive induction and decay which follow from this theory can be more rigorously tested. For instance, it should be demonstratable that cessation of responding during extinction of habits learnt for intracranial stimulation is a function simply of time since the last intracranial stimulus. In the case of habits learnt for a normal reward cessation of responding is almost entirely a function of the number of unreinforced trials, and not time since the last reward. Accordingly, a series of experiments was performed in the Skinner box (Howarth and Deutsch, 1962) to test this prediction. After the rats had been well trained to press the lever to obtain an intracranial stimulus, they were tested under two conditions. In the first condition the current was switched off and the number of responses to cessation of responding was counted. Then was counted the total number excluding those responses made during the first 2.5 secs.; then the total number excluding those responses made during the first 5, 7.5, and 10 secs. In the second condition, responding was prevented by withdrawing the lever at the beginning of extinction for 2.5, 5, 7.5, and 10 secs., and the number of responses to extinction counted after the lever was reinserted. If as in normal habits the number of responses to extinction was a function mainly of the number of unreinforced responses, the number of responses without lever withdrawal and after each interval of lever withdrawal should have been the same. On the other hand, cessation of responding could be a function of time since the last brain stimulus. According to such a hypothesis the number of responses made to extinction after the lever was reinserted after, say, 5 secs., should be the same as the number of responses made to extinction in the first condition when we exclude the presses made during the first five seconds. The data are presented in Figure 4–1, and it is clear that the prediction from the hypothesis is strongly supported.

To test the generality of the result in the Skinner box, another experiment was designed in a grid crossing situation. If drive decayed after an intracranial stimulus, speed of grid crossings in a well-learned habit should be slower after a delay of 30 secs. than after no delay between successive trials. On the other hand, with thirsty animals running to cross

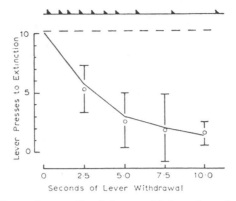

FIG. 4-1. Effect of seconds of lever withdrawal on lever presses to extinction. (The circles show the average effect of withdrawing the lever from the box for a given time before replacing it, on the number of lever presses to extinction which immediately follows the replacement of the lever. The dashed line shows the expected result if extinction were a function of the number of unreinforced lever presses. The solid line shows the expectation from the hypothesis that extinction in this case is a simple function of time since the last brain stimulus. The way this curve is derived is shown on the top line in the figure which represents a typical extinction record obtained on an event recorder. Ten presses altogether are made. Four of these occur before 2.5 seconds so that one would predict that six lever presses should be made if the lever were removed for 2.5 seconds before starting the extinction trials.) (From Deutsch, J. A., and Howarth, C. I., 1963, *Psych. Rev.* 70, courtesy of American Psychological Association.)

the grid, no slowing down after 30 seconds should be observed. The results of the experiment are in agreement with this prediction.

Because it could have been argued that all that had been shown in the previous experiments was some decrease in the level of general activity after an intracranial stimulus, with a consequent slowing down of activity, another kind of test was devised. In this test it was shown that it was the specific motivation to obtain an intracranial stimulus which decayed, and not some factor of general activity. Animals were trained to obtain water in one side of a T-maze and intracranial stimulation on the other. They were then run under varying degrees of thirst and were given a choice after varying delays after the previous intracranial stimulus. If run close to the last intracranial stimulus, they would choose it again. However, as the interval after the previous intracranial stimulus increased, so the probability of the choice of such a stimulus decreased. The results are presented in Figure 4-2. The motivation for intracranial stimulation falls off with the time after the previous intracranial stimulus.

The drive decay hypotheses of extinction in intracranial self-stimulation has been questioned by Pliskoff and Hawkins (1963). They trained rats in the Skinner box under two conditions. In the first, rats were rewarded by

FIG. 4–2. Probability of choice of brain stimulation as a function of delay and competing drive. (Effect of delay since last brain stimulus on the probability of choice of brain stimulation as against water, when the rat is 0, 5, and 22 hours thirsty.) (From Deutsch, J. A., and Howarth, C. I., 1963, *Psych. Rev.* 70, courtesy of American Psychological Association.)

an intracranial stimulus for returning to the lever after the current had been switched off for some time. In the second condition other animals were never rewarded for returning to the lever after the current had been switched off.

Pliskoff and Hawkins found that the first group emitted a larger number of responses after the current was switched off. Pliskoff and Hawkins argued that the drive decay hypothesis of extinction must be modified because differential training was shown to affect the number of responses to extinction. However, their results are perfectly compatible with the hypothesis. Given different amounts of training, a habit will need different degrees of drive to be evoked. The first group of rats had been given training to return to the lever, the second had not. The first group would therefore be expected to perform at a lower level of drive than the second, and so continue to press for longer as drive subsided.

## Relationship between Drive Induced by Intracranial Self-stimulation and Normal Motivation

It has been noted that many placements from which intracranial self-stimulation can be obtained are close to sites in the hypothalamic region which upon stimulation produce such motivated behaviors as thirst, hunger, or sex. On the hypothesis used to view the data one would expect that pathways which are held to be stimulated by intracranial self-stimulation are close to such areas. As the hypothesis assumes separate pathways for the various drives, such as hunger and thirst, we would expect an interaction between specific drive states and electrical stimulation. The internally generated messages down the motivational pathways would be expected to sum with the externally introduced message.

If animals are hungry, for instance, they—

a) Bar press more rapidly for a given level of electrical stimulus (Hoebel and Teitelbaum, 1962; Brady *et al.*, 1957; Olds, 1958).
b) Perform better on a task where brain stimuli are widely spaced (fixed ratio schedule) (Sidman *et al.*, 1955).
c) Learn to run complex mazes as in the experiment of Olds (1956), where the "rewards" are widely spaced.

It seems that in these cases the excitation proceeding from the physiologically excited groups of cells sums with the artificially "injected" excitation to increase the amount of "drive" excitation. The same summation would prolong the effect of the electrical stimulus at a level suprathreshold for action.

This idea was more directly tested by Deutsch and Metzner (quoted by Deutsch, 1963). They measured running speed in a T-maze as a function of delay between an intracranial stimulus and succeeding trial. They found that running speed decreased as a function of time since the last brain stimulus and the rate at which it decreased was significantly altered by thirst in some electrode placements.

As we have argued that normal "drive" excitation can sum with "injected drive" excitation, it is entirely possible that in the cases where performance has been obtained in a learning situation, even where brain stimulation is widely spaced (such as Seward, *et al.* [1959], normal "drive" was present.

However all the cases quoted above could be accounted for in other ways than by assuming a summation of internally generated and artificially produced drive excitation. It could be said that owing to biochemical changes during drive states, tissues were electrically more sensitive, or the stimulus became more rewarding. These arguments could not be used if it could be demonstrated that a habit previously learned for an intracranial reward could be evoked by a natural drive in the absence of further intracranial stimulation. Accordingly, two groups of rats were used by Deutsch and Howarth (1962), one with electrode implants in the lateral hypothalamus and the other with implants in the ventral tegmentum. Both groups were then trained to lever press in a Skinner box. When any of the rats were held away from the lever for a short while, they failed to return. When the rats were subsequently frightened by a buzzer or shock, only those animals with ventral tegmental implants returned to press the lever, which was now disconnected from the current. A further experiment showed that time to extinction was extremely prolonged when animals with tegmental implants were frightened, whereas those with hypothalamic electrodes tended to show such a prolongation when they were hungry. This supports the idea that the same pathways as produce normal motivated behavior when they are active are also stimulated during intracranial self-stimulation.

Herberg (1963) has recently claimed that the number of presses to extinction is uninfluenced by the drive state of the rat in placements which produce higher rates of responding during such a drive state. Unfortu-

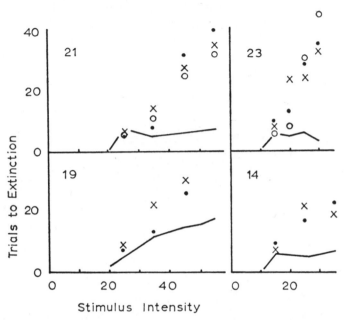

FIG. 4–3. Intensity, its effect on rate of responding and time and presses to extinction. (Effect of intensity of brain stimulation on lever pressing rates—solid line, number of presses to extinction—circles, time to normal extinction—crosses, and time to extinction without lever pressing—dots.) (From Deutsch, J. A., and Howarth, C. I., *Psychol. Rev.* 70, courtesy of American Psychological Association.)

nately it seems that his animals had been repeatedly extinguished during training so that the average number of responses to extinction was around three. Rats learn to stop pressing irrespective of drive level as soon as reward is withdrawn if the process of extinction is often enough repeated. In support of this interpretation of Herberg's failure to obtain the effect, there is the fact that he also failed to find in the same experiment a correlation between strength of current obtained by the rat for a lever press and number of trials to extinction. A high correlation exists as is shown by Deutsch and Howarth (1963) (Figure 4–3).

In fact, it has been found by Deutsch and DiCara (unpublished) that there is a very large effect of drive on the number of presses during extinction. Furthermore there is a high correlation between the number of presses during extinction and elevation of response rates when the animals are pressing for an intracranial reward when they are hungry in both conditions. To obviate the objection that a higher rate of responding (due to hunger) would lead to a larger number of responses before the extinction period and so indirectly perhaps to a larger number of responses during extinction (so leading to a spurious confirmation of the theoretical prediction) the rats were run on a current level which produced maximal rates of responding whether the rats were hungry or satiated. Elevation of rate due to hunger was measured after extinction trials had been concluded. Current was lowered during the elevation of rate determination to bring about a 25 percent reduction in rate of lever-pressing. In this way the ceiling effect which had been purposely used in the first part of the experiment was avoided.

It has been suggested above that Herberg obtained a different result (i.e., no effect of drive on number of lever presses in extinction in animals showing elevation of rate while under that drive) because repeated extinction had already taken place during training before the experiment proper was conducted. Accordingly, Deutsch and DiCara continued to test their animals, giving them repeated experience of rewarded bouts of responding followed by extinction. The extinction scores both during hunger and satiation conditions declined rapidly until they both reached the same low asymptote. A test conducted after six extinction sessions would have showed no difference in the number of trials to extinction between the hungry and satiated condition. It therefore seems that Herberg's discrepant finding can be accounted for (Figure 4–4).

An analogous prediction to that on extinction can be made concerning secondary reinforcement. Rats should continue to press to obtain a stimulus previously paired with intracranial reward only if some drive was present at the time of testing. For instance, rats which show an elevation of lever-pressing for an intracranial reward should press only if they are hungry for a tone previously paired with the intracranial reward (Gallistel, 1964). DiCara and Deutsch (unpublished) have found that there is a high correlation ($r = 0.89$, $N = 12$) between the rate of responding for brain stimulation measured during hunger and the degree of secondary reinforcement obtained under the same drive condition. Using group data, Stein (1958) has shown that a significant overall secondary reinforcement effect can be obtained when an intracranial reward is used as primary reinforcer. However, reporting individual scores, Seward et al. (1959) found that a secondary reinforcement effect appears in only a small proportion of their rats. This discrepancy can readily be explained if we take variability in placement into account and assume that the appearance of the secondary reinforcement effect depends on the presence of a relevant drive during testing.

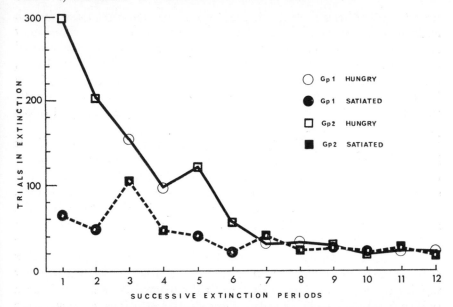

FIG. 4–4. Total number of lever-presses in successive 3-minute periods of extinction made by rats, displaying elevation of rate of lever pressing when they were hungry. The rats were divided into 2 groups for two extinction periods. One group was run satiated during extinction while the other was run hungry. Such an alternation was maintained until the end of the experiment. As can be seen there is a large discrepancy between extinction scores in the initial extinction periods. This difference disappears rapidly as the rats learn that once current is switched off no more intracranial reward will be available.

## Two Pathways in Intracranial Self-stimulation

The suggested hypothesis of intracranial self-stimulation assumes that two sets of pathways, each with a different function, have to be stimulated to produce the phenomenon. To test this feature of the theory, various electrical parameters were used to see if the presumed pathways showed differential sensitivity to them. It is known mainly from studies on peripheral nerves that nerve fibers differ among themselves in various aspects of electrical excitability. For instance, they show differences in rates of adaptation to a gradually rising electrical stimulus, in absolute threshold to an applied stimulus, and also in the time during which they are unexcitable following a suprathreshold stimulus (refractory period).

If the drive pathways had a lower threshold of excitability than the reinforcement pathways, then it should be possible to elicit drive without reinforcement simply by using a lower stimulating current. In such a way a learned response could be maintained even when the intracranial stimulus occurred randomly in relation to the previously rewarded action. Thus it should be possible to maintain the animal's responding during extinction.

If on the other hand the reinforcement system were also excited with each random stimulus, it should not only maintain motivation, but reward new actions and so lead to a diminution of performance of the already learned habit. In the experiment done to test this relation (Deutsch et al., 1962), it was found that stimulation at approximately half the intensity necessary for training would increase the number of emitted responses during extinction when such stimulation was applied randomly with respect to the previously rewarded act.

The next set of experiments (Deutsch, 1964) was concerned to find out if the refractory period of the reinforcement and motivation pathways was different. If two brief pulses are applied to a nerve, there is an interval during which the second will be ineffective in triggering a second spike. However, if the two pulses are shifted apart, there is a point at which the second pulse will also initiate a spike. In such a way if we stimulate, say, a motor pathway with double pulses, we should see a sudden increase in the effect of the stimulation as we apply the two pulses progressively further apart in time from each other. In a similar way if we stimulate a pathway which produces reward (or drive) with double pulses, we should see a sudden increment in the rewarding (or drive producing) efficacy of the physical stimulus as the second pulse falls outside the refractory period of the nerve. To test whether such a difference in refractory periods exists, animals were given stimuli consisting of two brief (0.1 msec.) pulses separated from each other by intervals varying from one test session to the next. These pulses were negative going because this is the more effective direction of stimulation and were repetitiously applied for 0.5 sec., 10 msec. elapsing between the first pulses in each pair. The intrapair distance was varied between 0.2 and 2 msec., this being the range within which to expect the appearance of the neural absolutely refractory period. This varies from 0.4 to 2 msec., depending on the diameter and type of fiber in peripheral nerve (Grundfest, 1940). A series of situations to measure reward and drive were then devised. These were designed to show at what interval between the two pulses reward or drive would suddenly increase. The rate of lever-pressing in a Skinner box was used as one measure of drive. The lowest level of voltage compatible with consistent lever-pressing with an intrapair pulse interval of 2 msec. was first determined and then rates of lever-pressing at this voltage were determined in random order for other intrapair pulse intervals. Five-minute rest intervals were given between tests to allow the drive induced by one test to decay before the next test. As can be seen (Figure 4–5), there is a sudden increase of the effectiveness of the second pulse when it is more than 0.8 msec. after the first. A second test of drive was also used. A rat was taught to traverse a straight alley for a reward of an intracranial stimulus which was always kept the same. Trials were spaced so that running did not occur spontaneously unless an intracranial stimulus was used as a "primer" in the start box. The drive-inducing effectiveness of double pulses at various spacings was measured by running speed. As in the lever-pressing test, an enhancement of effectiveness occurs after the pulses are spaced more than 0.8 msec. apart.

Tests to measure the reward effect of the intracranial stimulus were also devised. For instance rats were given a choice between two rewards in a T-maze, each consisting of an intracranial stimulus with a certain intrapair

FIG. 4–5. Rate of lever-pressing at different pulse-pair intervals with voltage kept constant. Each point represents a single score (lever presses during one minute). The curves of 3 rats are shown. 1P = 1 pulse per 10 msec. instead of 2 as in rest of tests. (From Deutsch, J. A., 1964, J.C.P.P. 58, courtesy of the American Psychological Association.)

pulse interval. It can be seen that 0.7 msec. is consistently preferred over smaller intervals, but treated as equal to longer intervals (Figure 4–6). This suggests that the second pulse is already having a full effect at 0.7 msec. unlike the result which emerged in the drive tests. A further reward test confirms this difference. Rats were trained to press in a Skinner box for a high 60 cps. stimulus. Repeated extinction trials were then run, until the rat stopped responding within five seconds. (During the first few extinction trials the rat would respond for over one minute.) In this way the animal was trained to stop when no further reward occurred. At this stage the irregular periods of extinction (in which the animal was abruptly

FIG. 4–6. Number of choices of goal containing stimulus at 0.7 msec. intrapulse-pair interval against other intrapulse-pair intervals at the same voltage in a T maze. (Each point represents the results of a session of 40 trials.) (From Deutsch, J. A., 1964, *J.C.P.P.* 58, courtesy of the American Psychological Association.)

shifted from receiving a high 60 cps. stimulus for a bar press to receiving nothing) were removed from the training schedule. Instead, the animal was abruptly shifted from receiving the high 60 cps. stimulation for a lever press, to receive some level of double pulse stimulation. Since the animals were in a high state of drive following the 60 cps. stimulation and had been taught not to press when reward was discontinued, it was expected that they would continue to press for voltage-pulse couple combinations which were above the threshold for reward when they were switched to these after the 60 cps. standard. However, it was thought they would cease pressing abruptly when the effective strength of the voltage-pulse couple combination was below the threshold of the reward effect. The criterion for the continuation of lever-pressing was that the animal should press for more than 30 seconds out of the minute after the stimulus obtained by lever-pressing had been changed from the high intensity 60 cps. standard to the pulse-pair stimulation at varying voltages. The duration of a minute after the standard was taken because lever-pressing initially persisted for at least a minute after the standard was switched off, thus showing that induced drive sufficient to motivate lever-pressing continued for at least this length of time. In this way the double-pulse stimulus would only need to supply reward, the drive component having already been induced by the standard 60 cps. stimulation. It was hoped by this method to measure the threshold of the reward component of intracranial self-stimulation. We would expect a higher voltage to be necessary to sustain responding after the standard has been switched off if only one pulse in each pulse pair is effective and a lower voltage to be sufficient if both pulses were effective. The curve plotting the lowest voltage necessary to sustain responding at each interval between the two pulses in each pair should then show a sharp inflection at the end of the refractory period. The obtained curves are illustrated in Figure 4–7. As can be seen, the inflection in the curve occurs at the same point as in the curve (Figure 4–6) plotting the data from the preference test of reward. Some of the advantages of the Skinner box single-lever method of measurement of reward threshold are that the same animal can easily be used both in the rate of lever-pressing experiment and in the reward threshold experiment, and that the voltages used in both experiments are comparable. Results from both experiments performed on the same animals are shown in Figure 4–8. Another way of showing that there are two components or two refractory periods involved in the phenomenon of intracranial self-stimulation is to measure the rate of lever-pressing for various pulse intervals at a higher voltage. In the original experiment, reported above, rats were run at a voltage sufficient to produce a steady level of responding when pulses were 2 msec. apart. Little lever-pressing occurs when the voltage is determined in this way when pulses are closer than 0.9 msec. apart. At a higher voltage, however, an increase in the rate of lever-pressing occurs as soon as the shorter refractory period is exceeded. It seems that at the lower voltage both refractory periods have to be exceeded to give rise to instrumental behavior. When the voltage is increased, only one refractory period has to be exceeded. (At higher voltages still ceiling rates of responding occur whether the pulse interval is within both refractory periods or not.) We can in this instance then obtain a "reward" curve using the same response as the one yielding the "drive" curve. (Figure 4–9)

Another interesting finding emerges from the experiments with double pulses which were reported above. It will be noticed that on many of the curves presented above, there is a short period of about 0.2 msec. during which the second of the two pulses does seem to have an effect on the animal's behavior. This is probably due to a neural phenomenon known as latent addition. For a nerve spike to be triggered, a certain threshold has to be exceeded. As a pulse of current is applied to the nerve a charge builds up and if the applied current is withdrawn before such a charge has built up sufficiently to trigger a spike, the charge will persist for a short while and finally decay. If during this period of decay, another normally

FIG. 4–7. Minimum voltage required to keep rat pressing for intracranial stimulation in reward test. Results for three rats. Each point represents a single determination. (After Deutsch, J. A., 1964, *J.C.P.P.* 58, courtesy of American Psychological Association).

subthreshold pulse is applied, the process of charging will resume, adding itself to the charge still left. In this way the two together may exceed the critical threshold where either one alone would not. The period during which two normally subthreshold pulses sum to produce a spike is called the period of latent addition. Now when we stimulate a large number of pathways simultaneously through an implanted electrode, the fibers close to the tip of the electrode, charging at a higher rate will produce nerve spikes. However, fibers at a longer distance will charge more slowly and will

FIG. 4–8. The upper two curves were obtained under the same experimental conditions as the curves in Figure 7. The middle two curves were obtained under the same conditions as the curves in Figure 5. The bottom two curves show the number of responses in the second minute of a session (sessions 5 min. apart) with a voltage at reward threshold is in rat no. 52. In the case of no. 52 rat also, the reward threshold was determined again in the critical beginning part of the curve after the test plotted in the bottom curve to check for possible order effects. The points thus repeated are also indicated in the top curve to give an indication of consistency. In the case of rat no. 54, the fixed voltage was two volts above threshold, as lever pressing could not consistently be induced at reward threshold. Where the voltages at which the test was conducted are the same for the two "number of responses" tests, they are plotted on both graphs. Again, each point represents the result of one determination. The inset point on the bottom curve shows the effect of raised voltage on responding at a pulse pair interval. (After Deutsch, J. A., 1964, J.C.P.P. 58, courtesy of American Psychological Association).

therefore not have reached the critical threshold when the electrical stimulus is withdrawn. However, if the identical subthreshold pulse is repeated within the period of latent addition (about 0.2 msec. for A and B fibers in the peripheral nerve), then the critical threshold will be exceeded. In this way fibers which are not normally excited by the electrode are recruited. It can therefore be surmised that the enhancement of effect at very short intervals (0.2 msec.) before the end of the refractory period is due to the recruitment of a different population of fibers in the subliminal fringe, whereas the enhancement of effect at the end of the refractory

FIG. 4–9. The top, second and bottom two graphs correspond to those described in Figure 8 in that order. They represent results for another two animals. The two graphs next to the bottom represent the rates of lever pressing at varying pulse intervals at a voltage higher than in the second two graphs. (After Deutsch, J. A., 1964, *J.C.P.P.* 58, courtesy of American Psychological Association.)

period is due to a doubling of activity within the same population of fibers. The effect might be useful in investigating fine differences in localization. However, whether such an effect is found is dependent, among other things, on the spatial arrangement of the stimulated fibers. For instance if the electrode is stimulating all the fibers to an adequate extent with the first pulse, then there will be no subliminal fringe.

The results of this last series of experiments support the view that "reward" and "drive" have a separate anatomical substrate in terms of separate pathways, and that both these pathways are stimulated to produce intracranial self-stimulation.

RAT NO. 1

RAT NO. 2

RAT NO. 3

RAT NO. 4

RAT NO. 5

RAT NO. 6

RAT NO. 7

1   2   3   4   5   6   7   8   9

TIME IN MILLISECONDS

FIG. 4–10. Evoked potentials recorded in the medial forebrain bundle by stimulating with one brief pulse through an electrode, known to produce responding for intracranial stimulation. The distance between recording and stimulating electrodes was about 0.5 cm. For rats 1–3 the stimulating electrode was in the posterior hypothalamus; for rats 4–7 it was in the lateral hypothalamus. Two evoked potentials arriving at different times can be seen. Each record is composed of at least 10 superimposed traces. (Deutsch, J. A., unpublished.)

As a check on the validity of the neurophysiological interpretation given above, direct recordings from animals exhibiting intracranial self-stimulation were undertaken. The rats were placed in a stereotaxic instrument under nembutal anesthesia and a recording macroelectrode inserted in the medial forebrain bundle 5mm. anterior of the previously implanted and behaviorally tested stimulating electrode. Stimuli were then applied through the stimulating electrode and evoked potentials recorded from the anteriorly placed recording electrode. The experiment was performed in two parts. In the first a single pulse was used as a stimulus. If two pathways with different refractory periods were being stimulated, they should also differ in conduction speed. The thicker the fiber, the lower the refractory period, and the faster the conduction speed. It should therefore be possible to see two evoked potentials arriving at different times at the recording electrode. This provides an independent check on the previous interpretation. It can be seen from Figure 4–10 that two evoked potentials appear, the first being smaller than the second. However, the distances available in the rat's brain are very small, so that the electrical stimulus used to trigger the neuronal discharge tends also to be picked up to an undesirable extent by the recording electrode, and it does not die down sufficiently by the time some fast traveling potentials have arrived at the recording site. This interference (or stimulus artefact) can act as a confounding factor when we interpret records. It could be that the first evoked potential which arrives is actually bigger than it appears. On the other hand, in some cases at least, it could simply be a stimulus artefact.

In the second part of the experiment, pulse pairs separated by varying intervals were used as stimuli. It is difficult to see anything of the faster arriving evoked potential as it tends to get obliterated by the second pulse. It can however be seen from various records that the second evoked potential only repeats when the time interval between the two pulses is on the order of 1 msec., showing a clear refractory period of the magnitude expected from the behavioral measure (Figure 4–11).

## REWARD

If an animal is deprived of food or water and then finds some food to eat or water to drink it will tend to repeat the sequence of actions which led up to its finding the needed substance. Various notions of what makes eating or drinking rewarding have been advanced. For instance, Hull (1951) believed that it was the reduction of a physiological need which originally led to a connection in the nervous system such that the behavior leading to this need reduction would occur again.

Sheffield and his associates have attempted to test this belief that physiological need reduction must occur for an activity to become rewarding. Sheffield and Roby (1950) have shown that saccharin, a sweet-tasting nonnutritive substance, will function as a reward in runway

FIG. 4–11. Evoked potentials recorded in the medial forebrain bundle by stimulating with two brief pulses at various time intervals from each other. These pulses were applied through an electrode known to produce responding for intracranial stimulation. The distance between recording and stimulating electrodes was about 0.5 cm. Each record is composed of at least 10 superimposed traces. The second pulse has no effect until it occurs after about 0.85 msec. thus showing that there is a refractory period. (Deutsch, J. A., unpublished.)

performance and that it will continue to do so without losing its effectiveness as a reward. This finding demonstrates that reinforcement can occur without need reduction.

This interpretation of the experiment has been questioned by Smith and Capretta. They point out that in the conditions of Sheffield and Roby's experiment the digestion of previously eaten food would have been taking place when saccharin was being drunk. They therefore argue that the reward value of saccharin to the animal is derived from the physiological need reduction due to the digestion of other substances at the time that the rat drinks saccharin.

In order to test this possibility, Smith and Capretta used two groups of rats. One group of rats was given saccharin only when the processes of digestion were complete. For this group, saccharin diminished in value as a rewarding agent during the course of the experiment. However, saccharin kept its effectiveness as reward for a second group to which saccharin was given not long after ordinary food. Such an experiment on the face of it would confirm this argument. Unfortunately, the effect of saccharin is not simple. Saccharin at high concentrations tastes bitter. It also produces a bitter taste when injected intravenously. The build-up of concentration of saccharin in the bloodstream when it has been drunk by an animal on an empty stomach may be very much swifter and rise further than when it is mixed with food in the intestine. In other words, saccharin drunk on an empty stomach may have unpleasant side effects. It would be interesting to repeat the experiment of Smith and Capretta on animals with esophogeal fistulae or with nonnutritious sweet-tasting substances other than saccharin where some of the complicating properties of saccharin are absent.

De Snoo (1937) found that fetuses in utero would respond to an introduction of saccharin into the amniotic fluid by drinking. It is difficult to see how the presence of saccharin could be correlated with the reduction of physiological need in this instance.

Some theorists have adopted an amended view that drive reduction, not necessarily accompanied by need reduction is reinforcing. A reduction in physiological need or deficit can, as for instance in hunger, take a long time. Further, there are cases where an activity is rewarding, as for instance mating, where there is no obvious physiological deficit which is corrected. Nor is it easy to argue that the rewarding nature of such an activity arises through association with a reduction of a physiological deficit of another kind. The shift of emphasis from need reduction to drive reduction is an easy one for a Hull-type theory. On this theory a physiological need or deficit is held to give rise to afferent stimuli (called drive stimuli). A rewarding state of affairs is said to arise when there is a rapid diminution of the physiological deficit, which in turn would cause drive stimuli to decrease. It is a simple modification of the theory to leave out physiological deficit and simply to talk in terms of reduction in drive stimuli.

Sheffield et al. (1951) set out to test the view that drive reduction is reinforcing. They used copulation as a reward for male rats. However, they allowed them to intromit without permitting them to intromit a sufficient number of times for ejaculation to take place. As we saw in the chapter on mating, a rat intromits and withdraws a number of times before the final ejaculatory mount. Sheffield *et al.* found that this procedure would function as reward for males with no previous sexual experience. In this situation it is difficult to argue that any reduction in drive stimulation had taken place, since the animals were not allowed to ejaculate. In fact, a commonsense view of the matter would be that there had been a drive increase. Of course, we can always say that if such a procedure was rewarding it must have been drive reducing, but this would make the concept of drive reduction circular and untestable.

Kagan (1955) has investigated further the reward value of incomplete coition in rats. He found that naive male rats not allowed to proceed to ejaculation would find copulation rewarding to begin with though they develop some kind of conflict. They run up to the female but show reluctance to mount her. It may be that the observed conflict is due to some kind of discomfort produced by incomplete coition. However, Whalen (1961) found no decrement in reward with incomplete copulation, and criticizes Kagan's design.

Sheffield on the basis of his findings proposes that it is the evocation of a consummatory response which is rewarding. However, it is unlikely that this is the case. Miller and Kessen (1952) found that a rat will learn to choose the arm of a T-maze where a nutrient solution is directly inserted into the stomach, showing that reward can occur even when the usual consummatory activities are absent. So it seems that both an explanation of reward solely in terms of consummatory activity or in terms of drive reduction are rendered implausible by the above evidence.

It is however possible to look at the evidence another way. We can assume that it is some specific stimulation which is correlated with reward. For instance, we may adopt the view that it is the taste of water which is rewarding to the animal. Putting this in more physiological terms, we can say that it is a signal ascending certain pathways which is correlated with reward when the animal is thirsty.

This can be illustrated by considering the physiological correlates of taste preference. In rat and man (Zotterman and Diamant, 1959) when water is placed on the tongue, there is a reduction in the spontaneous firing of a certain type of fiber. If a salt solution above a certain concentration is placed on the tongue, there is an increase in the amount of firing from the same type of fiber. If samples of water with an increasing admixture of salt are placed on the tongue, there is progressively less reduction of spontaneous firing. A reduction of spontaneous firing in this fiber signals water, and it seems to be the cumulated reduction of firing in this fiber while the animal drinks that determines how much the animal will drink. If the animal is presented with a solution of saline which reduces the spontaneous firing in this water-salt fiber by only a small amount, the animal will drink this solution for a much longer time than if it drinks water. Further, if the animal is given such a solution of saline in its cage together with water, the amount being unlimited, it will drink much more of the saline. However, when rats are presented with equal volumes of the same saline solution and water in the maze and they have to choose between them, they find the water more rewarding and learn to run to the water side. This can be explained by saying that the same volume of water will produce a larger cumulative reduction in the firing of the water-salt fiber (Deutsch and Jones, 1960). These findings indicate that it is a particular afferent message which leads to the neural changes which underlie the phenomena of reward. In terms of the system we discussed above, the function of the afferent message would be to make a connection between two sets of cells more permeable to the passage of excitation.

It seems that such an account of reward in terms of a specific afferent message can be applied to other types of activity. Hagstrom and Pfaffmann (1959) have pointed out that there is a correlation between the amount of activity in the chorda tympani nerve (a part of the afferent taste pathways) generated by various sweet-tasting solutions and the reward value of these solutions. This observation extends the previous work of Hutt (1954) and Guttman (1954). Hutt found that the rate of responding of rats in a Skinner box for a given solution was a function of the taste of the solution as well as of its amount. Guttman reported that those solutions of glucose and sucrose which are judged equally sweet by human observers are equally reinforcing to rats.

## Is the Association between Reward and Need Reduction Learned?

It might be suggested that the association between reward and need reduction is learned. For instance, it could be said that the animal learns that a particular sensory message brings in its wake a certain amount of physiological need reduction. In this way the role of afferent impulses would be a secondary and not a primary relation. However, Sheffield's work on the rewarding effects of coition (cited above p. 140) would be difficult to reconcile with this viewpoint, since he used naive rats. However, there is other work bearing on this question. For instance, Coppock and Chambers (1954) attempted to pair an arbitrarily chosen event with physiological need reduction. They tried to reward hungry rats with an injection of glucose into the bloodstream when they turned their heads in a certain direction. Their rats were 72 hours hungry, apparently without having been placed on a feeding schedule previously. This would have produced extremes of depletion. (It is usual to accustom animals to a regular feeding schedule before an experiment.) In spite of such extreme treatment the results of this experiment are highly equivocal. Though 32 animals were used in this study, significant differences were not obtained for absolute frequency of head turns or their absolute duration, or for the relative number of moves toward the rewarded position, but only for the relative duration of preference for the rewarded position. Further, the controls used in this study consisted of animals which had physiological saline injected. This would not have the same reviving effect as an injection of glucose in the experimental group. Any difference could therefore have been due to some factor of revival rather than of learning. At best, the experiment shows that such learning, if it occurs at all, is very inefficient. Chambers (1956a, 1956b) extended the experiment mentioned above to dogs and rabbits. His animals were given an injection of glucose when they were in one area in a box and xylose (a nonnutritive sugar) or saline in other areas. Chambers found that dogs (which were satiated, or starved one or three days) did not learn. The rabbits (starved six, four, or three days) did find the glucose injections rewarding. It was found that a relatively short time after glucose injection there followed a significant rise in body temperature. It seems likely that a sudden removal of noxious symptoms could in this situation serve as a reward. It is known (as we have seen in the chapter on hunger and thirst) that this can constitute a way in which animals learn to select certain dietary components. However, as we also saw, such a way of learning to ingest the appropriate substance in the quantity appropriate to a deficit is inefficient and breaks down when the choice given the animal is large.

The inefficiency of learning by need reduction alone is illustrated in an experiment by Thomson and Porter (1953) where the need was produced by sodium deficiency. In this experiment, six rats were rendered ageusic (unable to taste) and anosmic (unable to smell). These six rats and eight normal rats were fed on a sodium deficient diet. Saline, below taste threshold for the ageusic group, but not for the normal group, was placed in one arm of a T-maze, and water in the other. The normal group learned within ten days, in which four trials a day 15 minutes apart were given. The ageusic group received the same treatment but did not learn. They were then placed on a complex and lengthy training procedure, as a result of which four out of the six ageusic animals appear to have learned. The two animals which did not learn, learned promptly as soon as the strength of the saline solution in the maze was increased above their taste threshold.

That the reward value of the taste of salt is unlearned is further supported by an experiment of Epstein and Stellar (1955). They showed that rats would drink an amount of saline proportional to their deficit as soon as it became available, without previous experience.

In summary then, the most plausible way of interpreting experimental evidence on reward agrees well with common sense and introspection. It is the taste of water, the feeling of satiety, the sensations from the genitalia that an animal finds rewarding. The connection of these sensations with need reduction is not one which is made by each individual animal. Such a connection between reward and physiological deficit has been made by the process of natural selection. Only those animals which have found certain sensations rewarding have survived. Learning with physiological need reduction as reward has already occurred in the species; the individual need not recapitulate it.

## CONCLUSION

In this chapter we have reviewed some of the evidence both from physiological and behavioral experiments which show us something about the mechanism which produce the adaptive change known as learning. In the first part of the chapter we saw that it is unlikely that learning consists in the linkage of stimulus with response. In the section dealing with learning to obtain the reward of an intracranial stimulus, we showed how more specific models of brain function could be tested and verified by a combination of stimulation of the central nervous system in animals under simultaneous behavioral test. In the section on reward, it was shown that primary reinforcement was in all probability due to the excitation of certain receptor systems. It is in this area of learning that the distinction between experimental and physiological studies is becoming mainly obliterated, as physiological studies have shown themselves capable of testing theoretical issues generated by behavioral work.

# 5

## AROUSAL, SLEEP, AND ATTENTION

As we all know, the events which we notice form only a proportion of those which impinge on our sense organs. We fail to notice events when we are unconscious or asleep, and also when we are attending to some other aspect of our environment. In this chapter we shall deal first with factors underlying general arousal, and then with those underlying selective attention.

### THE ELECTROENCEPHALOGRAM (EEG) AND STATES OF ALERTNESS

An important difference between the conditions of the awake and the sleeping organism is demonstrated by means of the electroencephalogram (EEG). This is a record of the gross electrical activity of the brain, and is obtained by attaching two electrodes to the scalp without physiological interference with the organism. The electrical activity of the cortex, when the subject is awake and relaxed, is characteristically a 10/sec. synchronized wave form, known as the alpha rhythm (Figure 5–1). With increasing drowsiness, the frequency of the rhythm is reduced and low-amplitude slow waves occur occasionally. Light sleep is characterized by slow waves and occasional high-voltage "sleep spindles." In deep sleep, large, very slow waves appear in a random irregular pattern. When the subject is alert and attentive, low-amplitude fast waves appear which are only partially synchronized. In states of emotion, brain rhythms become totally desynchronized (Lindsley, 1952).

Although the correlation between states of alertness and type of EEG pattern is generally good, especially at the extremes, it is possible to separate the two. Gastaut (1954) quotes a number of clinical cases where certain states of alertness are accompanied by cortical rhythms characteristic of other states. For instance, in comas brought about by hypoglycemia, very frequently the most superficial comas are concomitant with the

145

slowest rhythms. When extreme coma is brought about in patients through some complication in the administration of anesthesia, the patient's EEG shows very rapid desynchronized rhythms. Also during artificial hibernation (a procedure in which coma is produced in a patient by means of the administration of drugs and the concomitant lowering of temperature) rapid, desynchronized rhythms may often accompany loss of consciousness. Similarly, normal alpha waves may be shown to occur during comas as in cases reported by Gastaut in which the coma was

FIG. 5–1. Characteristic EEG records from different stages of sleep and wakefulness. (From Jasper, H. H., Penfield, N., and Erickson, J. C., *Epilepsy and Cerebral Localization*, 1941, by permission of C. C. Thomas, Publisher, Springfield, Ill.)

produced by lesions in the lower brain stem. Feldman and Waller (1962) found that lesions in the posterior hypothalamus produced a permanent sleeplike state during which it was possible to produce electrical activation (desynchronized low-voltage rhythms in the cortex) either by stimulation of the midbrain reticular formation or by peripheral stimulation, without behavioral arousal or alerting. Desynchronized rhythms also occur periodically in normal sleep and this has been described as "paradoxical sleep."

But even more compelling are the cases cited of the concomitance of perfectly normal states of alertness with chronically slow cortical rhythms. Gastaut describes the case of a girl who had rhythms of a frequency of 3 cps. for some years following recovery from a coma and yet was, in fact, the brightest pupil in her class. Hess further observes (1954) in cats in which natural sleep was induced by stimulation of a "sleep center," that while in most cases there appeared an EEG pattern characteristic of sleep, on some occasions the electrical activity of the brain was found to have a waking pattern while the cat was lying in a sleeping position and vice versa. Feldman and Waller (1962) report that limited lesions of the midbrain reticular formation can lead to attentive behavior, though the EEG rhythm is of high voltage and low frequency; i.e., characteristic of sleep. It has also been observed that over-tired people, whose EEGs manifest a definite sleep pattern, may still perform calculations.

Certain drugs have also been shown to produce a dissociation between states of alertness and their characteristic EEG patterns. Funderbunk and Case (1951) demonstrated that atropine induces a synchronized EEG in animals which nevertheless seem quite alert. Bradley and Elkes (1953) and Wikler (1952) confirmed this finding. On the other hand, Killam et al. (1957) demonstrated that reserpine induces drowsiness in animals which nevertheless maintain a desynchronized EEG. And chlorpromazine causes a slight increase in stimulus threshold for EEG desynchronization upon brain stimulation, but greatly raises the threshold for behavioral arousal (alertness) upon stimulation of the same region. It seems therefore that it may be wiser to consider EEG patterns as by-products of the mechanism underlying arousal and sleep rather than as an integral part of this mechanism.

Many attempts have been made by neurophysiologists to correlate EEG rhythms with certain neural "states" of the cortex. However, little success has so far been obtained. Kogan (1960) reports that during conditioning, the presentation of an auditory CS results in generalized desynchronization in all cortical areas; yet some regions demonstrate increased excitability and other regions decreased excitability though they both show the same EEG patterns. Jasper, Ricci and Doane (1960) found that desynchronization of EEG rhythms in the cortex may be accompanied by an increase, decrease or no change in the discharge frequency of a cortical unit. And they conclude: "States of excitation or inhibition in the cortex are not related in a simple manner to the presence or absence of slow waves in the surface ECG as judged by rates of firing of cortical cells." Schlag (personal communication) feels, however, that though there may be a lack of correlation when we look at the activity of individual units with microelectrodes, a better estimate may be formed if simultaneous recording from a number of units is used. Using somewhat larger electrodes, Schlag did find a good correlation between unit activity and EEG rhythms. Desynchronization is accompanied by an increase in the activity of the majority of units.

## AROUSAL AND THE RETICULAR SYSTEM

The term "reticular system" refers to a number of subcortical structures thought to be concerned, amongst other things, with the regulation of wakefulness and the electrical activity of the brain. These structures have been divided into two main groups which to some extent subserve separate functions. The first group has been called the "brain stem reticular formation," and the second group, the "thalamic reticular system."

## The Brain Stem Reticular Formation

Anatomically, the brain stem reticular formation is found to extend upward from the medulla through the central core of the brain stem, traversing the pons, midbrain, hypothalamus, subthalamus and thalamus

FIG. 5–2. Lateral view of the monkey brain, on which is projected a representation of the ascending reticular system. (From Magoun, H. W., [Ed.], *Brain Mechanisms and Consciousness*, 1954, by permission of Blackwell's).

(Figure 5–2). It probably projects to the cortex by two routes, one via various non-specific thalamic nuclei, and the other by-passing the thalamus and reaching the cortex directly by way of the internal capsule.

Reticular regions of the brain are of vital importance for a number of functions (Magoun, 1963). Here we are concerned only with their relevance to arousal and attention. One of the first studies demonstrating the importance of brain stem structures in the maintenance of arousal was that of Bremer (1937) who placed an animal in a permanent state of sleep, indicated both behaviorally and by its electrocorticogram, by a midbrain transection (the "cerveau isolé" preparation). Bremer assumed at the time that his results were due to deafferentation of the cerebrum. However, in

1950 Lindsley *et al.* showed in the cat that if the classical afferent pathways are severed at the level of the midbrain, the animal is able to move around and demonstrates a waking EEG. Nevertheless, if lesions are made in the reticular formation and the specific sensory pathways are left intact, the animal is permanently asleep and shows a sleeping EEG (Figure 5–3).

French and Magoun (1952) demonstrated that in the monkey, too, injury to the cephalic brain stem produces a permanently comatose animal with a chronically synchronized EEG. Similar findings have been reported in man by various workers including Penfield (1938), French (1952), and Jefferson (1952). It was also found that increasing the size of chronic lesions in the brain stem reticular formation induces a progressively deepening stupor.

FIG. 5–3. A'. Waking EEG in a cat with bilateral section of the classical sensory pathways in the midbrain, sparing the central tegmentum. B'. Sleeping EEG in a cat with interruption of the mesencephalic tegmentum sparing the sensory pathways. (From Lindsley, D. B., *et al.*, 1950, by permission of *EEG Clin. Neurophysiol.*, 2.)

Corroborating evidence that the brain stem reticular formation is involved in arousal derives from experiments involving stimulation of various portions of this structure. Moruzzi and Magoun (1949) found that stimulation in the region of the brain stem led to a cessation of synchronized cortical rhythms and their replacement by low-voltage desynchronized activity. Further, using animals with chronically implanted electrodes, Segundo, Arana, and French (1955) found that stimulation of the reticular formation produced behavioral arousal from sleep, in addition to a desynchronization of EEG rhythms; and they argue that this effect did not seem to be secondary to pain or movement.

### Pathways into the Reticular Formation

Important sensory connections to the reticular formation have been demonstrated. Collaterals to the reticular formation from afferent pathways subserving all the sensory modes have been established at many levels. Starzl *et al.* (1951) recorded potentials evoked in the brain stem of cats by sciatic stimulation and auditory clicks. They concluded that collaterals from the ascending somatic paths feed into the brain stem reticular formation through almost its entire length from the medulla to the posterior thalamus, and that the distribution of collaterals from the auditory system is almost identical. Similar findings have been reported with reference to other modalities. Anatomical studies (Mehler *et. al.*, 1960; Bowsher, 1957, 1961) emphasize the connection with pain pathways. There does not seem to be any topographical subdivision of the reticular formation with respect to reception of impulses via the different modalities. Even single units have been shown to respond to stimulation via various sensory modes. However, the various modalities of stimulation are not equally powerful in exciting the reticular formation. Stimulation of the

A                          B                          C

FIG. 5–4.  Lateral (A) basilar (B) and medial (C) surfaces of the monkey cortex showing loci, stimulation of which induced evoked potentials in the central cephalic brain stem. (From French, J. D., *et al.*, 1955, by permission of *J. Neurophysiol.*, 18.)

visual system seems to be least powerful, and stimulation of the somatic pathways, most powerful. Magoun (1963) points out that the potent arousing quality of painful stimuli would lead one to expect pain pathways to have a particularly intimate relation with the reticular formation.

Important connections from the cortex to the reticular formation have also been shown to exist. Segundo, Naquet and Buser (1955) found in the monkey that single-shock stimulation of various cortical loci caused generalized EEG arousal. French, Hernandez-Peon and Livingston (1955) found, also in the monkey, that stimulation of certain discrete cortical regions gave rise to evoked potentials throughout the extent of the brain stem reticular formation. These regions were located in the frontal oculomotor fields, sensorimotor cortex, cingulate gyrus, orbitofrontal surface, temporal tip, first temporal gyrus and the paraoccipital region (Figure 5–4). It has also been demonstrated (Bremer and Terzuolo, 1953) that brief faradization of various cortical areas produces behavioral awakening in a sleeping animal as well as inducing desynchronized EEG rhythms.

The importance of these pathways from the cortex is indicated by the finding of Hernandez-Peon and Hagbarth (1955) in cats, that potentials evoked in the reticular formation by cortical stimulation are larger and more widespread than those evoked by afferent stimulation. Further, "meaningful" stimuli, which presumably must be analyzed as such by the cortex, seem to be especially efficient in inducing arousal. Gangloff and Monnier (1956) report that a rabbit will be aroused much more effectively by the appearance of a human being than by strong stimuli such as bright lights or loud noises. In the human case, a person will awake at the sound of his own name, a mother at the sound of her baby's cry, and yet be undisturbed by quite loud noises. Fischgold and Lairy-Bounes (1952) report that in the case of a comatose patient, calling his name would evoke EEG arousal, whereas intense stimuli were without effect.

One might explain spontaneous waking from sleep, for instance when a nightmare becomes out of hand, by means of such corticofugal messages. Stimulation of the superior temporal gyrus and hippocampal gyrus are extremely effective in evoking potentials in the reticular formation, and there is evidence that these areas play an important part in processes connected with memory and dreaming (Penfield, 1958).

Pathways to the reticular formation have also been found to arise from the cerebellum (Snider, 1952), basal ganglia (Sprague, 1953), and rhinencephalic structures (Adey, Sunderland, and Dunlop, 1957; Green and Adey, 1956).

### Convergence of Input to the Reticular Formation

It is characteristic of the reticular formation that it responds in a much more generalized fashion to incoming stimulation than do relay nuclei on the primary sensory pathways. Potentials may be evoked throughout this structure by excitation of various sensory systems (French et al., 1952; Starzl et al., 1951) and various cortical structures (Bremer and Terzuolo, 1954; French et al., 1955). Occlusive and facilitatory interactions between responses evoked in the reticular formation from very different sources have further been observed (Bremer and Terzuolo, 1952, 1954; French et al., 1955). Single unit studies have demonstrated a convergence of input from several sources (Amassian and DeVito, 1954; Scheibel et al., 1955; Palestini et al., 1957; Bradley and Mollica, 1958). Figure 5–5 shows the response of a single neuron in the reticular formation to several different stimuli. Neuroanatomical evidence further indicates that the reticular formation may function in a diffuse manner (Scheibel and Scheibel, 1958).

However, it has also been observed that the convergence of input onto individual reticular neurons is not absolute; i.e., that units could not be made to respond to all types of stimulation (Amassian and DeVito, 1954; Hernandez-Peon and Hagbarth, 1955; Scheibel et al., 1955). Furthermore, some reticular units have been found to be more responsive than others. Also, due to artefacts introduced by experimental techniques, it is difficult to assess just how generalized the reticular response to stimulation is under normal conditions. It has been found, for instance, that individual units exhibit larger receptive fields under chloralose anaesthesia than under syncurarine. We cannot say with certainty, therefore, how large the receptive fields would be in animals under no drug at all. Again, the type of stimulation employed is important. Hernandez-Peon and Hagbarth (1955) report that units which were unresponsive to stimuli applied as single shocks responded quite well when stimuli were applied repetitively.

Another finding which retains the possibility that information as to the

. FIG. 5–5. Convergence onto the same pontile reticular unit of tactile, acoustic and cortical stimuli. A. Spontaneous discharge. B. Tapping the ipsilateral forelimb. C. Rubbing the back. D. Touching whiskers. E. Hand claps. F. Single shocks to the ipsilateral sensorimotor cortex (indicated by the stimulus artefact). (From Palestini, M., *et al.*, 1957, *Archives Italiennes de Biologie*, 95.)

source of an incoming stimulus may be preserved in the reticular formation is that individual units will respond with different patterns and latencies of firing depending on their source of input. Theoretically, it is possible to encode information by means of such differences, though such a system would be cumbersome and would require a very complex decoding apparatus.

## Lack of Topographical Projection to the Cortex

French, Amerongen and Magoun (1952) stimulated various regions in the brain stem of monkeys and concluded that there was no correlation between the site of stimulation of the activating system and the area of cortical response. What they did find, however, was that some areas of the brain stem were more excitable than others, and stimulation of these areas gave rise to activation throughout the cortex. Stimulation of less excitable brain stem areas gave rise to a response which tended to be frontally oriented. The frontal and parietal areas of the cortex were found to be most easily excited, the temporal region less easily and the occipital region least. Magoun (1954) also found that stimulation of any part of the brain stem region gave rise to a desynchronization of the EEG which was generalized all over the cortex, though it was most pronounced and persisted for longer in the anterior part of the hemisphere.

## A Synchronizing Influence in the Lower Brain Stem

It has been demonstrated by numerous experiments, described earlier, that lesions in the brain stem reticular formation produce coma and a permanently synchronous EEG. However, a series of experiments initiated recently under Moruzzi have complicated this picture. It was found that cats with transections at the midpontine level show desynchronized EEG rhythms for most of the time, with only a few brief periods of synchrony. According to Batini *et al.* (1958), this preparation (the midpontine pretrigeminal preparation) displayed a waking EEG for at least 70 percent and frequently 90 percent of the total time it was recorded, as contrasted with a normal animal which displayed a waking EEG from 20 percent to 50 percent of the time. Such an animal could follow with its eyes an object passing across its visual field, and display pupillary dilation when an emotionally significant stimulus was presented. These ocular signs appeared only when the EEG was desynchronized.

Various experiments indicate that this effect may not be accounted for by irritative or humoral factors. It was postulated, therefore, that the midpontine transection excludes the influence of a synchronizing structure in the lower brain stem. If the transection is made a few millimeters rostrally (the rostropontine preparation), EEG synchronization is induced; so it was also inferred that structures immediately rostral to the midpontine transection were essential for producing a desynchronized EEG. (Figure 5–6).

## The Effects of Anaesthetics on the Reticular Formation

Activity in the brain stem reticular formation is easily depressed by anaesthetic agents (Arduini and Arduini, 1954; French, Verzeano, and Magoun, 1953) in contrast with activity in the cortex and primary sensory pathways (though activity in the latter regions is also modified). It has been suggested (Brazier, 1954) that this particular susceptibility is due to the fact that anaesthetic agents block synaptic transmission much more than they do nerve fiber conduction, and the reticular formation is a multisynaptic system. Generally, anaesthetics, as well as blocking activity

FIG. 5–6. EEG patterns following midpontine and rostropontine transections. Horizontal sections of the brain stem of the cat with cross-hatched areas indicating the level and extent of the brain stem lesion in the midpontine (A) and rostropontine (B) pretrigeminal preparations. Below each set of drawings are shown the EEG patterns typical for each preparation, recorded from the right (F.d.) and left (F.s.) frontal areas. (From Batini, C., *et al.*, 1959, *Archives Italiennes de Biologie*, 97.)

in the reticular formation, also produce EEG changes in the direction of synchrony.

## The Thalamic Reticular System

The thalamic reticular system consists of a closely interconnected network of neurons involving those thalamic nuclei which do not have specific projections to the cortex (Figure 5–7). These include the midline and intralaminar nuclei, the anteroventral nucleus, and the lateral reticular nucleus. Just as was found with the brain stem reticular formation, this system receives collaterals from the classical sensory pathways subserving various sensory modalities, and input from these pathways is distributed here in a non-specific fashion. Important projections from the cortex have also been demonstrated, as from other areas, such as the cerebellum and rhinencephalon (Lindsley, 1960).

Although its name implies that it is a single system, the thalamic reticular system does not in fact function in a unitary fashion. On the one hand, it appears to have an activating function similar to that found in the

| D. Pyr | —decussatio pyramydum, decussation of the pyramyds | | cellularis of Meessen and Olszewski |
|---|---|---|---|
| N. III, V, VI, VII, VIII | —root fibers of the third, fifth, seventh and eighth cranial nerves | R. p. c. | —nucleus reticularis pontis caudalis of Meessen and Olszewski |
| N. r. | —Nucleus ruber, red nucleus | R. pc. | —nucleus reticularis parvocellularies of Meessen and Olszewski |
| N. l. l. | —nucleus lemnisci lateralis | | |
| N. r. l. | —nucleus reticularis lateralis | | |
| N. r. t. | —nucleus reticularis tegmenti pontis | R. p. o. | —nucleus reticularis pontis oralis of Meessen and Olszewski |
| Ol. i. | —nucleus olivaris inferior, inferior olivary nucleus | Tr. | —corpus trapezoideum, trapezoid body |
| Ol. s. | —nucleus olivaris superior, superior olivary nucleus | Tr. sp. V | —tractus spinalis nervi trigemini, spinal tract of the trigeminal nerve |
| P. c. | —Pes pedunculi cerebri (or basis pedunculi) | | |
| Pyr. | —Pyramis, pyramid | V m. | —motor nucleus of the fifth cranial nerve |
| R. gc. | —nucleus reticularis giganto- | | |

brain stem reticular formation. On the other hand, it also has effects which antagonize the arousal system. We shall describe these latter effects first.

### The Recruiting Response

Morison and Dempsey (1942) discovered that during stimulation of the intralaminar nuclei of the thalamus at frequencies of six to twelve per second, there is an increment of response at the cortex with successive shocks. The cortical wave reaches a maximum after two to five successive stimuli. As repetitive stimulation continues, the response at the cortex may decrease again, exhibiting spontaneous waxing and waning (Figure 5–8).

**Frontal Plane 7.5**

| | |
|---|---|
| CC | Corpus callosum |
| CM | Centre median nucleus |
| fsc | Subcallosal fasciculus |
| Fx | fornix |
| GM | Medial geniculate body |
| H | field of Forel |
| HbL | Medial habenular nucleus |
| HbM | Lateral habenular nucleus |
| LD | Lateral dorsal nucleus |
| LME | External medullary lamina |
| LP | Lateral posterior nucleus |
| Ped | Cerebral peduncle |
| Pul | Pulvinar |
| PVA | Anterior periventricular nucleus |
| s | stria medullaris |
| THP | Habenulopeduncular tract |
| VPM | Ventral posteromedial nucleus |
| Zi | Zona incerta |

**Frontal Plane 6.0**

| | |
|---|---|
| BCI | Brachium of the inferior colliculus |
| CC | Corpus callosum |
| CP | Posterior commissure |
| Da | Nucleus of Darkshevitch |
| fsc | subcallosal fasciculus |
| Fx | Fornix |
| GC | Central gray matter |
| GM | Medial geniculate body |
| HbL | Lateral habenular nucleus |
| HbM | Medial habenular nucleus |
| Ip | Interpeduncular nucleus |
| Is | Interstitial nucleus |
| Lim | Nucleus limitans |
| mc | pars magnocellularis |
| NCP | Posterior commissural nucleus |
| NR | Red nucleus, nucleus ruber |
| P | Posterior nucleus |
| Prt | Praetectum |
| Pul | Pulvinar |
| SG | Supragenicular nucleus |
| SN | Substantia nigra |

FIG. 5–7. Diagram of the thalamic reticular system in the cat. Areas giving rise to recruiting responses are shown by the stippling. Successive frontal planes are shown. (From Jasper, H. H., 1960, in *Handbook of Physiology*, Vol. 2.)

This phenomenon is known as the recruiting response, and resembles the spindle bursts which occur spontaneously during sleep.

The exact pathways involved in this effect on the cortex are uncertain. It had been thought that connections were made with the cortex by way of the specific thalamic nuclei. However, Hanbery and Jasper (1953) demonstrated that recruiting responses could be obtained in a given cortical area after destruction of the specific thalamic nucleus known to be connected with this region. For instance, the recruiting response obtained from the visual area of the cortex was unimpaired after destruction of the lateral geniculate body of the thalamus. Similar findings were obtained for the auditory and somatosensory areas. Indeed, even better recruiting was obtained in a cortical region for which the appropriate specific thalamic

Frontal Plane 12.0

| | |
|---|---|
| AD | Anterodorsal nucleus |
| AM | Anteromedial nucleus |
| AV | Anteroventral nucleus |
| CC | Corpus callosum |
| Cd | Caudate nucleus |
| Cl | Claustrum |
| En | entopeduncular nucleus |
| Fil | Filiform nucleus |
| FSC | subcallosal fasciculus |
| Fx | fornix |
| HL | Lateral hypothalamus |
| Hvm | Ventromedial nucleus of the hypothalamus |
| IAM | Interanteromedial nucleus |
| MFB | medial forebrain bundle |
| Pt | parataenial nucleus |
| PVA | Anterior periventricular nucleus |
| PVH | periventricular hypothalamic nucleus |
| R | reticular nucleus |
| RE | nucleus reuniens |
| S | stria medullaris |
| ST | Stria terminalis |
| TO | Optic tract |
| VA | Ventral anterior nucleus |

Frontal Plane 10

| | |
|---|---|
| aHd | Dorsal hypothalamic area |
| Cc | Corpus callosum |
| Cd | Caudate |
| Cl | Claustrum |
| CL | Central lateral nucleus |
| En | Entopeduncular nucleus |
| Fsc | Subcallosal fasciculus |
| FT | Thalamic fasciculus |
| Hp | Posterior hypothalamus |
| LD | Lateral dorsal nucleus |
| LME | External medullary lamina |
| LP | Lateral posterior nucleus |
| MFB | Medial forebrain bundle |
| NCM | Central medial nucleus |
| Pc | Paracentral nucleus |
| Pt | Parataenial nucleus |
| RE | Nucleus reuniens |
| Sm | Submedian nucleus |
| ST | Stria terminalis |
| TMT | Mammillothalamic tract |
| TO | Optic tract |

FIG. 5–7—Continued

nucleus was destroyed. Generally, recruiting responses are easier to elicit and of higher voltage in the frontal and motor cortex and the anterior cingulate region than in the cortical sensory areas and posterior parietal areas.

FIG. 5–8. Recruiting response, showing waxing and waning, produced by repetitive stimulation of the intralaminar nuclei of the thalamus at the frequency indicated by the signal. This record was taken from the middle suprasylvian gyrus. (From Dempsey, E. W. and Morison, R. S., 1942, Am. J. Physiol. 135.)

Recently Sterman and Clemente (1962a) have reported that low-frequency stimulation of a circumscribed region in basal forebrain of the cat, just rostral to the optic chiasma, gave rise to an immediate and sustained cortical synchronization. This response was similar in many respects to the thalamic recruiting response. However, differences in the responses obtained from the two loci did exist. For instance, the synchronization evoked from basal forebrain stimulation was also prominent in the primary sensory areas. Further, this response was blocked by nembutal; in contrast, the recruiting response from the thalamus may even be potentiated by this drug.

### Behavioral Sleep Produced by Stimulation of Areas from Which the Recruiting Response Is Obtained

As Sterman and Clemente (1962a) observe, the relevance of the recruiting phenomenon consists in its similarity to the rhythms recorded from the cortex during sleep and allied states. It lies also in the fact that stimulation of areas from which the electrical phenomenon of recruiting can be induced, often produces behavioral sleep in freely moving animals.

For instance, Hess (1944, 1954) observed that repetitive stimulation in an area overlapping with that from which recruiting is obtained at low voltage and a frequency of eight per second produces sleep in cats. Hess stresses the resemblance of this phenomenon to that of natural sleep. The animal does not fall asleep suddenly but first chooses a convenient place and settles down in it. The EEG pattern is indistinguishable from that recorded in natural sleep (Hess, Koella and Akert, 1953), and the animal may be aroused by peripheral stimulation. Employing dogs as subjects, Akimoto et al. (1956) also demonstrated that repetitive stimulation at low voltage and low frequency (five to ten per second) in the intralaminar nuclei, induces sleep in unanaesthetized animals. Here also the EEG pattern produced was very similar to that found in natural sleep. Further, Sterman and Clemente (1962b), using cats, found that stimulation of the basal forebrain synchronized area, described above, induces the rapid onset of behavioral sleep. In this case the effect could be obtained by high- as well as low-frequency stimulation (5–250 cps.).

### Interaction between the Recruiting System and the Arousal System

Various kinds of evidence indicate that the activating effect of the brain stem reticular formation acts as an antagonist to the recruiting system. Best recruiting is obtained in animals with the mesial portion of the reticular formation destroyed. Furthermore, it is difficult to obtain recruiting in unanaesthetized animals which are aroused by sensory stimulation. Rapid stimulation of the brain stem reticular formation concomitantly with stimulation of the intralaminar nuclei to obtain recruiting will block the recruiting response. The interaction between the basal forebrain synchronizing area and the brain stem reticular formation is more complex. Here the order of application of the two types of stimulation is important. Cortical arousal produced by high-frequency stimulation of the brain stem reticular formation will be blocked if the basal forebrain zone is then stimulated simultaneously at low frequency; i.e., cortical synchronization will result. However, if the basal forebrain zone is stimulated first, the opposite will be the case (Sterman and Clemente, 1962a).

## The Activating Function of the Thalamic Reticular System

Large bilateral lesions of the anterior portion of the thalamic reticular system may produce coma analogous to that produced by lesions of the midbrain (French and Magoun, 1952; Lindsley et al., 1950), though the depth of coma invoked by the thalamic lesions is less profound. It seems therefore that the thalamic reticular system also has an activating function.

Further evidence arises from stimulation studies in this region. It is possible to produce EEG desynchronization upon high-frequency stimulation of the thalamic reticular system, though activation so produced is shorter lasting than is that mediated by the brain stem reticular formation. In the two studies cited above demonstrating the induction of sleep by low-frequency thalamic stimulation (Hess, 1954, Akimoto et al., 1956) raising the stimulus frequency in the same locus produced the opposite effect: it would arouse a sleeping animal.

Such findings have led to speculation as to whether these two opposite effects obtained from the same locus are due to stimulation of the same system in different ways, or to stimulation of two separate systems by the use of different stimulus parameters. Recent work has made it very likely that the latter interpretation is correct, and that the contrasting effects are due to the stimulation of two separate systems which partially overlap anatomically. Schlag and Chaillet (1963) were able to show that different points within the thalamic reticular system tended to give rise either to recruiting or to desynchronization in the cortex. Further, cortical desynchronization could not be elicited in a third of their cats when the connection of the thalamic reticular formation with the mesencephalic reticular formation was severed, whereas the recruiting response could still be elicited. Enomoto (1959) had shown that a sagittal section of the massa intermedia and corpus callosum abolishes the recruiting response on the contralateral cortex. Schlag and Chaillet were able to confirm this finding and to show in addition that stimulation at a high frequency at the same thalamic site in Enomoto's preparation was able to produce a desynchronization of the contralateral hemisphere. It may therefore be that the desynchronizing effect of stimuli to one component of the thalamic reticular system is actually transmitted to the cortex by first traveling back to the midbrain reticular formation. The path which transmits the synchronizing influence to the cortex appears to be more direct.

## Paradoxical Results Following Lesions of the Reticular System

Adametz (1959) and Chow and Randell (1960) report that if lesions are made in the midbrain reticular formation in several stages, allowing for recovery between each stage, animals with large lesions may yet remain alert and capable of learning. The explanation of why inflicting such lesions in stages should prevent coma is as yet unclear. Doty *et al.* (1959) also report that cats with massive midbrain lesions might recover and demonstrate EEG desynchronization if given intensive nursing care. Similar results have also been obtained by Sprague, Chambers and Stellar (1961) and Batsel (1960). It is possible, therefore, that the brain stem reticular formation might prove to be less vital for the maintenance of arousal than it has been considered to be. Chow *et al.* (1959) found also that massive lesions in the thalamic reticular system need not produce comas.

### THEORIES CONCERNING THE PROCESS OF FALLING ASLEEP

There have been two main approaches to the study of sleep. The first approach regards sleep as a "passive" process; that is, it is assumed that sleep is brought about by some impairment or depression of nervous system function. A modern version of this view stresses the finding that wakefulness depends on the integrity of ascending pathways from the brain stem reticular formation, and that coma results from lesions in these pathways. It is therefore proposed that sleep is brought about by reduction in the activating influence of the reticular formation. This may be produced by several factors, such as synaptic fatigue and reduction in sensory influx. This view was stated by Bremer (1954), when he wrote:

The physiological process of falling asleep may be explained, without necessary recourse to the hypothesis of a hypnogenic centre, by the cumulative de-activation (de-facilitation) of the encephalic neuronal networks resulting from synaptic fatigue and favored by a reduction in the exteroceptive and proprioceptive sensory afflux. In this process of neuronal de-activation which culminates in sleep the functional slackening of the brain stem reticular formation, by reason of the latter's central situation in the nervous apparatus of arousal, plays without doubt an essential role.

Another view suggests that sleep is brought about by the influence of an active sleep-producing mechanism. This view is supported by various lines of evidence. Firstly, lesions in the anterior part of the hypothalamus have given rise to states of sleeplessness both in encephalic patients (Von Economo, 1918) and in rats (Nauta, 1946). It may be suggested that sleep-inducing structures are damaged in these cases. Secondly, stimulation in various diencephalic regions (including structures in the anterior hypothalamus) can produce sleep, as shown by the experiments of Hess and his collaborators (1944, 1953, 1954), Akimoto *et al.* (1956), and Sterman and Clemente (1962) quoted above.

Moruzzi (1960) presents the hypothesis that sleep may be induced by an ascending flow of impulses arising from synchronizing structures in the lower brain stem which inhibit or antagonize the reticular activating system. He suggests that while the reticular activating system is excited by sudden environmental changes, "the synchronizing structures of the brain stem are endowed with the opposite property of responding with an avalanching increase of their activity whenever a prolonged sequence of monotonous sensory stimulations is applied to a large group of receptors." In support of this notion he cites experiments of Pavlov and his followers, which indicate that sleep may be brought about more quickly and consistently in the presence of repeated identical stimuli than if such stimuli were omitted. Moruzzi's hypothesis was not intended to account for the whole process of induction and maintenance of sleep, but he argues that it may be an important factor at least in the case of sleep initiation.

Moruzzi's hypothesis is supported by two main lines of evidence. Firstly, cortical EEG synchronization can be produced by stimulation in the region of the nucleus of the solitary tract in the medulla. The second line of evidence comes from experiments which surgically separate parts of the nervous system from each other. When a section is made between the medulla and the spinal cord (encéphale isolé preparation), EEG synchronization and ocular signs of sleep occur from time to time. However, if the section is made in the middle of the pons (the midpontine pretrigeminal preparation), desynchronization is present for most of the time (Figure 5–6). It is therefore argued that some structure which lies between the middle of the pons and the junction between the spine and medulla is responsible for exerting a synchronizing influence.

Further evidence that there are separate mechanisms for sleep and for arousal comes from experiments involving the injection of cholinergic and adrenergic agents into the relevant brain sites. Hernandez-Peon *et al.* (1963) report that injection of noradrenaline into sites in the preoptic area elicited alertness, whereas injection of cholinergic substances into the same sites produced sleep. This makes it very likely that separate arousing and sleep-inducing pathways exist and employ different chemical mediators, though they overlap anatomically. It is at present unclear how the active sleep-inducing process exerts its effect. It could for instance inhibit the arousal system directly, or it could antagonize its effects at various structures.

This does not mean that the reticular deactivation view of sleep is incorrect. It is apparent from common experience that the onset of sleep is facilitated by a quiet environment. Even when sleep was induced by brain stimulation, it was found that this could be affected by such conditions as

external stimulation and the animal's emotional state. It seems therefore
that a low level of activity in the arousal system is prerequisite for the
induction of sleep. Both processes, the active and the passive, are
important.

## PARADOXICAL SLEEP

Paradoxical sleep is so named because it is deep behavioral sleep
accompanied by a fast desynchronized EEG record, normally characteristic
of behavioral alertness (Dement, 1958; Hubel, 1960; Moruzzi, 1964). In
spite of this resemblance to the waking state, paradoxical sleep seems to be
a deeper stage of sleep than that characterized by slow synchronized
rhythms. For instance, on going to sleep, the organism passes from the
synchronized stage of sleep to the desynchronized stage. Further, on being
disturbed in the desynchronized stage by some externally applied stimulus,
the organism passes into synchronized sleep and then perhaps wakes up.
Also during paradoxical sleep, antigravity reflexes are diminished, as shown
for instance by loss of muscle tone in the neck muscles. However, this stage
of sleep is accompanied by fast eye movements, and it seems that it is
during this stage that dreaming occurs (Jouvet, 1962). It has been shown
that the desynchronized stage of sleep is induced by activity in the pontile
tegmentum (Jouvet, 1962). It appears that the pathways carrying this
effect from this nucleus run to the higher parts of the nervous system
through the ventral and medial part of the upper brain stem, and are
separate from the pathways responsible for desynchronization during
behavioral wakefulness.

## HUMORAL FACTORS INVOLVED IN CORTICAL
## ELECTROGRAPHIC CHANGES

Although most studies investigating the effect of reticular changes on
the electrical activity of the cortex have concentrated on the neuronal
pathways and mechanisms involved, it has also been demonstrated that
such an influence can occur in the absence of a neural pathway. Ingvar
(1955) observed that electrical stimulation of the reticular activating
system caused electrographic changes in neuronally isolated cortex, and
concluded that neurohumoral factors must also play a role in regulating
cortical electrical activity. Purpura (1956), using the cross-perfusion
technique in cats found that stimulation of the bulbar reticular formation
in the donor produced cortical EEG arousal in the recipient. He concluded
that this effect was due to the release of a neurohumor from the donor's
brain. In a similar situation, Kornmuller et al. (1961) found that
stimulating the central lateral nucleus, the ventral medial nucleus of the
thalamus and the caudate nucleus in the donor produced electrographic
sleep effects in the recipient as well as in the donor.

Monnier et al. (1963) performed cross-circulation experiments on rabbits. They found that stimulation of the mediocentral intralaminary thalamus in the donor produced a statistically significant increase in high-voltage slow activity in the recipient as well as in the donor. Stimulation of the midbrain reticular system in the donor produced a statistically significant decrease in high-voltage slow activity in the recipient as well as in the donor. This substantiates the hypothesis of an extraneuronal humoral agent influencing cortical electrical activity following reticular changes.

## HABITUATION OF THE AROUSAL RESPONSE

When a stimulus is repeatedly presented, it gradually ceases to elicit EEG arousal. This habituation of the arousal response may develop even when many minutes intervene between successive presentations of the same stimulus, and may persist for hours or even days. The presentation of a novel stimulus may abolish habituation established to an old stimulus (disinhibition), and pairing a stimulus with a motivationally relevant stimulus such as shock (conditioning) will greatly retard the habituation process. These findings show that habituation is a type of learning, and not just the result of receptor fatigue or nerve accommodation.

Even when extinction of the generalized arousal response is complete, the localized activation pattern in the cortical region receiving the afferent stimulus may persist for much longer. Voronin and Sokolov (1960) report that visual stimuli continue to produce blocking of the posterior alpha rhythm even after hundreds of presentations.

This type of habituation has been shown to be very specific to the stimulus parameters presented. Sharpless and Jasper (1956) recorded responses to auditory stimuli in naturally sleeping cats. They found that habituation was specific to the frequency of the tone used, and even to the pattern in which various tones were presented. For instance, an animal habituated to a tone falling in pitch from 5,000 to 200 cps. would be aroused by the same combination of tones rising in pitch. A comparison of the effect of Sharpless and Jasper's lesions on specificity of habituation, with the effect of similar lesions on the ability to discriminate between stimuli, suggests that habituation may be as specific as is the animal's ability to discriminate between stimuli. Bilateral lesions of the auditory cortex destroyed specificity of habituation to tonal patterns but did not destroy frequency-specific habituation. In comparison, tonal pattern discrimination is abolished by ablation of auditory cortical areas; yet animals with auditory cortex ablated can still make frequency discriminations (see Chapter 10).

Evidence from studies on human subjects also indicates that habituation of the arousal reaction is very sensitive to changes in stimulus parameters. Voronin and Sokolov (1960) found that a diminution in intensity of a light or sound stimulus, or even the omission of a stimulus which has been regularly repeated, will produce dehabituation. If habituation is established to a complex of three stimuli, then the presentation of one of these without the others will induce arousal. In experiments employing verbal stimuli they found that when habituation is established to a group of words similar in meaning but different in sound, then arousal occurred to a word with a different meaning. However, some generalization of habituation has also been demonstrated. The more similar a stimulus is to the habituatory stimulus, the less likely it is to produce alpha blocking.

Speed of habituation depends on the type of stimulus employed. Sharpless and Jasper (1956) report that habituation to a click stimulus needed only six trials, whereas habituation to a modulated tone changing continuously in pitch required sixty trials. Voronin and Sololov found that against a background of habituation to words indifferent to the subject, words with particular significance were not habituated to.

Habituation of the arousal response seems to be independent of changes in the primary sensory pathways. Sharpless and Jasper (1956) showed that after such habituation in sleeping cats, cortical potentials evoked by the habituatory stimulus were undiminished. Furthermore, it does not seem to depend on changes occurring in the nonspecific ascending pathways, since high amplitude potentials may also be recorded from the reticular formation in response to the habituatory stimulus (Jouvet, 1961). Parts of the cortex do seem vital to this function, however. Jouvet (1961) reports that it is not possible to obtain habituation of the arousal response in chronic mesencephalic or neodecorticated cats. In animals with partial cortical ablations, the smaller the area of cortical surface left intact, the longer it takes for an animal to habituate. Sharpless and Jasper (1956) showed that habituation to auditory stimuli occurred in animals with total ablations of the auditory cortex; so the primary cortical receiving areas do not seem to be essential to this process. The frontal cortex however does appear to be of critical importance. Jouvet found that almost complete ablation of the frontal cortex led to a considerable slowing down of the habituation process. Konorski (1956) reports that in the dog, ablation of the frontal lobes led to a substantial retardation of the process of inhibition. On the basis of such evidence, Jouvet (1961) postulates that habituation depends on the action of a rostral inhibitory system, of which the neocortex is an essential part, which acts downward on the reticular system.

## SELECTIVE ATTENTION

### Human Behavioral Studies

It is apparent from everyday experience that we are aware of only a limited sample of the happenings around us. Such a limitation is not due only to the relatively restricted range of our sense organs. Many things which excite our sense organs do not appear to be registered by us. Instead, we seem to select small samples of the input from our receptors and to deal with these samples one at a time. We can also switch from one sample to another when we wish, but we cannot attend to everything at once even if we would like to do so. Why this is the case is one of the main problems of selective attention.

An experiment by Cherry (1953) illustrates how very little we may be aware of from one information source when we are attending to another. Subjects were required to repeat back a continuous stream of speech delivered to one ear, while at the same time another stream of speech was being fed into the other ear. In the middle of the experiment the nature of the stimulus to the "irrelevant" ear was changed: some subjects were presented with a pure tone; others with a woman's voice instead of a man's; others with German instead of English words; and still others with "reversed" speech with the same spectrum as normal speech, though devoid of meaning. It was found that though the changes to a female voice and a pure tone were readily noticed, the subjects could say nothing about the content of the irrelevant message—not even what language it was in! And only some of the subjects presented with the reversed speech noticed "something queer" about it.

One question which arises here is where in the nervous system the messages to which we do not attend are lost. One of the ways of deciding where the nervous system discards information with which it is not at the moment dealing is to consider the complexity of selection between messages. If, for instance, the nervous system will only exclude a message on the basis of which ear is receiving it (as in the experiment of Cherry quoted above), then it would be plausible to assume that the selection is performed at a low level, simply by blocking the path leading from one ear. If, on the other hand, the meaning of messages is utilized in enabling us to attend to one message and to discard another, then it is evident that both messages must have been examined as to their content prior to the rejection of one. It is most unlikely that such an examination could be carried out at the purely peripheral level, and a central or cortical theory of selection therefore becomes plausible.

In the attempt to determine which cues we utilize in making such a selection, the experimental situation preferred by most workers has been the simultaneous presentation of two auditory sequences. Localization cues have been shown to be important in this situation. Broadbent (1954) presented, simultaneously, sequences of messages in pairs, and required subjects to answer only to one sequence. He found that the presentation of the messages through spatially segregated loudspeakers increased efficiency, as did stereophonic separation (which, as Broadbent remarks, controlled well for other possible factors such as changes in the quality of the sound produced by moving the speaker, or the subject's moving his head nearer to one speaker). Furthermore, he found that if the speech was reproduced through headphones stereophonically, better results were obtained than if the voices were presented through the headphones conventionally mixed. Further evidence for the importance of localization cues is presented by Poulton (1953), and by Spieth, Curtis and Webster (1954), and Webster and Thomson (1954), who investigated the monitoring of more than two channels at a time.

Experiments on listening to messages against a background of noise are also of relevance here, since "noise" may be considered a second channel competing for the subject's attention. Hirsh (1950) investigated this phenomenon in a well-controlled situation, using a room free of echoes. When the speech was delivered through one loudspeaker and the noise through another, he found that better results were obtained if the speakers were separated than if they were adjacent. Furthermore, if one loudspeaker was placed in front of the head and the other behind, efficiency was lower than if the speakers were separated but differently placed, and it is interesting that the latter condition provides more localization cues than the former, in which the only available cue is provided by the shadow of the external ear.

Another cue shown to be important in this respect is the frequency of the sound occurring in the messages. Increasing the difference between the mean frequency (pitch) of the relevant and the irrelevant messages increases efficiency in attending to the former and ignoring the later (Spieth, Curtis and Webster, 1954; Egan, Carterette and Thwing, 1954).

So far the evidence quoted is consistent with the notion that the separation of one message from another in selective attention may be done on the basis of relatively few simple characteristics, such as localization and frequency. If messages were discarded on some simple criterion such as frequency, then the selected message could proceed alone for more complex analysis. The mechanisms for more complex analysis could then handle the single message more efficiently than if they were being flooded by a large number of messages. Such a view has been put forward in a detailed form by Broadbent (1958). He supposes that messages are selected by a "filter" which is capable of simple and few discriminations. This filter only allows one message out of many to proceed to the central analyzing mechanisms, thus reducing the load of discrimination which they have to perform. Such a notion of a filter at the time agreed with neurophysiological observations on diminution of evoked potentials at relatively peripheral levels during attention (see below). However, further research has produced a more complicated picture of these phenomena, so that the neurophysiological findings on the whole do not really support the notion of a peripheral filter.

Further, behavioral research makes such a notion of a filter implausible, because of the complexity of discrimination required in many tasks involving selective attention. Various findings demonstrate that the selection of wanted from unwanted speech is a central phenomenon, and not due simply to the blocking of the unwanted information at a peripheral level. Peters (1954) found that if two messages similar in content are played simultaneously to the subject, it is more difficult for him to select one of them than if the contents of the messages are different. This tends to show that the contents of two messages is taken into consideration before one of them is selected.

The operations performed on incoming information before the selection of a message have been shown to be very complex. Gray and Wedderburn (1960) performed an experiment in which two meaningful sequences of syllables or words were used. Instead of playing one of these sequences consistently to one ear or the other, they took the two sequences and switched them between ears. Sequence A would start on the left ear and Sequence B on the right; thus a syllable or word would be fed one into each ear. However, the second word or syllable in Sequence A would be fed into the right ear, and the second word or syllable in Sequence B would go into the left ear. It was found that though the sequences were continually switched from one ear to the other, the subjects would select the speech in such a way that a meaningful sequence was reported back to the experimenter. The subjects were, therefore, analyzing the meaning of the speech sounds in the process of selecting some and rejecting others, and this analysis could not possibly have been carried out at the periphery. Gray and Wedderburn's (1960) experiment shows that the nervous system, prior to making its selection, can make use of its memory of the transition probabilities of the items presented. Some word or sound sequences are more probable than others, and it looks as if in this experiment the more likely combinations were chosen as belonging together, in spite of their occurring on different ears.

Further evidence of the use of such transition probabilities is presented by Treisman (1960). She played two messages, one to each of a pair of earphones. Subjects were asked to repeat back to her what they heard in one of their ears. In the middle of the experiment the messages were switched from one ear to the other. There was a tendency to stay with a message for a few words in spite of the switch, this tendency being proportional to the transition probability of the words in the message.

It has also been shown that there is a surprising specificity about the items which will redirect attention. Moray (1959) has shown that if a subject is attending to a message on one ear, it is possible to have him switch to the other ear on a certain proportion of instances by calling his name on the ear the message to which he was otherwise unaware. No other stimulus was found to be effective. The special status of one's own name in the attention process has been confirmed in other instances. In a well-controlled experiment, Oswald, Taylor and Treisman (1960) found that a subject shows EEG changes during sleep in response to his own name much more so than to any other name. Howarth and Ellis (1961) used another type of situation to investigate this problem. Subjects were required to identify various names when they were fully awake and listening with both ears, but when there was masking by noise. The investigators found that the probability of the subject recognizing his own name was significantly higher than that of his recognizing other names. Comparing the probabilities of recognition in their experiment with those derived by Moray (1959) and Oswald, Taylor and Treisman (1960), they conclude, "It seems an obvious conclusion to suppose that the same pattern analysing mechanism is required to account for behavior during dichotic listening or during sleep." If the same structure is responsible for recognition in the case of normal listening and during selective attention, it is then most likely that selection is performed at the highest neural level. The above evidence therefore leads us to conclude against the hypothesis that selection in attention is achieved by a two-stage process, including a preliminary discriminating mechanism or filter which allows only certain items to proceed to the highest level. It is more consistent with the behavioral evidence to suppose that messages proceed to the same destination whether they are selected in attention or not. Then, as a result of activity in the regions to which the messages proceed, further changes will take place in these and associated regions if such messages are selected for attention.

## Localized EEG Arousal

Since general behavioral arousal is correlated with widespread EEG desynchronization, it might be expected that selective attention to a specific stimulus would be associated with EEG arousal localized to the appropriate cortical region. Such an association has indeed been found under certain conditions. Adrian (1947) showed in human subjects that the presentation of visual stimuli led to the blocking of the occipital alpha rhythm. Shifting attention from the visual to an auditory stimulus caused the occipital alpha to return. He also found that visual stimuli, if confined to a part of the visual field, selectively block only the alpha rhythm in the contralateral parieto-occipital region. Penfield (1954) describes localized activation in a patient during operation. When the patient was told to make a fist of his hand, the resting rhythms in the hand area of the contralateral precentral and postcentral gyri disappeared, but they continued in the face area and in the cortex lying anterior and posterior to the Rolandic hand area. The resting rhythms returned as the patient maintained his hand in that position. While the patient, upon instruction, touched his thumb with one finger after the other of the same hand, resting rhythms in the Rolandic hand area disappeared again not to return until the maneuver was completed.

However, this localized activation can only be demonstrated under certain conditions. The presentation of a relatively novel stimulus gives rise to a number of behavioral reactions, involving the activation of widespread areas of the cortex. With repeated presentations of the same stimulus, however, most of these general reactions tend to disappear, and concomitantly the EEG arousal response becomes localized to the appropriate cortical region. For instance the initial presentation of a light stimulus induces blocking of the alpha rhythm in the occipital and motor areas of the cortex, along with other effects such as changes in respiration, GSR changes, and eye movements. After a few presentations these behavioral effects tend to disappear, along with the alpha blocking of the motor area. However, alpha blocking in the occipital region may continue for even hundreds of presentations. With the presentation of a tactile stimulus the blocking of occipital alpha disappears after the first few presentations while the GSR changes and blocking of the Rolandic rhythm continue. With proprioceptive stimuli, blocking of the Rolandic rhythm and the GSR changes continue for even longer. Thus the appearance of localized activation coincides with the disappearance of the generalized behavioral response to a novel stimulus (Voronin and Sokolov, 1960).

We may ask further what functional change such EEG activation reflects. When we attend to an object, various processes can be seen to occur by common observation. We may make receptor adjustments to see the object more clearly and to approach it, and we are in a state of readiness to respond to it. We are also able to report the various features of the object afterwards if called upon to do so. So it seems that when we are paying attention to certain stimuli, various circuits in the areas concerned with the reception of these stimuli are activated. These circuits are concerned with motor output, memory storage and so on. The generalized EEG arousal accompanying the presentation of a novel stimulus is thus associated with a considerable degree of activity in motor and autonomic pathways. However, with repeated stimulus presentations fewer of these circuits are activated and this is reflected in a more localized EEG desynchronization. Certain pathways, concerned with the reception and analysis of the signal, of course continue to be activated.

The discovery by Hubel, Henson, Rupert, and Galambos (1959) of units in the auditory cortex of the cat, which responded only when the animal was paying attention to a sound source, might be interpreted in this light. One unit they describe almost never responded to clicks, tones or noise, but responded readily to squeaks emitted by a toy mouse, to a human voice and to hissing when the animal was paying attention to these stimuli. Another unit responded to the sound of keys being jingled outside the room, but only when the cat looked towards the door. It also responded to the rustling of a paper but only when the cat looked towards the paper. The authors conclude that about 10 percent of the units in the auditory cortex of the cat are of this type. Other units, in contrast, responded reliably to stimuli presented by loudspeaker, regardless of whether the animal was awake or asleep. We might suppose that these "attention" units formed part of circuits responsible for such things as the appropriate motor response to the stimulus, or memory storage; or that they lay on the pathway to these systems. Thus we should expect these units to be inactive even if impulses evoked by auditory stimuli were reaching the cortex, provided the animal was not paying attention to these stimuli.

## The Selection Process in Selective Attention

So far we have concluded that the discarding of information to which we are not attending does not occur at a peripheral level, since the discriminations required to separate the ascending messages before one of these is selected are often extremely complex. The problem of how the nervous system discriminates or separates the vast mixture of ascending impulses so that they are appropriately grouped to correspond with the many concurrent events stimulating the organism is not basically one of selective attention. It is rather a problem in perception. However, there is another question which is more limited to the sphere of selective attention. This is how one of the messages, once they have been separated, is efficiently selected by the nervous system. There is an extremely large number of possible messages from which one is to be selected at any one time. If we wish to select one item out of a set according to some criterion, this involves us in a process of comparison among the items of such a set. If the set is large, it seems at first sight that the number of comparisons to be made among its various items will be enormous. For such a task to be performed by the nervous system, one would have to postulate a neural connection for every comparison that might have to be made.

However, we can envisage a much simpler system which would choose the largest item of a group (Deutsch and Deutsch, 1963). If there is a group of boys and we wish to select the tallest, we can proceed by placing a horizontal board over their heads to see which boy's head it touches. The boy whose head it touches will know he is the tallest boy in the group. If he leaves the group, then the board will descend until it touches the head of the tallest boy who is left. The principle of operation of this system is that the tallest will raise a general level to his own height and so will be the only one to be at that level.

Deutsch and Deutsch (1963) describe in detail how signals might be selected for attention on this analogy. In this paper it is proposed that the reticular system may, as part of its function, act as a diffuse system capable of taking up a level appropriate to the greatest amount of excitation being fed into it. Such excitation would occur as a result of cortical analysis of a signal. For those signals whose resultant excitation is lower than that appropriate to the level in the diffuse system, the relevant motor and memory storage pathways, etc., would be blocked. Thus only one signal would be attended to (Figure 5–9).

Such a system could be independent of the mechanism underlying

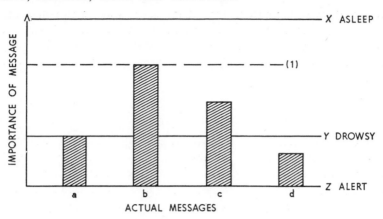

FIG. 5–9.  Diagram to illustrate the operation of a hypothesised specific alerting system and its interaction with the mechanism underlying general arousal. This system involves a shifting reference standard which takes up the level of the most important arriving signal. The interrupted horizontal line (1) represents the 'level' of importance in the specific alerting system which is raised and lowered according to the incoming messages. The solid horizontal lines represent levels of general arousal. At X the organism is asleep and none of the incoming messages produce alerting. At Y the organism is drowsy and only some of the incoming messages could produce alerting. At Ż the organism is awake and all incoming messages could produce alerting; however only *b* is heeded because of the operation of the specific alerting system. (Adapted from Deutsch, J. A. and Deutsch, D., 1963, *Psych. Rev.* 70.)

general arousal (though it need not be). Beh and Barrett (1965) present evidence for such an independence of general and specific alerting systems. This is a question which needs to be investigated further.

## Changes in the Evoked Potential Related to Shifts of Attention and Habituation

### 1. Attention Shifts

Hernandez-Peon, Sherrer, and Jouvet (1956) recording responses evoked in the dorsal cochlear nucleus to clicks, in unanaesthetized animals, found that the presentation of a visual stimulus (in this case, mice in a jar) or an olfactory stimulus (fish odors) greatly diminished the amplitude of the evoked response to clicks. When the "distracting" stimuli were removed, responses in the cochlear nucleus returned to their original amplitude. A similar effect has been reported in visual and somatosensory pathways (Hernandez-Peon, Guzman-Flores, Alcarez and Fernandez-Guardiola, 1957; Brust-Carmona and Hernandez-Peon 1959). In man, Jouvet (1957) studied the effect of various attentional states on responses in the optic radiations to light flash. When the subject was asked to attend to and count the flashes, there resulted an enhancement of responses in the optic radiations. The responses diminished when distracting stimuli were introduced, or when the subject was asked to perform calculations.

## 2. Habituation

It has been claimed that when a stimulus is repeatedly presented, evoked potentials recorded from the cortex and relay nuclei along the primary sensory pathways, as well as from the reticular formation and other subcortical structures, show a decrement in amplitude which follows a waxing and waning course. Various factors such as a period of rest and the presentation of extraneous stimuli (disinhibition) will bring about a return to high amplitude potentials. Such habituation has been alleged to occur at such peripheral levels as the dorsal cochlear nucleus (Hernandez-Peon and Scherrer, 1955; Galambos et al., 1956; Hernandez-Peon, Jouvet and Scherrer, 1957), the retina (Palestini, Davidovich and Hernandez-Peon, 1959), the olfactory bulb (Hernandez-Peon, Alcocer-Cuaron, Lavin, and Santibanez, 1957), and the lateral column of the spinal cord (Brust-Carmona and Hernandez-Peon, 1959). Habituation at higher levels on the primary sensory pathways including the cortex has been found in various structures (Hernandez-Peon, Guzman-Flores, Alcarez, and Fernandez-Guardiola, 1958; Moushegian et al., 1961). In the cortex, habituation of the evoked potential occurs often considerably faster in regions other than the primary projection area for the appropriate stimulus. It has also been reported that cortical evoked potentials may disappear at a faster rate than evoked potentials at lower levels (Hernandez-Peon, 1960).

### Involvement of the Brain Stem Reticular Formation in These Effects

It has been inferred from a variety of evidence that the changes in evoked potential described above are brought about by some mechanism involving the brain stem reticular formation. One such type of evidence is that stimulation of the reticular formation may cause a reduction in amplitude of the evoked response similar to that produced by distraction and habituation, or a facilitation of the evoked response similar to that obtained in conditioning (see Chapter 3).

Granit (1955) demonstrated both facilitation and inhibition of the firing of individual ganglion cells of the retina as a result of stimulating the midbrain tegmentum. A similar control of activity in the spinal and brain stem relays has been demonstrated: stimulation of the reticular formation inhibited responses in the posterior columns (Hagbarth and Kerr, 1954), and inhibited conduction in the nucleus gracilis (Hernandez-Peon, Scherrer and Velasco, 1956). Activity in the sensory nucleus of the fifth nerve could be similarly affected (Hernandez-Peon and Hagbarth, 1955).

Hernandez-Peon, Scherrer and Velasco (1956) report that stimulation of the reticular formation resulted in a depression of the evoked response to photic stimulation in the lateral geniculate. Under some conditions a facilitatory effect can also be demonstrated (Bremer and Stoupel, 1959). At the cortical level also, both inhibitory and facilitatory effects of reticular stimulation on the evoked potential have been shown (Bremer and Stoupel, 1959; Dumont and Dell, 1958). Lindsley (1958) found improved resolution of cortical response to two light flashes closely separated in time as a result of reticular stimulation.

Nevertheless, stimulation of other central structures may also influence the size of evoked responses. This has been shown, for instance, for the cortex, cerebellum and various structures in the rhinencephalon. Such effects are mentioned in other chapters in this book dealing with specific sensory afferents.

Further evidence that the brain stem reticular formation is involved in the habituation of the evoked response is based on the finding that lesions in this structure may eliminate such habituation (Hernandez-Peon, 1960). The reticular formation does not appear to act nonspecifically in this respect, however. Pontine lesions were shown to eliminate habituation of post-rotatory nystagmus but not to affect olfactory habituation. Yet mesencephalic lesions eliminated acoustic and olfactory habituation but did not prevent habituation to vestibular stimulation. Barbiturate anaesthesia is known especially to depress activity in the reticular formation. Animals under this anaesthetic will not demonstrate habituation, and if this anaesthesia is administered after habituation has taken place, evoked potentials will as a result return to their original high amplitude. On the other hand, such a return to high-amplitude responses does not occur under light physiological sleep (Hernandez-Peon, 1960). However, despite the seeming necessity for the intactness of reticular structures in some instances, it has also been shown that habituation of the evoked potential is possible in preparations lacking a reticular formation. Hernandez-Peon and Brust-Carmona (1961) report that habituation may occur in isolated spinal cord in cats.

## The Interpretation of the Changes in the Size of the Evoked Potential at the Peripheral Sensory Synapses

Hernandez-Peon (1960) suggests that the reduction in amplitude of response which occurs at the peripheral sensory synapses with attention shifts, habituation, and reticular stimulation, is due to "centrifugal plastic inhibition acting at those peripheral sensory synapses" originating from the brain stem reticular formation. There are indications from recent experiments, however, that these effects may at least in some cases be due to peripheral factors. Hugelin, Dumont and Paillas (1960) report that when the middle ear muscles were cut, stimulation of the reticular formation failed to produce an attenuation of the evoked response to clicks at the cochlear nucleus. They suggest that the reticular control of auditory input may be due to motor effects. They further point out that the mean diminution of microphonic potentials resulting from reticular stimulation was less than 5 decibels, which is very small from the point of view of auditory sensation.

Naquet *et al.* (1960) report that changes in the evoked potential at lower levels of the visual pathway resulting from reticular stimulation, may be due to accompanying changes in pupillary diameter. The pupil dilates during desynchronization of the EEG (whether or not this desynchronization is due to reticular stimulation) and contracts during EEG synchrony. It has been found that during desynchronization flash-evoked responses at the optic chiasma and lateral geniculate were increased, and that they were reduced at the visual receiving area of the cortex. The reverse occurred during synchrony. Now when the size of the pupil was fixed by topical application of atropine, the size of the evoked potentials remained constant at the optic chiasma and lateral geniculate though they continued to vary at the cortex.

Another line of criticism is put forward by Worden and Marsh (1963) in a study on cats with intact middle ear muscles. They found that fluctuations in the amplitude of evoked response occurring in the cochlear nucleus with repeated stimulus presentations were quite inconsistent. Increases in amplitude of evoked response occurred as well as decreases. Amplitude changes in opposite directions could be recorded between placements in the right and left cochlear nuclei, and also between two adjacent placements within one cochlear nucleus. No correlation was found between placement of electrode tip and direction of amplitude shift in the evoked response. Opposite results were even obtained from the same placement on different occasions. It may therefore be that earlier results showing a decrease in evoked potential at peripheral levels during repeated stimulus presentations were due to sampling bias.

## The Interpretation of the Changes in Evoked Potential at the Cortical Level

Changes in the evoked response at the cortex have not been shown to be due to peripheral factors. We saw above that when the size of the pupil was fixed by atropine, flash-evoked responses in the visual receiving area of the cortex continued to show lability (Naquet *et al.*, 1960). Further, Moushegian *et al.* (1961), using animals in which the middle ear muscles had been cut, found that evoked responses at the auditory cortex still demonstrated diminution with habituation and attention shifts as well as enhancement with conditioning (Figure 5–10).

However, some disagreement exists concerning the functional interpretation of these changes at the cortex. Using human subjects, Jouvet (1957)

HABITUATED          CONDITIONED          PRE-DISTRACTION

DISTRACTION

POST-DISTRACTION

MEM-3          50 μ VOLTS

I SEC.

FIG. 5–10.   Click-evoked potentials recorded from the auditory cortex of cats deprived of middle-ear muscles. The first column shows potentials taken from a cat in the 'habituated' state. The middle column shows enhancement of evoked potentials produced by the reinforcing of selected clicks with a puff of air directed at the cat's face. The last column shows evoked potentials recorded immediately before, during, and after visual distraction. (From "Evoked Cortical Potentials in Absence of Middle Ear Muscles," Moushegian, G., *et al.*, *Science*, Vol. 133, p. 282. 24 Feb. 1961. Copyright 1961 by the American Association for the Advancement of Science.)

and Garcia-Austt *et al.* (1964) found that the visual evoked responses to flash stimuli were enhanced in amplitude when the subjects were required to attend to and count the flashes. On the other hand, Horn (1960) recorded flash-evoked responses in the visual cortex of cats, both when the cat was watching a mouse and when it was resting. He found that when the cat was watching the mouse responses were attenuated, and when it ignored the mouse the amplitude of the responses remained high. Horn proposed therefore that diminution in evoked responses might indicate increased rather than reduced sensitivity in the appropriate region. Callaway *et al.* (1965) obtained results from human patients pointing to the same conclusion. They found that when the subjects were attending to auditory stimuli, they manifested a decrease rather than an increase in the auditory evoked response. A further conflicting result was obtained by Van Hof *et al.* (1962) who report that attending to and counting flash stimuli did not affect the amplitude of the evoked response to the flashes.

FIG. 5–11. Computer-averaged cortical evoked potentials for equal numbers of detected and missed signals in two human subjects. (From "Attention, Vigilance and Cortical Evoked Potentials in Humans," Haider, M. A., *Science*, Vol. 145, pp. 180–82, 10 July 1964. Copyright 1964 by the American Association for the Advancement of Science.)

Lindsley and his co-workers suggest that these conflicting results (in the human case) may have been due to differences in the methods by which an attentive set was established in the subjects. Some tasks also involve a degree of distraction of attention from the test stimuli (such as may occur if numerical calculation is required). In a situation which they felt minimized this factor, Spong, Haider and Lindsley (1965) required subjects to make perceptual discriminations. They recorded cortical evoked responses to flashes and to clicks, and found that when attention was directed toward the visual stimuli the responses to flashes evoked from the occipital area were larger and when attention was directed to the auditory stimuli the responses to clicks evoked from the temporal area were larger. Earlier, Haider, Spong and Lindsley (1964) found that signal detection performance in a vigilance task was associated with a reduced amplitude of visual evoked responses at the cortex (Figure 5–11). It is evident from these careful studies that close attention must be paid to behavioral variables in order to reach agreement on this question.

# 6

# EMOTION I

## WHAT IS EMOTION?

The word "emotion" is not itself amenable to precise definition. As pointed out by Mandler (1962), it is rather to be regarded as a "Chapter-heading term" which, in common with other such terms, does "no more than collect under one rubric what are believed to be related phenomena, experiments and observations. . . . The collection of these instances has no clearly definable boundaries; it arises historically and empirically, with the structure of the boundaries rarely spelled out, and, most frequently, appreciated intuitively." The study of emotion, therefore, consists in the investigation of various classes of events, such as emotional experiences, the environmental events which arouse emotion, behavior during emotional states, and so on. In this chapter we shall investigate the physiological changes which occur during emotional states. There are a large variety of conditions which are generally classified as emotions. These include for example love, joy, euphoria, hate, pity, disgust, sadness, fear and rage. However physiological psychologists studying emotion have been concerned mainly with fear and rage, since these are most readily produced in animals.

## Manifestations of Fear and Rage

The somatic manifestations of fear and rage, as is well known from common observation, include running, immobility, fighting, tremor, crying and screaming, to mention a few. A large number of autonomic changes accompany these states, including for instance changes in blood pressure, size of pupil, heart rate, skin temperature, respiration, salivary secretion, sweating, and gastrointestinal activity. Both the sympathetic and parasympathetic divisions of the autonomic nervous system are involved in these effects, though the sympathetic nervous system plays a predominant role on the whole (Gellhorn and Loofbourrow, 1963). Various endocrine changes also occur, notably the increased secretion of epinephrine by the adrenal medulla and the release of ACTH by the adrenal cortex. The electroencephalogram in emotion displays a pattern indicating a high degree of arousal, and Lindsley (1951) has emphasized the role of the reticular activating system in emotion.

## THE JAMES-LANGE THEORY AND THE ROLE OF AUTONOMIC AROUSAL IN EMOTION

It is apparent that in emotional states a high level of autonomic activity accompanies the emotional feeling. One of the major questions which has exercised psychologists of emotion is how these two conditions, i.e., the autonomic arousal and the feeling state, are related. Sherrington (1906) put the question thus:

Does (1) the psychical part of the emotion arise and its correlate nervous action then excite the viscera? Or (2) does the same stimulus which excites the mind excite concurrently and *per se* the nervous centres ruling the viscera? Or (3) does the stimulus which is the exciting cause of the emotion act first on the nervous centres ruling the viscera, and *their* reaction then generate visceral sensations; and do these latter, laden with affective quality as we know they will be, induce the emotion of the mind? On the first of the three hypotheses the visceral reaction will be secondary to the psychical, on the second the two will be collateral and concurrent, on the third the psychical process will be secondary to the visceral.

Basically, the James-Lange theory of emotion is hypothesis (3). It proposes that emotional feeling is produced by and is secondary to the autonomic discharge generated by the stimulus. James also included motor responses along with autonomic discharge as determiners of emotional feeling. Thus, for instance, our feeling of fear is our awareness of the bodily changes such as dryness of the mouth, muscular tremor, and so on, which are part of the state of fear.

If this hypothesis were correct, then depriving an organism of information as to the state of its peripheral autonomic and somatic apparatus should result in a lack of emotional feeling. However there are cases where injury to nervous pathways prevents the patient from feeling his body reactions, yet the patient nevertheless reports emotional states. Related experiments have been performed on animals. Sherrington (1906) demonstrated that dogs deprived of a considerable proportion of their sensory input would still manifest emotional behavior (anger, joy, disgust, fear). It could be argued against such animal studies that the hypothesis under discussion is one correlating feeling or introspectible states with autonomic and motor responses, and that this is only possible with human subjects. This objection is well taken if one is concerned only with James' original formulation. However, others have adapted his hypothesis to propose an effect of autonomic discharge on emotional behavior as well as on introspectible states, and the animal studies do argue against this amended hypothesis.

Some have argued against the objection based on interference with the nervous system, that before these lesions were made, central events had been conditioned together through the mediation of peripheral autonomic responses, and that once such conditioning had taken place the peripheral autonomic changes were no longer necessary. To test this hypothesis, it would be necessary to deprive animals of autonomic information very early in life, so that such conditioning would not have a chance to take place. It should be pointed out in this regard that a dog described by Sherrington was very young when tested, and had never before had a chance to display one emotion that it was tested for: that of disgust for dog's flesh, which is a highly specific emotion.

A further criticism of the James-Lange theory, put forward by Cannon (1929), is that the visceral changes apparent in various emotional states do not differ sharply, as might be expected on this hypothesis. In fact, Cannon argued, the visceral discharge accompanying emotion is diffuse, and could not form the basis of our clearly differentiated emotions. Following such objections, attempts were made to correlate different patterns of visceral discharge with different emotional states. Ax (1953) and Schachter (1957) found that fear and anger were correlated with a similarly high level of autonomic arousal, but that they differed on some indices. Wolf and Wolff (1947) were able to observe physiological responses of the stomach wall in a patient with a gastric fistula. They found that fear and anger were correlated with different visceral patterns. However, not enough work has been done on this problem to state with confidence that fear and anger can be reliably differentiated on this basis. In addition, these studies do not elucidate whether the visceral changes were caused by, or themselves caused, the emotions.

Another line of criticism stems from work by Mandler (1962) and his co-workers, who concluded on the basis of various experiments that although people may be aware of a rather diffuse and global condition of emotional arousal, they are unable to discriminate discrete changes in autonomic discharge. If we are unable to detect such differences, they argue, it is difficult to see how they could form the basis of clearly differentiated emotions.

Further studies point to the conclusion that autonomic arousal influences emotional states in a rather global and diffuse fashion. Marañon (1924) injected patients with epinephrine which mimics the action of the sympathetic nervous system. He found that some patients reported that they felt "as if" they were experiencing some emotion such as fear or happiness. A few experienced genuine emotion as a result, when reminded of emotion-arousing subjects. In a well-controlled study, Schachter and

Singer (1962) report that injection of epinephrine was found to invoke states of enhanced emotion, which were either anger or euphoria, depending on the social situation the subject was in. This effect depended on the subjects not being correctly informed of the autonomic effects of the drug. It appears therefore that the subjects, unless informed otherwise, interpreted the autonomic effects of the drug as part of their feelings of emotion.

Schachter and Wheeler (1962) injected subjects with epinephrine, a placebo, or chlorpromazine (a sympatholytic agent). The degree of amusement which these subjects then displayed to a slapstick movie was found to be correlated with the degree of sympathetic activation produced by the injections.

Singer (1963) reports that rats given epinephrine showed more fear than controls in fear-producing situations, but that there was no difference in situations which were not fear-producing. An analogous effect of depression of fear by chlorpromazine was also found.

These experiments indicate that the level of autonomic arousal does generally affect the degree of emotion manifest, though generalized autonomic arousal alone does not appear to produce specific emotions. It might be pointed out that epinephrine, besides mimicking the action of the sympathetic nervous system, also has various effects on the central nervous system. The effect of epinephrine on emotion may therefore be due to any of several factors. Of course, this does not invalidate the hypothesis that its effect on emotion is due to its sympathetico-mimetic action.

## THE SYMPATHETIC NERVOUS SYSTEM
## AND AVOIDANCE LEARNING

The adrenal medulla secretes epinephrine and norepinephrine, and this activity is controlled entirely by pathways from the sympathetic nervous system. Conditions of stress, such as cold, pain, anxiety, exercise, or anoxia, will greatly increase this activity. Epinephrine and norepinephrine themselves mimic the action of the sympathetic nervous system.

Several learning theorists believe that the activity of the autonomic nervous system is a vital link in the processes underlying avoidance learning. Mowrer (1950) suggests that autonomic responses produced by a noxious UCS become conditioned to a neutral CS by a process of classical conditioning. These autonomic responses themselves produce stimuli (SD), the termination of which is reinforcing to the animal. The animal therefore learns by instrumental conditioning to terminate those unpleasant SD which occur in the presence of the CS, by performing whichever act removes the CS. In this way the animal avoids the UCS. Mowrer considered the SD produced by noxious stimuli and conditioned to the CS to be exclusively autonomic. Now since the secretions of the adrenal medulla have an effect mimicking the action of the sympathetic nervous system, removal of the medulla should remove a large number of these SD and so should retard avoidance learning (since the degree of SD reduction should determine the degree of learning).

However, experiments investigating the effects of adrenal demedullation on avoidance conditioning have yielded conflicting results. Moyer and Bunnell (1959) performed a bilateral adrenal demedullation on a group of rats and found that this group did not differ significantly from operated or nonoperated controls with respect to number of trials to criterion or number of shocks during avoidance training in a shock alley. Nevertheless Levine and Soliday (1962) found using a shuttle box that with efficient training procedures adrenal demedullated rats did perform fewer avoidance responses than did controls. Also Caldwell (1962) reports that demedullated mice trained in a shuttle box before operation and then tested for retention took longer to reach criterion and showed longer latencies at first than did operated or nonoperated controls when they were first tested.

Other workers have studied the effects of injection of epinephrine on fear-motivated behavior. Kosman and Gerard (1955) injected rats with epinephrine and then tested them for escape and avoidance responding in a shuttle box. A decrease in the frequency of escape and avoidance responses was noted, but the authors considered the effect due to general debilitation caused by the drug. Moyer and Bunnell (1958) report that injections of epinephrine did not alter the acquisition of a CAR. However, Latané and Schachter (1962) conclude that if the correct dosage is given, a facilitation of avoidance learning can result from epinephrine injection. Rats injected with a·weak dose learned an avoidance response more quickly and effectively than did placebo-injected rats, but rats given a heavy dose did not differ significantly from placebo-injected rats.

In another experiment to test the importance of the autonomic nervous system in avoidance conditioning, Wynne and Solomon (1955) effectively blocked the peripheral autonomic reactions of dogs by various procedures, and trained them in a shuttle box. These animals were retarded both in their escape and avoidance of shock, though they could in fact learn. The authors conclude that autonomic responses play an important role in avoidance conditioning, but that aversive SD must also be produced in other ways.

A recent study by Wenzel (personal communication) is of particular importance in this regard. It has been reported (Cohen, 1960; Levi-Montalcini and Booker, 1960a) that a protein extract of mouse salivary glands, called the nerve growth factor (NGF), causes hypertrophy of sympathetic ganglia when injected into newborn mice. Levi-Montalcini and Booker (1960b) showed that an antiserum to the growth factor had the opposite effect: when injected into infant mice it caused gross underdevelopment of the sympathetic ganglia. It appears that such mice are indistinguishable from normal controls in every way, except that their peripheral sympathetic nervous system is grossly depleted. They are therefore ideal subjects for an experiment on the role of the sympathetic nervous system in conditioning, since it appears that other portions of their nervous system have not been interfered with.

Wenzel injected a group of mice daily for the first eight days after birth with this antiserum. Two and one-half months later they were trained in a shock-avoidance and a food-getting task. Practically no difference was found between the performance of this group of mice and that of saline-injected controls. This preliminary study is therefore evidence against the importance of autonomic arousal in avoidance behavior.

The suggestion that avoidance learning is critically dependent on the degree of autonomic arousal related to a fear state is not without difficulties on other grounds. Some have found that when measures of fear are taken at various stages of learning and extinction, they do not correlate with what should be expected on such a hypothesis. Kamin *et al.* (1963) for instance observed the suppressive effect of the CS in a Skinner box at various stages of acquisition and extinction of a shuttle box avoidance response. They found that subjects which had been trained to a moderate extinction criterion were still very fearful of the CS. The decline in fear seemed to be an effect rather than a cause of the extinction procedure. They write: "The data on the whole reveal a considerable lack of parallelism between fear and instrumental behavior." Using heart rate as an index of autonomic behavior during avoidance acquisition and extinction, Black (1959) also describes a lack of parallel between autonomic and behavioral responses during extinction.

## THE ADRENAL CORTEX AND AVOIDANCE LEARNING

The adrenal cortex secretes various steroids which are important for the maintenance of health and in combating the effects of stresses of various kinds, including cold, heat, pain, and infection. Bilateral removal of the adrenal cortex results in a very much greater susceptibility to all kinds of trauma. Adrenal cortical function is controlled almost completely by ACTH released from the pituitary. Almost any environmental change will increase the secretion of ACTH, including cold, heat, pain, fright, and infections.

Since fear is a potent stimulus to ACTH secretion, psychologists have been interested in the consequences of increasing or reducing the degree of adrenal cortical activity on fear-motivated behavior. For instance, Solomon and Wynne (1954) propose two ways in which neuroendocrine discharge might enter into the process of avoidance learning. Firstly, they propose that such a discharge is part of the pain-fear reaction to aversive stimuli, which also includes autonomic discharge, skeletal motor discharge, and higher nervous activity. This neuroendocrine discharge, they suggest, results in chemical feedback, the termination of which is reinforcing to the animal. They in effect espouse a two-factor theory such as that of Mowrer, except that they also assign a role to feedback stimuli other than autonomic. Secondly, in order to explain the extreme resistance to extinction displayed by animals after avoidance conditioning, they propose that avoidance training results in a permanent increase in the probability of occurrence of an anxiety reaction in the presence of the conditioned stimulus ('the principle of partial irreversibility'). They suggest that the action of the adrenal cortex may play an important role in this permanent change which they propose takes place in the central nervous system. Selye (1950) also proposes a "General Adaptation Syndrome" characterized by a permanent partial reorganization of hormonal functioning under conditions of stress.

The body of experimental evidence, however, has not led to any definite conclusions concerning this hypothesis. Mirsky *et al.* (1953) found that monkeys injected with ACTH showed less fear-motivated inhibition of a bar-press response for food than controls. Also monkeys injected with ACTH during extinction of a habit acquired to avoid shock showed more rapid extinction than controls. However, Murphy and Miller (1955) found, using a shuttle box procedure, that rats given ACTH during conditioning took significantly longer to extinguish than did controls. No significant effect was found on the number of trials to criterion however, and the administration of ACTH during extinction was found ineffective. Miller and Ogawa (1962) tested adrenalectomized rats and found that ACTH administration during learning delayed extinction of the avoidance response in this group too; and, as with Murphy and Miller's experiment, there was no effect on conditioning. Since these rats were adrenalectomized the authors conclude that ACTH must have exerted its effect through some extra-adrenal mechanism.

Moyer (1958) showed that animals subjected to bilateral total adrenalectomy were not retarded in the performance of an escape response, as compared with operated and nonoperated controls. Furthermore, Levine and Soliday (1960) made lesions in the median eminence of the tuber cinereum in the hypothalamus, which has the effect of blocking ACTH release to trauma (McCann, 1953) though constant amounts of ACTH continue to be secreted. They found that lesioned subjects paradoxically showed *superior* avoidance learning in a shuttle box, and suggest that a high degree of anxiety may make learning less efficient and that secretion of ACTH during stress may actually be a disadvantage in such situations. An alternative interpretation of these results is that the lesions made the animals hyperactive; but even if this were correct, the experiment still shows that releasing ACTH during stress does not appear of vital importance in learning situations.

## THE LIMBIC SYSTEM

The term "limbic system" refers loosely to a group of structures and their interconnections thought to be concerned with the development and elaboration of various emotions. Though different writers vary in their definition of the exact scope of the system, the structures involved generally include: the cingulate and hippocampal gyri, hippocampus, orbitoinsulatemporal polar region, amygdala, septum, hypothalamus, epithalamus, and the dorsomedial and anterior thalamic nuclei. Other terms such as "rhinencephalon," "olfactory brain" and "visceral brain" have also been employed to refer generally to the same group of structures. Historically the term "limbic system" derives from Broca's term "limbic lobe" which he employed to refer to the cingulate and hippocampal gyri. These regions have recently been held to be important components of the anatomical substrate of emotion.

Papez (1937) first emphasized the possibility that some anatomical "circuit" involving limbic structures may underlie emotional thought and expression. He wrote:

The central emotive process of cortical origin may then be conceived as being built up in the hippocampal formation and as being transferred to the mammillary body and thence through the anterior thalamic nuclei to the cortex of the gyrus cinguli.

He thus hypothesized a circuit underlying emotion which ran as follows: hippocampus—fornix—mammillary bodies—mammillothalamic tract—anterior thalamic nuclei—thalamocortical radiations—gyrus cinguli.

The basis for Papez's choice of these structures rested mainly on a few clinical observations. For instance in rabies, a disease characterized amongst many other things by emotional outbursts, brain lesions occur in the hippocampus (as well as in other areas). He also cites a case report of the association of degeneration in the gyrus cinguli with emotional outbursts. But in spite of this paucity of evidence, his hypothesis gave rise to a vast amount of animal experimentation, involving stimulation and ablation of these and related structures. As other regions of the brain were also found by these experiments to be implicated in emotional processes, various attempts were made to elaborate and subclassify this ever-growing group of related structures and interconnections.

Maclean (1949) was one of the first to elaborate the Papez circuit. Later, different investigators tended to include different structures and classify them along different principles. Brady (1958, 1960) divided limbic structures into three main groups. The first group, the paleocortical or allocortical portions of the system, comprised those surface structures meeting the criteria for "cortex" suggested by Rose and Woolsey (1948), and included the hippocampus, pyriform lobe and the olfactory bulb and tubercle. The second group, the juxta-allocortical portions of the system, intermediate between the phylogenetically old and phylogenetically young cortex, included the cingulate gyrus, presubiculum and frontotemporal cortex. The third group was made up of subcortical structures, and included the amygdaloid complex, septal region, certain portions of the thalamus and hypothalamus, and also perhaps the caudate nucleus and the midbrain reticular formation.

Pribram and Kruger (1954) subdivided the limbic system according to a different principle, this time by olfactory connections. The first group, termed rhinal, consisted of structures with direct connections with the olfactory bulb. These included the olfactory tubercle, area of diagonal band, prepyriform cortex, and corticomedial nuclei of the amygdaloid complex. The second group, termed paleol, consisted of structures with

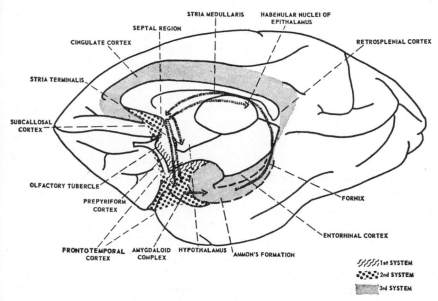

FIG. 6–1. Mediobasal surface of the monkey brain, showing limbic structures classified into three systems according to olfactory connections. (From Pribram, K. H., and Kruger, L., 1954, Annals, The New York Academy of Sciences, 58: 109–38, p. 116.)

direct connections with the first system but none with the bulb, and included subcallosal and frontotemporal juxta-allocortex, septal nuclei of the amygdaloid complex, and "olfactory" portions of the corpus striatum. The third group, termed hippocampal-cingulate, consisted of structures with direct connections with the second system but none with the bulb or with the first system, and included Ammon's formation, and the entorhinal, retrosplenal, and cingulate juxta-allocortex (Figure 6–1).

It should be pointed out, however, that though there is some usefulness at present to be derived from classifying these limbic structures in an orderly fashion, a "true" classification of the system as it is involved in emotion can only be arrived at after the exact nature of the involvement of each of these structures and their interrelations in emotional processes has been thoroughly understood. At present we are far from this goal. We shall now investigate what is known from stimulation studies of the involvement of central nervous structures in fear and rage.

## STIMULATION STUDIES

## Midbrain and Diencephalon

Stimulation of various regions in the midbrain and diencephalon has been found to give rise to reactions of fear and rage. Using lightly anesthetized cats, Ranson and Magoun (1933) obtained spitting movements upon stimulation of the subfornical component of the medial forebrain bundle. Magoun *et al.* (1937) obtained in the lightly anesthetized cat and monkey coordinated facial and vocal activity closely resembling that occurring during the expression of unpleasant emotion in the normal animal, when they stimulated the central grey matter and tegmentum of the midbrain, and also certain hypothalamic areas. In the unanesthetized cat, Hess (1928) obtained various manifestations of rage from brain stem areas. Masserman (1941) produced rather stereotyped and undirected rage manifestations from the hypothalamus. Later Hess and Brugger (1943) and Hess, Brugger and Bucher (1945) obtained from the perifornical nucleus and preoptic area of the hypothalamus and the ventral septal region complex manifestations of rage during which the animal would effectively direct its attack. Ingram (1952) found that stimulation of the dorsomedial nucleus of the hypothalamus gave rise to expressions of rage. Spiegel, Kletzkin and Szekely (1954) produced defensive behavior when they stimulated the periaquaductal grey matter and neighboring areas. Delgado, Roberts and Miller (1954) obtained a fear-like reaction in cats upon stimulation of the superior part of the tectal area and the lateral nuclear mass of the thalamus. Maclean (1957) found that chemical stimulation in the region of the central grey would produce a furious animal.

Some have observed a distinction between brain stem placements yielding flight and those yielding aggression. Hess (1954) reports that stimulation of the posterior hypothalamus yielded flight and more anterior placements yielded rage. Hunsperger (1956) obtained in the cat an aggressive reaction from the perifornical region of the hypothalamus and also from the central grey matter of the midbrain. These two regions he found to be surrounded by a larger common field from which flight responses were obtained (Figure 6–2). Nakao (1958) reports in the cat that aggressive responses were generally elicited from sites in the middle hypothalamus and flight reactions from rostral hypothalamic or preoptic sites.

Roberts (1958a) also divides aversive responses elicited from the brain stem into two main groups. The first, which he termed "flight," was obtained upon stimulation of a small area in the posterior hypothalamus.

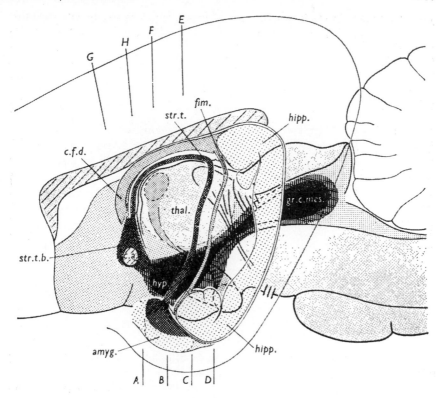

amyg.        amygdala
c. a.        commissura anterior, anterior commissure
c. f. d.     columna fornicis descendens, descending column of the fornix
fim.         fimbria
gr. c. mes   griseum centrale mesencephali, central gray matter of the mesencephalon
hipp.        hippocampus
hyp.         hypothalamus
str. t.      stria terminalis
str. t. b.   stria terminalis bed
thal.        thalamus

FIG. 6–2.  Regions in the forebrain and brain stem of the cat from which affective responses were obtained by Hunsperger (1956) and de Molina and Hunsperger (1959). Two saggital levels are plotted in this one figure. (From de Molina, A. F. and Hunsperger, R. W., 1959, courtesy of *J. Physiol.* 145.)

The second, which he termed "alarm," and which included a much more heterogeneous group of responses, could be obtained from placements scattered widely through the midbrain and diencephalon (Figure 6–3). Roberts (1962) obtained fear-like behavior upon stimulation of the cat thalamus. He classified these responses into three groups: a visual searching response, a pain-like response (elicited mainly from the postero-ventral nucleus), and a crouching response (elicited mainly from a region around the dorsomedial nucleus).

| | |
|---|---|
| ▮ | "FLIGHT" POINTS USED IN AVOIDANCE TESTS |
| ▯ | OTHER "FLIGHT" POINTS |
| ◆ | "ALARM" POINTS USED IN AVOIDANCE TESTS |
| ◊ | OTHER "ALARM" POINTS |
| Χ | POINTS ELICITING LITTLE OR NO EMOTIONAL BEHAVIOR |
| ? | POINTS RESEMBLING BOTH "FLIGHT" AND "ALARM" |

FIG. 6–3. A series of frontal sections through the diencephalon and midbrain of the cat, showing sites yielding 'flight' and 'alarm' responses. (From Roberts, W. W., *J. Comp. Physiol. Psychol.*, 51, Courtesy of the American Psychological Association.)

The dissociation between the two different types of effect obtained by these various authors is not complete. Hess (1957) reports that with the same stimulation, one type of reaction may be transformed into another. Also Hunsperger (1959) found that increasing the intensity of the stimulation in the same placement may sometimes change an aggressive reaction to one of flight or the other way round. Nakao (1958) writes that in some animals the reaction appeared mixed, including both attack and escape elements. Also, the fear and rage areas suggested by the various authors differ considerably, and there is considerable overlap in the pooled results. Further caution should be added in view of the report (de Molina and Hunsperger, 1959) that the individual character of the animal may affect the type of response obtained: a timid cat would tend to show flight, for instance. Since reported findings represent the pooled effects obtained from many animals, it is difficult to say how much this factor of individual differences may have influenced results. Nakao, who used 50 cats, reports that only in three animals could he elicit either flight or aggression depending upon which placement was used, and this is a very small number.

## The Interpretation of the Effects

*1. Are "True" Rage and Fear Produced by This Stimulation?*  Masserman (1941, 1943) claimed on the basis of his observations on hypothalamically elicited "fear" and "rage" responses that stimulation merely evoked the motor manifestations of fear and rage, and that the reactions did not indicate true emotionality. He gave various reasons for this:

a) An animal made "aggressive" by hypothalamic stimulation would not appropriately direct its attack, neither would an animal thus made "fearful" appropriately direct its escape.

b) The induced reaction ceased abruptly and completely upon cessation of the electrical stimulus.

c) The stimulus, while inducing the reaction, would not also inhibit any other behavior in which the animal was indulging. A cat would continue to lap milk, clean itself, and purr in response to petting while at the same time exhibiting the motor and autonomic manifestations of rage and fear.

d) No conditioned reaction to a light or sound stimulus could be obtained after it had been paired for a very large number of times with the hypothalamic stimulation.

He therefore concluded (1941) that "the activity induced by hypothalamic stimulation is mechanical, diffuse, stereotyped, stimulus-bound, and seems to carry no greater emotional connotation than would the contraction of a skeletal muscle induced by the stimulation of an efferent nerve."

However, the findings of later investigators are on the whole at variance with those of Masserman. An animal stimulated in this way would be provoked to a well-directed attack on the experimenter (Hess and Akert, 1955; Akert, 1961; Nakao, 1958) or would make well-directed attempts to escape (Nakao, 1958; de Molina and Hunsperger, 1959). After cessation of the stimulus the threshold for angry behavior remained at a low level for a longer period (Hess and Akert, 1955), and mewing and snarling often persisted after discontinuation of the stimulation (Nakao, 1958). Eglin (1953) (reported by MacLean, 1955) found (corroborating Masserman's findings) that animals receiving injections of physostigmine and acetylcholine in the lateral and posterior groups of nuceli in the hypothalamus also showed hissing, growling, and other manifestations of aggressive behavior while at the same time licking the examiner's face between growls. However Nakao (1958) reports that a hypothalamic stimulus too weak even to cause overt responses repeatedly caused a cessation of other behavior—e.g., the animal would stop lapping milk.

Furthermore a number of recent studies have shown that such hypothalamic stimulation may indeed serve as an unconditioned stimulus in conditioning experiments. Cohen *et al.* (1957) point out that in the usual avoidance conditioning situation the unconditioned stimulus, such as pain, produces an innate response on which the conditioned reaction may be based (e.g., electric shock applied to the feet induces running or jumping). They therefore selected for their experiment only those animals which included locomotor behavior of the running and jumping kind as part of their response to the hypothalamic stimulation. They then demonstrated that animals would learn to shuttle from one compartment to another in response to a tone in order to avoid the hypothalamic shock. They noted further that presentation of the CS would evoke generalized agitation in these animals.

Nakao (1958) found that after many presentations of a buzzer followed by hypothalamic stimulation, the buzzer alone induced various signs of agitation. Animals learned to escape from a compartment in which the hypothalamic stimulation had been given and to avoid a dish of milk in the observation cage when this had been associated with stimulation. Further, animals which had learned to push a paddle to escape and avoid shock to the feet pushed the paddle on the first trial that hypothalamic stimulation was administered. Earlier Delgado et al. (1954) reported that stimulation of brain stem areas which elicited a fear-like reaction in cats could motivate the performance of a response previously established to avoid shock. Such animals would also learn to escape from a compartment in which they had been stimulated, and to avoid food which had been associated with the stimulation. Delgado et al. (1956) also found that stimulation of various subcortical structures in the monkey, including the amygdala and central grey matter, elicited a previously learned avoidance response.

It has been suggested (Akert, 1961) that the reason why Masserman failed to obtain conditioning to hypothalamic stimulation may have been that this stimulation set up afterdischarges antidromically in the hippocampus. Such hippocampal seizures have been shown to disrupt learning.

Another possibility as to why Masserman's animals would not react to a conditioned stimulus is that the hypothalamic stimulation may have been rewarding as well as aversive. Roberts (1958a) reports that animals with "flight" placements would not show an emotional reaction to a CS, nor would they learn a response to avoid the stimulation. They would, however, learn to escape it. In contrast, "alarm" placements did elicit avoidance learning. Roberts (1958b) then showed that stimulation of "flight" placements was also rewarding to the animals, and concluded that this was probably the cause of the lack of avoidance. Bower and Miller (1958) also produced rewarding along with aversive effects when they stimulated placements in the middle to anterior portions of the medial forebrain bundle.

Finally, various investigators (e.g., Hunsperger) have reported that in addition to placements yielding integrated defense reactions, other placements have yielded various components of aversive responses, such as growling, without eliciting the whole pattern. It is possible that Masserman was studying these borderline placements. In sum, it appears that stimulation of some placements yields reactions which appear to have the properties of a true emotion, and with other placements there is some doubt about this.

2. *The Causes of such "Rage" and "Fear" Reactions.* Assuming that true fear and rage can be produced by stimulation of at least some brain stem loci, there are two main possibilities to account for this. The first is that some central mechanisms specifically concerned with fear and rage are being stimulated, and the second is that these effects are due to pain or some other unpleasant sensation. If the latter were the case, then these findings would be more relevant to the study of central somesthetic mechanisms than to the study of emotion. On the other hand, if the sensory explanation could be effectively discounted, it would look as though we were tapping regions which are normally excited in the presence of certain stimuli (such as the sight of a predator or prey) to produce behavior connected with fear and aggression. Of course nothing definite can be concluded about an animal's sensations. This is where stimulation studies on human patients provide us with valuable information.

The hypothesis that these emotional responses are due to pain has been examined by several investigators. With stimulation of these areas it is always possible that current spread to structures such as the dura, blood vessels, or classical pain pathways might cause pain; or that pain pathways as yet uninvestigated are being stimulated. Miller (1961) describes an animal in which a rage reaction was evoked upon stimulation, and in which the tip of the electrode was later found to be below the base of the brain. Further, the exact course of the nervous pathways mediating sensation including pain is still unclear (see Sweet, 1959; Perl, 1963), but it appears diffuse and may well include several of the regions from which emotional responses have been elicited. And some workers have actually concluded that their effects probably were due to pain. An animal when hurt displays a characteristic set of reactions which an experimenter may come to recognize. Such reactions have been reported from hypothalamic stimulation in cats and monkeys by Karplus and Kreidl (1928), by Spiegel *et al.* (1954) in cats upon stimulation of the mesencephalic tectum, and by Delgado (1955) in the monkey upon stimulation of the lateral part of the tegmentum, central grey, posteroventral nucleus of the thalamus, crus of fornix and posterior hippocampus.

Further evidence that stimulation of the midbrain tegmentum may produce pain arises from human studies. Spiegel and Wycis (1961) report that after lesions involving a large area of the spinothalamic system (the classical pain pathway), stimulation a few millimeters ventrally, apparently in the midbrain tegmentum, elicited conscious pain sensations. Also Reyes *et al.* (1951) found that stimulation of the mesencephalic tectum produces pain in patients.

However, others have concluded that the reactions they obtained from animals upon stimulation in these areas were definitely not pain-suggestive. For instance, a description which is often chosen of a cat so stimulated is that it behaves as if confronted with a dog, or barking dog (Hess, 1957; Hunsperger, 1959). But this does not exclude the possibility of a sensory artifact of some sort. Different unpleasant sensations may give rise to different behavioral reactions. Consider for instance the development of an intense itch, or a feeling of suddenly being too hot. One sensation might make an animal feel that another animal is responsible, and so make it attack the nearest object in sight, and another might make it want to run away. This possibility should especially be considered if we bear in mind that some brain stem areas yielding defense and flight responses overlap with areas yielding other types of response. For instance, with stimulation of the preoptic area of the hypothalamus, "the animal then behaves as if exposed to a rather high ambient temperature" (Akert, 1961). Sneezing, retching and vomiting also occur from regions overlapping with some of the areas evoking affective responses.

Roberts (1958a) reports that animals with "alarm" placements showed very variable behavior, with a number of interfering effects, and suggests a possible sensory explanation for effects obtained from these regions. Behavior elicited from "flight" placements however did not give this impression.

In human patients, although White (1940) reports no sensory changes resulting from hypothalamic stimulation, Heath and Mickle (1960) write that the patients report "marked discomfort" in the form of tachycardia, flushing, etc., resulting from stimulation.

Perhaps the answer is that with some placements the effect is due to sensory phenomena, but that with other placements this is not so. Placements in the anterior hypothalamus investigated by Roberts and Kiess (1964) appear to be related directly to aggression. Stimulation of these regions caused normally placid cats to attack rats ferociously, and during such stimulation, cats would learn a Y-maze to obtain a rat which they could attack, i.e., the performance of the attack was positively reinforcing. With regard to fear, a recent experiment by Deutsch and Howarth (1962) indicates that stimulation of certain placements is related to fear motivation, and here it is very difficult to see how a sensory artifact could account for the results. Deutsch and Howarth first trained rats to press a lever to obtain brain stimulation, and then held them away from the lever until they lost interest. They then found that fear-producing stimuli (buzzer and shock) recalled the rat to the lever (though its pressing on these occasions never produced further brain stimulation), and also increased rates of lever-pressing for long periods. This occurred often in animals with tegmental placements but infrequently in animals with hypothalamic placements. The authors conclude that "electrical self-stimulation in some sites may be caused by an activation of mechanism underlying normal fear and escape."

## Amygdala

Manifestations of fear and rage have also been obtained upon stimulation of the amygdala. Kaada, Anderson, and Jansen (1954) obtained these manifestations when they stimulated the lateral part of the basal nucleus and the lateral nucleus. Ursin and Kaada (1960) obtained an attention response, and fear and rage effects, from the basal and lateral nuclei and also from an area extending medially through the area of the central nucleus and into the internal capsule. Magnus and Lammers (1956) implicated the central, medial, basal and mediobasal nuclei in emotional responses. Shealy and Peele (1957) implicated basal, lateral, central and medial components. Wood (1958) obtained emotional responses from basal and central nuclei. de Molina and Hunsperger (1959) produced affective responses from the dorsal portion of the basal nucleus and adjacent parts of the central nucleus and medial nucleus, i.e., in a field from which several components of the stria terminalis arise. They also traced affective reactions along the pathway of the stria terminalis into the bed nucleus of this tract at the level of the anterior commissure. At this level, they report, the field spreads out and joins the region producing emotional effects in the hypothalamus and midbrain (Figure 6–2).

Opposite effects have however also been reported. Anand and Dua (1956) found that amygdaloid stimulation in some cases had a quieting effect on animals. In one case sleep was produced. Fonberg and Delgado (1961) report that in some cases amygdaloid stimulation appeared to make cats friendlier and less hostile. Egger and Flynn (1963) write that in some cats normal mousing was blocked by amygdaloid stimulation. Also hypothalamically elicited attack of rats was blocked by amygdaloid stimulation. Amygdaloid placements producing these effects were found in the medial portion of the lateral nucleus and the magnocellular portion of the basal nucleus. However in other regions, noticeably in the area of the dorsolateral portions of the lateral nucleus, electrical stimulation facilitated the attack response.

Various investigators have claimed that regions yielding fear and rage are to some extent topographically separate. Ursin and Kaada (1960) conclude that the two areas yielding fear and rage run approximately parallel in a medio-dorso-caudal direction. Fear results from stimulation in an area extending from the rostral part of the lateral nucleus and the preamygdaloid area through the region of the central nucleus. Anger is induced from more ventro-medial, and caudal regions. Both zones extend into the internal capsule (Figure 6–4). They write, "In our experience fear and rage have been obtained from the same electrode on two occasions only." Magnus and Lammers (1956) report that fear occurred from the periamygdaloid area and the central, medial and mediobasal nuclei. Anger was elicited from the medial nucleus and the ventral part of the basal nucleus. Shealy and Peele (1957) obtained an escape reaction from basal

| a. amyg. a. | area amygdalae anterior, anterior area of the amygdala |
| caps. int. | capsula interna, internal capsule |
| clans. | claustrum |
| cort. pyr. | cortex pyriformis, pyriform cortex |
| f. rhin. | fissura rhinalis, rhinal fissure |
| n. trac. olf. lat. | nucleus tracti olfactorii lateralis, nucleus of the lateral olfactory tract |
| tr. opt. | tractus opticus, optic tract |
| v. lat. | ventriculus lateralis, lateral ventricle |

FIG. 6–4.  A series of frontal sections through the amygdala in the rostro-caudal direction showing points yielding 'attention', anger, fear and combined effects. (From Ursin, H. and Kaada, B., 1960, by permission of *EEG Clin. Neurophysiol.* 12.)

and lateral components and a few central placements and a rage reaction from medial and central areas.

Others have concluded that no such topographical division exists. de Molina and Hunsperger maintain that points yielding flight lay scattered between those yielding rage, the former being much less common than the latter. Some have gone even further and asserted that fear or rage may be elicited from the same placements. Gastaut *et al.* (1952) report that attention occurs with low stimulation, fear and flight with higher intensities, and rage with intensities which are higher still.

### The Interpretation of These Effects

As was discussed for brain stem stimulation, the question arises as to whether the induced fear and rage may be secondary to some unpleasant

gl. pal.                    globus pallidus
hip.                        hippocampus
n. bas. amyg.               nucleus basalis amygdalae
n. bas. amyg. p. lat.       nucleus basalis amygdalae pars lateralis (large celled portion
n. bas. amyg. p. med.       nucleus basalis amygdalae pars medialis (small celled portion
n. caud.                    nucleus caudatus, caudate nucleus
n. cent. amyg.              nucleus centralis amygdalae
n. interc. amyg.            nucleus intercalatus amygdalae
n. med. amyg.               nucleus medialis amygdalae

Fig. 6–4—Continued

sensation caused by the stimulation. In a large proportion of cases, stimulation of the amygdala produces fear or rage also accompanied by other effects, such as micturition, defecation, spitting, salivation, motor effects, behavior resembling an attempt to eject a foreign body from the mouth or throat, and so on. Magnus and Lammers point out that licking movements obtained upon weak stimulation may change into gagging and vomiting with higher intensities and finally to flight and attack with the highest intensities.

One argument against the sensory explanation is that these supplementary effects are also elicited from regions outside those producing affective reactions (de Molina and Hunsperger, 1959; Ursin and Kaada, 1960). This argument is not entirely conclusive however, since the degree of resultant distress might be the factor determining whether or not the animal will react emotionally.

In some cases the effects may be caused by unpleasant hallucinations. Ursin and Kaada (1960) write that anger elicited from rage placements "seemed to be directed towards something imaginary." Extracts quoted by

Magnus and Lammers from their protocols include: "Looks as if she were seeing something." "Shrinks back to the Lt. and tends to turn over to the Lt. as if she had a disagreeable hallucination."

*The Possibility of Seizures.* Naquet (1954) has pointed out that stimulation of the amygdala may give rise to an electrical after-discharge projected to the septum, hypothalamus, and parts of the cortex. Such a discharge may produce various autonomic and motor phenomena and also sometimes growling and fear manifestations. Injection of alumina cream into the amygdala will produce spontaneous seizures which mimic clearly the effects of stimulation, including the fear manifestations. Amygdaloid stimulation will also sometimes trigger hippocampal seizures which may give rise to fear and rage manifestations.

One should be able to decide on behavioral grounds whether fear symptoms produced by stimulation are actually the result of a seizure process. With seizures, the behavioral symptoms occur after a delay and may considerably outlast the stimulation. The animal underreacts to external stimuli and its fear does not appear to be related to any object in the environment. This fits some descriptions of stimulated animals, but other experimenters report symptoms which arise and cease concomitantly with the stimulation, during which time the animal is prone to attack any object in its environment. It therefore appears that only some fear and rage symptoms resulting from amygdaloid stimulation are due to a seizure process.

## Hippocampus

Fear and rage reactions have been produced by some upon stimulation of the hippocampus (Kaada, Jansen and Anderson, 1953; Gastaut *et al.,* 1952; MacLean and Delgado, 1953), though negative results have also been reported (Liberson and Akert, 1955). DeMolina and Hunsperger (1959) write that the hippocampus is on the fringe of the area which produces affective reactions, and only marginally yields emotional responses.

Delgado (1955) obtained pain-suggestive responses in monkeys upon stimulation of the posterior hippocampus and crus of fornix. Kaada *et al.* (1953) favor an interpretation in terms of hallucinations for the affective reactions which they evoked upon hippocampal stimulation in cats. The animals would direct their attention towards something imaginary, and there was a diminished reactivity to actual stimuli in most cases. The possibility that these effects are due to seizure discharge is very strong.

## Neocortex

Fangel and Kaada (1960) obtained definite manifestations of fear and flight in cats upon stimulation of a few points in the lower ends of the posterior sylvian, ectosylvian, and suprasylvian gyri, and from some placements in the cingulate cortex. Rage was never obtained from cortical placements by these experimenters. Sano (1958) also reports anxiety and fear in cats upon stimulation of the posterior suprasylvian gyrus, but not rage. A much lower proportion of "affective" placements was found in this area as compared with the amygdala. Kaada, Jansen and Anderson (1953) obtained behavioral effects upon stimulation of the cingulate and hippo-campal gyri similar to those found for the hippocampus and fimbria. Finally Anand and Dua (1955) found that stimulation of the temporal tip in cats and monkeys produced "irritability." Stimulation of the posterior orbital surface of the frontal lobe produced viciousness in cats only for placements very near the tip of the temporal lobe. Stimulation of other placements in this area both in cats and monkeys made the animals very quiet. Stimulation of the anterior cingulate gyrus produced irritability in monkeys and intense rage in cats.

However, since high intensities are necessary to produce "affective" responses from the cortex as opposed to the amygdala and the brain stem, one cannot be certain that these cortical structures are really responsible for the effects (Hunsperger, 1959).

## Temporal Lobe Stimulation in Patients

The responses of patients to brain stimulation are particularly enlighten-ing since they provide introspective reports as well as behavior to study. Such reports may help us to decide whether the fear and rage manifesta-tions observed in animals are due to direct activation of fear and rage mechanisms, or whether they are secondary to some unpleasant sensation or hallucination.

During operation, epileptics have been found frequently to report feelings of fear upon stimulation of parts of the temporal lobe. Such feelings appear to be a genuine result of the stimulation, and not due to a general fear of the operative procedure since they occur only with stimulation of some regions, and not others. Such effects have been obtained from the anterior and inferior surfaces of the temporal lobe (Penfield and Jasper, 1954; Penfield, 1958; Roberts, 1961). In contrast, anger and other types of emotion were not evoked.

Jasper and Rasmussen (1958) found practically no emotional responses upon stimulation of the amygdala and hippocampus. However, sensory responses, sometimes unpleasant, were often produced. They concluded from these findings that the amygdala and hippocampus are not important integrating centers for emotional experience. Pampiglione and Falconer (1960) further report that out of 17 patients suffering temporal seizures, stimulation of the hippocampus evoked fear or rage in none. Sensory effects occurred sometimes.

In contrast, Chapman et al. (1954) and Chapman (1958) describe feelings of fear and anxiety upon amygdaloid stimulation in four out of five epileptic patients. Assaultiveness was never obtained even though the patients were spontaneously assaultive. Heath and Mickle (1960) report reactions of both fear and rage resulting from stimulation of the amygdala and rostral hippocampus in schizophrenics. Heath *et al.* (1955) found that in one schizophrenic woman the evoked response, using the same placement and the same parameters of stimulation, was variable, sometimes fear being elicited and sometimes rage.

### Interaction with the Patient's Illness

The advantages of being able to obtain introspective reports from patients undergoing electrical brain stimulation are qualified by the fact that all such patients are seriously ill. The responses of schizophrenics should be viewed with suspicion since their spontaneous speech and behavior are very abnormal. Further, many have affirmed that temporal lobe stimulation only produces psychical responses in patients who had previously had epileptic discharges in the temporal lobe (Baldwin, 1960; Penfield and Jasper, 1954; Jasper and Rasmussen, 1958). Stimulation of the temporal cortex even in patients with epileptic foci in the parietal or frontal lobe does not result in such responses. It has also been observed that the responses emitted by these patients may closely resemble those forming part of the patient's seizure pattern, though this is only sometimes true. This does not necessarily mean that such data obtained from epileptics do not shed light on normal function. It may simply be that epilepsy renders the cortex more susceptible to stimulation, and the results obtained may genuinely reflect the function of these regions under normal conditions. This is especially so when a good topographical agreement between different types of response can be shown upon comparing results from different individuals.

## CLINICAL STUDIES OF BRAIN PATHOLOGY

Emotional changes have been shown to occur in patients with brain lesions caused by various factors including physical trauma, infections, disease, and hereditary and other disorders.

Encephalitis Lethargica is an example of an infectious disease which produces acute emotional changes. This disease affects the whole of the central nervous system in small disseminated foci, but particularly affects the brain stem (Von Economo, 1931). In its acute form great apathy is often manifest, and lack of emotion also occurs often in its chronic form. Outbursts of extreme emotion can also appear. In rabies, which also produces lesions located mainly in the brain stem, extreme emotional outbursts occur too.

Patients with tumors involving the hypothalamus and surrounding structures may show emotional changes. Alpers (1937) describes a patient with extensive destruction of the hypothalamus who became very aggressive and defensive. Cushing (1932) reports cases of tumors in the pituitary region which were accompanied by emotional changes such as periods of fright or emotional negativism. A case of a tumor involving the chiasm and spreading into the ventricle was associated with extreme symptoms of rage, such as shrieking, clawing and scratching, alternating with periods of somnolence. From another point of view, Gibbs (1956) correlated abnormalities of electrical activity in the brain with various abnormalities of behavior and concluded that the presence of rage was correlated with abnormal activity assumed to emanate from the thalamus and hypothalamus. However, it should be stressed that emotional changes are not listed amongst the most common symptoms produced by hypothalamic lesions (Le Gros Clark *et al.* 1938).

Zeman and King (1958) note that a clinical syndrome of hyperemotionality including outbursts of violence and constant crying may be associated with tumors of the anterior midline structures, especially the septum pellucidum and the fornix.

Patients with brain disease involving frontal tissue often show outbursts of emotionality. In addition, a pathological appearance of frontal tissue was found by Slocum *et al.* (1959) to be associated with symptoms of extreme anxiety and depression. Ackerly and Benton (1948) describe a case of bilateral frontal lobe defect in which the patient was unable to form any but superficial and transient emotions.

In psychomotor epilepsy, which results from seizure discharges originating in the mesial temporal region, feelings of fear may occur at the start of an attack (Macrae, 1954; Weil, 1956; Williams, 1956). Such ictal symptoms of fear have been shown not to be due to fear of the oncoming fit or to any other such circumstance, but to occur simply in isolation as auras, analogous to the somatic, gustatory or other sensations which may occur at the onset of an attack. Rage has only rarely been reported to occur as an aura (Gastaut *et al.*, 1955). However, aggressive behavior often appears once the attack is in full swing. This may be related to the finding that stimulation of the amygdala only very rarely causes aggression in patients, even those about to be operated for intractable assaultativeness (Chapman, 1958, 1960). Perhaps for aggression to occur, the discharge must spread from the amygdala to other structures.

Patients suffering from psychomotor epilepsy often exhibit personality disturbances which may be described as in some ways the reverse of the Kluver-Bucy syndrome (see Chapter 7): a tendency to explode into violent anger, loss of sexual urge, and appetite disturbances (Gloor, 1960). This may result from a continuous irritative process due to the lesion.

Finally, in view of the many though divergent findings on limbic system structures, a report of normal mentality associated with gross anatomical defects in rhinencephalic areas is of special interest. Nathan and Smith (1950) report the case of a man who died of cancer and who before death was intensively studied as part of a program concerned with operation for the relief of pain. He was intelligent, sociable and popular, and appeared perfectly normal both intellectually and emotionally. When he died and his brain was examined it was found, however, that in place of a corpus callosum and gyrus cinguli there was an irregular mass of white matter covered by overlying grey matter. The fimbria and fornix were absent, as was the septum pellucidum. The amygdala was grossly abnormal. The hippocampus was very small and abnormal and its only efferent pathway was to its fellow on the opposite side. This well-documented study demonstrated that at least in one individual a number of limbic structures are not indispensable for emotion.

# 7
# EMOTION II: ABLATION STUDIES

## EARLY ABLATION AND TRANSECTION STUDIES AND THE PROBLEM OF SHAM RAGE

Early experimenters investigated emotional changes resulting from extensive ablation or transection procedures. The early preparations were classified into two main groups: (*a*) *Decorticate preparations* typically (Dusser de Barenne, 1920; Rothman, 1923; Cannon and Britton, 1925; Bard, 1928) exhibited fully fledged rage responses which were, however, poorly directed. These responses would often occur not only to noxious stimuli but also to normally innocuous stimuli such as those produced by light stroking. (*b*) *Decerebrate preparations* (Woodworth and Sherrington, 1904; Bazett and Penfield, 1922) did exhibit signs of rage, sometimes even to normally innocuous stimuli (Keller, 1932) but their repertoire of response was limited compared with that of decorticate preparations.

Later, full-scale experiments utilizing large numbers of animals were carried out, in order to define more precisely the nature of the emotional changes resulting from various lesions. From such studies Bard and his collaborators arrived at the following generalizations:

1. Bilateral removal of neocortex alone induces a state of extreme placidity.

2. Further destruction of certain forebrain structures, even ablations large enough to include most of the diencephalon, produces a ferocious animal, with much lower rage threshold than normal, but with poorly directed attack.

3. This integrated rage response may be elicited in preparations with extensive forebrain damage, provided the caudal half of the hypothalamus remains intact. When this is removed, as in the decerebrate preparation, the rage response becomes more circumscribed, less well integrated, and of higher threshold.

4. The lower the level of decerebration, the more fragmentary the rage response becomes (Bard and Macht, 1958).

Bard and Mountcastle (1948) concluded that destruction of the amygdaloid complex and the transitional cortex of the mid-line was crucial to whether or not decortication rendered an animal placid or ferocious. They therefore concluded that the cortex normally exerts an inhibitory (as well as facilitatory) influence on rage-provoking mechanisms in the brain stem, this inhibitory influence being mediated via the amygdaloid complex and transitional midline cortex. When this inhibitory influence is removed the rage threshold is lowered.

Bard adopted the term "sham rage" (introduced by Cannon and Britton, 1925) to describe animals with a lowered rage threshold resulting from decortication. He explained (1934) that the term "sham" was chosen

FIG. 7–1. Diagrams showing the extent of lesions produced in cat 4. Solid black: regions removed in the first and second operations, which resulted in a state of placidity. Stippled areas: regions left intact in the first and second operations but ablated in the third operation, which produced a state of ferocity. (From Bard, P. and Mountcastle, V. B., 1948, courtesy *Res. Publ. Assn. Nerv. Ment. Dis. 27.*)

not as a behavioral description but because the conscious aspects of emotion are assumed to be missing in animals without neocortex. However, the term is really generally employed to refer to a characteristic group of symptoms. Bard and Mountcastle (1948) present a vivid description of such an animal, whose lesions are shown in Figure 7–1.

When the cat was lifted from her cage she growled, spat and bit. Light pinching of the skin of her tail, flank or back produced growling, spitting, biting and striking, acceleration and deepening of respiration, marked dilatation of pupils, and piloerection. In her poorly directed attack she bit herself viciously.

From the second day after the third operation until she was sacrificed 160 days later, *Cat 4* invariably responded to the most trifling disturbance by a savage exhibition of rage. Tactile, pressure and vibratory stimuli were equally effective in eliciting all the motor phenomena which make up the full expression of feline anger. Merely placing a hand lightly on her flank or back produced hissing with lips retracted and tongue curled, growling, flattening of the ears, tail-lashing, acceleration of respiration, dilatation of pupils, erection of hair over tail or back, and profuse sweating from the the toepads. Any stimulus of the body extremities or tail greater than a gentle stroke evoked in addition savage biting and striking with unsheathed claws. If the stimulus was applied to the tail or near the midline of the body the attack was directed forward or downward and sometimes she bit her forepaws. When it was applied well to one side of the midline she turned a little to the stimulated side but never sufficiently to reach the source of the stimulation. The threshold for effective tactile stimulation was higher around the neck, occiput and top or sides of the head than over the trunk, tail and extremities. A light puff of air directed at her face sufficed to provoke spitting, growling, retraction of ears, widening of pupils, piloerection, and the assumption of a belligerently defensive stance, but this reaction was not produced by tapping her on the nose. The cat occasionally hissed in the absence of any apparent external stimulus but we never observed any spontaneous development of an integrated rage reaction. . . .

Provided she was in her cage, tapping it always elicited several definite signs of anger. The same response could be obtained by knocking on a table when she was sitting or crouching on it. We were never able to induce any sign of pleasure. Stroking her back or lightly rubbing her head or cheeks invariably caused growling and spitting.

One explanation of decorticate sham rage, alternative to that of a release of rage mechanisms from cortical inhibition, is that the changes observed are really sensory in origin, and that these animals are hyperalgesic. Human cases of hyperpathia resulting from subcortical lesions present a picture with various relevant features (see Chapter 9). Often the response to noxious stimulation is greatly exaggerated, and a discrete stimulus such as a pinprick may give rise to a very disagreeable diffuse sensation localized over a large area of the body. Later, stimuli not usually considered painful at all, such as light touch and vibration, may produce this same intense disagreeable sensation. In some cases a state of perpetual intense pain may develop. In comparison, sham rage preparations exhibit rage to normally innocuous stimuli; the rage reaction is typically poorly localized (which may indicate a diffuse sensation); and different parts of the body have different "rage thresholds." The animals' reactions appear at times more appropriate to pain than to rage: they were described on occasion as licking themselves, and as biting themselves rather than their environment. Such animals would also constantly rub themselves. The stimulus threshold for rage often became progressively lower, until sometimes the animal would bite itself constantly. Finally, although most of these preparations were bilateral, Bard and Rioch (1937) do report several animals with unilateral ablations which exhibited a lower rage threshold only to stimuli on the ipsilateral side. Cat 244, for instance, which sustained ablation of the right cortex, exhibited violent rage upon light mechanical stimulation of the right side. The threshold, though low over the entire right half of the body, was especially low at the ear and the feet. Stimuli adequate to evoke the reaction on the right side failed to do so on the left.

If decorticate sham rage phenomena are really due to sensory changes, then the notion of a cortical inhibitory influence on brainstem rage mechanisms should be reexamined. Perhaps future experimentation will elucidate this further.

## LESIONS IN VARIOUS BRAIN STRUCTURES AND THEIR EFFECTS ON EMOTIONALITY

### Midbrain

Kelly, Beaton and Magoun (1946) found in cats that lesions in the central grey matter of the midbrain and adjacent parts of the tegmentum produced a specific loss in certain kinds of emotional response. Facio-vocal expression of negative emotions was greatly impaired, whereas other ways of expressing these emotions, such as clawing and flight reactions, were preserved, as were other facio-vocal activities such as purring. Recent experiments of Hunsperger (1956) and deMolina and Hunsperger (1962) on the cat indicate that midbrain structures are indeed critically involved in fear and rage. They found that after bilateral lesions in the midbrain region from which hissing was obtained upon stimulation, hissing could no longer be elicited from the hypothalamus. Further, a unilateral lesion in this midbrain area suppressed ipsilaterally but not contralaterally the aggressive response obtained upon stimulation of the amygdala. Finally, bilateral lesions in this region produced a permanent impairment of naturally elicited aggressive reactions. Since this placidity did not occur with similar lesions in the hypothalamus or amygdala, deMolina and Hunsperger conclude that the central grey of the midbrain is of supreme importance in the elicitation of defensive behavior.

### Hypothalamus

Lesions involving various parts of the hypothalamus have been found to produce either a loss in emotional responsiveness, or an increase in fear and rage reactions, or no emotional changes. Such differences can to some extent be correlated with the locus of the hypothalamic lesion.

Bard considered the presence of the caudal half of the hypothalamus to be of critical importance for the elicitation of a well-integrated rage response. This conclusion was arrived at as a result of observations on large numbers of animals in which varying amounts of forebrain had been removed (Bard, 1928, 1934; Bard and Rioch, 1937). Bilateral lesions in the caudal hypothalamus have been found by others (Ranson, 1939; Ingram et al., 1936) to produce a loss in emotional responsiveness, in addition to somnolence and depression of general activity. Masserman (1938, 1943) reports similar findings. He cautions, however, that animals in this condition suffer gross impairment of bodily functions, so that this loss in emotional responsiveness is difficult to evaluate. This is especially so since those animals which survive long enough to reestablish their bodily functions to nearly normal levels also recover emotionally.

Others have described animals with large circumscribed hypothalamic lesions which can exhibit well-integrated rage reactions. Kelly, Beaton and Magoun (1946) report that two cats in which the hypothalamus was completely destroyed at the mammillary level exhibited growling, crying, and spitting to nociceptive stimulation; and pupillodilatation, retraction of the nictating membranes, piloerection, spitting and striking movements in the presence of barking dogs. Magoun and Bard (quoted by Bard and Mountcastle, 1948) observed three cats with very extensive hypothalamic lesions which displayed "vigorous well-integrated rage reactions."

In an earlier experiment Keller (1932) produced a "typical rage response" in what was essentially a pontile animal, this differing from the normal only in that the "somatic effectors are not coordinated into an escape or defensive pattern." This, he remarks, is only to be expected in an animal which "lacks sight, hearing, smell, and the ability to localize disturbances at the periphery." The threshold for rage in such an animal was found to be very low, since it was evocable by gentle handling and even the animal's own sneezing. From such experiments it appears that hypothalamic mechanisms are not indispensable for the elicitation of rage.

DeMolina and Hunsperger (1962) also conclude that hypothalamic mechanisms are less critical than midbrain mechanisms in the elicitation of rage. They observed that bilateral lesions of the hypothalamic zone which yielded hissing upon stimulation abolished the electrically induced affective response obtained from the amygdala, but did not abolish the response obtained from the midbrain (Hunsperger, 1956). In contrast, midbrain lesions abolished the response from the hypothalamus. A unilateral hypothalamic lesion produced an ipsilateral suppression of the pattern evoked from the amygdala. However, naturally evoked aggressive behavior was unaffected by such lesions, in contrast with midbrain lesions.

Wheatley (1944) describes a dramatic increase in ferocity in cats with lesions in the ventromedial nucleus of the hypothalamus. Similar results were obtained by Anand and Brobeck (1951) on rats. Wheatley suggests that the ventromedial nucleus usually exerts an inhibitory influence on rage-producing mechanisms. Hunsperger (1959) however favors the possibility that the effect is due to a chronic irritative effect of the lesion on structures from which fear and rage may be elicited. Wheatley himself doubts the irritative hypothesis since the effect is long-lasting, but this is not conclusive, since permanent irritative scars can be formed.

## Thalamus

The dorsomedial and anterior nuclei of the thalamus project to the granular cortex of the frontal lobe and the cingulate gyrus respectively;

these areas are of special interest to neurosurgeons concerned with
providing relief from various neurotic and psychotic symptoms (see
below).

### Anterior Thalamic Nuclei

Schreiner et al. (1953) report that destruction of the anterior thalamic
nuclei in the cat produced an elevated rage threshold and overly solicitous
responses to pleasurable stimuli. However, Brierley and Beck (1958) found
no such changes in either the cat or the monkey.

### Dorsomedial Nuclei

Although Spiegel et al. (1949, 1951) observe that a reduction in
aggressiveness and anxiety results from lesions in the dorsomedial nuclei in
animals as well as in patients, Schreiner et al. (1953) found increased
irritability and rage to result in cats. Chow (1954) obtained no behavioral
changes as a result of bilateral lesions in the dorsomedial nuclei (but his
lesions were small). Pechtel et al. (1955) stress that the preoperative and
postoperative treatment of the subjects are crucial in determining the
ultimate effects of such a lesion. On the whole, increased aggressiveness
seemed to occur only if the cats had been made experimentally neurotic
before operation. Also, regular contact with other cats and human beings
after the operation led to increased friendliness which was not shown by
animals kept in isolation. Brierley and Beck (1958) write that bilateral
dorsomedial lesions in cats produce no changes in emotionality. However,
the same lesions in the monkey produce hyperactivity, loss of fear
reactions, and distractibility together with a vacant facial expression. They
conclude that the symptoms observed appear to be those characteristic of
the frontal lobe syndrome, therefore justifying the attention of those
interested in therapeutic effects of lobotomy and similar procedures.

## The Temporal Lobe

Kluver and Bucy (1937) found that bilateral anterior temporal lobectomy in monkeys results in a variety of extraordinary behavioral changes.
(These were first noted by Brown and Shäfer, 1888, but later forgotten.)
These changes include (1) a loss of fear and rage reactions; (2) changed
dietary behavior often described as "indiscriminate," for instance the
monkeys, usually frugivorous, would eat all kinds of meat; (3) an increase
in sexual activity and also "perverted" sexual behavior; (4) hypermetamor-
phosis, or a tendency to attend to and if possible touch all things seen; (5)
a tendency to examine all objects by mouth; and (6) visual agnosia, or an
inability to recognize the meaning of objects presented visually.

Faced with this wide variety of symptoms resulting from one extensive ablation, other investigators have attempted both to separate the different symptoms anatomically by making more discrete lesions, and also to explain the various symptoms by postulating a change in a single underlying factor. A dissociation of the symptoms by anatomical means has not been very successful. There is, however, some evidence that visual agnosia may be separated from the loss of fear and rage reactions. Lesions in the ventrolateral portion of the temporal lobe produce considerable impairment in visual discrimination, seemingly alone (Mishkin, 1954; Mishkin and Pribram, 1954). Orbito-insulatemporal lesions or more restricted anteromedial lesions appear to produce the other components of the Kluver-Bucy syndrome without impairment of visual discrimination (Pribram and Bagshaw, 1953, Walker *et al.*, 1953). However Akert *et al.* (1961) found that in monkeys, ablations restricted to the neocortical gyri of the temporal lobe and in which encroachment on rhinencephalic structures was functionally insignificant, produced a partial Kluver-Bucy syndrome, including psychic blindness, oral tendencies, and a taming effect. However, in this case the symptoms other than psychic blindness diminished considerably after three months.

## The Amygdala

It is now generally believed that the structure most critically involved in the emotional (along with some other) changes in the Kluver-Bucy syndrome is the amygdala. Lesions in the amygdala (which also usually damaged the pyriform area in the cat and the uncus in the monkey) have been observed by many to result in increased tameness. This has been found true for rats (Anand and Brobeck, 1952; Woods, 1956), cats (Shreiner and Kling, 1953, 1956), lynxes and agoutis (Schreiner and Kling, 1956), and monkeys (Rosvold *et al.*, 1954; Weiskrantz, 1956; Schreiner and Kling, 1956).

However, ablation of the amygdala has also been found to result in entirely opposite changes. Spiegel *et al.* (1940) and Bard and Mountcastle (1948) report a drastic increase in aggressiveness resulting from bilateral amygdalectomy. Wood (1958) observed the same effect with discrete bilateral lesions in the basal and central nuclei of the amygdala. (Interestingly, these were the structures found by the same author to produce fear and rage when stimulated.)

Extensive amygdaloid ablations have been reported by others to produce no change in overt emotionality. King (1958) makes this observation in the rat, though he suggests that his animals may not have been emotional enough initially for a taming effect to become manifest. Hunsperger (1959) also found that extensive lesions in the amygdala produced no change in emotionality.

A complex result has recently been obtained by Ursin (1965a). He found that in wild cats, flight behavior was significantly reduced by small bilateral lesions in the flight zone of the amygdala, previously mapped by stimulation experiments (Chapter 6, Figure 6-4). However, no significant correlation was obtained between lesions of the previously mapped defense zone and a reduction of defensive behavior, though such a reduction was also obtained. However, in tame cats neither type of behavioral change was noted.

Various explanations for these discrepancies have been put forward. For instance, it has been suggested that the symptoms resulting from amygdalectomy are really due to inadvertent damage to other structures. Hunsperger (1959) suggests that concomitant damage to the pyriform area may be a critical factor. In support of this is the finding of Adey *et al.* (1956) who observed that damage to this area leaving the amygdala intact produces tameness. However, Wood (1958) reports that discrete lesions in the pyriform cortex result in no behavioral changes.

Green, Clemente, and de Groot (1957a) emphasize that amygdalectomy may interfere with the blood supply to the hippocampus, producing damage which may in turn render the animal prone to hippocampal seizures. Such seizures may include manifestations suggestive of fear and rage (see Chapter 6). Indeed Green *et al.* (1957b) observed that bilateral lesions in the amygdala and surrounding tissue produced increased aggressiveness only in those animals which developed seizures, and in all of these there was extensive hippocampal involvement. In addition, these animals appeared hyperesthetic to peripheral stimulation.

Schreiner and Kling (1954) observed that animals made initially placid by amygdalectomy became hostile at the onset of hypersexuality, and suggest that this may be the basis for the reported discrepancies. However, as Gloor (1960) points out, Bard and Mountcastle's cats were not hypersexual, so this cannot wholly explain the differences.

Other writers have stressed that the emotional changes produced cannot simply be described in terms of "increased" or "decreased" aggressiveness or fear. In a study on dogs in which there were extensive lesions in the pyriform area and hippocampus in addition to the amygdala, Fuller *et al.* (1957) found that different tests yielded very different results. For instance, though these operates would not take the initiative and start a fight with other animals, they were capable of fighting as fiercely as the controls when aroused. Again, though they tended to keep away from people, they did not display various submissive forms of behavior usually associated with such timidity. Similarly Rosvold *et al.* (1954) report that amygdalectomy in monkeys results in all the subjects appearing more aggressive in the individual cage situation. However in the group cage situation two out of three animals fell from top to bottom of the hierachy.

The preoperative and postoperative treatment of the animals have also been considered crucial (Masserman and Pechtel, 1956). In the experiment of Rosvold *et al.*, though two operates fell from top to bottom of the hierarchy, the third appeared more aggressive. This animal had been dominant for the longest time, and was after operation confronted with only submissive animals. Weiskrantz (1956) has also emphasized the importance of the way animals are treated in the postoperative recovery period. If the animals are constantly "tested" for reactivity to noxious stimulation for instance, the constant unpleasant stimulation could make them become very wild. He suggests also that the effect of amygdalectomy may be mainly cognitive. The animals may find it difficult to recognize reinforcing stimuli as such, whether they be positive or negative. Sometimes this difficulty may be apparent in overgeneralization, as when an animal attempts to ingest anything or copulate with anything. On the other hand, it may also be manifest in an absence of response to normally fear- or rage-producing stimuli.

This cognitive hypothesis is attractive since it purports to explain other effects of amygdaloid lesions simultaneously with the resultant loss of fear and rage. Schwartzbaum (1960) carried out an experiment demonstrating that amygdalectomized monkeys did not react to a change in the degree of reinforcing value of stimuli as did normals. The amygdalectomized monkeys did not show the usual change in rate of lever-pressing when the amount of reward was changed. However, a lack of emotionality could also have accounted for Schwartzbaum's results, as he points out. One difficulty with the cognitive hypothesis is that it does not explain why the amygdalectomized animal tends to eat *more* things but be afraid *less*, for instance, rather than eat less and be afraid of more; that is, the *direction* of the changes is not explained. Perhaps this could be related to the difference between autonomous drives and drives depending on peripheral stimulation for their arousal. Eating is not dependent on peripheral stimulation but fear and rage are. Sex is to some extent, but considerably less so than fear or rage.

### Combined Lesions Involving the Amygdala and Other Structures

*Amygdala and Ventromedial Nucleus of the Hypothalamus.* In an experiment by Schreiner and Kling (1953) one male cat, rendered docile by amygdalectomy, later sustained lesions of the ventromedial nucleus of the hypothalamus. The effect of this second lesion was to make the animal very ferocious. However Anand and Brobeck (1952) report that one rat, made ferocious as a result of lesions in the ventromedial nucleus, and which then sustained lesions in the lateral group of amygdaloid nuclei, was rendered quite tame by the second operation.

The above studies obviously did not employ enough animals for any definite conclusions to be drawn from them. In a larger study by Kling and Hutt (1958), four cats rendered ferocious by bilateral lesions in the hypothalamus, three of them in the ventromedial nuclei, sustained bilateral amygdalectomies. The second lesion in no way reduced the ferocity of these animals. Also cats which had been rendered tame by lesions of the amygdala were rendered ferocious by the superimposition of bilateral hypothalamic lesions.

These findings set a limit to the number of possible hypotheses concerning the functions and interactions of these two structures with regard to fear and rage. One hypothesis consistent with the findings is that the amygdala exerts an inhibitory influence on structures in the ventromedial nucleus and that this nucleus in turn inhibits other structures responsible for the elicitation of fear and rage. The results of single unit studies also indicate that the amygdala may exert an inhibitory influence on the ventromedial nucleus. Sawa *et al.* (1959) write that stimulation of the lateral, medial, and intermediate nuclei of the amygdala in cats caused either an inhibition of single unit firing in the ventromedial nucleus or a transition of the responses from inhibition to facilitation, usually depending upon the characteristics of the stimulus. However, with repetitive stimulation of the amygdala the effect on single unit discharge in the ventromedial nucleus became much more strongly inhibitory. Evidence of other interactions between the amygdala and various other hypothalamic areas is discussed in the section on stimulation studies.

*Amygdala and Septum.* King and Meyer (1958) studied the effects of superimposed septal and amygdaloid lesions in the rat. They found that rats showed a striking increase in emotionality with septal damage, and the effect of superimposing an amygdaloid lesion (mainly the lateral and basal nuclei were damaged) was to suddenly reduce this hyperemotionality to approximately preoperative levels. When the first lesion produced was in the amygdala, this had the effect of preventing the appearance of a full-blown septal syndrome.

*Amygdala, Hypothalamus, and Midbrain.* On the basis of certain stimulation and lesion studies in the cat, DeMolina and Hunsperger (1962) propose a different system of interaction between the regions yielding emotional responses in the amygdala and brain stem (Chapter 6, Figure 6–2). They found that unilateral coagulation of the affective region in the midbrain suppressed ipsilaterally the affective pattern evoked from the amygdala. Bilateral coagulation of the midbrain field suppressed the pattern evoked from the hypothalamus. Unilateral coagulation of the affective field in the hypothalamus also suppressed ipsilaterally the pattern evoked from the amygdala. However, unilateral and bilateral coagulation of the amygdala did not affect the response obtained from the hypothalamus. Furthermore, unilateral coagulation of the stria terminalis suppressed ipsilaterally the pattern obtained from the amygdala, but did not affect the pattern obtained from the hypothalamus. In addition, coagulation of the amygdala or the hypothalamic affective region did not affect spontaneous affective behavior, whereas coagulation of the midbrain region produced placidity. On the basis of these findings, DeMolina and Hunsperger suggest that the system governing defensive behavior is organized at three levels of progressively increasing importance; the amygdala ranking lowest in the hierarchy and the affective region of the midbrain highest.

## The Hippocampal Fornix System and Septum

Ablation experiments involving the hippocampal fornix system and the septum have also produced equivocal results. Spiegel *et al.* (1940) report that lesions in the hippocampal fornix system, particularly those in which the lesions of the fornices encroached on the septum pellucidum, produced marked aggressiveness. Brady and Nauta (1953) observed that rats with septal lesions showed a significant increase in emotional reactivity and startle response. They demonstrated later however (Brady and Nauta, 1955) that these symptoms disappeared within sixty days after operation. Study of the lesions led the authors to the conclusion that the fornix and hippocampus were probably involved in these effects. King (1958) also reports that rats with septal lesions show a dramatic increase in overt emotionality. However, Rothfield and Harmon (1954) found that bilateral interruption of the fornix resulted in a definite lowering of the rage threshold only in cats in which the neocortex had been removed.

However, many negative results have also been obtained. Hippocampal ablation in rats (Brady, 1958) and cats (Bard and Mountcastle, 1948) did not lower the rage threshold. Allen (1948) observed no emotional changes in dogs following removal of Ammons horn or transection of the fornix on both sides. Destruction of the fornices produced no behavioral changes in cats (Wheatley, 1944) or monkeys (Garcia-Bengochea *et al.*, 1951). Bond *et al.* (1957) found that bilateral lesions of the septum and fornix in cats resulted in no increase in rage reactions; and Kling *et al.* (1960) report that lesions of the posterior septum, fornix, and anterior commissure did not produce even transient irritability.

One possible explanation for these discrepancies is that the regions investigated here are on the fringe of those for producing definite affective responses upon stimulation (de Molina and Hunsperger, 1959). The lesions may therefore sometimes produce chronic irritation of these areas. The sometimes reported transient nature of the emotional effects together with the variability of the findings would tend to indicate an irritative factor. The exact placement of the lesion may be an important factor determining whether such an irritative effect occurs.

Green (1960) points out that the hippocampus has an extremely low threshold for seizure discharge. In addition to other symptoms, behavior suggestive of fear and rage often occurs during such seizures, and the animal may appear hyperesthetic. Such lesions may produce an irritative scar which results in a chronic tendency to seizure discharge. Of course, if the behavioral effects under discussion occur during seizures, we cannot be sure that the hippocampus is involved in this particular behavior, since it may be initiated in some other part of the brain to which the seizure is propagated. It must also be stressed that different experiments have employed different species of animal, and some of the discrepant results may be due to anatomical differences between the species investigated.

## Temporal Ablations in Human Patients

Many unilateral ablations of the anterior temporal lobe in man have been carried out for the relief of seizures, and no significant emotional effects have resulted. Bilateral lesions in the anterior temporal area have been produced in patients with severe psychomotor epilepsy, and in patients with assaultive psychosis. A decrease in aggressiveness has been obtained in several instances (Green, Duisberg and McGrath, 1951; Pool, 1954; Terzian and Ore, 1955), though the results have been very variable. Increased rage immediately after the operation, which later subsided, was observed in some cases (Sawa et al., 1954). Other symptoms analagous to those found in animals upon similar operations have also been reported by several investigators (Terzian and Ore, 1955; Pool, 1954; Sawa et al., 1954). On the whole, however, the findings in this area have been very variable, and it is difficult to conclude much from the studies since the patients involved were all very deteriorated before operation.

## Anterior Cingulate Region

A temporary alteration in behavior, best generally described as a decrease in fear, has been reported by several investigators after anterior cingulate ablation in monkeys. Smith (1944) found this, as did Ward (1948) who also observed a lack of aggression and of affection, and a general social indifference towards other animals. Glees et al. (1950) made similar observations, stressing the general abnormality of response to animate objects, which resulted both in decreased fear and aggression, and yet also an increased tendency to act in a provocative fashion. However, Mirsky et al. (1957) report that though such monkeys appeared less fearful of man, no gross abnormalities were apparent in the group cage situation, and the animals did not appear socially indifferent. Pribram and Fulton (1954) found that the sole effect of bilateral anterior cingulate lesions was a decrease in the duration of an avoidance reaction caused by a sudden frustration.

However, increased aggressiveness and a general over-reactivity have also been observed with such lesions. Kennard (1955a) made this observation on cats, though she found the equivalent lesion in monkeys to produce a nonaggressive attitude (1955b). It has been pointed out that the lesions sustained by Kennard's animals were not really in the anterior cingulate area; however, Brutkowski et al. (1961) found a similar increase in rage in dogs resulting from lesions in the genual portion of the anterior cingulate area, and so well within the region ablated by the above experimenters. Pechtel *et al.* (1958) also found an increase in aggression and a lowered threshold for startle responses as a result of ablation of the anterior cingulate area in cats and monkeys. Brutkowski *et al.* favor the hypothesis that increased rage is here due to hyperalgesia and is therefore sensory and not emotional in origin. Their animals appeared afraid of being touched. Such an interpretation is also very consistent with the other descriptions of such animals. Smith (1944) also observed an apparent increased cutaneous sensibility and vigorous reaction to very slight cutaneous stimulation.

## Clinical Studies of Frontal Lobotomy

Following a report by Fulton and Jacobsen in 1935, that bilateral prefrontal lesions in chimpanzees may reduce reactions to frustrating situations, Moniz (1936) carried out frontal lobotomies on several mental patients, with encouraging results. Relief from anxiety was found to follow this procedure, along with a certain "flattening" of the emotions, i.e., such patients may be prone to emotional outbursts, but they are said to feel emotions less deeply and more briefly. Patients after this operation also display a general lack of perseveration.

More recently, attention has been focused on the more limited ablations of the anterior cingulate area and of the posterior orbital cortex. Following reports from animal studies that anterior cingulate ablation appears to reduce fear, this operation was performed by various neurosurgeons in place of the more extensive lobotomy procedures to provide relief for patients suffering from chronic anxiety and obsessions (Tow and Whitty, 1953; Tow and Armstrong, 1954; Le Beau, 1954; Whitty, 1955). Success has been claimed especially for the treatment of chronic anxiety. Pathological worrying was greatly reduced, and, at least according to some investigators, this was accompanied by a reduction of other associated traits, such as self-consciousness, timidity, and excessive perseveration (Tow and Whitty, 1953). No intellectual deficit resulted from these lesions, and less "blunting of personality" than occurred following standard lobotomy.

A limited ablation of the posterior orbital cortex has been attempted especially for patients who are depressed and suffer from low psychomotor activity, mainly on the basis of the finding that posterior orbital ablations cause hyperactivity in monkeys (Dax and Radley-Smith, 1943). Some success has been claimed for this procedure (Fulton, 1951).

Recently, Slocum, Bennett and Pool (1959) carried out a very thorough long-term study on 18 patients which they had selected for frontal lobe surgery. All were suffering from very severe long-term anxiety which had proved unamenable to other treatment. They claim that excellent results were obtained. Interestingly, the operation revealed a pathological appearance of frontal tissue in a high proportion of patients. The authors therefore suggest that some organic brain disease may sometimes underlie such extreme anxiety symptoms.

## LEARNING EXPERIMENTS INVOLVING LESIONS

Recently, investigators have become dissatisfied with the use of simple observation or rating scales for the detection of changes in fear-motivated behavior and have increasingly been testing animals in learning situations. They have hoped by this method to obtain a clearer picture of the nature of the resultant changes; for instance, in the case of decreased fear, whether fear responses were simply lost or whether they extinguished more rapidly, or whether perhaps the deficit was one of retention of previously learned fear responses.

However, once the animal is tested in a learning situation, many more factors must be taken into consideration in accounting for the observed changes than is necessary with simple observation. One reason why an animal may not learn an avoidance habit is that his fear and therefore his motivation to avoid has been reduced; an alternative explanation is that his general learning capacity has been rendered defective.

Another factor concerns the direction of the motivational change. When fear is extremely low, avoidance performance will obviously be inefficient. However, it appears that in some situations performance may also be less efficient when fear is very high. In a study on children, Penny and Croshery (1962) found that anxious subjects performed an avoidance response less well than nonanxious subjects. Levine and Soliday (1960) report that animals deprived of the ability to release ACTH under stress learned a shuttle box avoidance problem faster than controls, and this study also suggests that highly anxious animals may perform less well than animals which are less anxious. More specifically, in the shuttle box situation, one important factor in the acquisition of an avoidance response is that of overcoming a tendency to perform competing responses, such as freezing or leaping straight up into the air. From observation of animals in this situation it appears that those which have been made very anxious do tend to perform more of these competing responses. Therefore if a lesioned animal is shown to perform less well in a shuttle box, then in the absence of further behavioral criteria to go on, one may hypothesize that the animal is either much less frightened or much more frightened.

Another methodological point is made by Harvey et al. (1965). They found that septal-lesioned rats showed a deficit in shock-produced suppression of a lever-pressing response for water. However, the manifestation of this deficit depended critically on the strength of shock employed. They state: "had the study employed only strong shocks the lesion would have appeared to be without effect; had it employed only weak shock the lesion would have appeared to block the aversive conditioning completely. The quantitative character of the effect only appeared with intermediate shock intensities." The parameters of the aversive stimulation used are therefore of critical importance in avoidance experiments.

A further possible source of error has been emphasized in a very interesting paper by McCleary (1961). Following the findings of Kaada (1951) that stimulation of the subcallosal cortex produced motor inhibitory effects, whereas stimulation in the medial and anterior cingulate gyrus resulted in facilitation (Figure 7–2), McCleary hypothesized that subcallosal lesions should disrupt avoidance behavior under circumstances requiring inhibition of responding (passive avoidance) and that lesions in the cingulate gyrus should disrupt avoidance behavior under circumstances requiring the making of an active response (active avoidance). He indeed

::: inhibitory

+ facilitatory

FIG. 7–2. Midsaggital drawing of the cat brain, indicating the regions on the mesial cortex yielding inhibitory and facilitatory motor effects. (From McCleary, R. A., 1961, data from Kaada, B., courtesy of *J. comp. physiol. Psychol.* 54. Courtesy of American Physiological Association.)

found that when avoidance was tested by measuring the degree to which a cat was inhibited in returning to a food trough after it had been shocked while eating, animals with subcallosal lesions appeared totally incapable of inhibiting their approach response, whereas both normal and cingulate lesioned animals very quickly inhibited their response. It was shown later (Lubar, 1964) that cingulate-lesioned animals actually avoided a source of punishment for longer than normals. Yet when avoidance was tested in a shuttle box situation, cats with bilateral cingulate lesions were grossly deficient in avoidance though they exhibited clear fear responses to the CS, whereas cats with bilateral subcallosal lesions were at least as efficient as normals, and the data suggest that their performance was in fact superior.

It has yet to be clarified to what the dichotomous results found by McCleary are due. One possibility is that they are due to changes in general activity. It has been found that animals with posterior orbital ablations suffer from motor restlessness. McCleary also reports that his subcallosal subjects were hyperactive in their home cages. Such hyperactivity might prevent them from avoiding a source of shock but might if anything facilitate shuttle box conditioning. McCleary did not observe any activity changes in his cingulate-lesioned animals, though he did not test specifically for this.

Another possibility is that such lesions interfere with the animals' ability to *initiate* a voluntary movement, or else to keep still purposely to attain some end—i.e., that the deficits are in the "start" and "stop" systems (Vanderwolf, 1962). Thus an animal might be "reflexly" hyperactive but still be unable to initiate a movement to attain an end.

Thirdly, the effects may be specific to fear-producing situations. In such a situation, an animal has two innate responses: it can run or it can freeze. A lesion may increase a tendency to freeze in an avoidance situation and so interfere with the animal's ability to escape effectively, but not with its ability to passively avoid a source of food. Or the lesion may increase the animal's tendency to run rather than freeze, so that it becomes unable to inhibit a movement to avoid shock. In a related study, Hearst and Whalen (1963) report that administration of d-amphetamine facilitated discriminated avoidance performance in a lever-pressing situation. However, rates of lever-pressing in non-CS periods were unaffected. They interpret these results as due to the effect of amphetamine in breaking up freezing patterns.

Further, Vanderwolf (1963) found that rats which had been subjected to a series of electroconvulsive shocks learned a shuttle box task more readily than controls. The convulsed subjects were not hyperactive, however, and the author attributes their improved performance to the breaking up of freezing patterns by the ECS.

A further complication in the interpretation of these experiments arises from the findings that when cingulate-lesioned cats were trained in a one-way active-avoidance apparatus (instead of the shuttle box), they did not perform significantly worse than controls (Lubar, 1964). Two possible reasons for these contrasting results may be considered. Firstly, since the shuttle box task is a harder one to learn than either the passive avoidance or the one-way active avoidance tasks, the cingulate-lesioned animals may really be suffering an intellectual impairment. Secondly, it may be that freezing tendencies become particularly strong in the shuttle box situation. This is not unexpected, since in the shuttle box the animal is required to return to the compartment which it had just been required to avoid, and thus a "position conflict" is set up.

An experiment by Thomas and Slotnick (1963) makes it very likely that the explanation in terms of increased freezing in the shuttle box is correct. They conditioned sham-operated control and cingulate-lesioned rats in a double-grill box under high and low hunger drives. They found that although cingulate-lesioned rats under a low drive showed a significant deterioration in avoidance performance, cingulate-lesioned rats under a high hunger drive showed no performance deficit. It therefore appears that the hyperactivity caused by hunger counteracts the increased freezing tendency of the cingulate-lesioned animals. If their original deficit had been due to intellectual impairment, hunger should not result in improved performance.

Lubar (1964) also found that animals with cingulectomies in addition to limbic cortex-septal lesions showed normal passive avoidance. Thus the reduction in activity produced by the cingulate lesions counteracted the increase in activity produced by the limbic cortex lesions.

Other studies also point to the conclusion that cingulate lesions result in an increased tendency to freeze. Peretz (1960) reports that rats with anterior cingulate lesions required a greater number of trials to learn a shuttle box avoidance response than did sham operates. However, they performed better than normals on bar-pressing and discrimination tasks with food as the motivation. But in both the control tasks used, decreased motility may be associated with improved performance (see Maher and McIntire, 1960). Also active avoidance deficits may be due to a tendency to freeze. Thus this experiment does not argue against McCleary's hypothesis.

Thomas and Slotnick (1962) observe that in rats bilateral damage to the cingulum produced significant retardation in the acquisition of an avoidance response in a double-grill box. However maze learning was not significantly affected by the lesion. They hypothesize that this impaired acquisition of the CAR derives from an increased tendency to freeze. The worse performers in the experiment did indeed freeze more.

Another interesting approach has recently been adopted by Hunt and his colleagues (Harvey et al., 1965; Harvey and Hunt, 1965). They point out that passive avoidance tasks rely heavily on appetitive drives. In one passive avoidance measure, the CER (conditioned emotional response), a lever-pressing habit is established for a reward (e.g., water). The animal is then presented several times with a CS followed by shock. The CS soon comes to elicit a suppression of the lever-pressing rate, together with crouching and defecation. The degree to which lever-pressing is inhibited is then taken as a measure of avoidance. In other passive avoidance tasks the animal is required to inhibit its response to obtain food and water in order to avoid shock. One would therefore expect an animal's desire for food or water to affect its performance in these situations.

However, active avoidance tasks (such as shuttle box conditioning) do not also rely on appetitive drives. Supposing therefore that a lesion had the effect of making the animal more hungry or thirsty, this would reduce the effectiveness of shock in suppressing a food or water-obtaining response. However, this would not also impair shuttle box performance. It might be suggested further that the facilitation observed in shuttle box conditioning in such animals is also due to increased appetitive drive. Thomas and Slotnick (1963) found that cingulate-lesioned rats improved their shuttle box performance when they were hungry.

The hypothesis that passive avoidance deficit is secondary to increased hunger or thirst has been intensively investigated for the septum. Animals with septal lesions exhibit a diminished strength of CER and also a deficit in the suppression of lever-pressing by punishment (Brady and Nauta, 1953; Harvey *et al.*, 1961). Further, the lesions with which McCleary (1961) obtained deficits in passive but not active avoidance (his "subcallosal" group) also invaded the anterior septal region. Also Kaada *et al.* (1962) produced deficits in passive avoidance (avoidance of an electrified water dish) in rats with septal lesions. However, such animals will learn a shuttle box avoidance problem more rapidly than normals (King, 1958).

Harvey *et al.* (1965) found that septal lesions produced deficits in discriminated shock-produced suppression of lever-pressing for water reward. However, they also found that lesions in the septal region caused a consistent increase in water intake after deprivation. Furthermore, increasing the amount of water deprivation in sham-operated controls offset the differences in suppression between them and the septal animals. Harvey and Hunt (1965) showed that the effect of increased thirst on lever-pressing is manifested to a greater or lesser extent depending on the type of lever-pressing schedule used. Very careful controls are therefore necessary to establish whether or not a change in hunger or thirst occurs as a result of a lesion.

Septal lesions also increase food intake in the rat and the cat (Harvey and Hunt, 1961). A similar interpretation of the effect of septal lesions in impairing a shock-produced inhibition of responding for food therefore also appears reasonable.

Another factor to be considered in evaluating the effect of a lesion which alters avoidance responding is that of sensory changes. Harvey *et al.* (1965) measured the latency to tail flick in response to radiant heat in septal lesioned and sham-operated control rats. No differences were obtained. However, it appears that septal rats are slightly more sensitive to painful electrical shock as measured by the flinch-jump technique. Unfortunately very few studies of this nature have been performed.

## Thalamus

Studies on animals with medial thalamic lesions point to the conclusion that such lesions produce an exaggeration of the freezing component of the reaction to fear-producing stimuli.

Thompson (1963) observed in the rat that bilateral lesions in either the diffuse thalamic nuclei or the dorsomedial nucleus impaired the performance of a jumping and gripping response to avoid shock which was acquired prior to operation. However, such rats also clearly showed fear reactions to the CS in spite of not responding. It appears unlikely that this deficit was motor in origin since the majority of the subjects that failed to relearn the habit (with the exception of those with dorsomedial lesions) made many spontaneous responses.

Vanderwolf (1962) investigated the effects of lesions in the medial thalamic nuclei (including habenulae, medial nuclei of the thalamus, intralaminar nuclei, and nuclei of the midline). Animals were required to run from a black compartment into a white one within five seconds, in order to avoid shock. The lesioned animals were found quite unable to avoid shock, although they showed all signs of fear to the black box (squealing, defecating, etc.). However, they were able to *escape* shock as well as normals. They also performed better if allowed fifteen seconds to run instead of five. Such animals typically sat motionless in this situation, and if they ran, they did so with explosive suddenness. They were also shown capable of sitting still on a platform surrounded by a charged grid in order to avoid shock, so they showed no passive avoidance deficit. Yet in spite of this inability to run quickly to avoid shock, animals with such lesions tend generally to be hyperactive, and will run faster than normals to obtain food (Replogh, quoted by Vanderwolf, 1962).

Roberts and Carey (1963) studied cats with dorsomedial lesions (which also encroached on other medial thalamic nuclei). These animals displayed a considerable increase in crouching and decrease in flight attempts in classical fear conditioning. Their tendency to crouch excessively also interfered with the learning of a locomotor flight response. However, these cats did not differ significantly from controls in speed of approach to a food box.

It therefore appears from these studies that medial thalamic lesions result in an increased tendency to freeze in avoidance situations, thus producing an inefficiency in avoidance performance. This reduction in motility appears to be specific to fear-producing situations since it does not occur in food-getting tasks. A further study by Vanderwolf (1964) also demonstrates that this reduced capacity to avoid is not due to learning impairment. He found that rats with medial thalamic damage which fail on an active avoidance test will improve their avoidance performance as a result of a second lesion in the septal area. Septal lesions have the effect of making normal animals hyperactive (see above) and so would break up the freezing patterns. If the original deficit were due to learning impairment, a further lesion would not lead to an improvement in performance.

## Amygdala

The nature of the effect of amygdaloid lesions on avoidance learning is unclear. Brady *et al.* (1954) observe that amygdalectomy in cats produced an increase in the number of trials needed to learn an avoidance response in a double-grill box, though it did not impair retention of such a habit. However, King (1958) in a study on rats found that amygdaloid lesions lengthened response latencies but did not alter rates of acquisition of an avoidance response. He points out however that the task he used was simpler than that set by Brady *et al.* and so perhaps his test was less sensitive. Weiskrantz (1956) reports that amygdalectomized monkeys also tended to take longer in acquiring a conditioned avoidance response. They also extinguished more rapidly a habit acquired preoperatively, though no difference in the degree of retention of such a habit was found.

Horvath (1963) obtained different results in a study on cats depending on task difficulty. He found that cats with lesions restricted to the basolateral division of the amygdala showed a severe deficit in acquisition of a complex active avoidance response, and significant but smaller deficits in the performance of a passive avoidance response and in the acquisition of a simple active avoidance response. For the complex active avoidance response there was a very good correlation between retention deficit and damage to the basolateral nuclei. No such correlation was shown for the other tests. He therefore suggests that the basolateral nuclei are essential for the performance of an avoidance response of a high order of complexity.

However, Ursin (1965b) using different experimental procedures, arrived at a different conclusion. He found that lesions in the rostral part of the lateral nucleus and in the region containing fibers projecting from it (his 'flight' zone, Chapter 6, Figure 6-4) inpaired the acquisition of an active-avoidance response. Lesions encroaching on the medial nucleus or the stria terminalis impaired passive-avoidance.

## Hippocampus

The results of studies on the effect of hippocampal lesions on avoidance responding on the whole support the notion that increased activity is an important factor here. This increased activity may be due to increased hunger or thirst but this has not been investigated yet. On the whole, deficits have been demonstrated in passive avoidance but not in active avoidance situations.

Brady (1958) reports that lesions in the hippocampus can virtually eliminate the CER in the rat. Teitelbaum and Milner (1963) found that hippocampal rats were hyperactive compared with normal and brain-damaged controls. Others (e.g., Kim, 1960; Kaada et al., 1961) observed little if any increase in activity, but their measures of activity were different. Teitelbaum and Milner also found that these animals were unable to inhibit movement to avoid shock. The animals were unable to sit still on a "safe" platform as did normals, but instead kept jumping on and off.

Kimura (1958) reports that whether or not hippocampal animals show a deficit in a passive avoidance task depends on the exact placement of the lesion. He tested latency of running to food after the rat was shocked while eating and found that rats with lesions in the posterior part of the dorsal hippocampus were deficient in this avoidance compared with normal controls. However, those with anterior lesions showed no such difference.

Some negative results have also been obtained. Kaada *et al.* (1962) presented water-deprived rats with an electrified water dish and recorded the total number of shocks accepted by the animals. He found that though lesions in various other brain structures greatly increased the number of shocks accepted, the number received by hippocampal operates did not increase significantly. There was no significant difference found between animals with anterior and those with posterior hippocampal lesions. Kimble (1963) also found that although hippocampal rats showed less passive avoidance following shock than did normals, they did not show significantly less than did cortical-lesioned controls.

It might be expected from the above findings that in active avoidance tests hippocampals should perform if anything better than normals. This has been observed in several instances. Brady *et al.* (1954) report that cats with hippocampal lesions do not show poorer learning than normals in a double-grill box situation. Isaacson *et al.* (1961) found that when rats with extensive hippocampal lesions were tested in a shuttle box avoidance problem, they actually reached learning criteria sooner and exhibited lower response latencies than did normals.

## Frontal Lobotomy and Fear-Motivated Behavior

Various studies involving passive avoidance have been carried out in order to investigate the effect of lobotomy on anxiety. Lichtenstein (1950) reports that lobotomized dogs showed a partial or complete loss of a preoperatively acquired feeding inhibition. This may be due to a reduction in anxiety, but there are two other factors which may also account for this finding. First, prefrontal lobotomy increases feeding (Brutkowski, 1959), so the results may simply be due to increased feeding activity. Second, prefrontal lobotomy increases motility, as has been studied by several authors, including French and Harlow (1955), and this should be expected to produce a passive avoidance deficit.

Streb and Smith (1955), using the rat, measured the amount of crouching displayed after several trials to be the sound of a buzzer which terminated with shock. They found that frontal lobotomy resulted in fewer crouching responses and also a greatly increased motility score. It would therefore be difficult to conclude anything about anxiety here since this effect also may simply be due to increased motility.

Maher and McIntire (1960) carried out an experiment to test the increased motility explanation of CER reduction following frontal ablation. Rats in which a CER (immobility and defecation) had been established were subjected to bilateral frontal ablation. Postoperatively the subjects showed a loss of immobility but no loss of the defecation component. They conclude that the effect of the operation is to increase motility rather than reduce anxiety. These findings were confirmed by Maher *et al.* (1962) using a different apparatus.

In a different type of experiment, Waterhouse (1957) trained monkeys to overturn one cup to obtain food and another to avoid shock, using discriminant CSs. Prefrontal lobotomy led to a marked loss in performance accuracy for both tasks, though retraining was possible. A slightly greater effect on fear than on food responses was noted. However, since lobotomy produces an increase in food-related responses (Brutkowski, 1959) an effect on anxiety is not conclusively shown here.

Indeed Auleytner and Brutkowski (1960) claim that bilateral prefrontal lobotomy in dogs produces an increase rather than a decrease in responsiveness to noxious stimuli and defensive behavior when the classical conditioning procedure is used. However, Brutkowski (1959) also demonstrated an increased responsiveness with other types of behavior, so we cannot be sure that his effect is specifically related to fear.

In general, it appears that deficits in passive avoidance situations resulting from lesions are secondary to some effect other than on emotion. It may well be that with lesions producing an increase in passive avoidance and a deficit in active avoidance, these effects are due to an increased freezing tendency; though the exact causes of this change have yet to be elucidated.

# 8

# PERIPHERAL SOMESTHETIC
# MECHANISMS

In this chapter we shall be concerned with the physiological processes underlying the various types of sensation which are elicited by stimulation of the skin surface. These include for instance, warmth, heat, cold, touch, pressure, vibration, pain, tickle, itch and sexual feelings. Of course a much larger list could be made up of such sensations, and an even greater variety are introspectively apparent. The study of these processes is made complex by the fact that many distinct sensations cannot be identified with particular physical stimuli in any simple way. Apart from differences in the type of stimulus energy employed (such as heat, mechanical stimulation, acid), differences in spatial and temporal patterning of stimulation alone may give rise to qualitatively distinct sensations. For instance the sensations produced by stroking, itch and vibration are qualitatively distinct, yet they are all brought about by light mechanical stimulation.

For this reason, experiments correlating activity in the nervous system with sensory quality are best classified into two groups. The first group correlates neural activity with physically defined stimuli, and the second group correlates neural activity with experienced sensation (or in the case of animals, with behavior). Both groups of experiments are of importance. Much knowledge may be gained by the study of nervous activity in response to physical stimulation yet this does not tell us how such activity is interpreted by central structures. For instance, if a nerve fiber is found to respond to two distinct types of physical stimulus, this may mean one of two very different things. Either the fiber is treating the stimuli as the same, i.e., it is confusing them, or it is relaying information concerning both types of stimulation. In the latter case the fiber would be relaying more information than one which responds specifically only to one type of stimulus. In some cases, experiments correlating neural activity with

223

sensation can decide to which of the two categories such a fiber might belong.

The way in which the different sensory qualities are transmitted in the nervous system has been one of the major interests of workers studying the skin senses. The classical theory maintains that there are four "primary sensory modalities," namely touch, warmth, cold and pain, and that other sensations are just derivations of these. Each primary sensory modality has its own morphologically distinct receptor type. Another view is that different physical stimuli activate the same pathways, but cause a different temporal and spatial patterning of activity in these pathways. The different sensations result from these different temporal and spatial patterns. A third view was suggested by Head (1920) who proposed that apart from the system subserving deep sensibility there are broadly two peripheral sensory systems: the phylogenetically older *protopathic system*, which subserves rather poorly defined sensations; and the phylogenetically younger *epicritic system*, which is capable of relaying the finer grades of sensation. It has further been suggested (Bishop, 1961) that not two but several sensory systems may exist in the same organism, each representing a different level of phylogenetic development. The newer the system phylogenetically, the more discrete the sensory information which it carries.

A further view is that some pathways may become less specific as they progress from periphery to center. Wall (1960) presents evidence that there are cells at the level of the first relay which behave as though several fibers, conveying different sensory modalities, terminate on them. Or a system of temporal patterning at the periphery may lead to a spatial separation according to modality at more central structures (in some cases) as suggested by Hunt and McIntyre (1960d). We shall return to this question of modality transmission several times during the course of this chapter.

## SPATIAL DISTRIBUTION OF THE SKIN SENSES

The ease with which different sensory qualities may be elicited varies for different regions of the skin surface. This is true firstly when large regions of the body surface are compared. Sensitivity to pressure, as measured by stimulus threshold, varies considerably over the body surface, the threshold being very low at the tip of the tongue and the fingers, and high for instance on the abdomen and forearm. Sensitivity to pain also varies considerably, but in a different fashion. The cornea and conjunctiva of the eyes are very sensitive to pain, and the fingertips are insensitive. The mucous lining of the cheeks are particularly insensitive to pain, one region here, known as Kiesow's Area, being totally analgesic. The thresholds for thermal sensation also vary depending on body region. The threshold for warmth is low on the forehead and high on the foot for instance (Maréchaux and Schäfer, 1949). Secondly, if a small area of the skin is systematically tested spot by spot, it is found that some spots are particularly sensitive to touch, some to pain, some to warmth and some to cold. Figure 8–1 shows typical maps of cold and warm spots. The number of spots per unit area sensitive to a certain type of stimulus varies for different regions of the body. Further, those body regions which contain a very large number of spots for one type of stimulus often do not contain such a proportionately large number of another type of stimulus.

When physiological techniques were not so well developed, so that it was difficult to analyze directly the activity of neural structures, much of the discussion concerning specificity within the skin senses centered around whether or not the sensory spots for the different modalities were

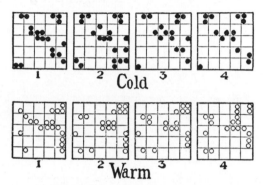

FIG. 8–1. Maps of cold and warm spots on the skin of the upper arm. The same square centimeter of skin was mapped repeatedly to locate sensory spots. The results are presented in the upper four squares for cold spots and in the lower four squares for warm spots. (From Dallenbach, K. M., 1927; permission of *Amer. J. Psychol.*, p. 39.)

stable when tested on different occasions. For it was argued that if spots sensitive to a particular modality appeared consistently in the same locations, then receptors sensitive to this stimulus modality must be located beneath these spots. This would not of course prove the point. Variations in skin sensitivity, even consistent variations, could occur for many different reasons. Yet it was disputed by others that such sensory spots were not stable, but varied from day to day mirroring only temporary differences in local skin sensitivity. Many experiments were therefore conducted to determine how stable such sensory spots were, and many varied results were obtained. However, modern electrophysiological methods have enabled us to provide much more direct and convincing answers to questions concerning specificity of skin receptors, so the controversy over the stability of sensory spots now assumes less importance.

An interesting group of mapping experiments concerns the application of nonadequate stimuli to previously mapped sensory spots. A nonadequate stimulus is one to which a spot is relatively insensitive. Von Frey (1894) found that a painful stimulus (sharp needle) applied to a pressure spot often gave only a sensation of pressure. Kiesow (1895) reported that applying pressure or electrical stimuli to a previously mapped cold or warm spot often gave reports of cold or warmth. These experiments indicate the existence of receptors which may be activated by more than one type of stimulus, yet their excitation is always interpreted as signaling one particular sensory mode.

Another example is the phenomenon of paradoxical cold. Von Frey (1895) found that previously mapped cold spots will respond to hot stimuli with a sensation of cold. The stimulus temperature needed to

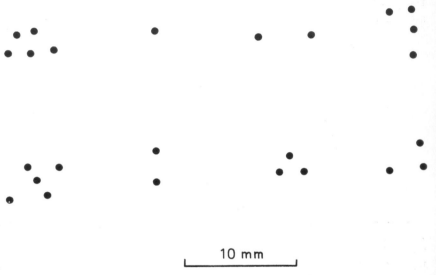

FIG. 8–2. Examples of the distribution of receptive spots taken from eight touch units in the sural nerve of the cat. (From Hunt, C. C. and McIntyre, A. K., 1960; by *courtesy of J. Physiol.*, 15.)

obtain this effect had to be high—around 45 degrees C or above. This fits in very well with the neurophysiological finding that single cold receptors maintain a steady discharge at temperatures below 41° C, and also at 45° C and above (see below).

It is still not really known whether sensory spots are regions innervated by single modality-specific receptors, or whether they are simply due to favorable conditions for transfer of the appropriate form of stimulus energy. However, neurophysiological studies have shown that in at least some cases the hypothesis of single receptors is likely to be correct. Hunt and McIntyre (1960a) describe a group of fibers in the sural nerve of the cat which respond to tactile stimulation, with receptive fields limited to a few distinct spots arranged about 1–5 mm. apart (Figure 8–2). These spots might correspond to touch spots in human skin. Other experimenters have also described peripheral fibers with punctate receptive fields (Maruhashi *et al.*, 1952). This unevenness of sensitivity within a receptive field is not limited to peripheral fibers. For instance Perl *et al.* (1962) describe single neurons in the nucleus gracilis in which there is a spotlike distribution of sensitivity over the receptive field.

## MORPHOLOGY OF THE SKIN RECEPTORS

In man, most of the body surface is composed of hairy skin. Here there are present *free nerve endings*, which are formed by repeated division of fibers as they near their terminations. After several divisions, the fiber branches lose their myelin sheaths and then the neurilemma, leaving only the naked axis cylinders. These free nerve endings are arranged in plexiform fashion, and the nerve nets formed by different fibers overlap freely. Other fibers end in basket-like networks around hair follicles. A specialized type of ending known as *Merkel's discs* appears on the back of the hand (Weddell and Miller, 1962).

Nonhairy skin (palms of the hand, soles of the feet, etc.) also contain free nerve endings, and in addition Merkel's discs, and *Meissner's corpuscles*, an encapsulated ending. In various specialized body areas, such as the lips, nipples, and genital organs, there occur in addition a large variety of encapsulated endings. These include *Krause end bulbs* and *Ruffini cylinders* among others, which are so varied and numerous that it is difficult to classify them. Present in many body regions, especially in deep locations, are *Pacinian corpuscles*. This corpuscle is very large (often large enough to be seen with the naked eye) and is composed of a large number of thin layers of tissue surrounding the end of a large fiber, rather like onion layers (Figure 8–3).

## Functions of the Different Types of End Organs

It was once thought that the different sensations could be attributed to the activation of end organs of the appropriate morphological type. Von Frey concluded that the Krause end bulb was the organ responsible for the sense of cold, the Ruffini cylinder for warmth, Meissner's corpuscle for touch and the free nerve ending for pain. This proposal has been attacked on the grounds that most of the skin surface, which is composed of hairy skin, contains only free nerve endings and terminations around hair follicles, and yet all the sensory qualities are perceived from such skin. Sinclair, Weddell and Zander (1952) found that all sensory modalities were adequately represented in the human auricle (hairy skin). Hagen *et al.* (1953) compared thresholds for warmth and cold for the mucous membrane of the lip (which contains many encapsulated endings) with those for an adjacent piece of hairy skin (no encapsulated endings) and found no significant differences between them. Further, the cornea has been found to contain only free nerve endings, yet Lele and Weddell (1956) were able to evoke in addition to reports of pain (which was

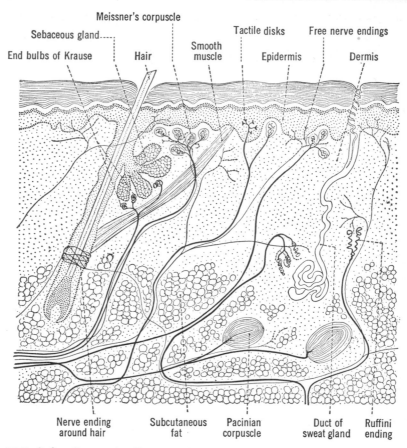

FIG. 8–3. Composite diagram of a cross-section of the human skin. (From Gardner, E., 1947, *Fundamentals of Neurology*; by courtesy of W. B. Saunders Co., after Woollard, Weddell and Marpman, *J. Anat.*, 1940.)

classically supposed to be the only sensation obtainable from the cornea) consistent reports of touch at contact with a fine nylon thread, and of warmth and cold at contact with copper cylinders and jets of air at the appropriate temperature. Indeed, no differences in sensation were found when the skin and the exposed mucous membranes of the lip were similarly stimulated. It is clear from this that the various skin sensations may be perceived without the presence of encapsulated end organs.

Weddell and his colleagues have argued that since a variety of sensations may be aroused through the activation of free nerve endings, then these endings are not modality-specific. They propose instead that the various sensory modalities are conveyed by means of different patterns of activation of the end organs. However, this conclusion does not of necessity follow from the findings. These have shown only that different sensory modalities may be conveyed by receptors which do not with our present techniques exhibit any morphological differences. As will be described later, recordings from single fibers in the peripheral nerve have disclosed many examples of receptor specificity. It is to be expected that advances in microscopic techniques will lead to the discovery of morphological differences amongst free nerve endings.

The question still remains of whether the various types of encapsulated end organ are modality specific, as suggested by the classical hypothesis of Von Frey. Strughold and Karbe (1925) mapped the cold spots on the conjunctiva of the eye and found good agreement between this map and that of Krause end bulbs as seen under the microscope. In a later experiment, Bazett et al. (1932) attempted to correlate the number of cold and warm spots found in the prepuce with that of Krause end bulbs and Ruffini cylinders respectively. Making various allowances they found that the two counts agreed fairly well.

However, Weddell and Miller (1962) point out that encapsulated end organs appear to occur increasingly with age, or with injury to the skin, and are likely therefore to represent degeneration processes, or protective devices against hardening of the skin. To link both types of evidence it may be suggested that for the transmission of each modality there are required specific protective devices, and that a nerve ending develops the type of capsule appropriate to its particular needs.

The Pacinian corpuscle provides an example of a capsule as a protective device which occurs on an end organ which is highly modality-specific. This is a very sensitive mechanoreceptor which is highly specific in its pattern of activation. It is covered by a capsule as shown in Figure 8–3. It might be thought that this very distinctive capsule was intrinsically involved in the transducing of mechanical into electrical energy by the end organ. However, Loewenstein and Rathkamp (1958) showed that when the capsule of the Pacinian corpuscle was peeled off, the responsiveness of the end organ was not changed.

## RESPONSES IN THE PERIPHERAL NERVE

## Classification of Fiber Type

Fibers in the peripheral nerve are found to vary with regard to diameter size, height and characteristics of action potential, and degree or presence of myelination—these characteristics all correlating with each other. Various classifications of fiber type on the basis of these attributes have been made, but the one most commonly used is that proposed by Gasser and his collaborators (Gasser, 1943). Gasser denoted as A fibers all the myelinated fibers in the somatic nerves (though some in the visceral nerves were also included). He further subdivided the A fibers into five groups of diminishing diameter and conduction velocity: $a$, $\beta$, $\gamma$, $\delta$, and $\epsilon$. Their diameters varied from 16 to 20 $\mu$ for $a$ fibers, to 2 to 4 $\mu$ for $\epsilon$ fibers; and their velocity varied from 90 to 115 m/sec for $a$ fibers, to about 10 m/sec for $\epsilon$ fibers. He denoted as C fibers the unmyelinated fibers in the sensory nerves, and these have diameters of 2 $\mu$ or less and conduct at from .6 to 2 m/sec. Also, each component of the action potential of a C fiber lasts much longer than does the corresponding component of an A fiber's action potential. B fibers are myelinated, and have a very different type of action potential from those of A and C fibers, but since they occur only in visceral nerves we shall not be concerned with them.

It was originally hoped that different fiber sizes might be correlated with the various sensory modalities; that is, that fibers of one size might be concerned with touch, fibers of another size with pain, and so on. As it turns out, however, the sizes of fibers responding to different sensory modalities overlap considerably.

A number of experiments have shown that mechanical stimuli may evoke responses in fibers throughout the spectrum of sizes. This was shown in the early work of Adrian (1930), and Zotterman (1939) amongst others. More recently Wall (1960) demonstrated that fibers sensitive to pressure occur throughout the A fiber range. Hunt and McIntyre (1960b) divided A fibers responding to mechanical stimulation into several groups: hair, touch, pressure and probably nociceptive. They plotted the number of fibers in each group against conduction velocities and calculated diameters as shown on Figure 8–4. Each class of units has a characteristic distribution, but it is obvious that considerable overlap occurs, even amongst these subgroups. Furthermore, recent studies (Douglas *et al.* 1960; Iggo, 1960; Iruichijima and Zotterman, 1960) have confirmed that many C fibers respond to mild mechanical stimulation.

Zotterman (1936) recorded responses in the lingual nerve of the cat and judged fibers activated by cold to be in the thinly myelinated $\delta$ group of A fibers, and those responding to warmth to be slightly larger. Maruhashi *et al.* (1952) found thinly myelinated fibers in the saphenous nerve which responded to cold, and in addition, described C fibers sensitive to thermal stimuli. Various other experimenters (Douglas *et al.*, 1960; Hensel, Iggo, and Witt, 1960; Iruichijima and Zotterman (1960) have confirmed the presence of C fibers responding to mild temperature changes.

Regarding nociceptive stimulation, Zotterman (1939) found that burning, without inducing mechanical deformation of the skin, gave rise to A $\delta$ and C potentials in the saphenous nerve. Etching the skin with acids produced similar results. Needle prick gave rise to initially large potentials (accounted for by mechanical deformation of the skin) followed by A $\delta$ and C potentials. Maruhashi *et al.* (1952) also found small myelinated and C fibers responsive to noxious mechanical stimuli and to acid. Iggo (1959a) and Iruichijima and Zotterman (1960) describe some C fibers which responded to temperature changes only when they were extreme enough to be considered painful.

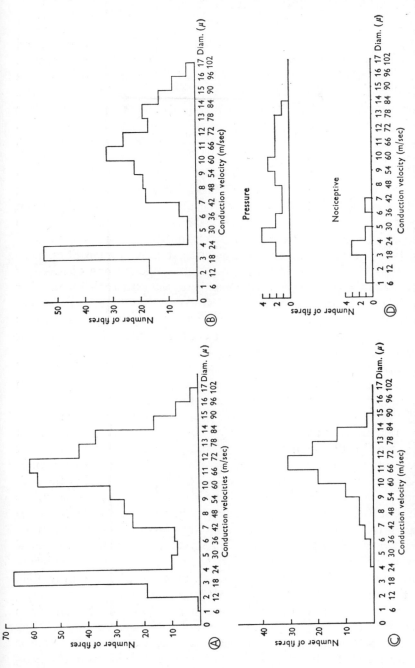

FIG. 8-4. Distribution of fibers in the sural nerve of the cat according to conduction velocities and calculated diameters. A. Total sample of 421 sural fibers. B. Hair units. C. Touch units. D. Pressure and nociceptive units. (From Hunt, C. C. and McIntyre, A. K., 1960, courtesy of *J. Physiol.* 153.)

## MODALITY SPECIFICITY IN THE SENSORY PATHWAYS

Information from the environment reaches our skin surface in temporal and spatial patterns, and is relayed by the nervous system in temporal and spatial patterns. It is obvious that some of our sensations can only be obtained by the preservation of such patterning; amongst these are included the sensations of tickle, vibration, roughness and smoothness. However, there are basically two competing views regarding the importance of such patterning in the overall analysis of skin sensation. On one view, the somatosensory system is regarded as divisible into several subsenses, each with a separate transmission system; the total sensory picture is thought of as more or less a sum of the different types of information arriving at the various central analyzing mechanisms. This view does not deny that interactions take place between the different senses. A pain on one part of the body will cause someone to ignore a tactile stimulus to another part. At the physiological level there are many examples of interaction between units subserving different sensory modalities, both inhibitory and excitatory. However, the basic picture is one of relatively independent transmission systems which interact with each other. After all, such interactions at both the experiential and the physiological levels are known also to take place between entirely different senses—such as vision and audition—but this does not detract from the basic picture of two separate senses in these instances.

Another view emphasizes the importance of spatial and temporal patterning of neural activity, and would rather regard the whole of the skin senses as one great transmission system, with different types of output. In the first place it is held that a perceived sensory quality should be regarded not as resulting from the activation of one particular type of fiber, but rather as a function of the activity together of fibers of many different types. On this view, if one type of fiber were to be rendered inactive, there should not result a sensory loss limited to only one modality, but the total sensory experience should change; since the overall pattern of impulses arriving at the central analyzing mechanism would be changed. With relevance to this expectation, clinical studies on partial sensory loss are particularly important. For if the skin senses were divided into several subsenses with separate transmission systems, then a loss of one modality should leave other modalities on the whole undistrubed. But on the other view there should be a total disturbance of the sensory apparatus.

Secondly, proponents of the "pattern theory" hold that information concerning different sensory modalities may be conveyed in the same fiber by different temporal patterns of activity. For instance, one stimulus modality may be conveyed in a particular fiber by firing in the high-frequency range, and another modality by firing in the low-frequency range. On such a system, confusions would be expected to arise between the different sensory modalities. This however is not an argument in itself against the pattern theory, since such confusions do indeed arise. The study of such confusions and the attempt to correlate them with what is known of unit activity is one of the most fascinating aspects of this problem.

Of course, if the reasonable assumption is made that at the final level of integration, spatially separate structures underlie the different sensory modalities, then the proposed system of temporal patterning would require some analyzing mechanism at the highest level to decode the transmitted information. If information concerning the different modalities were transmitted independently, this would not be necessary. This makes a system of separate mechanisms preferable on the principle of parsimony.

To confirm or disconfirm the hypothesis of temporal patterning, investigators have studied the response of single fibers to different modalities of stimulation. For those fibers which respond to only one modality, the temporal pattern theory cannot hold. For those which respond to more than one modality this theory provides a possible interpretation of the findings: such a fiber may be relaying information concerning both modalities. Alternatively, however, the fiber though responding to both types of physical stimulus, may instead be treating them as one. For instance touch and cold stimuli may activate the same fiber, the activity of which is always interpreted by the central structures as conveying touch. The only type of evidence which will convincingly decide between these interpretations is evidence involving subjective experience, both clinical and experimental.

In some cases, such "nonspecific" fibers may not be concerned with sensation at all, but with some reflex activity. Certain types of reflex activity such as the flexor reflex and startle response are to a large extent independent of stimulus modality. "Nonspecific" fibers may mediate such responses.

## Neurophysiological Evidence

Both fibers responding specifically to one modality of stimulation and fibers responding to more than one have been described. In an early report, Zotterman (1936) described an experiment demonstrating not only that some mechanoreceptors are unresponsive to thermal stimuli, but also that some thermoreceptors are unresponsive to mechanical stimuli, and some pain receptors unresponsive to mild mechanical and thermal stimuli. Recording from a fine branch of the lingual nerve in the cat, Zotterman found that when the tongue was laid free in the air there was evoked a volley of small spikes which increased in number when the tongue was exposed to draft or to a fine stream of air from a syringe. However, if the air in the syringe was warmed these small spikes disappeared, so Zotterman concluded they came from cold fibers. If the air from the syringe was forceful enough to produce a deformation on the tongue large spikes also appeared, and remained whether the air was cool or warm. Thus they must have come from specific pressure fibers. Similar large spikes appeared at the impact of a drop of water falling onto the tongue. When a drop of hot water was applied to the tongue, besides the large pressure spikes two different types of spike appeared, one of which Zotterman concluded came from warm fibers, and the other from pain fibers.

A large number of later experiments have demonstrated the existence of fibers specifically responsive to thermal or mechanical stimuli and of others which responded to more than one stimulus modality. Many of these are summarized in Table 8–1.

### Fibers Responding Specifically to Mechanical Stimuli

It is apparent from the table that there are many fibers which respond specifically to warming, to cooling, or to mechanical stimulation. But the degree of specificity shown by many of these fibers is much greater than is suggested by these three classifications. Within the class of mechanoreceptors, for instance, various types of specificity have been demonstrated. In a study of individual A fibers in the sural nerve of the cat, Hunt and McIntyre (1960a and b) found several patterns of response to mechanical stimulation. One group of fibers, which they termed "hair receptors," were activated by hair movement, which did not necessarily involve skin deformation. These fibers adapted rapidly, even if the hair was maintained in a bent position. Their receptive fields varied widely in size (in general between 3 mm.$^2$ and 185 mm.$^2$) and showed a large amount of overlap. These fibers would not respond to temperature changes. A second group termed "touch receptors" would usually discharge only upon actual touching of the skin. They were slow in adapting, and would usually maintain their discharge for the duration of the tactile stimulus. Their receptive fields were discrete, and limited to a few distinct spots, clustered about 1 to 5 mm. apart. These fibers also responded to temperature changes. A third group, designated "pressure receptors," discharged only to pressure stimuli of considerably greater intensity than that necessary to activate touch receptors, though such stimuli were not noxious. These fibers were slowly adapting, but did not exhibit discrete receptive spots, and did not respond to temperature changes. A fourth group called "probably nociceptive receptors" discharged only to heavy pinching of the skin or pinprick.

Iggo (1960) recorded impulses in C fibers from the saphenous nerve, and found further grounds for subclassifying mechanoreceptors. The C mechanoreceptors exhibited a discharge of impulses for as long as 10 seconds following brief stimulation of the skin. A fibers did not do this. Some very sensitive units could be excited simply by touching the tips of hairs, yet others, which were more sensitive to direct skin pressure, were

# TABLE 8–1

## Electrophysiological Studies of Cutaneous Receptors

| References | Type of lead | Fiber size | Specific fibers | | | Nonspecific fibers | | | |
|---|---|---|---|---|---|---|---|---|---|
| | | | *Cool & cold* | *Warm & hot* | *Mech.* | *Cold & mech.* | *Hot & mech.* | *Hot, cold, & mech.* | *Temp. mods. mech.* |
| **CAT** | | | | | | | | | |
| *Tongue* | | | | | | | | | |
| Hensel & Witt, 1959 (55) | Single | A | + | | | | | | |
| *Infraorbital nerve* | | | | | | | | | |
| Boman, 1958 (8) | Single | A | + | | | + | | | |
| Iriuchijima & Zotterman, 1960 (63) | Single | C | + | + | + | + | + | + | |
| *Saphenous and sural nerves* | | | | | | | | | |
| Iggo, 1959 (60) | Single | A | | + | | | | | |
| Witt & Hensel, 1959 (153) | Single | A | + | + | | + | | | |
| Hunt & McIntyre, 1960 (56) | Single | A | | | + | + | + | + | |
| Hunt & McIntyre, 1960 (57) | Single | A | | | + | + | + | + | |
| Wall, 1960 (127) | Single | A | | | + | | | + | + |
| Douglas & Ritchie, 1957 (23) | A-dromic | A | | | + | | | | |
| Iggo, 1959 (59) | Single | C | + | + | + | + | | | |
| Iggo, 1959 (60) | Single | C | + | + | + | + | + | | |
| Iggo, 1960 (61) | Single | C | + | + | + | | | + | + |
| Hensel, Iggo & Witt, 1960 (54) | Single | C | + | + | | + | | | |
| Iriuchijima & Zotterman, 1960 (63) | Single | C | + | + | + | + | + | + | |
| Douglas & Ritchie, 1957 (23) | A-dromic | C | | | + | | | | |
| Douglas & Ritchie, 1959 (24) | A-dromic | $C_1$ | + | | + | + | | | |
| | | $C_1$ | + | | | | | | |
| Douglas, Ritchie & Straub, 1959 (25) | A-dromic | $C_1$ | + | | + | + | | | |
| Witt, 1961 (152) | Single | $C_1$ | | | | | | + | |
| | | $C_2$ | | + | | | | | |
| *Pacinian corpuscle* | | | | | | | | | |
| Ishiko & Loewenstein, 1960 (64) | Single | A | | | + | | | | + |
| Loewenstein, 1961 (89) | Single | A | | | + | | | | + |
| *Cornea* | | | | | | | | | |
| Lele & Weddell, 1959 (81) | Bundle | A | | | | | | + | |
| Weddell, 1960 (122a) | Bundle | A | | | | + | + | + | |
| **DOG** | | | | | | | | | |
| *Infraorbital nerve* | | | | | | | | | |
| Boman, 1958 (8) | Single | A | + | | | + | | | |
| Iriuchijima & Zotterman, 1960 (63) | Single | C | + | + | + | + | + | + | |
| *Saphenous nerve* | | | | | | | | | |
| Iriuchijima & Zotterman, 1960 (63) | Single | C | + | + | + | + | + | + | |
| **RAT** | | | | | | | | | |
| *Infraorbital nerve* | | | | | | | | | |
| Boman, 1958 (8) | Single | A | + | | | + | | | |
| *Saphenous nerve* | | | | | | | | | |
| Iriuchijima & Zotterman, 1960 (63) | Single | C | + | + | + | | | + | |
| **RABBIT** | | | | | | | | | |
| *Ear* | | | | | | | | | |
| Weddell, Taylor & Williams, 1955 (142) | Bundle | A | | | + | | | | |
| **MAN** | | | | | | | | | |
| *Radial nerve, superficial branch* | | | | | | | | | |
| Hensel & Boman, 1960 (53) | Single | A | + | | + | + | | | |
| Hensel, 1961 (52) | Single | A | + | | + | | | + | |

Crosses indicate fibers activated by the cutaneous stimuli indicated. On account of wide variations in experimental approach, it is impossible to make any quantitative comparisons. See papers cited against each author for more detailed information.

*Type of lead.*—Single: single fiber preparation, either teased or isolated by collision technique, or microelectrode intracellular recording. Bundle: lead from a bundle. A-dromic: antidromic recording technique.

*Nerves tested.*—A: fibers described by the authors as Group A or myelinated. C ($C_1$ or $C_2$): Group C fibers.

*Specific fibers.*—Cool and cold: warm and cold: fibers activated by stimuli below or above skin temperature respectively. Mech.: fibers activated by any kind of mechanical stimulus.

*Nonspecific fibers.*—Cold and mech.: cold or cool fibers responding also to mechanical stimuli. Hot and mech.: warm or hot fibers responding also to mechanical stimuli. Hot, cold, and mech.: fibers activated by positive and negative heat transfer and to mechanical stimuli. Temp. mods. mech.: mechanoreceptors, the afferent discharge of which is modulated by a change of temperature.

(From Weddell G. and Miller S., Annu. Rev. Physiol. 1962.)

FIG. 8–5. The response of an isolated Pacinian corpuscle to vibration. Afferent impulses were found to follow each cycle of vibration in a 1:1 ratio over a frequency range from 90 to 600 c/s. The upper trace displays nerve impulses; the lower trace displays the frequency of vibration applied to the corpuscle. Final frequencies (c/s): A 90, B 102, C 180, D 550, E 650, F 700, G 1000. Time marker, 10 msec. (From Hunt, C. C., 1961; courtesy of J. Physiol. 155.)

not activated by such hair movements. C hair receptors tended to display a persistent discharge when the hair was maintained in a bent position, in contrast with the A hair receptors which always adapted rapidly. These mechanically sensitive C fibers were insensitive to heat, but discharged briefly to cooling of the skin.

Another example of specificity within the group of mechanoreceptors lies in their ability to follow the frequency of repetitive stimulation. A large number of mechanoreceptors discharge with each cycle of low-frequency vibration (around 40 c/s) but cannot follow higher frequencies. Yet the Pacinian corpuscle will follow vibration at frequencies in the range of about 50 to 800 c/s (Figure 8–5).

### Fibers Responding Specifically to Thermal Stimuli

The thermal receptors studied by Zotterman and his colleagues in the chorda tympani and lingual nerve of the cat (e.g. Hensel and Zotterman, 1951a; Dodt and Zotterman 1952a) demonstrated an exquisite degree of specificity. The different fibers were found to have optimal discharge frequencies at different temperatures, and each fiber exhibited a finely gradated response, which varied with the different conditions of thermal stimulation.

If the surface of the tongue is maintained at a constant temperature, cold fibers will maintain a steady discharge, the frequency of which depends on the temperature, over long periods, sometimes hours. The maximum frequency of this discharge lies at around 10 imp/sec.; and the temperature at which it is elicited varies from fiber to fiber, but lies within the range of 20° to 34° C. The frequency of the steady discharge as a function of temperature falls on both sides of this maximum (Figure 8–6); the highest temperature at which the steady discharge may be elicited

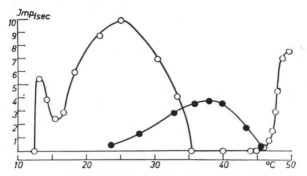

FIG. 8–6. Graph showing the steady discharge frequency of a single cold fiber (open circles) and a single warm fiber (filled circles) as a function of static temperature level within the range of 10 to 50° C. (From Zotterman, Y., 1953; courtesy of *Ann. Rev. Physiol. 15.*)

being around 41° C, and the lowest temperature being around 10° C. At temperatures above 45° C, however, the steady discharge gradually returns, the frequency of discharge increasing with increasing temperature to a maximum of 7 to 7.5 imp/sec. at around 50° C. Above this temperature the discharge disappears. (This discharge at high temperatures is known as the paradoxical discharge of cold fibers, and is held to be the explanation of the "paradoxical cold sensation" described by Von Frey, who discovered that stimulating single cold spots with temperatures above 45° C produced a sensation of cold.)

Zotterman stresses that the frequency of discharge of these cold fibers at constant temperatures is determined solely by the prevalent temperature, and not at all by how it was reached.

When the temperature of the tongue is made to drop suddenly, a cold fiber will produce a short burst of high-frequency discharges, though it will quickly adopt the steady discharge frequency appropriate to the new temperature (Figure 8–7). The frequency of this rapid discharge depends mainly on the rate of temperature change, though the temperature range in which the drop occurs also affects it. The maximum discharge frequency observed to sudden cooling was 140 imp/sec., which occurred to rapid cooling from 40° to 2° C. Rapid cooling may produce this discharge from cold fibers even when the temperature range concerned is above the upper limit for steady discharge.

When the temperature is made to rise rapidly, a cold fiber will briefly cease to discharge before adopting the frequency appropriate to the new temperature. The rate of warming and the temperature range in which it occurs both determine the length of this inhibition of discharge. If the rate of warming is slow, or the degree of warming small, the discharge may not disappear entirely.

It was found that warm fibers, as well as cold fibers, maintain a steady discharge at constant temperatures, the frequency of the discharge

**FIG. 8–7.** Discharge frequency of a single cold fiber in the lingual nerve of the cat during sudden lowering of the temperature of the tongue. Cooling starts at time 0. (From Hensel, H. and Zotterman, Y., 1951; courtesy of *Acta Physiol. Scand.* 23.)

depending on the temperature (Figure 8–6). The maximum frequency of steady discharge occurred in the temperature range of 37.5° C to 40° C, and was around 1.5 to 3.7 imp/sec. The upper temperature limit necessary to evoke a steady discharge was in the region of 47° C, and the lower limit around 20° C. In contrast to the discharge recorded in cold fibers, the discharge exhibited by warm fibers tended to be rather irregular.

A rapid rise in temperature produces in warm fibers a brief high-frequency discharge, before they adopt the frequency appropriate to the new temperature. A fall in temperature of 8° to 15° also gives rise to a brief increase in discharge frequency of very short latency, the effect being greater for more rapid temperature drops.

Cutaneous thermoreceptors in rats, cats, and dogs (Iruichijima and Zotterman, 1960; Hensel, Iggo and Witt, 1960) of C fiber diameter have been described whose behavior is very similar to that of the A thermoreceptors in the tongue described above. However, the warm fibers show no paradoxical discharge during cooling (Hensel, Iggo and Witt, 1960).

### Fibers Responding Specifically to Painful Stimuli

Pain sensations may be aroused by a variety of means. Extreme mechanical stimuli of various types, such as pinching, needle prick, extreme heat, extreme cold, and the application of various chemicals to the skin, may all cause pain in man. Yet these stimuli all differ from each other physically. The problem of specificity in pain pathways is therefore particularly interesting; for we must ask not only whether fibers exist which respond only to pain-producing stimuli, but also whether these fibers respond to *all* pain-producing stimuli, or whether instead a modality separation amongst pain fibers themselves exists.

It has been found that an adequate stimulus for pain in the skin is either potentially or actually productive of tissue damage. Hardy *et al.* (1952) found that the thermal radiation threshold for pain is at a skin temperature of around 45° C. This temperature is at the threshold range for tissue damage (Moritz and Henriques, 1947). Lewis (1942) showed that needle prick at pain threshold will produce skin damage as manifested by redness later. A chemical change accompanying a slight degree of tissue damage may therefore be the common basis for the perception of pain. This will be discussed in greater detail below.

Fibers have been found which are activated only by painful stimuli. In this category fall fibers responding only to those mechanical stimuli judged painful by man, such as pinprick and pinching of the skin. These have been found in the A δ range (Dodt, 1954; Hunt and McIntyre, 1960b) and the C range (Iggo, 1959a, 1960).

Some fibers have also been reported to respond only to those temperature changes judged painful by man. Pain thresholds in man are variable, but such reactions occur roughly at skin temperatures above 45° C (Hardy *et al.*, 1952) and below 17° C (Wolfe and Hardy, 1941). Fibers activated by warming the skin only to high temperatures exist in the A δ range (Dodt, 1954) and the C range (Hensel, Iggo and Witt, 1960; Iggo, 1959b; Iruichijima and Zotterman, 1960), and those activated by cooling the skin only to very low temperatures (Boman, 1959) in the C fiber range (Iggo, 1959a; Iruichijima and Zotterman, 1960).

However, it is not possible to make the generalization that all individual pain fibers respond to all painful stimuli. Instead it appears that some fibers respond only to one kind of painful stimulus, others to two kinds, and yet others to more. For instance, Dodt (1954, 1959) found that A δ fibers in the lingual nerve of the cat responded to extreme heat and to painful mechanical stimuli but not to cold. Iggo (1959a), recording impulses from C fibers in the saphenous nerve of the cat, found some fibers sensitive only to intense mechanical stimuli and heat from stimulators 48° C or hotter; others responded to intense mechanical stimuli and cold from stimulators 10° C or cooler; only one fiber was found which responded both to heat and to cold. He further describes C fibers sensitive to noxious mechanical stimuli but not to temperature change. Some fibers appear to respond to heat, cold, and mechanical stimulation not necessarily noxious. Iruichijima and Zotterman (1960) describe C fibers which responded to strong thermal changes in the skin in both directions, and also to mechanical stimulation such as touch and pressure as well as pinching and pinprick. One might wonder whether such fibers are really nociceptive in function since they respond to touch. Yet Iggo (1959b) describes C fibers sensitive to extremes of temperature which were initially responsive to mechanical stimuli only if they were severe. Repeating heating and cooling of the skin sometimes led to a lowering of the mechanical threshold. Such behavior parallels the development of hyper-algesia as a result of trauma (see below), and may form part of its basis.

The scatter in the responsiveness of the various pain fibers makes it unlikely that there is a common physical basis for the perception of different types of pain. An attempt to classify nociceptive fibers together was made by Fjallbrandt and Iggo (1961). They hoped that injection of pain-producing substances into the skin might cause those fibers activated by other nociceptive stimuli to be excited. Maruhashi et al. (1952) had described earlier single fibers responding to noxious mechanical stimuli and also to acid. Other fibers responded to mild mechanical stimuli and were insensitive to acid. Fjallbrandt and Iggo (1961) made close-arterial injections of histamine, acetylcholine, and 5-hydroxytryptamine into the saphenous artery and recorded afferent activity. However they did not succeed in identifying nociceptors by this method, and they suggest that nociceptors may instead be modality-specific.

### Fibers Responding to Both Mechanical and Thermal Stimuli

A number of fibers have been described which responded both to mechanical stimulation and to cold. Hensel and Zotterman (1951b) describe a group of mechanoceptive fibers in the lingual nerve which may be activated by cooling. However their response to cooling was different from that of the "true" cold fibers which they had studied, for they could only be activated by severe cooling and ceased to respond as soon as the low temperature was made constant. A different pattern has been described by Hensel and Boman (1960) in fibers from a superficial branch of the radial nerve in human subjects. Here fibers responded sensitively to mechanical stimulation and in addition exhibited a steady discharge at indifferent skin temperature without mechanical stimulation. Cooling led to an increase in discharge frequency, but this increase was small compared with that due to mechanical stimulation. Witt and Hensel (1959) describe similar receptors in the cat.

It is probable that the receptors described above mediate a mechanical sensation. Firstly, their thermal sensitivity is very low compared with their mechanical sensitivity. Secondly, this assumption would explain the illusion of pressure which is produced by cooling, known as Weber's illusion. On the other hand, mechanical stimuli may produce a cold sensation (Kiesow, 1895).

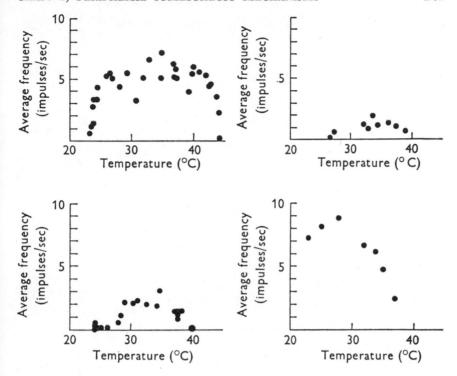

FIG. 8–8. The relation between baseline discharge frequency and static temperature level in four touch units in the sural nerve of the cat. (From Hunt, C. C. and McIntyre, A. K., 1960, by courtesy of *J. Physiol.* 153.)

Lippold *et al.* (1960) report that a proportion of the muscle spindles which they studied in the cat, responded to cold in a fashion similar to that found in specific cold fibers, while still having a normal response to stretch. The function of such a response is as yet unknown.

Hunt and McIntyre (1960a) describe a group of fibers which they call "touch units." These fibers were highly sensitive to mechanical stimulation, and yet displayed a background discharge in the absence of mechanical stimulation. The average frequency of this discharge depended on skin temperature. One group of such units showed a maximum discharge frequency in the 28° to 38° C range, the frequency gradually falling on either side of the optimum temperature, which varied for different units (Figure 8–8). Other units discharged only at high skin temperatures. Others responded with an increased discharge to cooling, and an inhibition of discharge to heating, in a manner similar to that of specific cold receptors. It was also found that responses to constant tactile stimuli varied depending on temperature. Below 22° C and above 42° C touch units often failed to respond to mechanical stimulation. In the temperature range between these extremes, warming or cooling led to rapid adaptation of the receptor, and to the evocation of fewer discharges by the mechanical stimulus.

Hunt and McIntyre suggest that in this group of units, sensory information relating to both touch and temperature may be conveyed by the same fibers—possibly that low discharge frequencies convey temperature and high frequencies touch. Such a system would not provide very good differentiation of the two types of information. The finding that sufficient raising or lowering of the skin temperature causes faster adaptation and fewer discharges in response to a tactile stimulus may be related to whàt is known of variations in tactile threshold with temperature changes. Allers and Halpern (1921) found that pressure thresholds are related to skin temperature by a concave function, with maximal sensitivity between 36° and 38° C.

Wall (1960) also describes pressure-sensitive fibers which responded to temperature changes. Some were spontaneously active and responded to an increased temperature with an increased discharge frequency; some became constantly active when skin temperature was increased; in others the rate of adaptation was decreased by heating the skin.

### Explanation of Double Specificity

When a fiber responds both to mechanical and to thermal stimulation this may have several possible causes. One possibility is that the double response is due to a physical artefact. For instance, changes in skin temperature might cause movement of blood vessels, and so excite mechanoreceptors. However, in well-controlled experiments, such artefacts may be ruled out (Wall, 1960). Secondly, one receptor responding to mechanical stimuli and another responding to temperature changes, may originate impulses converging onto the same fiber. Thirdly, a single receptor might itself respond to the two different types of stimulation. But even here one cannot conclude without very careful controls that the receptor in question can be excited independently by both forms of energy. It has been found that the amplitude and rate of rise of a mechanically elicited generator potential in the Pacinian corpuscle increases greatly with temperature. Yet it has been domonstrated (Ishiko and Loewenstein, 1960) that here the receptor membrane is excited by mechanical stimulation, yet not by temperature change per se. However, changes in temperature alter the rate and amount of charge transferred through the mechanically excited receptor membrane. Loewenstein (1960) has also shown that in the Lorenzinian Ampulla of selachians, temperature changes will alter activity, but only when physiological levels of pressure in the ampulla are maintained. When pressure is reduced to subphysiological levels the receptor will not respond to thermal changes. In each receptor type under investigation therefore very careful studies have to be performed before the nature of the double response can be determined.

## Experiential and Behavioral Evidence Regarding Modality Specificity

In the spinal cord, fibers are to some extent segregated according to modality, and so studies on patients with limited lesions of the cord have been very fruitful in the investigation of modality specificity from the sensory point of view. Unfortunately fibers in the peripheral nerve are not grouped according to modality, so such studies cannot be performed here. However, some evidence for sensory modality specificity does exist for the peripheral nerve.

That only tactile sensations may be aroused when only certain tactile fibers are conducting is indicated by the correlation of the results of certain psychophysical and neurophysiological experiments in which conduction in the peripheral nerve is blocked by cocaine. In man, cocaine block leads to a disappearance of the various modalities of sensation in sequential order, touch being the last to remain. Gasser and Erlanger (1929) showed that injection of cocaine blocked conduction first in the smallest fibers, then the middle ones, and finally the largest. It can thus be inferred that the largest fibers in the cutaneous nerves convey only tactile sensations. More direct evidence on this point derives from an experiment by Heinbecker, Bishop and O'Leary (1933). They were able to stimulate directly exposed peripheral nerves in conscious man and found that activating the largest fibers in these nerves gave rise to tactile sensations, and no other, though they evoked painful sensations when smaller nerve fibers were activated.

In a study on the frog, Adrian, Cattell and Hoagland (1931) also present evidence that large tactile fibers are not concerned with nociception. They found that stimulating the skin by an intermittent air blast gave rise to discharges of frequency as high as 200 to 300/sec., which is almost the maximum frequency the nerve fiber can carry. However, intact frogs, when stimulated in this fashion, showed no pain reactions. A similar conclusion was drawn by Gernandt and Zotterman (1946) in a study on the cat. They report activation of large medullated fibers in the splanchnic nerve in response to the most gentle pressure to the exposed mesentery. However, stimulation of such fibers would not elicit any viso-enteric reflex or any other noticeable response. The authors thus conclude that these fibers are not concerned with nociception.

Though these experiments do not absolutely prove the point, they present convincing evidence that at least some tactile fibers (in the large group) convey only messages concerned with touch, even though they might be activated in response to noxious stimulation.

Heinbecker et al. (1933) correlated δ fiber activity with the sensation of pain. They stimulated exposed nerves in the leg of a conscious man and report that he gave a response of pain at that stimulus which produced a $\delta$ elevation in the electroneurogram.

Further, Collins, Nulsen and Randt (1960) stimulated the exposed sural nerves of eleven human subjects, and simultaneously recorded the action potentials. They found consistently that A-$\beta$ and A-$\beta$-$\bar{\gamma}$ stimulation was not painful; however, when the A $\delta$ group was also stimulated this produced definite pain.

In another study, Clark, Hughes and Gasser (1935) found that in the saphenous nerve of the cat, when C as well as A fibers were activated, this produced greater effects on blood pressure and respiration than when only A fibers were activated. When all fibers other than those in the C group were blocked by compression or asphyxia, then stimulating the C fibers alone was sufficient to produce reflexes. Further, under those experimental conditions where it can be shown in animals that all fibers other than C fibers were blocked by asphyxia, then human subjects give reports only of pain and warmth when stimulated.

## MECHANISMS OF IMPULSE INITIATION

### Mechanoreceptors

Little is as yet known about the mechanisms involved in impulse initiation by mechanical stimuli. Recently various possibilities have been suggested for the Pacinian corpuscle. Loewenstein (1961) recorded the generator potential in the Pacinian corpuscle resulting from mechanical stimulation of the nerve terminal after he removed the outer lamina. He found that potentials evoked by stimuli applied to different places along the receptor axons summated. Also the generator potential decreased with distance from the site of stimulation. From this among other evidence he concluded that the size of the generator potential was determined by the area of the receptor membrane excited.

### Thermal Receptors

Various theories have been put forward to explain the initiation of impulses by thermal stimuli. It has been suggested (Ebbecke, 1917; Bazett, 1941) that this is based on a thermal gradient existing between the different skin layers; that is, a difference in the temperature of the skin at various depths. It was thought that the receptors were activated by an alteration in such thermal gradients. However, Hensel and Zotterman (1951c) demonstrated that thermoreceptors were excited by thermal stimuli independently of intracutaneous gradients. They used nerve preparations containing cold fibers innervating only the upper surface of the tip of the tongue. Cooling the upper or lower surfaces of the tongue, or injecting cold solutions in the lingual artery, all produced cold receptor discharges, and at latencies expected from the time the cold would take to penetrate to the regions supplied by the cold fibers. Yet the spatial temperature gradients would differ in each case. Arrest of blood flow for a short while did not materially affect the results.

Another suggestion put forward was that a temporal thermal gradient is necessary for excitation of thermal receptors; that is, that the receptor must be subjected to a changing temperature. However, we have seen that although a change in temperature produces briefly a rapid discharge in the appropriate fiber, warm and cold fibers have been found to discharge at a steady rate for several hours to a constant thermal stimulus. A temporal thermal gradient is therefore not necessary for the excitation of thermal receptors either. Zotterman (1959) concludes that thermal receptors are probably excited by some chemical process, since they do not depend for their activation on any exchange of thermal energy. The nature of such a chemical change is at present unknown.

### Pain

It is believed that the excitation of pain fibers is chemically mediated; though it is not definitely known yet which chemicals are involved. Lewis (1942) reports that pain can be produced by intradermal injection of extracts of freshly excised human skin. Rosenthal (1950) presents evidence that the chemical concerned is histamine or a similar substance. He found that a very small amount of histamine, when injected into the skin, caused pain. Habgood (1950) found a similar effect to the sensitization of receptors caused by scraping the skin of the frog was produced by antidromic stimulation of a cutaneous nerve. He demonstrated that some chemical substance was liberated at the nerve endings by this procedure and presented evidence that the substance was histamine or similar to histamine.

However, other workers claim that chemicals unlike histamine in their properties are also involved. Armstrong *et al.* (1957) found acetylcholine and serotonin as well as histamine to produce pain when applied to the area exposed by removal of blistered skin. They also found an unidentified pain-producing substance which was unlike histamine or serotonin (and which they called PPS) to appear in blister fluid and various other body fluids, immediately after they are brought into contact with glass.

### PAIN STATES

## Cutaneous Hyperalgesia

When an area of skin is traumatized, for instance by scratching, heating, freezing or electrical irritation, there results a lowering of the pain threshold in this region. In addition, the pain sensation now felt has an intense burning, diffuse quality. This hyperalgesia may last for hours or even days.

Echlin and Propper (1937) found that scraping the skin of the frog produced an increase in the number of impulses traveling at speeds appropriate to pain fibers, and a lowering of threshold for their evocation. Recently, Iggo (1959b) found C fibers sensitive to temperature extremes which responded at first to mechanical stimuli only if they were severe. Repeated heating and cooling of the skin sometimes led to a lowering of the mechanical threshold. This provides a possible basis at the nerve fiber level for hyperalgesia.

The hyperalgesic region gradually spreads, and may finally extend over a much larger area than the original region of trauma. Lewis (1942) suggests that a special system of fibers with large receptive field must be involved in this effect, but this view has come under criticism, mainly that such a system of fibers has not been found. A second line of explanation rests on two phenomena. The first is that a peripheral nerve fiber is divided into fine branches in the area which it innervates. When one of these branches is stimulated, the evoked activity not only travels up the main fiber, but also propagates antidromically down the other branches. The second phenomenon, demonstrated by Habgood (1950) in the frog is that antidromic stimulation of pain fibers releases some substance in the skin which then evokes activity in neighboring pain fibers. Accordingly it is supposed that a noxious stimulus in the normal case provokes activity in a branch or branches of a nociceptive fiber. Some of this activity spreads antidromically to neighboring skin areas via the other branches of this same fiber. There is a release in these further areas innervated by these fibers of a substance which in turn is capable of stimulating branches of fibers not originally involved. In such a way the pain spreads from the point to which the noxious stimulus was applied.

Another suggestion is that this spread of hyperalgesia is centrally produced. A constant barrage of impulses up one pain pathway may cause irritation of adjacent pain pathways from neighboring regions of skin. Stimulation of a nerve proximal to a procaine block can cause hyperalgesia (Hardy et al., 1950), and this would suggest the hypothesis of a central origin.

It may well be that both the peripheral and the central explanations are correct. Hyperalgesia after trauma has a very important function in that it tends to prevent an injured region from being further traumatized, so that healing processes will be unimpeded. It is very possible that in this case more than one mechanism exists to produce the same end result.

## Hyperpathia Resulting from Peripheral Nerve Lesions

When one or more cutaneous nerves is cut there appears in the corresponding peripheral field a region which is totally anaesthetic, surrounded by a region which is partially anaesthetic. Sensation in the region of partial anaesthesia soon develops an altered quality. The threshold for touch is still raised, but once a stimulus is above this elevated threshold, it may appear painful. Pinprick now gives rise to a diffuse poorly localized pain which is very unpleasant. Sometimes a spontaneous burning pain appears. As regeneration proceeds, stimulation of the previously anaesthetic zone may also produce such sensations.

Such effects have also been produced when a peripheral nerve trunk is blocked with a local anaesthetic, or when a limb is compressed with a pressure cuff (Weddell *et al.*, 1948).

Various explanations for this have been suggested. Prominent among these is the explanation of Head (1920). He suggests that, apart from the system subserving deep sensibility, the peripheral sensory apparatus consists of two systems. The phylogenetically older "protopathic system" is capable of responding to painful cutaneous stimuli and to extremes of heat and cold. The response of this system is diffuse, and not accompanied by any real appreciation of the location of the stimulus. The phylogenetically younger "epicritic system" responds to light touch with a well-localized sensation. It is responsible for our capacity to discriminate two points: localize stimuli effectively and appreciate the finer grades of temperature.

Head proposes that normally the epicritic system exercises an inhibitory influence on the protopathic system. After a nerve has been damaged, the protopathic fibers regenerate more quickly than the epicritic fibers, so for a while the protopathic system is released from inhibitory control. The hyperpathia is due to the uncontrolled activity of the protopathic system.

Foerster (1927) also suggests that hyperpathia is produced by the activation of pain pathways without the concomitant activation of pathways for touch and pressure, which have an inhibitory action.

Against this explanation, it has been pointed out that the regions in which pain has this abnormal quality are not directly correlated with the regions of anaesthesia to touch. Trotter and Davis (1909) found in one case that there were more spots hypersensitive to pinprick actually outside the region of anaesthesia. Lanier *et al.* (1935) describe a region in which pain sensibility was diminished and the peculiarly unpleasant pain was felt, although there was no loss of touch sensibility.

Another version of the explanation in terms of a loss of inhibition which would meet the above objection is that this abnormal pain is usually inhibited by the normally felt pain. Landau and Bishop (1953) conclude from their experiments on differential nerve block that the block of A $\delta$ pain fibers releases the perception of C fiber pain.

Others, such as Trotter (1926), have suggested that the phenomenon is due to abnormal activity in the regenerating fibers. Granit *et al.* (1944) have demonstrated the appearance of "artificial synapses" at the point of injury, and through such a mechanism abnormal activation could appear.

Another finding which may have bearing on the phenomenon is the ingrowth of fibers from adjoining nerves. Pollock (1919) postulated such an ingrowth, since recovery was not lost after second section of the regenerating nerve. Weddell (1941) actually demonstrated historically that unmyelinated fibers do grow into the anaesthetic area. How such an ingrowth could explain the findings on hyperpathia is, however, still obscure.

### THE SENSATION OF PAIN

Pain may be aroused by a variety of means. It may be aroused from the skin surface by severe mechanical, thermal, chemical, or electrical stimulation. It is possible that there is a common basis underlying pain produced on the skin surface, perhaps the release of some chemical which occurs at intensities of stimulation strong enough to produce tissue damage though this has not been demonstrated—see pp. 245–46. Distention of various visceral organs also causes pain. Severe arterial dilation and arterial constriction producing ischaemia have also been shown to produce pain. Inflammation has the effect of lowering the pain threshold both for the skin and for deeper structures.

In a well-controlled situation, it can be demonstrated that differences in intensity of pain can be well detected. Hardy *et al.* (1952) have shown that 21 j.n.d.s of pain may be distinguished by trained observers. With a constant pain stimulus, it has also been shown (Dallenbach, 1939) that pain sensations adapt to eventual disappearance.

## Are There Two Types of Pain?

From neurophysiological studies described in a previous section it appears that fibers mediating pain may be found both in the group of small myelinated fibers and also in the C group. It has been held further that these two groups of fibers subserve two distinct types of pain, which have been called fast pain and slow pain.

There have been three main lines of argument for the existence of two separate types of pain. The first is that two temporally discrete sensations are often felt to noxious stimulation, such as pinprick. The second is that during experimental nerve block the type of pain felt when only A fibers are conducting is qualitatively quite different from that felt when only C fibers are conducting. And the third is an attempted correlation of the delay in pain perception and reaction time to pain when the peripheral nerve is blocked by ischaemia with the extra time taken by C fibers in conduction.

Many early experimenters (e.g., Gad and Goldscheider, 1892; Thunberg, 1902) have reported two painful sensations to a noxious stimulus separated by a time interval, and many have confirmed this experience. Yet others have asserted that such two distinct sensations were not clearly apparent. Jones (1956) points out that it is very easy in this type of experiment to stimulate two receptors sequentially and thus produce a double sensation of pain by an artefact. For instance heat stimuli, which are considered very effective in producing double pain, will penetrate the tissues with time and stimulate more remote receptors even after the stimulator is removed. Pinprick too may stimulate more than one receptor sequentially, especially if the needle is not rigidly mounted; also pulling the needle out restimulates the receptor. When Jones employed as stimulus a square-wave pulse from a Grass stimulator, this type of stimulation ensuring that if more than one receptor were stimulated they would be stimulated simultaneously, no reports of double pain were given. She also noted that there was no case cited in the literature of double pain provoked by a single electrical stimulus.

The second argument for the existence of two types of pain, this time identifying the different types with transmission by different fiber groups, is that different qualities of pain are produced when the two groups of fibers are blocked differentially. Following perineural injection of cocaine, the C fibers in the peripheral nerve are blocked first and the A fibers last. And if a cuff is placed around the limb so as to block circulation, conduction in A fibers disappears first and that in C fibers last. It has been asserted by many that when only A fibers are conducting, the pain felt is a brief, pricking pain; when only C fibers are conducting, the experience is of a slow, long drawn-out burning pain. Some assert further that "C-fiber pain" is much more unpleasant than A-fiber pain. However, others have criticized such experiments on the grounds that such introspective data have not been reproduced consistently (Sinclair and Hinshaw, 1950a and b). Thirdly, there have been attempts to correlate changes in reaction time to a painful stimulus when only C fibers are conducting with the difference in conduction rate between A and C fibers. Zotterman (1933) reports that when A fiber conduction is blocked, the pain that persists is a delayed pain the reaction time to which agrees well with that reported by Thunberg (1902) for second pain. Attempting to calculate conduction rate in fibers mediating this delayed pain, from this reaction-time data he concluded that it agreed with the known conduction velocity of C fibers. Various other workers have obtained similar correlations. This work has, however, come under heavy criticism. (See, for instance, Sinclair and Hinshaw, 1951). Delays in reaction time to a stimulus under abnormal conditions may occur for a large number of reasons of which difference in peripheral conduction time is only one. Also *all* cutaneous sensory systems show a delay in perception under ischemic conditions. A delay also occurs with procaine blocks, during which A fibers alone are conducting and therefore there should be no delay.

## THE SENSATION OF PRESSURE

The absolute threshold for pressure sensation has been found to be constant, for any one locus of stimulation, at a given degree of tension, or force per linear extent of skin surface contacted (Von Frey and Kiesow, 1899). The application of pressure alone does not arouse a pressure sensation, as can be demonstrated by dipping a finger into a jar of mercury. Under these conditions a pressure sensation is felt only at the surface of the mercury where there is a difference between the pressure exerted by the mercury and by the air above it.

Von Skramlick (1937) showed that the incremental threshold for pressure varied for different regions of the body, on the whole correlating with the absolute threshold. It also varies depending on the state of adaptation to the initial stimulus. Thus it is smaller when the increment is applied rapidly, and if both stimuli are brief it is larger with short interstimulus intervals (Kolbe, 1936; Grindley, 1936).

The pressure sense adapts very rapidly. Von Frey and Goldman (1915) found that after three seconds of application of a pressure stimulus, it appeared weaker than a momentary pressure of only 25 percent of its value. We have seen that there are many types of rapidly adapting receptor responsive to mechanical stimulation. The time orders of adaptation to pressure found may be a result of the sequential stimulation of various fast-adapting receptors as the skin adjusts to the pressure stimulus. Nafe and Wagoner (1941) showed that pressure sensations due to the application of a weight on the skin occurred only while the skin was moving. When the skin stopped moving, the subject reported no pressure; yet when the weight was removed so that the skin started returning to its normal position, the subject again reported a pressure sensation.

## TEMPERATURE SENSATIONS

The absolute threshold for temperature sensation varies with different bodily regions, and is lower when the number of spots stimulated is increased (Hardy and Oppel, 1938). The rate of change of the stimulus temperature is an important factor governing the size of the threshold. The slower the rate of change, the higher the threshold. Another factor is the temperature to which the skin is adapted before application of the stimulus. At room temperature, thermal stimuli of around skin temperature (32° C) do not arouse sensations of warmth or cold. When the fingers are dipped in warm or cool water, a change of .15° C in either direction is needed to produce a thermal sensation. When the skin has previously been adapted to a higher or lower temperature, a greater temperature change is needed to produce a thermal sensation.

The course of temperature adaptation is in the form of a negatively accelerated curve (Hahn, 1930). The time taken to adapt depends upon the temperature applied. At temperatures close to normal, this time is very short, and as temperatures deviate from normal skin temperatures, adaptation time becomes increasingly lengthened. At temperature extremes (below 20° C and above 40° C) the thermal sensation does not disappear (Hensel, 1950). However, when only single spots are stimulated, adaptation is rapid, even at temperature extremes.

Adaptation to a certain temperature brings with it not only a lack of sensation at this temperature but also a change in the perception of other thermal stimuli. Thus when the skin is at normal temperature (around 32° C), temperatures above this will appear warm, and those below cold. After the skin has adapted to 38° C, stimuli below 38° C will appear cold, and those above 38° C will appear warm. Similarly with an adaptation temperature of 26° C, temperatures above 26° C will appear warm, and those below it cold. In other words, physiological zero corresponds to the temperature to which the skin is adapted, and stimuli are felt as warm or cold depending on whether they are higher or lower in temperature than physiological zero at the time.

The increase in time to adaptation as temperature extremes are approached would be easily explicable if warm and cold peripheral fibers each showed a monotonic increase in rate of steady discharge with increased constant warm and cold temperatures respectively. One would simply have to assume that the peripheral warm and cold fibers projected onto central neurons of the same sign which adapted to their discharges. The time to complete adaptation would be longer the higher the frequency of incoming impulses; and therefore as temperature extremes were approached.

The shift in physiological zero could also be easily explained on this model. For at a given state of adaptation, a central neuron would only fire to a new temperature which produces an increased steady discharge rate in peripheral fibers. Thus, at an adaptation temperature of 38° C, and a new temperature of 39° C, the peripheral warm fibers would increase their steady discharge rate, and the peripheral cold fibers would decrease theirs. Therefore, only the central warm neurons would fire. With the same adaptation temperature of 38° C, and a new temperature of 37° C, the peripheral warm fibers would decrease their steady discharge rate and the peripheral cold fibers would increase theirs. Therefore only the central cold neurons would fire.

However it is not clear from the neurophysiological data that peripheral warm and cold fibers do indeed show a monotonic increase in steady discharge frequency depending on temperature, or that this function is derivable from averaging the activity of several neurons. Some figures support this model (see, for instance, Figure 8–9), but others show instead fibers with a peak firing frequency at a certain temperature, with a gradual decline in steady discharge frequency with temperatures on either side of this optimum (Figure 8–6). On such a model, the sensory data could not be explained in the same way. One explanation of the adaptation findings applicable to the second model (and the first too) is that peripheral warm and cold fibers in addition to exciting central neurons of the same sign, also have inhibitory connections to central neurons of opposite sign. On this hypothesis it is the reciprocal inhibition which causes adaptation. Making the simple quantitative assumption that peripheral warm and cold fibers progressively inhibit central cells of opposite sign at a rate proportional to the degree to which they excite central neurons of their own sign,

FIG. 8–9. A graph plotting the frequency of steady discharge against constant skin temperature in a single "cold" fiber from a superficial branch of the radial nerve in a conscious human subject. (From Hensel, H., and Boman, K., 1960; courtesy *J. Neurophysiol.* 23.)

one would predict the curve relating time to adaptation with stimulus temperature that has been obtained. This would follow since the proportional difference in steady discharge of cold and warm fibers is lowest in the medium temperature range and increases toward the temperature extremes. One would also expect that at those temperatures where only either the warm or the cold peripheral fibers show a steady discharge, but not both, there should be no adaptation. Such a correlation is indeed obtained. According to Hensel (1950) who used very carefully controlled thermal devices, constant sensations appear at above 40° C and below 20° C; and the upper limit for steady discharge of the cold fibers is 41° C and the lower limit for warm fibers is 20° C (Zotterman, 1959).

It has been found that when single warm or cold spots are tested, adaptation is very rapid, even at temperature extremes, in contrast to the findings when relatively large areas of skin are tested. This would follow if reciprocal inhibition were the cause of thermal adaptation. Suppose a large skin area were stimulated at 41° C, this stimulus would cause the cold fibers to stop discharging. Therefore they would not inhibit the central warm neurons and so no adaptation would take place. However, if only one warm spot were stimulated, this will not cause neighboring cold fibers to stop firing. They would continue to fire at a steady rate approximately appropriate to room temperature, and would therefore still exert an inhibitory influence on the central warm neurons to which the stimulated warm fiber projected, and so adaptation would occur.

## ITCH

Itching is a unique sensory experience, with a unique and well-defined behavioral response—that of scratching. Yet the stimuli which will evoke it are not unique. Mechanical, thermal and electrical stimuli may produce itching, as can the application of various chemicals to the skin.

The aversive nature of itching, as well as its arousal by a variety of stimuli, gives rise to the possibility that it is related to pain. This is made more probable by the finding that itching cannot be aroused from skin made analgesic by severing the spinothalamic tract, nor in cases of congenital analgesia, yet it is unaffected in cases of touch anaesthesia (Foerster and Gagel, 1932; Arthur and Shelly, 1959). Yet whether or in what way it is related to pain is not clearly known. Certainly itching is not simply diminutive pain, as some have suggested; for a gradual reduction in the intensity of a pain stimulus produces simply a gradual lessening and final elimination of the pain, without producing itching (Keele, 1958; Moulton, Spector, and Willoughby, 1957).

With punctate stimulation it can be shown that some spots on the skin are sensitive to itch, and others insensitive (Von Frey, 1922) as with other types of sensation. Hyperalgesia greatly increases the number of itch points on an area of skin. It is generally held that itching is conveyed by C fibers. In the frog, topical application of itch-producing substances produces impulses characteristic of C fiber activity. Also, only C fibers display an after-discharge to stimulation and may be activated by extremely mild mechanical stimulation (Zotterman, 1939), and such an after-discharge may partly underlie the prolonged itch sensation which occurs even after withdrawal of the stimulus.

The release of various chemical substances in the skin has been suggested as the cause of itching. Histamine may produce itching when introduced into the skin, and it has been suggested that histamine liberation is the cause of itching. However, whenever histamine produces itching it also invariably produces whealing, and if diluted may produce whealing without itching. Yet itching can occur in skin with normal appearance. Arthur and Shelly (1955, 1959) report that protinease produces itching very effectively without also producing gross changes in the appearance of the skin. Protinease is a naturally occurring substance which may be released or activated to produce itching, and Arthur and Shelly (1959) suggest that this happens in various states leading to pruritus.

## VIBRATION

The sensation produced by vibration of a tuning fork or other device against the skin is quite distinct from that of pressure. The lower limit of frequency needed to produce the feeling of vibration is difficult to define, but it would not be under 10 c/s or as high as 100 c/s. The upper limit is also ill-defined, but may be as high as 10,000 c/s or higher (Geldard, 1953).

Studies on patients with neurological lesions have demonstrated that the sense of vibration may be impaired by specific lesions. Damage to the posterior columns often results in impairment, whereas damage to the anterolateral columns does not. Superficial cortical lesions usually do not impair vibratory sensibility though deep lesions, which may involve the thalamus more often do.

At the level of the peripheral receptor, there has been considerable controversy over whether the same receptors are used to convey both pressure and vibration, or whether separate receptors are responsible for the two.

At the sensory level, Geldard (1940) conducted a convincing experiment indicating that touch and vibration are conveyed by the same receptors. He mapped out pressure-sensitive spots on an area of skin and found that these had low and consistent vibratory thresholds. Those spots which were pressure-insensitive had much higher vibratory thresholds (Figure 8–10). Geldard (1953) also points out that vibratory sensitivity varies as a function of skin temperature, in a similar fashion to pressure sensitivity. Weitz (1941) showed that vibratory thresholds were lowest at around 4° C above normal skin temperature, and rose rather steeply on either side of this optimum. Allers and Halpern (1921) also found pressure thresholds to be lowest at around 36° to 38° C and to rise on either side of these temperatures.

However, neurophysiologists have recently taken another view. They point out that Pacinian corpuscles are exquisitely sensitive to applied vibration, but they are less suited to convey pressure. These corpuscles have been found in the periosteum, near tendons, joints, and muscles, where they are very well located for sensing vibration transmitted through the skeletal system. Hunt (1961) reports that various hair and touch receptors can follow low-frequency sinusoidal vibration (around 40 c/s), i.e., they can discharge with each cycle of movement. Muscle receptors can follow vibration frequencies up to about 150 c/s. But the only known receptor capable of following frequencies above 200 c/s is the Pacinian corpuscle. This responds to sinusoidal vibration in the range of about 50 to 800 c/s (Figure 8–5).

It might be concluded from this that a correspondence between pressure and vibration spots should be found with low vibration frequencies but not with high. But this has not been the finding. Geldard (1940) obtained a correspondence between pressure and vibration-sensitive spots for frequencies including from 64 c/s to 1,024 c/s.

It may then be concluded that vibration sensitivity does not rest on the ability of a fiber to follow the vibration frequency of the stimulus. The function of vibration frequency discrimination is much more likely to

FIG. 8–10. Vibratory thresholds for two populations of sensory spots, one very sensitive to pressure and the other very insensitive. The dotted lines indicate the variability of measurement. (From Geldard, F. A., 1940; courtesy of *J. Gen. Psychol.* 22.)

depend on the ability of a fiber to follow different stimulus frequencies. This is a difficult function to test, since subjective intensity also varies with frequency. Goff (1959) controlled for this variable by using equal-loudness stimuli varying in frequency. Under these conditions she found that at very low frequencies, frequency discrimination was good, but starting from below 100 cps. it very rapidly deteriorates (Figure 8–11). It is obvious therefore that vibration frequency discrimination at high frequencies must be very poor indeed. There is therefore no need to exclude as possible vibration receptors those which cannot follow high frequencies accurately. In addition the Pacinian corpuscle will not itself follow frequencies above 1,000 cps., and we can perceive stimuli vibrating at frequencies higher than this.

This does not mean that Pacinian corpuscles are not involved in vibration perception, but only that there is no reason to exclude other mechanoreceptors from this function. Geldard (1940) has shown that with areal stimulation, the skin is most sensitive to vibration of around 250 c/s, thresholds rising on either side of this. Plumb and Meigs (1961) recently confirmed that sensitivity was greatest in the region between 200 and 400 cps. This correlates with the behavior of the Pacinian corpuscle, which has its lowest threshold at around 300 c/s (Sato, 1961). Variations in sensitivity with temperature change in the Pacinian corpuscle found by Sato are to some extent consistent with the data obtained by Weitz (1941) on human vibratory sensitivity.

FIG. 8–11. Differential frequency discrimination of mechanical vibration applied to the finger tip, in a single subject. Reprinted from *Sensory Communication* edited by Walter Rosenblith (figure from F. A. Geldard after G. D. Goff) by permission of The M.I.T. Press, Cambridge, Mass. ©. (1961 The M.I.T. Press.)

Taking all this evidence together, it seems that vibration may be subserved both by pressure receptors and also by specialized receptors which do not respond to maintained pressure.

Mountcastle (1961) reports that with very light anaesthesia, cortical neurons follow repetitive cutaneous stimuli beat for beat, at frequencies up to about 75 to 100 per second. At higher frequencies, the response equilibrates. It may be that vibration frequency discrimination depends on the ability of central neurons to follow the stimulus frequency.

### HEAT

At temperatures roughly of above 45° C, a sensation of "heat" which is quite distinct from that of warmth, emerges. It has long been thought that this sensation is linked to the paradoxical discharge of cold receptors. As described above, Von Frey (1895) found that at temperatures above 45° C, previously mapped cold spots will respond with a sensation of cold. Dodt and Zotterman (1952b) placed this on a neurophysiological basis by showing that at temperatures above 45° C a steady discharge of cold fibers occurs, with a maximum frequency at 50° C (Figure 8–7).

Alrutz (1900) proposed that the sensation of heat was due to a fusion of warmth and paradoxical cold. That mixed warm and cold sensations can cause the impression of "heat" is demonstrated by the "heat grill." This consists of a grill made of parallel tubes which are alternately warm and cold (but none hot). Touching this grill will often give an impression of "heat." Also the simultaneous stimulation of a single cold spot with a cold stimulus and a single warm spot with a warm stimulus may produce the impression of "heat" (Alston, 1920). However, under normal conditions, stimuli described as "hot" are also above the pain threshold. Therefore a discharge from pain receptors usually also underlies the sensation of heat.

# 9

# CENTRAL PATHWAYS FOR THE SKIN SENSES

## PROJECTION PATHWAYS

### Spinal Cord to Thalamus

Fibers conveying sensory information through the spinal nerves enter the spinal cord by way of the dorsal roots. The cell bodies of these fibers lie in the spinal ganglion, which is an enlargement or swelling of the dorsal root. A dermatome is that skin area which is supplied with afferent fibers by one dorsal root. There is considerable overlap between dermatomes of neighboring roots. As each dorsal root enters the cord, it branches into many filaments. Each filament separates into a large medial division which contains large fibers, and a small lateral division containing small fibers.

Fibers of the medial division enter the ipsilateral dorsal columns without synapse and there ascend the cord. Some terminate at various levels in the grey matter of the cord. The remaining fibers terminate in the dorsal column nuclei of the medulla (the nuclei gracilis and cuneatus) and there synapse with second-order neurons.

Fibers arising in the dorsal column nuclei cross the midline and ascend in the tract of the medial lemniscus to end mainly in the lateral part of the ventrobasal complex of the thalamus. Some fibers terminate in portions of the posterior nuclear group of the thalamus, especially the magnocellular and suprageniculate nuclei of the medial geniculate complex (Bowsher, 1961; Perl and Whitlock, 1961).

Fibers ascending the dorsal columns give off collaterals at various levels, which synapse in the dorsal horns. Second-order neurons arising therefrom cross to the opposite side and ascend as part of the spinothalamic tract in the anterolateral region of the cord.

Fibers of the lateral division of the dorsal root enter the tract of Lissauer (dorsolateral fasciculus) located at the tip of the dorsal horn, ascend there a segment or two, and terminate in the substantia gelatinosa Rolandi. From here arise second-order neurons which cross to the opposite side and ascend there as part of the spinothalamic tract.

It is generally believed that the collaterals of the dorsal column fibers contribute to the ventral spinothalamic tract, and that fibers from the lateral division of the dorsal root contribute to the lateral spinothalamic tract. However, this dissociation has been questioned.

The spinothalamic pathway projects bilaterally onto the thalamus which it enters as lateral and medial bundles (Bowsher, 1961). The main lateral distribution is to the lateral part of the ventrobasal complex of the thalamus. Some fibers end in portions of the posterior nuclear group (Poggio and Mountcastle, 1960), especially the magnocellular and supra-geniculate nuclei of the medial geniculate body. The medial part of the tract is distributed to several intralaminar nuclei, and also to the centrum medianum, according to some definitions but not others (Bowsher, 1961; Whitlock and Perl, 1961).

Instead of ascending to the thalamus, many spinothalamic fibers terminate in various portions of the brain stem reticular formation (Mehler et al., 1960; Mehler, 1961). In return there is a strong input from the reticular formation to the diffuse thalamic nuclei.

In the cat, a further afferent pathway has been demonstrated which ascends in the dorsomedial part of the lateral funiculus (Morin, 1955; Lundberg and Oscarsson, 1961). The first neuron relays in the dorsal horn on the same side as its entrance to the cord (Eccles, Eccles and Lundberg, 1960). The second neuron relays in the lateral cervical nucleus of the same side, and the third in the ventrobasal complex of the contralateral thalamus (Busch, 1961).

## Trigeminal Pathways to the Thalamus

Fibers transmitting sensory information from the face and head enter the pons through the sensory root of the trigeminal nerve. Most of these fibers bifurcate, a fine branch ending in the main sensory nucleus of the pons and a larger branch following the spinal tract of the trigeminal nerve to end in the spinal nucleus of the medulla (Cajal, 1955). Other fibers connect only with the main nucleus, and yet others only with the spinal nucleus.

Fibers arising in the main sensory nucleus cross the midline and, lying adjacent to the medial lemniscus, ascend to the medial component of the ventrobasal complex of the thalamus. Other fibers originating in the main sensory nucleus form a dorsal pathway, which some believe to be both crossed and uncrossed, others only uncrossed. This pathway is believed to terminate in the medial component of the ventrobasal complex, or in the centrum medianum, or both.

Fibers arising in the spinal nucleus ascend as the bulbothalamic tract, the exact course of which is unclear, though it does run for a while in the reticular substance of the brain stem tegmentum. This tract is believed to terminate in the medial component of the ventrobasal complex and the centrum medianum. Some fibers of the spinal nucleus appear to contribute to the medial lemniscal projection (Gordon, Landgren, and Seed, 1961).

Pathways from the glossopharyngeal and vagus nerves also exist, but these have been less well worked out.

## Thalamus to Cortex

The primary cortical sensory receiving area (SI) is located in the postcentral gyrus and receives projections from the ventrobasal complex of the thalamus, and possibly also from the posterior nuclear group. The second somatic area (SII) is located in the anterior ectosylvian gyrus in the cat (and the corresponding region in primates) and probably receives projections both from the posterior nuclear group of the thalamus and also from the ventrobasal complex (Andersson, 1962). The precentral gyrus also receives sensory projections (Gardner and Morin, 1953; Kruger, 1956), and the lateral and suprasylvian gyri should probably also be included as part of the cortical sensory projection area (Albe-Fessard and Rougeol, 1955).

### SOMATOTOPIC ORGANIZATION

## First- and Second-Order Neurons

Centrally projecting fibers in the dorsal columns are arranged in an orderly lamination, such that fibers from each progressively higher body segment are arranged just lateral to those from the segment immediately below (Figure 9–1). There is very little overlap between fibers from different segments, though overlap between fibers from the same segment occurs. In the dorsal column nuclei the lamellar arrangement is preserved; fibers from the caudal segments terminating medially, and those from the higher segments laterally (Kuhn, 1949). At all rostro-caudal levels of the dorsal column nuclear complex, a somatotopic organization is apparent both along the medio-lateral axes and the dorso-ventral axes, with the caudal regions of the body represented medially and the limb apices dorsally (Kruger *et al.*, 1961).

A somatotopic representation of the face, with the mandibular division lying dorsally, the opthalmic division ventrally, and the interior of the buccal cavity medially, occurs at all rostrocaudal levels of the sensory trigeminal nuclear complex. That is, each point on the face is projected onto a column of cells extending from the rostral portion of the main sensory nucleus to the caudal portion of the spinal nucleus (Kruger and

FIG. 9–1. Diagram of the cervical spinal cord showing lamination in various tracts. Since there is considerable overlapping and intermingling of fibers, the dividing lines shown here are arbitrary. C. cervical. T. thoracic. L. lumbar. S. sacral. (From Ranson, S. W. and Clark, S. L., 1959, *The Anatomy of the Nervous System*, after Walker, A., courtesy of W. B. Saunders Co. Philadelphia.)

Michel, 1962a; Wall and Taub, 1962; Eisenman *et al.*, 1963). In fact, if a cross-section were taken through the dorsal column nuclei and the caudal part of the descending trigeminal nucleus together, then the "distribution can best be visualized as a cat lying on its back which forms the floor of the DCN complex, with its tail extending to the midline; the hindlimb, forelimb and face successively more lateral, and the paws of each foot pointed up and located at the dorsal edge of the DCN complex" (Kruger *et al.*, 1961). This representation is shown on Figure 9–2. The projection

FIG. 9–2. Sensory representation in a crosssection through the dorsal column nuclei and the caudal part of the descending trigeminal nucleus of the cat. (From Kruger, Z., *et al.*, *J. Neurophysiol.*, 1961, 24.)

here is entirely ipsilateral, except that the perioral region has some bilateral representation.

Fiber tracts in the anterolateral columns are also laminated. Here fibers from the more caudal body segments lie lateral to those from higher segments (Figure 9–1). However, much intermingling of fibers from different skin segments takes place. This considerable overlap is confirmed in the spinothalamic tract in midbrain regions by stimulation studies in man during mesencephalectomy for the relief of intractable pain (Spiegel and Wycis, 1961).

## Thalamus

Neurons of the trigeminal nuclear complex project onto the medial division of the ventrobasal complex of the thalamus, and those from the dorsal column nuclei onto its lateral division, in an orderly fashion. Spinothalamic neurons projecting onto the ventrobasal complex intermingle in the same somatotopic organization (Whitlock and Perl, 1959). A similar organization is apparent at the thalamic level as at the level of first relay, though reversed mediolaterally (Kruger *et al.*, 1961).

In detailed studies on the rabbit, cat and monkey, Mountcastle and his collaborators (1949, 1952, 1959) have shown that the body surface is projected contralaterally onto the ventrobasal complex, with the head posteromedial, the tail anterolateral, the back superior and the feet inferior. The perioral and intraoral regions project ipsilaterally as well as contralaterally. Stimulation studies on patients during the course of thalamotomy for the relief of intractable pain have yielded a map of the body surface similar to that found in the monkey with the use of recording techniques (Monnier, 1955).

No clear somatotopic organization is apparent in the posterior nuclear region of the thalamus (Whitlock and Perl, 1961; Poggio and Mountcastle, 1960). Neither does such an organization exist at the centrum medianum or the intralaminar nuclei.

## Cortex

The projection of fibers from the ventrobasal complex to the postcentral gyrus of the cortex is orderly, so that the topographic relationships present in the former region are preserved in the latter, though in reverse position. The medial region of the ventrobasal complex (face area) projects near the Sylvian fissure. The lateral region of the lateral portion of the ventrobasal complex (leg area) projects dorsomedially. Fibers from intermediate regions of the ventrobasal complex also project into intermediate regions of the cortical area (Figure 9–3). Penfield and his collaborators have shown by studies on patients that a somatotopic organization exists in the postcentral gyrus in the human case also (Figure 9–4).

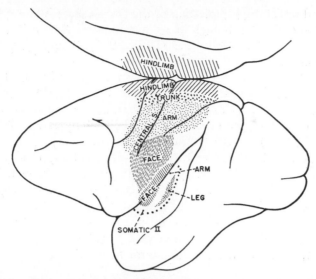

FIG. 9–3. Sensory representation in the cortex of the monkey. In this diagram the medial aspect of the hemisphere is shown as adjoining the dorsolateral aspect. Somatic area II extends into the superior bank of the Sylvian fissure. The area enclosed by open circles is normally in the depths of the fissure and so not visible in this view. (From Terzuolo, P., and Adey, W. R., in *Handbook of Physiology*, Vol. II; by permission of the American Physiological Society.)

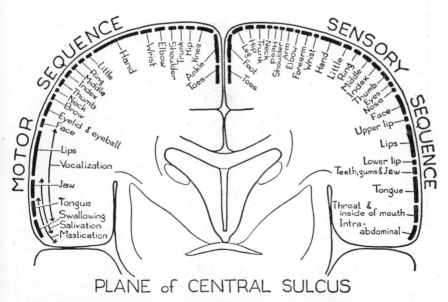

FIG. 9–4. Diagram of sensory and motor sequences in the cortex of man. The bars indicate roughly the extent of cortical area devoted to each body region. (From Rasmussen, G., and Penfield, W., *Fed. Proc.* 1947, 455.)

A detailed somatotopic projection of the body surface is also apparent at the second somatic area, though in a different order. The face areas of SI and SII are adjacent to each other (Figure 9–3). The projection to SII however is bilateral.

The somatosensory cortex is organized in a series of vertical columns oriented perpendicular to the cortical surface. All neurons forming part of a vertical column appear to have roughly similar receptive fields and to respond to the same type of stimulus modality. This is true both of SI (Mountcastle, 1961) and SII (Carreras and Levitt, 1959).

The proportional amount of tissue accorded centrally to a given body region does not mirror its actual proportional size. Regions which possess greater peripheral innervation density are accorded a correspondingly larger portion of central tissue. Receptive fields in these areas are also smaller. For instance receptive fields located on progressively more distal portions of a limb are found to be progressively smaller. Table 9–1 shows such a relation at the level of the dorsal column nuclei and Figure 9–5 at the

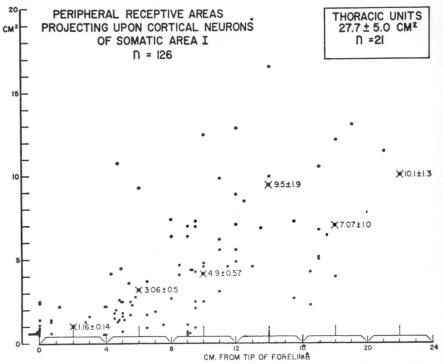

FIG. 9–5. A graph plotting the areas (in sq. cm.) of excitatory peripheral receptive fields of cortical neurons against the distances of the centers of these receptive fields from the tip of the contralateral foreleg of the cat. The crossed dots represent the means of these peripheral receptive field sizes when these are grouped into classes by 4 cm. distances from the limb tip. Standard errors are also given. (From Mountcastle, V. B., *J. Neurophysiol.*, 1957, 20, 408.)

somatosensory cortex. The same variation in receptive field size may exist at the level of the peripheral nerve (Yamamoto et al., 1956). These factors are further correlated with the degree to which the animal employs the body region in question. Thus the face is always accorded a disproportionately large amount of central tissue, as are the distal as opposed to the proximal portions of the limbs. Also, when different species of animal are compared, the amount of central tissue devoted to a body region varies with the degree to which that species of animal employs this particular organ. Thus the rabbit has a very large trigeminal representation. And in the monkey, much more than in the rabbit, the paws are extensively represented.

These correlations are of course to be expected, since the more complex or sensitive the functions carried out by a body region, the more

### TABLE 9-1

| Region | A: Hair | | B: Touch | |
|---|---|---|---|---|
| | Avg. Area, Sq. Mm. (Range) | No. of Units | Avg. Area, Sq. Mm. (Range) | No. of Units |
| Digit | 48 (6–200) | 46 | 444 (228–765) | 3 |
| Foot | 280 (28–900) | 30 | 1,818 (500–4,500) | 19 |
| Leg | 733 (50–1,140) | 5 | 4,121 (950–7,100) | 13 |
| Thigh | 1,620 (100–2,550) | 4 | 6,416 (3,150–12,000) | 16 |
| Hip and flank | 2,010 (600–6,600) | 7 | 10,742 (4,050–28,900 | 13 |
| Tail | 1,466 (900–2,300) | 5 | 6,800 | 1 |

Average receptive field sizes for two types of neuron in the nucleus gracilis of the cat: hair units (A) and touch units (B). The neurons are here classified by their location on the limb. For both types of neurons, the receptive fields located on progressively more distal regions of the limb are shown to be progressively smaller. (From Perl, E. R., et al., J. Neurophysiol., 1962, 25).

information has to be conveyed from the periphery and processed by central structures. One measure of somesthetic function, the two-point threshold, has been shown to correlate well with these factors. Receptive field sizes have been determined mainly in subhuman species, and a meaningful comparison cannot be made in absolute terms between these and the two-point threshold in man. However, the relative sizes of receptive field in animals taken from different regions of the body correlate very well with relative differences in two-point threshold determined in man for the different bodily regions.

## RECEPTIVE FIELD CHARACTERISTICS

It has been found at the level of the peripheral fiber that a receptive field may show a gradient of sensitivity. Stimulation at the center of the field may evoke discharge at shortest latency, highest frequency and slowest adaptation. Sensitivity diminishes with distance from the center of the field (Iggo, 1960). In some cases this would be expected on physical grounds. For instance, if the head of a pin is pressed into the skin, the resultant skin deformation would be maximal at the center. A discrete thermal stimulus would also transfer most heat at the center of the field of stimulation. This explanation would only hold under some conditions, for instance if the receptive field were not larger than the zone of deformation produced by a mechanical stimulus.

At the level of the first relay, several peripheral fibers converge onto the same central cells, and the same peripheral fiber sends branches to several central cells. Receptive fields at this level are therefore considerably larger and also overlap more than those of peripheral fibers. This pattern of convergence-divergence would be expected in itself to give rise to a gradient of sensitivity, sensitivity being again greater in the middle of the receptive field since here the synaptic linkages are the strongest. Such is in fact the case. The studies of Mountcastle and Powell (1959) on single units in the cortex have shown that cells in the middle of the cortical discharge zone discharge the largest number of impulses with the greatest probability and at shortest latencies. The further from the center a cell is located, the fewer the number of discharges and the longer the discharge latencies. Reciprocally, a given cortical cell will be excited maximally by one point on the receptive field, and less so by points located nearer the periphery of the field. This gradient of sensitivity could provide a means whereby information as to the locus of a peripheral stimulus is preserved in spite of enlarged and overlapping receptive fields.

Some neurons with extremely large receptive fields have been found at each stage in the sensory pathway. Several units in the thalamus and cortex were found to cover one half of the entire animal; some cover the entire body surface (see below). The functions of these units remain unknown. Many are activated only by noxious stimuli. It may be that these mediate gross withdrawal responses. In other cases where the units also respond to light mechanical stimuli, it may be that they are integrating information arriving simultaneously from various body areas. Greater sensitivity can also be obtained by summing information over large regions of the body.

## Lateral Inhibition

Evoked responses in many central neurons may be inhibited by stimulation of a different region of skin. The inhibitory receptive field may surround the excitatory field, or may lie adjacent to it or even be removed from it. In those cases where the zone of inhibition surrounds the zone of excitation this has the effect of sharpening the receptive field and therefore providing better spatial acuity. Lateral inhibition has been found as early in the somatosensory pathway as the nucleus gracilis (Perl et al., 1962) and as far up as the cortex (Mountcastle, 1961; Andersson, 1962). Temporal

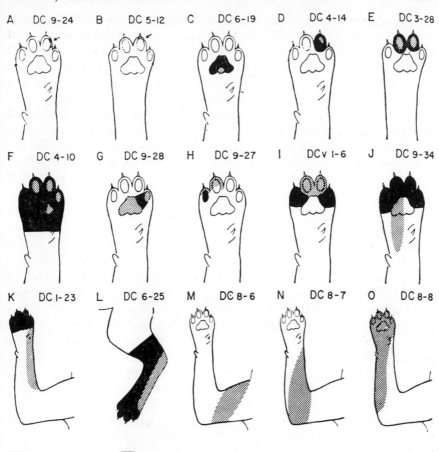

LIGHT TOUCH     INHIBITION

FIG. 9–6.  Typical excitatory and inhibitory receptive fields for units in the second somatic area of the cortex in cats with intact dorsal columns. These units were activated by light stimulation of the skin of contralateral limbs. B, E and L represent hindlimbs; all the drawings represent forelimbs. (From Andersson, S. A., *Acta, Physiol. Scand.*, 56 suppl. 194, 1967, 16.)

and spatial summation of such inhibitory effects occur (Mountcastle, 1961). Figure 9–6 shows some inhibitory and excitatory fields in the second somatic area of the cortex. Lateral inhibition also occurs in other sensory systems and is especially prominent in the visual system (see Chapter 11).

## MODALITY SPECIFICITY IN THE CENTRAL PATHWAYS

### Dorsal Columns

In the spinal nerve, fibers sensitive to different kinds of sensory stimulation are intermingled. In the cord, however, some separation according to modality occurs. The clinical evidence shows that the dorsal columns contain fibers subserving touch, pressure and kinesthesis, and complex discriminatory functions related to these. Destruction of the dorsal columns in man leads to an inability to determine the position and movement of limbs as well as to recognize vibratory stimuli. There is also an impairment of localization of sensory stimuli and of appreciation of spatial and temporal stimulus sequences. These symptoms are also found in tabes dorsalis, a disease in which there is degeneration of the dorsal columns.

In man, pain is generally held not to be mediated by the dorsal columns. Very good evidence for this view lies in the high success rate of anterolateral cordotomy for the relief of intractable pain. This operation spares the dorsal columns. However, the evidence in this regard is not completely clear-cut. Severe tingling has on occasion been obtained upon stimulation of the dorsal columns (Foerster and Gagel, 1932; Sweet, 1959). Also Browder and Gallagher (1948) found that relief of pain in a phantom limb was obtained in three out of four patients by division of the dorsal column.

In animals it may be that the dorsal columns also play a role in pain perception. Lesions in the anterior region of the cord do not abolish pain responses in dogs or monkeys (Cadwalder and Sweet, 1912; Mott, 1892) in contrast to the human case.

Single unit studies in the nucleus gracilis have also yielded information concerning modality transmission in the lemniscal pathway (Wall, 1961; Perl et al., 1962). Perl et al. (1962) found that most of the units here could be classified into three groups. The first group of units discharged to hair bending and adapted rapidly. The second group responded to light touch and adapted slowly to a maintained tactile stimulus. They also demonstrated a background discharge in the absence of mechanical stimulation, the frequency of which varied with changing temperature. The relation between discharge frequency and skin temperature depended on the rate and duration of the temperature change, rather than on the absolute temperature level. The third group responded well to jarring or vibratory stimuli, and were able to follow the frequency of applied vibration in the range from 70 to 350 c/sec. A few units responding to joint movement were also found. The response characteristics of the first three types of unit were considered very similar to these of certain peripheral units studied by Hunt and McIntyre (1960a and b) and Hunt (1961) (see Chapter 8). The authors conclude that these receptors had separate and specific projections to gracilis neurons. However many of the receptive fields of these second-order neurons were much larger than those of the peripheral fibers. Many second-order touch units for instance had fields which extended almost throughout the lateral or medial half of the hind limb (though quite small receptive fields were also found). It was therefore concluded that several peripheral fibers of the same modality converged onto a single second-order neuron.

In the case of hair units, it was further found that evoked responses could be inhibited by stimulation of the skin surrounding the excitatory receptive field. The other types of unit did not show this inhibitory interaction.

This study therefore demonstrates both the preservation of response characteristic and also some further organization of the incoming information at the level of the second-order neuron.

## Anterolateral Columns

Clinical evidence shows the spinothalamic tract to contain fibers subserving pain (including visceral) and temperature as well as touch. In syringomyelia, a disease in which fibers crossing in the anterior commissure are disrupted, there occurs a loss of pain and temperature sensibility in the corresponding body segments though tactile sensitivity appears unimpaired. Also anterolateral cordotomy, i.e., surgical interruption of the anterolateral columns (generally undertaken for the relief of intractable pain) produces little change in tactile sensibility, though there is an increase in tactile threshold; however, pain and temperature sensations are lost. (Visceral pain is lost if the operation is bilateral.) Sometimes the sense of tickle may also be lost and disturbances in sexual sensations occur.

Classically it is thought that the ventral spinothalamic tract is concerned with touch and the lateral with pain and temperature. However, there is no concrete evidence that this is the case (Rose and Mountcastle, 1959). The difficulty in establishing the exact locus of tactile fibers is partly due to the fact that since the dorsal columns also mediate tactile sensations there is little demonstrable loss in tactile sensibility when the anterolateral columns are sectioned.

It is also classically believed that fibers concerned with temperature lie separate to those concerned with pain in the lateral spinothalamic tract (Foerster, 1936; Foerster and Gagel, 1932). However, when anterolateral cordotomies are performed, analgesia and thermanesthesia usually occur together. Yet a few cases have been reported of the loss of thermal sensibility without loss of pain sensibility, and vice versa. There also occur sometimes cases of dissociated loss of sensibility to heat or to cold (Head, 1920). The existence and yet rarity of such dissociations leads one to conclude that there probably are separate pain and temperature fibers in the spinothalamic tract but that they are on the whole intermingled. Sweet (1950) found that stimulation of the spinothalamic tract in conscious patients yielded reports of either pain or temperature (mainly heat) though no touch. The fibers mediating the different sensations appeared intermingled.

Single unit studies on dorsal horn cells have added some further potential information concerning modality transmission in the spinothalamic pathways. However, the projections of the axons of the neurons studied are in most cases unknown, so it is difficult to draw specific conclusions from these studies. Some neurons investigated responded only to one modality such as touch or noxious stimulation; others responded to more than one (Kolmodin and Skoglund, 1960; Wall, 1960). Receptive fields varied from small to very wide, some being scattered (Hunt and Kuno, 1959). In some cases, stimulating one skin area produced an increased discharge frequency while the same stimulus to another area produced inhibition of discharge in the same neuron. Here it is apparent, as in the dorsal column nuclei, that many peripheral fibers must converge onto a single second-order neuron. But it seems that here the convergence is not restricted to fibers of the same modality.

Wall (1960, 1961) describes a group of neurons in the dorsal horn which responded in a different manner to several types of peripheral stimulus. They responded as though afferent fibers sensitive to different degrees of pressure converged onto them. Also, single cells responded both to pressure and to warming of the skin, to the latter with an increased average frequency of spontaneous discharge. Effects of high pressure and high temperature stimulation (which both produce pain in man) were similar; and application of vibration and an itch-producing substance to the skin also produced characteristic patterns of response.

Unfortunately, it is not known whether these neurons studied by Wall form part of a true sensory pathway, or whether they are involved merely in the formation of reflexes for which discrimination amongst the different modalities of stimulation would be unnecessary. However, Wall and Cronley-Dillon (1960) present some evidence that these cells may actually be transmitting information concerning different sensory modalities by means of different patterns of discharge.

Wall argues that if information concerning stimulus modality were transmitted via the discharge pattern of a cell, then factors altering the discharge pattern should also alter the experienced sensation. Further, where the discharge pattern to two types of stimuli were identical, one should expect these stimuli to be confused at the sensory level. Wall points to two such examples. The first concerns the effect of a vibratory stimulus applied to a given region of skin on the simultaneous application of another stimulus to the same region. Such vibratory stimuli cause the cells under discussion to produce a characteristic pattern of alternating activation and inhibition, and considerably raises their threshold for the emission of the high-frequency discharge which is characteristic on the presentation of other types of stimulus to the skin. Wall argues that if these cells really did convey information concerning stimulus modality, then vibrating an area of skin in man should cause sensitivity to other modalities of sensation in that region to decrease. It was indeed found that light vibration raises the threshold in this region in man for touch, pain and temperature. Another example is the similar response of such cells to extreme heat and high distorting pressures to the skin which cause similarly painful sensations in man.

The lateral tract located in the dorsomedial part of the lateral funiculus appears to transmit specific tactile information. Lundberg and Oscarsson (1961) report that single units in this tract responded effectively to light touch over a restricted receptive field and did not respond with increased activation to stronger mechanical stimuli. Further, Norsell (quoted by Andersson, 1962) reports that in dogs, unilateral interruption of the lateral tract in the dorsomedial part of the lateral funiculus abolished unilaterally a conditioned response established to puffs of air applied to the hindlimbs.

## Sensory Trigeminal Nuclear Complex

The clinical evidence indicates that the main sensory nucleus is primarily concerned with tactile information and the spinal nucleus with pain and temperature. Sjöqvist (1938) found that sectioning afferent fibers to the caudal part of the spinal nucleus (trigeminal tractotomy) produced a severe loss of pain and temperature sensibility in the face, yet very little impairment in tactile sensibility. However, single unit studies in the cat have produced results at variance with these findings. Many authors have reported the presence of neurons in the spinal nucleus as well as in the main sensory nucleus sensitive to light tactile stimuli (Gordon et al., 1960; Kruger et al., 1961; Kruger and Michel, 1962b; Eisenman et al., 1963). Also, differences could not be found between these two nuclei concerning responsiveness to noxious stimuli. Kruger and Michel (1962b) and Wall and Taub (1962) were unable to find units in either of the trigeminal nuclei which responded specifically to noxious stimulation. In contrast, Eisenman et al. (1963) found many cells which discharged only to noxious stimuli. Some responded to noxious mechanical stimuli but not to noxious thermal stimuli; others to both. However, these units were found in the main sensory nucleus as well as in the spinal nucleus, and the authors conclude that the two nuclei could not be separated on this basis.

Specific temperature fibers in the trigeminal nuclear complex have not been found. However, Wall and Taub (1962) describe certain pressure-sensitive cells that also responded to changes in temperature.

Single unit studies performed on the cat have failed to explain the clinical evidence on separation of function within the sensory trigeminal nuclear complex in man. It may be, however, that this is due to the difference in species investigated. Perhaps similar studies on the monkey will produce results more in line with the clinical evidence.

## Brain Stem between Spinal Cord and Thalamus

Lesions in the brain stem between the spinal cord and the thalamus may give rise to analgesia and thermanesthesia. However, appreciation of pain, warmth or cold may be impaired independently (Von Monakow, 1908; Mann, 1892; Head, 1920). There may result a raising of the tactile threshold, and sometimes an impairment of more complex functions, such as tactile localization, two-point discrimination, or appreciation of passive movement. In some cases, a pain syndrome may result. The affected regions lie in contralateral side of the body. Stimulation of the spinothalamic tract in patients during mesencephalotomy for the relief of intractable pain may produce pain of a tingling, burning or pricking quality. "Electrical" sensations have also been reported (Spiegel and Wycis, 1961). These sensations are usually projected to the side opposite that of stimulation, though bilateral sensations can occur. In some cases the pain is diffusely localized; in others it occurs in relatively specific regions of the body, such as the face, arm, chest, or leg.

## Central Midbrain Structures

It will be recalled that many spinothalamic fibers feed into various regions of the brain stem reticular formation. There is good reason to suppose that at least some of these fibers are concerned with pain, for if the spinothalamic tract is interrupted at the midbrain level, a pain syndrome may develop. Various writers (Walker, 1943; Bowsher, 1957; Spiegel and Wycis, 1961) attribute this pain sensibility following mesencephalic tractotomy to the functioning of the more medially placed structures.

Also, stimulation of various centrally placed midbrain regions has been found to give rise to reactions of fear and rage, and though some of these have been interpreted as demonstrating the existence of fear and rage "centers," the possibility that this stimulation causes pain or some unpleasant sensation is very strong in some cases. Spiegel et al. (1954) interpreted the reactions of cats upon stimulation of the mesencephalic tectum as being pain-suggestive, and Delgado (1955) came to a similar conclusion upon observing the reactions of monkeys upon stimulation of the inferomedial part of the mesencephalic central grey matter. Further, Spiegel and Wycis (1961) report that, in patients, stimulation in the midbrain tegmentum, probably of neurons of the reticular system, elicited pain sensations which were projected mainly contralateral to the point of stimulation; and Reyes et al. (1951) found that stimulation of the midbrain tectum produces pain in patients, projected to the contralateral side.

## Thalamus

### Ventrobasal Complex

Studying single unit responses to various forms of mechanoreception, Poggio and Mountcastle (1960) concluded that neurons in this region showed a high degree of modality specificity, with small contralateral receptive fields. Perl and Whitlock (1961) also found, in animals with spinal lesions sparing only the anterolateral tracts, that single units in the ventrobasal complex demonstrated a high degree of specificity, responding either to light touch, joint rotation, hair displacement, deep pressure, or heat of tissue-damaging intensity, with very restricted contralateral receptive fields. The effect of thermal stimuli in the medium ranges were not investigated in either of these studies.

Landgren (1961), studying responses of single ventrobasal units to stimulation of the tongue, also found that most of the neurons here were responsive to only one stimulus modality. Of these, touch cells comprised a large proportion. Cold cells were also numerous. One thalamic cell was activated by warming. He found some cells which responded both to touch and cooling.

Some ventrobasal neurons were found to be exquisitely sensitive to the stimulus parameters employed. The cold cells investigated by Landgren behaved in a fashion similar to those found in peripheral nerve fibers (see Chapter 8). Sudden drops in temperature caused an immediate increase in discharge frequency, and warming the tongue caused a decrease in firing frequency. With a constant temperature the fiber adapted to a steady discharge. These cold cells also discharged to very high peripheral temperatures (paradoxical cold discharge). The frequency of steady discharge in these thalamic neurons was both higher and less regular than that of peripheral cold cells. Other ventrobasal neurons only responded phasically to drops in temperature.

A similar exquisite sensitivity to stimulus parameters has been found in units activated by joint rotation (see below).

### Posterior Nuclear Region

Units in the posterior nuclear region were found regularly to have very large receptive fields, which were often stocking-like in shape and frequently bilateral (Poggio and Mountcastle, 1960; Perl and Whitlock, 1961). Some receptive fields here were so large as to include all four limbs; some were scattered. Perl and Whitlock (1961) found that most of these units responded to light mechanical stimuli. In contrast, Poggio and Mountcastle (1960) found that nearly 60 percent of these neurons could be activated only by noxious stimulation, the remaining cells responding to light mechanical stimuli. Some units were activated by light mechanical stimuli over one part of their receptive field and by noxious stimuli over another (Figure 9-7). This discrepancy between the two sets of findings may be due to a difference in the anaesthetic levels employed, or to a difference in anatomical location of the units studied. Complex patterns of excitation and inhibition exist in this region. Some cells were activated from one side of the body and inhibited from the other side. Others were excited from small fields and yet could be inhibited from almost the entire remaining body area.

Receptive fields of units driven by mechanical stimuli

Receptive fields of units driven by noxious stimuli

FIG. 9–7. Typical receptive fields for neurons in the posterior nuclear group of the thalamus. The right hand side of each figurine drawing represents the ipsilateral side of the body, relative to the recording electrode. (From Poggio, G. F. and Mountcastle, V. B.; *Bull. Johns Hopkins Hosp.*, 1960, 106.)

Some cells in this region were found to be activated by acoustic and vibratory as well as simple somatic stimuli; occlusion between somatic and auditory inputs occurred commonly. Other cells in this region were sensitive only to acoustic stimuli. Also although discrete thermal stimuli were not employed, changes in general skin temperature produced profound changes in the activity of these cells.

### Intralaminar Nuclei and Centrum Medianum

Units located in the intralaminar nuclei and centrum medianum responded only to noxious stimuli, receptive fields being very large, and bilateral (Perl and Whitlock, 1961). Albe-Fessard and Kruger (1962) report that cells in the centrum medianum-parafascicular complex responded only to noxious stimuli localized anywhere on the body. Some neurons fired at short latency, and others only after a delay. A few units emitted both short and long latency responses. The long latency response of such units may be related to the phenomenon of second pain (see Chapter 8).

Lesion studies in patients have further implicated this area in pain sensitivity. Ervin and Mark (1961) report that lesions in the ventroposterior nuclei did not alleviate pain of terminal cancer in patients. However, lesions in the centromedian and intralaminar nuclei did provide relief of pain. Hécaen *et al.* (1949) found that a marked reduction in the perception of painful stimuli resulted from lesions located mainly in the centrum medianum. Interestingly enough, however, they did not produce pain upon stimulation of this structure. Another finding which is against the supposition that these units underlie pain sensitivity is that they will not respond to a slowly applied pinprick, nor to light touch on the cornea, both of which are painful (Kruger, 1959).

### Thalamic Lesions and Deficits in Sensibility

Thalamic lesions often result in a raising of tactile thresholds in the affected regions, which lie on the side of the body contralateral to the lesion. Vibration sense is often disturbed. Appreciation of posture and passive movement are often affected, as are stimulus localization, two-point discrimination, and other tests of discriminative function. The appreciation of heat and cold may be defective. Pain sensibility is often disturbed, and a pain syndrome may develop (Head, 1920).

## Cortex

### First Somatic Area

Mountcastle (1961), studying the response of SI neurons only to various forms of mechanoreception, concluded that most neurons were specific as to mode and place. However other cells in this region displayed very large receptive fields and showed complex patterns of excitation and inhibition (Mountcastle and Powell, 1959). For instance some could be excited by ipsilateral stimuli and then inhibited by stimuli located in the equivalent region on the opposite side. Others could be activated only by noxious stimuli and then inhibited by light tactile stimuli applied to the same body region.

Landgren (1957, 1961) studied cortical neurons responding to stimulation of the tongue. He found the majority of these cells to respond only to one modality, these being mainly touch and cold cells, though one warmth cell was isolated. Some cells responded to two modalities, and some to even more. All cortical cells which responded to more than one stimulus modality fired at short latency to touch or "stretch" stimuli. Yet thermal and taste stimuli activated these same cells more effectively, though at longer latencies.

As at the thalamic level, cold cells were found to have different discharge patterns in response to cooling. Some manifested only phasic responses, but others behaved very like the peripheral cold fibers described by Hensel and Zotterman (1951).

Another example of exquisite sensitivity to the parameters of stimulation employed is given by neurons activated by joint rotation. Some only respond phasically to joint rotation. However, most of these neurons both respond rapidly to transient rotation of the appropriate joint and also discharge steadily when the joint is maintained at a certain angle, adapting to this only very slowly. The angle of joint displacement which causes excitation varies for different neurons. The degree and rate of joint movement determine the onset transient, whereas the joint angle alone determines the steady discharge. Some pairs of neurons were described which are reciprocally related to a given joint. The first neuron but not the second is activated when the joint moves in one direction, and when the

FIG. 9–8. Graph showing the impulse frequency of two neurons which responded reciprocally to alternating flexions and extensions of the contralateral elbow. The neurons, located in the postcentral gyrus of the cat, were observed simultaneously. The graph plots continuously the average frequencies for each consecutive 400 msec. period. During the fourteenth and fifteenth seconds the joint was held steady. (From Mountcastle, V. B., *J. Neurophysiol.*, 1957, 20.)

direction of movement is reversed the second cell is activated but not the first. The behavior of two such neurons is shown in Figure 9–8. It can be seen that the discharge frequency for each neuron reaches zero when the joint is in the position which maximally excites the other neuron. As yet it is not known whether this reciprocity is central or peripheral in origin.

## Second Somatic Area

Many units in SII respond specifically to one modality of stimulation over small contralateral receptive fields (Andersson, 1962). However, receptive fields in this area vary greatly from small to very large (Carreras and Levitt, 1959). In animals with spinal lesions it was shown (Andersson, 1962) that some units had very large receptive fields, often stocking-like, sometimes bilateral and symmetrical, sometimes discontinuous and sometimes including the whole animal. Some units were only responsive to strong stimuli; others were activated by light stimuli over one area but only by strong stimuli over another. These units were very slowly adapting. Some showed no adaptation and continued to fire with a gradual decrease in frequency after the stimulus was withdrawn. Some units were also activated by auditory stimuli, and interaction between responses to somatic and auditory stimuli was observed. A few units were driven by vibratory stimuli.

These units are similar to those found in the posterior nuclear complex of the thalamus (Poggio and Mountcastle, 1960; Perl and Whitlock,

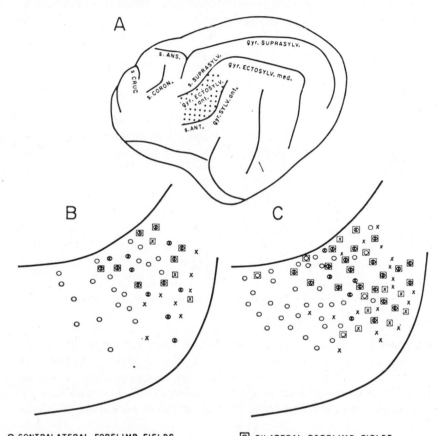

O CONTRALATERAL FORELIMB FIELDS
X CONTRALATERAL HINDLIMB FIELDS
⊕ CONTRALATERAL FORE- AND HINDLIMB FIELDS

◻ BILATERAL FORELIMB FIELDS
⊠ BILATERAL HINDLIMB FIELDS
◉ BILATERAL FORE- AND HINDLIMB FIELDS

FIG. 9–9. Distribution of penetrations in the second somatic area of the cat. A. Schematic drawing of the cortex of the cat with the area investigated stippled. B. Distribution of 47 penetrations with intact dorsal columns. C. Distribution of 87 penetrations with intact lateral tract. In both B and C each point was classified according to the maximum peripheral field, estimated both by single units and by evoked potential waves at all levels in the penetration. (From Andersson, S. A., *Acta Physiol. Scand.* 56, Suppl. 194, 1962, 60.)

1961). Andersson (1962) suggests that this type of response is mediated via the posterior nuclear complex whereas the specific type of response is mediated via the ventrobasal complex. He further suggests that in the intact animal the less specific pathways are inhibited both by descending tracts exerting a tonic inhibitory influence at the first relay, and also by inhibitory effects from ascending specific projection pathways interacting at higher levels.

Andersson found that the responses evoked from large body regions were obtained mainly in the posterior portion of SII. The more anterior portion of the area contained units which were much more specific in their response patterns; that is, similar to those typical in SI (Figure 9–9).

## Sensations Evoked in Patients by Cortical Stimulation

Stimulation of various cortical structures in patients has been found to evoke sensory responses. Most of these responses are obtained from the postcentral gyrus, though some are obtained from the precentral gyrus and a small number from neighboring points. Sensations evoked from the postcentral gyrus are somatotopically organized with respect to the body surface (Figure 9–4). The sensations evoked are generally contralateral but may be bilateral. Foerster (1927) reports that sensations obtained upon postcentral stimulation were discretely localized, but those obtained from the superior parietal lobule were localized much more diffusely.

The most commonly occurring sensations described are tingling, a feeling of "electricity," and numbness (Penfield and Jasper, 1954). Pain has occasionally been reported (Foerster, 1927) including visceral pain.

### CORTICAL LESIONS AND DEFICITS IN SENSIBILITY

In man, parietal lesions may produce a variety of symptoms, notably in the somatosensory field. With superficial lesions, sensory thresholds are often little affected, but marked deficits in discrimination and synthesis of sensory information may appear. There may be impairment of postural sensibility, the recognition of passive movement of a joint, or of the position in space held by a limb. The affected limb may appear too heavy or too light. Deficits may occur in stimulus localization, two-point discrimination, or stereognosis (the recognition of objects by tactile means). Also the patient, though able to perceive a stimulus to the affected limb when presented alone, may yet be unable to perceive it when presented together with a stimulus to the normal side of his body (Critchley, 1953).

Sometimes parietal lesions may give rise to anaesthesia instead of or in addition to the above symptoms. In this case, the anaesthesia is not usually distributed evenly over one half of the body; instead scattered islands of sensory loss with blurred boundaries appear. Sometimes a dissociated loss for some but not other sensory modalities occurs. Kleist (1934) reports deficits in pain and temperature sensation, or pain alone, in some patients. Foerster (1936) and Kroll (1930) report pain deficits. Marshall (1951) showed by careful investigation that pain sensation could be severely impaired as a result of such lesions, yet in other cases temperature sense could be severely impaired with no loss of pain.

Sometimes a pain syndrome may develop, as discussed in the next section. Occasionally asymbolia for pain is found; the patient may feel pain, but does not react aversively to it and may even seek it.

More severe symptoms may also result from parietal lesions, such as an inability to copy simple drawings, or simple models (constructional apraxia), or to write (agraphia) or perform calculations (acalculia). The patient may manifest considerable right-left disorientation in his movements.

The body image may become severely impaired or distorted. Sometimes there develops what is known as "unilateral neglect." Here, there is considerable poverty of movement on the affected side, but if specifically commanded to do so, the patient will use affected limbs. In extreme cases the patient will not tend to one half of his anatomy: he will comb his hair only on one side of his head, shave only one side of his face, leave unclothed one half of his body. Yet reflex movements on the affected side remain normal. An interesting test of this syndrome demonstrates that it is the sensory needs of the affected side which suffer rather than the desire to move it. If the left side is deficient and the patient is told to put on a pair of gloves, he will use his left hand to put a glove on his *right* hand (but not vice versa).

A striking concomitant of such disorders is that the patient often evinces complete unconcern for the affected limbs. Even in cases of paralysis, the patient is not troubled by the deficit. In fact, he often goes to great lengths to deny this very loss. He will assert that he can indeed move his paralyzed limb, and invent many excuses to explain his not using it. In worse cases, the patient will disown his affected part, complain of it, ask that it be removed, claim that it belongs to someone else. Sometimes bizarre delusions are formed concerning the identity of the affected limbs. At other times, the patient may feel as though nothing existed in the affected regions. Interestingly, Critchley concluded that it is injury to the *non*dominant parietal lobe which is best correlated with disorders of the body image.

It is difficult to know to what extent the extreme symptoms related to disorders of the body image are somatosensory in origin, and how much is due to a general loss of spatial sense, or even to personality disorder. Sensory loss alone cannot explain the refusal to admit paralysis, or denial of ownership of a limb, since this does not happen in cases of sensory loss and paralysis due to peripheral lesions. One consideration still involving the sensory system, but which may explain a part of these bizarre symptoms, is that in the case of normal sensory loss, the central representation for the affected area is intact, and the patient decides that a limb is paralyzed or numb on the basis of certain types of information, or lack of it, which is registered in the central representation. However, if the central representation itself is lost, this cannot happen. The information that there is a lack of sensation, or lack of movement, cannot be registered in the usual way. This might explain the feeling of nothingness in place of a limb, and the feeling that the limb is not really a part of one's body. Some such factor may be the basis of denial of a defect such as paralysis, if the registration of movement or lack of it does not occur.

However, it is unlikely that such considerations can explain the bizarre confabulations that some patients adopt to account for their deficit. A patient may believe that his limb has embarked on a long journey, or that he is attached to a limb belonging to some person of his acquaintance, or he might hold long conversations with his affected part. Other evidence of extreme personality disorder is also often apparent in such patients, and it may be necessary to postulate an additional general personality disturbance to account for these extraordinary symptoms. However, it is not very surprising that a consistent and extreme distortion of an individual's sensory world should alone cause a collapse of the sense of reality.

## Correlation of Different Subdivisions of the Sensorimotor Region with Different Types of Sensory Function in Man

Various clinicians have attempted to assign special functions to the different subdivisions of the sensorimotor region. According to the traditional view, the postcentral gyrus (or primary receiving area), is concerned with basic sensations, and the posterior parietal lobule (the association area for somaesthesis) is concerned with analysis and integration of these experiences. One might therefore expect lesions confined to the postcentral gyrus to give rise mainly to deficits in tests of simple sensation, such as sensory threshold. Lesions of the posterior parietal lobule might be expected to give rise to deficits in tasks testing integrative functions, such as stimulus localization, two-point discrimination, sense of movement, and so on.

On the other hand, Head (1920) proposed that in general, lesions of the precentral gyrus lead to a deficit in the appreciation of spatial relationships, lesions in the postcentral gyrus lead to a deficit in the recognition of similarities and differences between objects, and lesions of the posterior parietal area result in defect in response to graduated intensities (such as pressure sensitivity).

A completely different view is taken by Goldstein (1927, 1942) who denies that separate functions are localized in different areas. He suggests that lesions wherever placed result in the same basic disorder of function, which manifests itself differently on the various tests employed, but varies according to the individual patient. According to his hypothesis, one should not be able to point to any consistent variation in type of performance deficit resulting from lesions differently localized.

Semmes *et al.* (1960) carried out an extensive study on war veterans with discrete long-standing lesions of the sensorimotor cortex. They classified lesions as involving various subsectors of the sensorimotor area (precentral, postcentral, and posterior parietal regions), contralateral to the hand tested, or other cortical regions. For each hand, they then studied pressure sensitivity, resolution of two points, point localization, and discrimination of the direction of passive movement of a joint. They concluded that it was not possible to correlate lesions involving a particular subsector of the sensorimotor region with specific deficits, as measured by these tests. Their study therefore failed to support either the classical hypothesis or Head's hypothesis of gross anatomical localization of function. However, though they found that scores for the right hand on all tests were highly related, this was not the case for the left, forcing the postulation of more than one basic disturbance of function. Therefore Goldstein's hypothesis of a unitary impairment of function was also not corroborated.

Semmes *et al.* made a further interesting observation when they compared performance of the right with the left hand. Although they found that the presence of defects in the right hand was maximal after left sensorimotor injuries compared with lesions in other regions of the left hemisphere, right sensorimotor lesions did not have a significantly greater effect on the left hand than did other lesions in the right hemisphere. It therefore appears that sensory mechanisms, at least for the hand, are more concentrated in the left hemisphere than in the right.

## Animal Studies

In rats, Zubek (1951a, 1952) found that lesions in SI and SII did not lead to a complete abolition of the capacity to perform roughness and tactile form discriminations, though there was some loss. In one cat, Zubek (1951b) found that ablation of SI and SII did lead to a permanent loss of the ability to make roughness discriminations. However, one cannot conclude much on the basis of one animal. In dogs, Allen (1947) found that bilateral lesions of SI and SII did not abolish a positive CR to tactile stimulation, although a differential foreleg response was abolished.

Ruch and Fulton (1935) and Ruch, Fulton and German (1938) report that in the monkey, chimpanzee and man, lesions in the postcentral gyrus or posterior parietal region did not abolish the ability to discriminate differences in weight, roughness or tactile form. However, retraining was needed to reestablish the ability. Blum *et al.* (1950) found in one monkey with ablation of the entire parietal cortex, that with prolonged retraining somesthetic discrimination was possible.

Kruger and Porter (1958) found that ablation of SI and SII led to a severe tactile deficit in the contralateral limbs, though with unilateral and bilateral ablations a single somesthetic form discrimination could be relearned. Ablation of the precentral cortex led to a temporary tactile deficit but no deficit in somaesthetic form discrimination. Unilateral ablation of the precentral and postcentral arm area combined led to a severe sensory loss in the arm contralateral to the lesions. The two subjects tested were unable to carry out the somaesthetic task with the affected limb, though they were able to perform a visual discrimination task utilizing that limb.

## CENTRIFUGAL CONTROL OF SENSORY INFLOW

As in other sensory systems, there is evidence that centrifugal fibers modulate sensory information arriving at the somatosensory relay stations. Kuypers (1960a, 1960b) demonstrated that fibers originating in the precentral, postcentral, and posterior parietal cortices descended in the pyramidal tract to end in the dorsal column nuclei. Occlusive interaction has been found in units of the dorsal column nuclei between pyramidal and sensory inflows (Magni *et al.*, 1959). Some units here can be driven by sensorimotor cortex stimulation; others inhibited (Chambers *et al.*, 1960; Guzman *et al.*, 1961). Some reticular fibers also end in the dorsal column nuclei (Kuypers *et al.*, 1960). Stimulation of the midbrain reticular formation produces inhibition in this area; however, when the sensorimotor cortex is ablated, this changes to facilitation (Guzman *et al.*, 1961).

There also appear to be descending fibers originating in the cortex and ending in the ventrobasal complex of the thalamus. Iwama and Yamamoto (1961) found that stimulation of the somatosensory cortex altered activity in the ventrobasal complex evoked from the dorsal columns.

## SENSORY PATHWAYS FROM THE VISCERA

Sensory information from the viscera is carried peripherally by sympathetic and parasympathetic fibers, as well as by some somatic afferents which innervate the visceral cavities. Some types of stimulus which cause pain when applied to the skin do not produce sensation when applied to the viscera. Procedures as drastic as cutting or burning a visceral organ need not cause sensation. However, visceral afferents will discharge effectively for instance to certain chemical irritants, spasms or sudden distention. Inflammation renders visceral pain fibers more sensitive. Visceral pain is subjectively different from cutaneous pain, being in general more severe and long-lasting and having a diffuse irradiating quality.

Many visceral afferents are concerned only with the initiation of reflexes and do not have a sensory function. Such reflexes are mediated mostly by the parasympathetic system, though reflexes secondary to pain may be mediated by sympathetic fibers.

Most visceral pain impulses are carried by sympathetic nerves. However, there are exceptions to this. The parasympathetic pelvic and vagus nerves convey pain impulses from organs which they innervate (White, 1943).

## Fiber Size and Modality Specificity in Visceral Afferents

Gernandt (1946), and Gernandt and Zotterman (1946) found that noxious stimulation to the diaphragm and the intestine set up impulses in the Aδ and C range in the phrenic and splanchnic nerves respectively. Light stimulation of the mesentery gave rise to Aβ fiber activity in the splanchnic nerve. The diameters of the fibers responding to the two different types of stimulation were therefore similar in these instances to those found in afferents from the skin.

## Central Pathways

Not very much is known about the central visceral pathways. According to Aidar et al. (1952), splanchnic afferent pathways in the cat appear to traverse two routes. A fast route was found to travel by way of the ipsilateral posterior columns, and nucleus gracilis; from there to the contralateral medial lemniscus and lateral portion of the ventrobasal complex. Splanchnic impulses occurred in regions between those for the fore and hind limbs. Much slower impulses were also traced bilaterally in the region of the lateral spinothalamic tract in the cord, and also bilaterally in the posterior hypothalamus and caudal thalamus. Amassian (1951a) also recorded impulses evoked by splanchnic stimulation bilaterally in the anterolateral region of the cord, using rabbits, cats and dogs. Patton and Amassian (1951) demonstrated a splanchnic projection to the lateral part of the ventrobasal complex of the thalamus, intermingled with the topographic projection of the somatic afferents. It has been hypothesized that the sensation of visceral distention is mediated by the posterior columns and that of visceral pain by the anterolateral columns.

Cortical responses to visceral afferent stimulation have also been found. Amassian (1951b) showed that stimulation of the splanchnic nerve evokes activity in the contralateral postcentral gyrus, in a region between the arm and leg areas. Stimulation of the cortex in conscious patients has yielded visceral sensations (Penfield and Jasper, 1954). Foerster (1936) also reports visceral pain (cardiac and abdominal) upon stimulation of the postcentral gyrus in the appropriate regions of the topographic projection field.

Convergence has been observed between the somatic and visceral systems at the thalamic and cortical levels (MacLeod, 1956; Amassian,

1952). Central responses to visceral afferent stimulation may be blocked by preceding somatic stimulation.

HYPERPATHIA

Various lesions of the central nervous system may give rise to an alteration in the quality of pain sensation felt in the corresponding region of the body. Although the threshold for the experience of pain may not be lowered and may even be raised, the pain once felt is more intense and much more disagreeable. The term "hyperpathia" is employed to describe such abnormalities of sensation.

## Hyperpathia Due to Midbrain Lesions

Pain syndromes have been noted to occur after midbrain lesions. Dogliotti (1938) reports that patients in which pain pathways in the midbrain had been cut on one side experienced diffuse unpleasant sensations in the contralateral half of the body. Drake and McKenzie (1953) and Walker (1943) report similar findings. It was suggested that such pain could be mediated by fibers in the midbrain reticular formation or tectum, probably together with activity in the hypothalamus. Bowsher (1957) also proposes that while the spinothalamic system might mediate short-latency, sharply localized pain, the spinoreticulothalamic system might mediate the diffuse long-lasting pain found in these syndromes. One might assume, therefore, that the spinothalamic system, or some other pathway traversing the same area, normally inhibits the more diffuse system, and that the lesions had the effect of releasing the latter from inhibition. Or alternately one could suppose that the lesion had the effect of irritating the diffuse sensory pathways, so as to cause an abnormal increase in their activity, this producing the abnormal sensations.

## Hyperpathia Produced by Thalamic Lesions

The thalamic syndrome of Déjérine and Roussy (1906) occurs when a large portion of the thalamus, including much of the ventrobasal complex, is destroyed as a result of thrombosis of the thalamogeniculate artery. After an initial period of sensory loss, sensory stimuli come to evoke pain of long latency, which is persisting, diffuse, poorly localized, and intensely unpleasant. Though the threshold for their perception may be high, it often happens that painful sensations come to be provoked by normally innocuous stimuli, such as touch, vibration, or even sound. This condition may become steadily worse until the patient is in a state of spontaneous agonizing pain.

Whether it is due to irritation or loss of inhibition (see below), one may speculate about the possible thalamic regions involved in this syndrome. In the posterior nuclear region, receptive fields are commonly very large, and activity in such units might explain the diffuseness and poor localizability of the sensations experienced. Also several of these units have been found to be activated by vibratory and auditory stimuli (Perl and Whitlock, 1961; Poggio and Mountcastle, 1960), which also produce these unpleasant sensations in such patients. Another region which may be involved is the centrum medianum and adjoining structures. Here units respond only to noxious stimuli over very large receptive fields (Perl and Whitlock, 1961; Albe-Fessard and Kruger, 1962). Some of these neurons respond only at long latency (Albe-Fessard and Kruger, 1962). Against implicating this region is the finding that receptive fields here are bilateral. However, Walker (1943) reports a case of pain syndrome in which autopsy revealed destruction of almost the entire ventrobasal complex and the equivalent of the posterior nuclear group, but in which centrum medianum and intralaminar nuclei were spared. Also Hécaen et al (1949) found that centrum medianum lesions produce an improvement in thalamic pain.

## Hyperpathia and the Cortex

Pain syndromes have also been described following lesions of the cerebral cortex. Kleist (1934) reports cases of hyperpathia resulting from localized parietal lesions. Michelson (1943) also reports several cases of pain states resulting from cortical lesions, and Hamby (1961) corroborates this. Further, central pain may sometimes be abolished by excision of the appropriate parietal regions (Hamby, 1961; Eriksen et al., 1952). Biemond (1956) suggests that the second sensory area may be involved in the experiencing of such abnormal sensations. He reports a case of hyperpathia and spontaneous pain over the entire half of the body, contralateral to an area of softening involving SII, with retrograde degeneration in the posteroventral nucleus of the thalamus. Davison and Schick (1935) also describe a case of hyperpathia and spontaneous pain where there was a lesion largely in SII and here there was no thalamic lesion.

In SII, as in the posterior nuclear group, many units have been found with wide receptive fields, and many were activated only by noxious stimulation. And, as in the posterior nuclear group, many units were also activated by vibratory and acoustic stimuli. These findings increase the likelihood of the involvement of this region in pain states.

## The Explanation of Hyperpathia Caused by Lesions of the Central Nervous System

Head (1920) suggests that the thalamic syndrome is due to a release of the thalamus from the inhibitory control of the cortex. He proposes that the cortex and the thalamus are two separate "centres of consciousness." The thalamic center is concerned with the emotional aspects of sensation, and the cortex with discriminative aspects. Also, the threshold of the thalamic center is high, but once this is reached, its response is "of excessive amount and duration, and this it is the business of the cortical mechanism to control. The low intensity of the stimuli that can arouse the sensory cortex and its quick reaction period, enable it to control the activity of the cumbersome mechanism of the thalamic centre." Head suggests that corticofugal inhibitory fibers end in the lateral nucleus of the thalamus, so that destruction of this thalamic nucleus destroys the termination of most of these pathways. On this hypothesis those cortical and subcortical lesions, which are so situated that they destroy such corticofugal inhibitory pathways, should also produce hyperpathia.

The suggestion that as one ascends the phylogenetic scale, new and more discriminative integrating centers for sensory experience are produced, which exert an inhibitory influence on the older, cruder centers, has been proposed by others with reference to the problem of pain states. Walker (1943) proposes that there are three such integrating centers which may be related in this way: the oldest in the tectum mesencephali, the next in the thalamus and the third in the cortex. Bishop (1961) has reaffirmed this conception of a hierarchy of brains, on the basis of embryological studies.

An example of direct observation at the unit level of tactile pathways inhibiting pain pathways is provided by Mountcastle (1961). He reports the existence of units in the postcentral gyrus which respond only to noxious stimuli, but are then inhibited by the presentation of tactile stimuli to the same peripheral locus. Another related neurophysiological study is that of Andersson (1962). He found that lesions in the spinal cord produce a considerable increase in the proportion of cortical units with wide receptive fields, including those which respond only to noxious stimulation. He attributes this change to the severing of a centrifugal inhibitory pathway as well as to the loss of inhibitory effects from ascending specific projection pathways interacting at higher levels. There are also neurophysiological grounds for supposing that the sensory cortex modulates activity in the sensory region of the thalamus. It has been shown (Iwama and Yamamoto, 1961) that stimulation of the somatosensory cortex may affect activity in the ventrobasal complex of the thalamus which is evoked from the dorsal columns.

One argument against Head's hypothesis concerns the lack of complete correlation between pain syndromes and loss of discriminative sensibility. It very often occurs that there is a loss of discriminative ability without a pain syndrome being produced. Destruction of the dorsal columns, both as a result of disease and through operation, results in a loss of discriminative sensibility (Browder and Gallagher, 1948; Pool, 1946; White and Sweet, 1955). However, in the vast majority of instances, pain syndromes are not produced. Such findings are also common with lesions elsewhere in the central nervous system. The reverse dissociation has also been noted. Pain syndromes have been shown to occur as a result of lesions in the CNS without a concomitant loss of discriminative sensibility. Biemond (1956) reports a case of hyperpathia due to cortical lesions in which the discriminative senses of the patient were all intact. Michelson (1943) also remarks on the occasional absence of disturbances in discrimination in patients with centrally produced pain states.

These are not watertight arguments against Head's hypothesis. One could argue that provided some impulses reached the cortex, it could still control the thalamus effectively, even if its discriminative capacity was impaired. Also it might be possible to sever a centricifugal inhibitory pathway discretely without disturbing the discriminative capacities of the cortex. But they do cast doubt on this view.

An alternative explanation is that such syndromes are caused by irritation of structures adjacent to the lesion. Several factors may be pointed out in favor of this latter hypothesis. Firstly, it is more parsimonious to postulate an irritative factor affecting certain structures, than to propose a loss of a postulated inhibitory pathway which has not been shown to have the necessary characteristics. A second, and very strong, factor is the variability and unpredictability of the pain states produced. For example, mesencephalic tractotomy has in various cases given rise to pain states, as has been described. But this is by no means always the case; similar operations have not produced pain. Also, although surgical operation of the posterolateral thalamus may produce pain states, many such operations have produced no pain syndrome (Ervin and Mark, 1959). Further, a patient's symptoms may vary considerably during the course of his illness. Discussing patients with pain due to cortical lesions, Michelson (1943) stresses the variability and reversibility of their symptoms and concludes that irritative factors are probably the cause of the pain states.

## REFERRED PAIN

Although pain from a visceral organ may be correctly localized, at times it appears to arise instead from some area on the skin surface. Such pain is referred to those regions of the skin, or dermatomes, which are supplied by the same posterior roots as those through which the visceral afferents enter the spinal cord. Pain arising from other deeply placed structures may also at times be referred to the skin surface.

Various hypotheses have been put forward to account for referred pain. According to one view, irritation of pain pathways from the skin by neighboring visceral pathways may occur. Another suggestion is that visceral and cutaneous afferents converge into the same neurons at some level in the central nervous system, so that in these instances the information as to whether the impulses are visceral or cutaneous in origin is lost. The fact that the opposite confusion does not arise (i.e., pain arising from the skin does not get referred to a viscus) may be explained by assuming that the central mechanism always interprets pain coming from these common pathways as arising from the skin. Another explanation is that since the skin is a much more frequent source of afferent impulses than the visceral organs, a message which may have arisen from either is interpreted as coming from the skin, as this is the most likely place of origin.

Direct evidence of convergence of impulses from visceral and cutaneous sources onto the same neuron has been obtained in the posterolateral ventral nucleus of the thalamus. McLeod (1956) found that most of the cells here which responded to splanchnic delta afferents were also activated by stimulation of the skin, usually in the trunk region. He found occlusion to occur between impulses derived from the different sources. At the cortical level Amassian (1952) also found convergence of visceral and cutaneous afferents onto single neurons.

Various writers have suggested that a factor in referred pain is the existence of a constant barrage of impulses from the skin which are usually not numerous enough to cause the perception of pain, and which may be facilitated by visceral discharges so that the pain threshold is exceeded. To test this hypothesis experimenters have injected procaine into the cutaneous area of reference to see whether this would abolish the pain. Some have found no effect of procaine injection (e.g., Woollard *et al.*, 1932) who investigated pain caused by stimulation of the phrenic nerve). However, others have found that the pain was ended or made to migrate by these means (e.g., Weiss and Davis, 1928). Another demonstration of facilitation was reported by Cohen (1944) on two patients with cardiac anginal pain, both of whom referred their pain to the elbow region after trauma to the elbow but not before. These findings, though variable, are not inconsistent with each other. In some cases pain impulses arising from the viscera alone may be numerous enough to give rise to pain; in other cases pain may not be experienced unless facilitated from other sources, because the visceral barrage is not quite powerful enough to produce the sensation of pain. It is also likely that suggestion is an important factor in pain reference.

## DEPRESSED REACTIONS TO PAIN

### Insensitivity to Pain

Very occasionally individuals are found who do not appreciate painful stimuli as such. This appears to be not a psychologic or emotional but a sensory loss. It may be accompanied by other sensory changes. Kunkle and Chapman (1943) report the case of a young man with almost complete insensitivity to pain, and also a moderate impairment of heat and cold sensation. He also showed an absence of itching. However, the reflexes shown to be associated with activation of pain pathways were not all lost.

For instance the cold pressor effect was retained. (Immersing the hand in ice cold water produces a rise in arterial blood pressure, together with slight tachycardia, and this has been shown to be mediated by pain fibers [Wolff and Hardy, 1941].) Thus in this case it appeared that pain impulses did travel far enough to elicit a reflex blood pressure rise, but yet did not go far enough to reach consciousness.

## Pain Asymbolia

Cases of pain asymbolia may arise as a result of parietal lesions. In these cases pain is felt, but the aversive reaction to it is lost. The patient may even seek out painful stimuli. There is often a concomitant lack of concern over threatening gestures and other potential dangers. Such patients often show other extreme symptoms associated with parietal disease (see above) and this pain asymbolia may therefore be related to the other symptoms.

## Indifference to Pain after Frontal Lobotomy

Frontal lobotomy typically produces a state of indifference to pain, and therefore has been performed in cases of intolerable and intractable pain. Here the indifference does not appear to be to the pain immediately felt, but to lie rather in a considerable diminution of the prolonged psychologic disturbance which constant pain induces. Thus lobotomized patients are still distressed by painful events such as childbirth (Freeman and Watts, 1950), and their actual pain threshold appears if anything lower than normal (Chapman et al., 1948). However the pain does not make them so miserable, and they appear less engrossed in their feelings and sensations, and make fewer spontaneous complaints. It is suggested that lobotomy produces a loss of perseveration which extends also to disturbing thoughts, whether connected with pain, or with other anxiety-producing situations.

# 10

# HEARING

Before embarking upon a description of the organ which enables us to detect sound, it may be well to say a few words about some elementary physical properties of the stimuli which excite the ear. In the present context it is not necessary to consider how sound is generated or propagated, but simply what kind of changes are sensed by the ear when they arrive at its receptor surfaces. Such changes can be brought about by straightforward mechanical stimulation, as was done by Wilska (1935). He placed a thin rod against the membrane of the eardrum and was in this way able to move this membrane rapidly in and out, producing a sensation of sound. When we hear sounds in the normal manner, the eardrum is moved in and out in a similar way, but the movements are imparted by rapid in and out motions of the air molecules impinging on the eardrum, instead of a solid rod. In order to produce such a sensation of sound, the number of in-out movements has to be between about 30 per second to about 20,000 per second. The displacement of the drum membrane which will produce a just detectable sensation of sound when the number of in-out motions is 1,000 per second is about $10^{-8}$ cm., a surprisingly small distance.

In describing sound vibrations or waves, it is customary to specify the number of times per second the in-out cycle occurs, e.g., 1,000 cps. (cycles per second). Further, the physically most simple and important case of in-out movement is depicted by a sine wave. This is a curve which traces the up-down movement of a point traveling on the periphery of a circle rotating at a constant speed around its center and displays this up-down movement of the point as a function of time. For instance, such a curve would show how the height of the crank handle on a wheel rotating at a constant speed varies with time (Figure 10–1). The usefulness of such a specification of sound will be apparent when it is stated that any wave

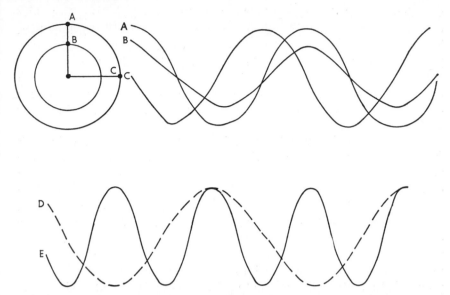

FIG. 10–1a.   The three curves A, B, and C are sine waves traced by the points A, B, and C as the disc on which these points are drawn rotates at a constant speed. Curves A and B do not vary in phase, because points A and B lie on the same straight line passing through the center of the disc. The curves A and B are however of different amplitude as point A lies on a circle of larger radius than point B. Curves A and C are 90° out of phase because the lines connecting them to the center of the circle form an angle of 90°. They are however of the same amplitude because the points A and C whose motions they trace are on the same circle.

FIG. 10–1b.   Curves D and E depict two sine waves traced out by the same point on the periphery of a circle. In the case of curve E the circle was rotating at twice the speed than when it was tracing out curve D. Consequently, the frequency depicted by curve E is double of the frequency depicted by curve A.

motion can be represented as a sum of sine components of differing frequencies and extents of movement, according to Fourier's theorem.

If we take vibrations which can be described by a simple sine wave, the frequency per second of these vibrations moving the eardrum corresponds closely to a perceived attribute of sound—its pitch. Another property of the sound wave that it is useful to consider is its phase. For instance, if we take the example we used above, we can imagine a wheel with two crank handles rotating at a constant speed. We can plot the height of the two handles separately as a function of time. If the two handles are set 90° apart on the wheel (the angle having its apex at the center of the wheel), then the two sine waves traced by the two handles are said to be 90° out of phase. If this is the case it can easily be seen that as one wave attains its peak, the other is always halfway between them and vice versa. If the two waves are generated by points 180° out of phase, the lowermost portion of one curve occurs at the same time as the uppermost portion of the other. The excursions above the center of the imaginary wheel may be regarded as positive (pushing the eardrum inward) and those below as negative (pushing the eardrum outward). This is important, as the eardrum in responding to such movements adds them so that two sound waves of the same frequency and in-out movement will cancel out completely if they are 180° out of phase.

When considering vibrations, it is useful to specify not only their frequency and phase but also the distance of the displacement of the vibrating body. For instance, two sounds can be identical in frequency, but one may produce larger vibrations. To specify their difference, it would be possible to refer to the distances of displacement caused by the two sounds. However, owing to the extremely small size of such distances, they are difficult to measure. Consequently, measurements are made in terms of pressure generated by sounds on a surface on which they impinge. Such pressure is directly proportional to the displacements during vibration provided also that the frequency of vibration is kept constant, and also the physical properties of the vibrating medium. Given the same amount of displacement of a medium (to-and-fro extent of movement), then pressure increases in direct ratio as the frequency of vibration goes up. Thus a measurement of pressure is another way of specifying the displacement during a vibration, except that the frequency of the vibration and the physical properties of the vibrating medium are also taken into account.

However, measurements of the amplitude of sounds are not made directly in terms of pressure (dynes per square centimeter). Instead, a logarithmic measure of comparison is used, and this for two main reasons. In making discriminations of loudness, the ear works according to Weber's law; thus a threshold difference is always approximately the same logarithmic increment. Second, the range of pressures that the ear can respond to before sound becomes painful is of the order of $10^{6.5}$ to 10 (630 dynes per sq. cm. to 0.0002 dynes per sq. cm.). Direct numerical comparisons of sound pressures would therefore be unwieldy. Consequently, sound pressures are compared by using the decibel (db.) notation. The difference in the pressure of two sounds in decibels is the 20th multiple of the logarithm (to base 10) of the ratio of the two sound pressures being compared. For instance, a tenfold increase in pressure is an increase of 20 db.

The organs of hearing make it possible for animals to respond to the minute rapid vibrations described above. Most of the features of the outer and middle ear are such as to minimize the loss of energy when such vibrations are transferred from air to the rather denser media of which the apparatus of the inner ear is composed. This apparatus in the inner ear translates the vibrations imposed upon it into neural activity, extracting their temporal characteristics, such as frequency, time of arrival, and amplitude.

The outer ear consists of the pinna or auricle, the familiar ear flap, which apparently is of little functional significance in hearing in man, and a short tube, about one inch in length, called the auditory meatus, which leads to the eardrum of tympanic membrane. The characteristics of this tube are of functional significance since it acts as a resonator by virtue of its length and shape. Because of its resonant characteristics, the meatus produces a pressure amplification of between 5 and 10 db. over the range from 2,000 to 5,500 cycles per second, dropping off outside these limits.

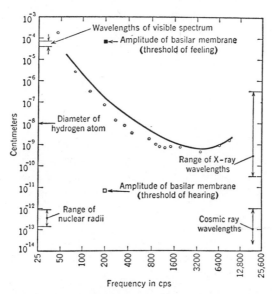

FIG. 10-2. **Amplitude of vibration of the eardrum at threshold of hearing. Circles—Data of Wilska. Solid line—Amplitude of vibration of air molecules at threshold intensity as calculated by Stevens and Davis. (From Békésy and Rosenblith, Chapter 27 in** *Handbook of Experimental Psychology,* **S. S. Stevens, (Ed.) New York: John Wiley and Sons, 1951.)**

This range corresponds to the region of greatest sensitivity of the ear (see Figure 10–2). Further, the meatus protects the eardrum mechanically against damage which it would sustain were the eardrum mounted on the body surface, and against variations in humidity and temperature which would greatly affect its elastic characteristics.

The eardrum is a thin membrane at the base of the meatus; it has the form of a flattened cone with its apex pointing inward relative to the exterior of the head. Most of the cone is relatively rigid; a flaccid fold on the lower rim permits the cone to move in response to imposed vibrations. Such movements in response to sounds encountered at the threshold of hearing are exceedingly minute, being of the same order as the diameter of a hydrogen molecule ($10^{-8}$ cm.). The eardrum has an area of 69 sq. mm.

The motions of the eardrum are then transmitted to the apparatus of the middle ear. This consists of a chain of little bones or ossicles. The first, the malleus (hammer), is connected to the eardrum and also to the second ossicle, the incus (or anvil), which in turn is attached to the stapes (or stirrup). The footplate of the stapes is implanted in the oval window by the annular ligament. The three ossicles are connected by the articulate ligaments. The whole system of ossicles is suspended in the cavity of the middle ear by eight ligaments, two of which lead to small muscles, the tensor tympani and the stapedius. These two muscles contract reflexly with a latency of about 10 msec. in response to strong sounds in such a way as to decrease transmission of sound down the ossicular chain. This tends to

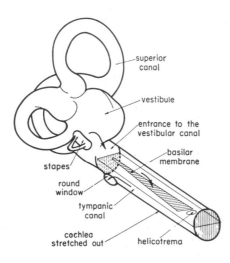

FIG. 10–3. Schematic drawing of the cochlea and labyrinth. The cochlea, normally wound, has been stretched out to form a straight tube. Note that the basilar membrane widens towards the helicotrema. (From Rasmussen, G. L., and Windle, W. F., *Neural Mechanisms of the Auditory and Vestibular Systems;* courtesy of Charles C. Thomas, Publisher, Springfield, Ill.)

protect the mechanism of the inner ear against potential damage by loud sounds. The middle ear has a second mode of defense against loud sounds. The ossicles are so suspended on their ligaments that they can vibrate in two different modes. Normally the stapes rotates on an axis at one end of the footplate and perpendicular to it. When, however, vibrations of large amplitude occur, the stapes rotates about an axis at right angles to the first mode, on an axis lying through and parallel to the footplate, thus reducing the efficiency of transmission to the oval window.

Though the detailed motions of the ossicular chain in transmitting sound are not completely agreed upon, there seems no doubt that the complex ossicular chain performs two functions. First, it performs the function of a lever in reducing the amplitude of excursion at the eardrum to a much smaller displacement at the oval window. The second function is to apply the energy acting on the larger surface of the eardrum to the much smaller surface of the oval window under the footplate of the stapes, which is about 3.2 sq. mm. This means therefore that the pressure (force per unit area) to the oval window is much greater than the pressure applied to the eardrum. The effect of these two functions of the middle ear is to increase the efficiency of energy transfer from the air to the denser media of the inner ear, acting like a transformer to match the two impedances. It can be calculated from the mechanical properties of the inner ear and air that 99.9 percent of the intensity of sound (30 db.) falling on the ear would be lost by being reflected back if it were not for the mechanism of the middle ear. Such a figure is in agreement with the degree of hearing

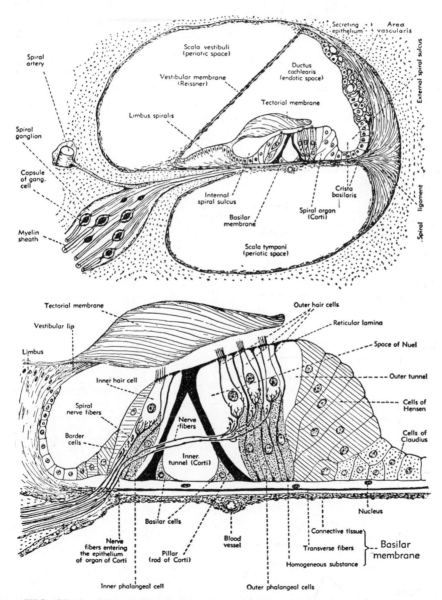

FIG. 10–4.   Upper: Vertical section of human cochlea. Lower: Organ of Corti, basilar membrane and tectorial membrane in greater magnification.

loss (again upward of about 30 db.) in patients who have lost their middle
ear apparatus. The middle ear has a resonant frequency of about 1,700 cps.
This in combination with the resonant frequency of the auditory meatus
gives the ear its overall sensitivity curve (Figure 10–2).

The vibrations of the stapedial footplate are transmitted to the cochlea
via the oval window (Figure 10–3). The cochlea is shaped like a snail shell
—a spiral bony duct. This duct is further divided into three divisions: the
scala vestibuli, the scala tympani, and the cochlear duct or scala media
(Figure 10–4). The scala vestibuli and the scala tympani contain perilymph and are joined at the apex of the cochlea through a small opening
called the helicotrema. At the basal end of the scala tympani lies the round
window closed by a thin membrane. Thus the stapedial footplate can move
into the oval window as it can displace the incompressible fluid in the
inelastic bony duct out through the round window. The scala vestibuli is
divided from the cochlear duct by the thin Reissner's membrane, which
does not seem to contribute significantly to the mechanical properties of
the inner ear. On the other side, the cochlear duct is divided from the scala

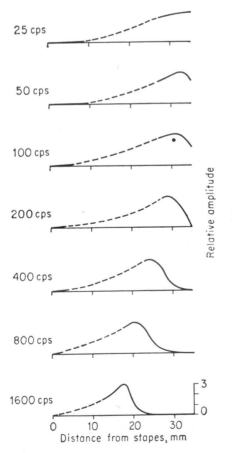

FIG. 10–5a. Maximum of displacement of the basilar membrane at
various imposed frequencies of sound.
(From Békésy, *Akust Zeits*, 1943. 8.
66. Courtesy of S. Hirzel Verlag.)

tympani by the basilar membrane. The length of the basilar membrane in man is about 35 mm. It is about 0.04 mm. wide at the stapes and actually increases in width towards the helicotrema (as the cochlea itself narrows) to 0.5 mm. The membrane is not under tension but exhibits a decrease in stiffness of at least 100 to 1, and an increase in mass as we ascend from the end near the stapes to that near the helicotrema. Because of this gradation in its mechanical properties, the basilar membrane serves to analyze the incoming sound waves.

When the stapes vibrates, pressure is transmitted to the fluid in the cochlea which travels virtually instantaneously to the round window. Hence a driving force is applied to the whole of the basilar membrane almost simultaneously. As Békésy (1960) was the first to observe (in 1928), when this occurs a wave appears to travel up the basilar membrane from the stapes. The amplitude of such traveling waves increases as they go from the oval window up the basilar membrane, reaching a maximum at a

FIG. 10–5b.  A schematic drawing of an actual displacement pattern at an instant of time existing on the basilar membrane when a sound is transmitted to the cochlea. (From Rasmussen, G. L., and Windle, W. F., (Eds.); *Neural Mechanisms of the Auditory and Vestibular Systems*, 1960, courtesy of Charles C. Thomas, Publisher, Springfield, Ill.)

point on the membrane, the location of which depends on the frequency of the imposed oscillation (Figure 10–5). High frequencies give rise to waves which end very close to the stapes. Lower frequencies produce waves which travel further towards the helicotrema before tapering off. The direction of travel from the stapedial end towards the helicotrema is the same whether or not the initiating vibrations are applied from the stapedial end or not, as for instance, where sound is transmitted through the bone of the skull. According to Békésy (1960) such a system is closely analogous to a set of reeds each with increasing resonant frequency. If a driving signal of a certain frequency is applied simultaneously to all the reeds, that reed whose resonant frequency is closest to the driving signal will vibrate maximally. This is essentially the model of the basilar membrane's action put forward by Helmholtz (1863) just over a century ago. However, in Helmholtz's model there is no traveling wave. The appearance of traveling waves in such a model, to conform to observations

FIG. 10–6. Arrangement of resonant reeds to demonstrate traveling wave. (From Békésy, *J. Acoust. Soc. Amer.* 27; courtesy of Acoustical Society of America.

of the basilar membrane, is easily provided by elastic coupling between the reeds. This is done by weaving a narrow rubber band to connect the reeds to each other. In this way a mechanical interconnection between the resonators is obtained as it presumably exists in the basilar membrane which is, after all, a continuous strip (Figure 10–6). In the model of interconnected reeds, traveling waves originate at one end independent of where the driving frequency is applied. As in the cochlea, the largest amplitude of movement of the waves occurs close to the point where the resonant frequency of the reeds corresponds to the frequency of the driving waves. As can be seen from the illustrations (Figure 10–7), there is a fairly sharp falling off beyond this point. In such a way, the frequency of a sound wave is translated into a place of maximum movement along the basilar membrane. However it should not be assumed from the foregoing that the traveling wave generated on the basilar membrane adds nothing to the resonance analysis of sound impinging on the cochlea. Tonndorf (1962) suggested that the traveling waves generated especially by brief sounds (e.g., clicks, thumps) probably provided an important method of analysis and identification of such sounds.

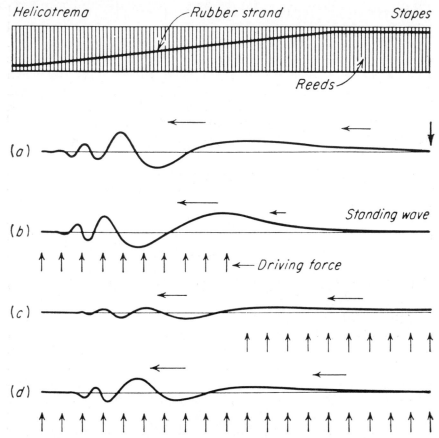

FIG. 10-7. The upper drawing shows how the rubber band was inter-
laced among the reeds to give coupling that produced traveling waves like
those of the cochlea. The waves shown below represent different ways of
actuating the system. In (a) vibrations were applied to one reed on the right,
in (b) to the more flexible half of the reeds on the left, in (c) to the stiffer
half of the reeds on the right, and in (d) to the support. (From Békésy,
J. Acoust. Soc. Amer. 27; courtesy of Acoustical Society of America.)

So far we have seen how the minute vibrations of the sound waves are
transmitted to the basilar membrane and how they are translated into
motions of this organ. We have now to consider how the motions of the
basilar membrane produce nervous activity giving information about the
pitch and loudness of sounds. The translation from movement to neural
activity in the cochlea is accomplished by the expedient of placing sensory
cells all along the length of the cochlear duct.

These sensory cells lie in the organ of Corti, which in turn lies on the
basilar membrane, on the side of the basilar membrane which bounds the
cochlear duct. The sensory cells are known as "hair" cells because hairs
protrude from them. These hairs protrude into the tectorial membrane

(and so are imbedded on their other end in it) (Figure 10-4). The tectorial membrane overlaps the organ of Corti in the cochlear duct and is hinged on one side of the cochlea only, a little way above the basilar membrane. In this way when the basilar membrane is displaced, the tectorial membrane moves also. However, being hinged at a different point, a shearing action occurs between it and the basilar membrane, carrying the organ of Corti. That is, as the basilar membrane takes the tectorial membrane up with it, a sideways displacement of the two membranes occurs, because they are hinged at different points. As the hairs of the "hair cells" are effectively imbedded in the membranes simultaneously, the hairs are bent sideways as the membranes vibrate up and down. This lever-like arrangement is thought to increase the efficiency of energy transfer from fluid to the cells themselves.

The hair cells are divided into two groups: the internal and external hair cells. The internal hair cells lie in one row close to the bony shaft around which the cochlea is wound. They are flask shaped, about 12 $\mu$ in diameter, and there are about 3,500 of them in the cochlea. The external hair cells lie in three or four rows. They are about 8 $\mu$ in diameter and 20,000 in number. Each external hair cell has a large number of hairs protruding out of it (more than 100 in man) set in the form of a W. In the internal hair cells, the hairs are set in two almost straight rows. Such morphological differences may be correlated with differences in function (Keidel, 1962).

The bending of the hairs by the displacement of the basilar and tectorial membrane somehow initiates activity in the auditory nerve. Such activity in the nerve itself is of the usual all-or-none type. The triggering of the auditory nerve by the bending of the hairs, however, seems to be mediated through an intervening electrical process, called the cochlear microphonic. The movement of the hairs in some way causes changes in electrical potential which can be recorded from the round window of the cochlea. This change in electrical potential follows with considerable fidelity the sound transmitted by the stapes, in the manner of a microphone. If electrodes are placed in the scala tympani or scala vestibuli, the potential variations recorded from them give a good index of the movement of the basilar membrane closest to the electrode. A second type of potential which arises on stimulation is called the summating potential. This seems to be produced by loud sounds, is slowly changing in comparison to the cochlear microphonic, and may be either negative or positive in sign. It is possible that the source of the electrical energy of these varying potentials may be the endolymphatic potential. The cochlear duct is filled with endolymph, a fluid unusually rich in potassium. The cochlear duct has a steady positive potential of about 80 millivolts which appears to originate in the stria vascularis (which lines one of the sides of the cochlear duct). It may be that this steady energy is released by the bending of the hairs on the organ of Corti to produce the cochlear microphonic, which in turn stimulates the auditory nerve.

FIG. 10–8. Two cross sections of a dimensional model of the cochlea, (b) made near the driving end and (a) made near the other end. (c) Detailed view of the model. (From Békésy, *J. Acoust. Soc. Amer.* 29; courtesy of Acoustical Society of America.)

The nerve endings of the auditory nerve reach the hair cells through the bony spindle around which the cochlear is wound. In the hollow of this spindle is a long spiral ganglion (the spiral ganglion of Corti) containing some 28,000 cells. The axon-like dendrites of the cells then pass through fine openings in the bone of the cochlea to reach the inner and outer hair cells. Whereas the fibers running to the internal hair cells innervate from one to three such cells, most of these crossing to the external hair cells may be connected to a large number of cells and each cell in its turn to a large number of fibers.

This is a good point at which to consider the contribution of the mechanical part of the hearing apparatus to our overall hearing ability. It was seen that different parts of the basilar membrane show a maximum vibration depending on the frequency of vibration imposed upon them. It was also noted that different parts of the organ of Corti lying upon the basilar membrane stimulate different nerve fibers. It looks, therefore, as if information concerning the frequency of sound impinging on the ear could be read off simply by seeing what nerve fibers are made active. However, if we look at the diagrams of the traveling wave as it has been observed by Békésy (Figure 10–5), a relatively large portion of the membrane seems to be vibrating at roughly the same amplitude. That is, the crest of the disturbance on the basilar membrane is rather flat. On the other hand, our ability to discriminate pitch is much finer than would be expected from these properties of the basilar membrane. For tones of up to 2,000 cps., we are able to discriminate differences of 2 to 4 cps. at 40 db. above threshold.

To overcome such a lack of selectivity at the mechanical level, Gray (1900) suggested that neural impulses arising each side of the peak of excitation were somehow suppressed. This idea he called the "principle of maximum stimulation." Békésy (1960) has proposed a "funneling" action on the part of the nervous system. This is a combination of the principles of lateral inhibition and summation. There are instances in which a stronger stimulus adjacent to a weaker one suppresses it. There are also instances where neighboring stimuli simply sum. Békésy proposes that in the cochlea they sum to produce a sensation of loudness but inhibit each other to produce a sharply localized sensation of pitch. He has shown such ideas to be plausible by ingenious experiments involving the sensation of vibration along the skin. In one experiment to show inhibition, he applied traveling waves such as he had observed in the cochlea to the skin of the forearm by means of a large mechanical model of the cochlea (Figure 10–8). He was able to show that the sensation of vibration was sharply localized to the peak of traveling wave, and not felt at other neighboring points though the physical extent of vibration was almost identical. In

FIG. 10–9.   Arrangement of a series of vibrators to show funneling (inhibition and summation). (From Békésy, *J. Acoust. Soc. Amer.* 29; courtesy of Acoustical Society of America.)

another experiment, he set off vibrators at different frequencies at equally spaced points on the forearm (Figure 10–9). These were individually adjusted in amplitude so as to produce a sensation of equal magnitude. When they were set to vibrate together, the vibration was only felt at a peak in the center of the whole row of vibrators. The frequency of vibration felt was that of the vibrator in the center. However, the amplitude of vibration felt was much larger than when the center vibrator was the only one vibrating. Such an experiment confirms the notion of funneling. Only one frequency is felt since other frequencies are inhibited. However, the other frequencies, though not perceived, contribute to the felt amplitude of the frequency which inhibits them. Of course, experiments on the properties of skin sensitivity can serve only as analogies. But if the sensory innervation of the skin produces a sharpening effect, it is plausible to believe that a similar sharpening effect can take place on the basilar membrane.

## Other Mechanisms of Frequency Discrimination

A mechanism reading off the place of the biggest bulge on the basilar membrane as outlined above could determine what sound frequency was impinging on the ear. However, such a mechanism would lose certain information about the incoming sound wave. It would not indicate for instance the precise point in time, during each cycle of pressure change, when a certain portion of the cycle occurred. In other words, such a mechanism would indicate frequency while losing information about phase. To obtain information about phase, messages must be sent indicating when in time an increase or decrease in pressure is occurring during each sound cycle. That such accessory information about the phase of a cycle is available can be seen from the performance of the observer in sound localization. It is possible for an observer to localize the source of a continuous sine wave by differences in phase at the two ears. The two ears are some distance apart and sound takes time to travel. Therefore, if the source of sound is nearer one ear, an increase of pressure at the nearer ear will be followed by a similar increase at the other ear some while later. This suggests that information about the precise time of a particular portion of the sound wave is picked up by the ear. There is also evidence from simultaneous unit recordings of firing in the auditory nerve and pressure changes that neural elements fire on the same position on the sound wave. Such information is useful in localizing tones up to frequencies of 1,500 cps. (Cherry, 1961). It therefore seems that information about the temporal spacing of pressure changes is useful up to this frequency even when comparison has to be made between the two ears about the precise timing of a portion of a pressure wave. The usefulness of such timing in identifying pitch might extend to even higher frequencies if successive events occurring in the same ear were being measured by the nervous system and so might serve as an accessory mechanism of pitch recognition.

One of the apparent limitations of such a system of identifying pitch is the refractory period of the nerve fiber. Having initiated a spike discharge, an auditory nerve fiber cannot fire again for about 1 msec. after, being only 3–5 $\mu$ in diameter. This would place an upper limit of about 1,000 cps. on the frequency at which any single neuron could follow. However, due to differences between neurons, some neurons could fire on one cycle and others on the next, so that information about frequency could be preserved in a whole bundle of fibers taken together. This is known as the *volley principle*, and direct recordings of the auditory pathway shows that such a principle could operate up to a frequency of 4,000 cps. Whether information about pitch is actually extracted from the incoming signal simply by an analysis of the frequency of neural impulses is difficult to know. A phenomenon, known as the residue phenomenon of Schouten is often quoted in support of the idea that the true temporal relations between events in the auditory nerve can produce sensations of pitch. Schouten (1938) has been able to demonstrate that if a high-frequency tone (e.g., 3,000 cps.) is turned on and off at 100 times per second, we can hear a 100 cps. tone. It is generally argued that such a sensation cannot be due to a place of resonance at the cochlea, but simply to the periodicity of interruption of the high-frequency tone. However, whether such an argument is entirely correct is open to question. Voots (1962) has shown that the tone corresponding to the frequency of interruption can be heard by patients who cannot hear the high tone being interrupted. This would indicate that the frequency of interruption was somehow separately signaled by the mechanics of the cochlea, as suggested by Tonndorf (1962). Whatever the outcome of this controversy, it seems probable that a place coding of frequency by the cochlea through its mechanical characteristics is the most important way that pitch is represented in the auditory system.

Some interesting consequences emerge from the reliance of the auditory system on an analysis of frequency by the mechanical properties of the cochlea. Because of the rather broad somewhat flat response of the basilar membrane to a single frequency, a neural mechanism is superimposed to inhibit neurons which are excited on each side of the peak. In this way the information about the movements of the surrounding basilar membrane which does not mirror the incoming frequency pattern is disregarded and only the incoming frequency is heard instead of a whole band of frequencies around it. In order to achieve such a suppression efficiently, the inhibitory function of the peak of oscillation of the basilar membrane should not be symmetrical. It will be remembered that the basilar membrane oscillates only at one end (the basal end) when high frequencies are applied to the cochlea and that the cutoff of the vibration is sharp towards the other, apical, and, where the lower frequencies have their maximum effects. We would, therefore, expect that the neural inhibition generated by a maximum of vibration will be smaller towards the apical portion of the basilar membrane than towards the basal, because the basal portion of the membrane tends always to move if any portion more apical is moving also, especially at the higher intensities of imposed vibration. This means that if there was no neural inhibition superimposed on the mechanism of the basilar membrane, real lower tones would always introduce a wide band of higher tones, but real higher tones would not in their turn lead to an illusion of a wide band of accompanying lower tones.

That a mechanism of suppression or inhibition operates in this way seems to be demonstrated by the phenomena of auditory masking. Two tones fairly close in frequency do sometimes actually sound together in the environment, and unfortunately the nervous system still acts according to its usual rule for suppressing illusory tones and tends to inhibit the activity produced by one of the real tones. The tones affected in this way are what we would expect from the considerations about the efficient suppression of illusory tones. That is, lower tones mask higher tones to a much greater degree than higher tones mask lower tones. In this way the auditory system, by excluding signals which it itself introduced, also on occasion excludes information about the environment. The inhibition of unit responses in central structures to one tone by the presentation of another tone is described later.

In the following sections we shall discuss the neural substrate of hearing. We shall discuss what is known of unit activity in central auditory structures, examine the results of ablation studies, and finally report on the efferent control of messages arising in the cochlea.

## CENTRAL AUDITORY MECHANISMS

## The Classical Auditory Pathway

The axons forming the cochlear branch of the eighth cranial nerve arise in the spiral ganglion of Corti; and are arranged in an orderly fashion, preserving their original positions relative to each other. As they reach the cochlear nuclei, those fibers arising in the apex bifurcate lateroventrally, those arising in the base, dorsomedially, with each fiber sending branches to the dorsal and ventral cochlear nuclei respectively. Each fiber branch terminates on many cells in the cochlear nuclei, and it is inferred that each cell in the cochlear nuclei receives many fibers.

The cochlear nuclei are composed of a number of different cell groups, and these are usually divided into two major groupings—the dorsal and ventral cochlear nuclei. However, for various reasons, especially because of recent evidence concerning the organization of frequency sensitive neurons in this complex, it has been argued that the ventral group should be further divided into the posteroventral nucleus and the anteroventral nucleus. No significant differences have been shown regarding the functioning of single units in these different subgroupings.

Most of the fibers leaving the cochlear nuclei cross the reticular formation and terminate in the contralateral superior olivary complex. Some, however, terminate in the reticular formation, others travel to the ipsilateral superior olivary complex and yet others join the tract of the lateral lemniscus. The superior olivary complex may be divided into five main nuclear masses: the S-shaped segment, the accessory nucleus, the nucleus of the trapezoid body, the medial preolivary and the lateral preolivary (Galambos et al., 1959).

The tract of the lateral lemniscus arises mainly in the superior olivary complex and terminates mainly in the inferior colliculus, though some of its fibers immediately join the brachium of the inferior colliculus to pass to the medial geniculate body of the thalamus. Scattered groups of cells lying amongst the fibers of this tract constitute the nucleus of the lateral lemniscus.

The brachium of the inferior colliculus, though containing some lemniscal fibers, consists mainly of fibers arising in the ipsilateral and contralateral inferior colliculi. The tract terminates in the medial geniculate body of the thalamus.

The medial geniculate body may be divided into two main portions: the small-celled, densely populated pars principalis, and the larger-celled, loosely packed pars magnocellularis. Of these, only the pars principalis should be considered a major auditory area (Rose and Galambos, 1952).

The main outflow of the pars principalis of the medial geniculate is to the auditory areas of the cortex, which are described in detail below. Connections to these areas are made by way of the posterior limb of the internal capsule.

## Other Auditory Pathways

In addition to the classical afferent pathways described above, various other auditory pathways should be mentioned. Galambos et al. (1961) have demonstrated that a more medial pathway of considerable importance must also exist, since transection of the classical pathway at the level of the brachium of the inferior colliculus does not significantly alter the pattern of evoked activity at the cortex following click stimulation to the ear. Behavioral studies involving lesions of the classical pathway confirm this supposition (see below). Responses to auditory stimulation have been found to occur in the brain stem reticular formation and also in the more medially placed thalamic nuclei. A fairly direct pathway to the cerebellum must also exist, though its exact course is unknown. Further, there are a complex set of descending connections, which are described at the end of the chapter.

## Single-Unit Responses to Auditory Stimuli

Many units in the auditory pathway do not respond to pure tones, but are sensitive instead to more complex sounds, such as clicks and noise. The proportion of units which are relatively frequency specific to those which are not, appears to decrease as one ascends the auditory pathway. A considerable number of elements have been found to be much more sensitive to clicks or noise than to pure tones at the level of the inferior colliculus (Thurlow *et al.*, 1951; Katsuki *et al.*, 1958), the pars principalis of the medial geniculate (Galambos, 1952; Gross and Thurlow, 1951) and the cortex (Erulkar *et al.*, 1956; Galambos, 1960). It also appears that as

**TABLE 10-1**

**Summary Table of Single Unit Responses in Cat Auditory Cortex***

| *Units respond:* | $A_i(n = 96)$ | | $E_p(n = 68)$ | |
|---|---|---|---|---|
| To some acoustic stimulus | 79 | (82%) | 42 | (60%) |
| In more than 50 percent of | | | | |
| trials | 59/96 | (62%) | 21 | (31%) |
| To pure tones | 62/88 | (70%) | 27/61 | (44%) |
| Sustained driving | 18/62 | (29%) | 3/27 | (11%) |
| Sustained suppression | 9/62 | (15%) | 2/27 | ( 7%) |
| At "on" and "off" | 20/62 | (32%) | 1/27 | ( 4%) |
| At "on" | 4/62 | ( 6%) | 0/27 | ( 0%) |
| At "off" | 6/62 | ( 8%) | 1/27 | ( 4%) |
| Broad-band | 5/62 | (10%) | 20/27 | (74%) |
| Consistently to single click | 26/99† | (26%) | 3/52 | ( 8%) |
| Consistently to noise | 27/41 | (66%) | 12/59 | (20%) |
| Best to odd sounds | 6 | | 13 | |

* Microelectrodes were chronically implanted and therefore the records were taken from unanesthetized animals. (From Galambos, R., 1960 in Rasmussen, G. L. and Windle, W. F. (Eds.), *Neural Mechanisms of the Auditory and Vestibular Systems.* Courtesy of Charles C. Thomas, Publisher, Springfield, Ill.)
† Additional data from 3 cats are included.

the pathway is ascended a higher proportion of units responsive to tones emit only "phasic" responses to these stimuli, i.e., that they discharge only at "on" or at "off" or at "on-off" of a stimulus. An illustration of this variety of responsiveness in units at the auditory cortex is provided in Table 10-1.

### *"Following" of Stimulus Frequency in the Auditory Nerve*

When a "click" is sounded, the auditory nerve responds with a well-synchronized volley of action potentials. This is followed by a second smaller volley when the click is of moderate intensity; and this in turn is followed by a third even smaller volley when the click is loud. (These volleys are designated $N_1$, $N_2$, and $N_3$ respectively). If a steady tone of frequency below 4,000 cps. is sounded, the auditory nerve responds with a series of small volleys, the frequency of which reproduces that of the tone. The neural response lasts while the tone is sounded. The frequency is not reproduced by the individual fibers but by the summated response of the fibers. There is considerable variability in response latency both between different fibers and between responses of the same fiber on different occasions. Response thresholds amongst different fibers also vary. This allows the auditory nerve as a whole to follow the frequency of a given stimulus. When the stimulus frequency exceeds 4,000 cps., however, such following ceases. In any case, the upper limit of following drops drastically as the auditory pathway is ascended.

## RESPONSE AREAS

When discussing peripheral auditory mechanisms we saw that different parts of the basilar membrane vibrated maximally at different frequencies, and therefore that different auditory receptors were maximally stimulated at different frequencies, depending on their location on the organ of Corti. We saw further that the crest of the traveling wave on the basilar membrane was rather flat, and therefore that some additional mechanism would have to be postulated to explain the fineness of our ability to discriminate pitch. One such possible mechanism is lateral inhibition, i.e., an inhibitory interaction between neighboring fibers such that the fiber firing more strongly would suppress the fiber firing more weakly.

One of the aims of the study of the central auditory pathways is to shed light on how this sharpening of frequency discrimination is brought about. To this end, investigators have compared excitatory and inhibitory response patterns to sounds of different frequencies, at all levels of the auditory pathway. One method of making such a comparison is the plotting of response areas. The response area for a unit is obtained by plotting the intensities of stimulation necessary to activate that unit at various stimulus frequencies. It might be hoped that the response areas in the auditory nerve would correspond with what would be expected from the mechanical characteristics of the cochlea, but that further along the auditory pathway the response areas of some units would show much more specificity with regard to sound frequency. (Such specificity would only be expected of some units. Other units, concerned for instance with the analysis of loudness or sound localization, would not be expected to show such characteristics.) However, at the present writing, it has not been possible to form such a neat conclusion.

## Response Areas of Single Auditory Nerve Fibers

Recording from the auditory nerve of the guinea pig, Tasaki (1954) reports that response areas were characterized by a steep rise in threshold intensity when the stimulus frequency exceeded a certain optimum, and a gradual rise as the stimulus frequency declined. The frequency at which the intensity threshold was lowest was found to be a function of the position of origin of the fiber at the cochlea. Those fibers arising in the basal turn of the cochlea had high cut-off frequencies, and those arising in the apical turn had low cut-off frequencies and therefore responded only to low tones. Similar findings have been reported for the cat (Tasaki and Galambos, reported by Tasaki, 1957; Katsuki *et al.*; 1958, Katsuki, 1961). The general shape of this threshold-frequency curve corresponds well with what might be expected on Békésy's model of traveling waves in the cochlea, yet the high-frequency cut-off in auditory nerve fibers is much

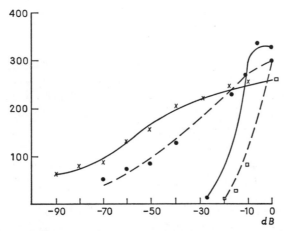

FIG. 10–10. The rate of increase of discharge with increasing intensity of sound of four neurons. Two of the neurons are of the low threshold type and two are of the high threshold type. The rate of increase of the high threshold neurons is higher. (From Katsuki, Y., *et al.*, *J. Acoust. Soc. Amer.* 34, 1962; courtesy of Acoustical Society of America.)

sharper than that of the mechanical movement of the cochlear partition or of the amplitude of the microphonic response recorded in the upper turns of the cochlea. Tasaki suggests that this sharp cut-off might be due to a complex mechanical motion of the cochlear partition near the point of maximum vibration.

Katsuki (1961) reports in cats the occurrence of a second type of response area in addition to the type described above. The second type was obtained mainly from units with low characteristic frequencies, and in it the threshold rose gradually on the high-frequency side of the optimum frequency as well as on the low-frequency side. He suggests that neurons with such response areas may innervate the outer hair cells, and that neurons with response areas of the former type may innervate the inner hair cells. Katsuki *et al.* (1962) demonstrated the existence of two types of unit with different shapes of response area in the monkey also. They describe two partially overlapping populations of neurons: those with low intensity thresholds and those with high intensity thresholds. Their rates of firing were the same, however, for sounds of very high intensity. This is because the low-threshold units increased their frequency of firing at a more gradual rate than those with high thresholds. The units with high thresholds were unresponsive to sounds of low intensity. However, as soon as their threshold was exceeded, any further increment of intensity brought about a much larger increase in rate of firing than did the same increment in the low-threshold neurons (Figure 10–10). Such a division into high and low threshold elements was apparent only in the low- and middle-frequency range.

Further evidence that there are two populations of receptor cells—one with a high and the other with a low threshold—is reported by Davis (1961). He recorded summed neural activity in the auditory nerve with intracochlear electrodes. As intensity was increased, the output of the auditory system did not rise smoothly. Instead there were two distinct humps on the curve suggesting two distinct but overlapping populations of receptor elements—a small one with low thresholds and a larger one with high thresholds.

## Response Areas of Units Higher in the Auditory Pathway

Several investigators have studied the response areas of units in the cochlear nuclei. Some found areas very similar to those obtained in the auditory nerve (Tasaki and Davis, 1955) with perhaps a less gradual decline on the low-frequency side (Tasaki, 1954; Katsuki et al., 1958; Katsuki, 1961). Recently, however, much more complex response areas have also been found at the level of the ventral cochlear nucleus. It appears that areas here have a large variety of shapes. In some cases, ineffective bands exist within the limiting frequencies of the response area, and such a tonal band may be inhibitory as well as ineffective (Moushegian et al., 1962). Further, a unit may be responsive to scattered frequency bands outside its response area (Figure 10–11).

Various studies have been made of response areas at levels higher in the auditory pathway; in the superior olivary complex, the inferior colliculus, the medial geniculate and the cortex (see, for instance, Galambos, 1952; Galambos et al., 1959; Hilali and Whitfield, 1953; Katsuki et al., 1958, 1959, 1962; Rose et al., 1963). These have employed varying techniques, and it is very difficult to draw any general conclusions from them. Investigators often note the similarity between response areas higher up to those lower down on the auditory pathway. Ades (1959) concluded that "the sharply restricted frequency specificity of fibers for theshold intensity in the cochlear nerve persists in units of the medullary auditory nuclei but in the thalamus and cortex gives way to restricted though broader bands of threshold sensitivity. On the other hand, the very broad frequency response for tones below the high frequency cutoff, characteristic of the cochlear

FREQUENCY IN KILOCYCLES

FIG. 10-11. Frequency response areas of ventral cochlear nucleus units. All units shown in this figure excepting E 40-15 and E 80-11, are from unanesthetized cats. *a,b*: classical response areas. Solid lines indicate tone band over which units respond, *c*: unit showing two response areas as well as additional response bands at −20 and −30 db. (arrows). *d*: unit responding to frequency bands higher and lower than those found in its response area. Unit lost after measurements at 30 db. were made. *e*: an inhibitory response area for unit of Fig. 10 driven at 7.8 kc. only. Hatched area encloses tones inhibiting spontaneous discharge. Note (arrow) the additional sharp inhibition outside the inhibitory response area. *f*: asymmetrical response area showing inhibition (hatched regions) within and bordering it. (From Moushegian *et al.*, *J. Neurophysiol.* 25, 1962.)

nerve fibers, diminishes steadily in width as we ascend the pathway and the sharp high frequency cutoff is lost."

On the other hand, Katsuki (1961) concluded on the basis of his own investigations that response areas become gradually more narrow the higher the level of unit studied, up to the level of the medial geniculate. At

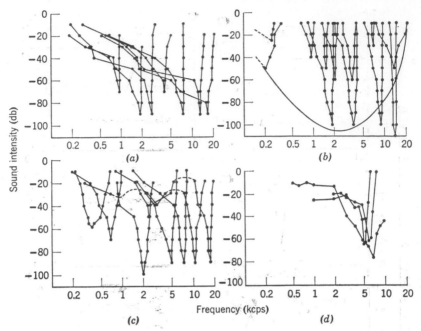

FIG. 10–12. Response areas of single neurons obtained from (a) cochlear nerve, (b) inferior colliculus, (c) trapezoid body, and (d) medial geniculate body. (Reprinted from *Sensory Communication*, Walter Rosenblith, Ed., by permission of The M.I.T. Press, Cambridge, Mass. Copyright 1961, The M.I.T. Press.)

the cortical level, however, he found very wide response areas. Some response areas plotted by Katsuki at four different levels of the auditory pathway are shown on Figure 10–12). However, taking more recent work also into consideration, one would hesitate to draw any generalizations of this nature. Certainly the study of response areas has not so far shown us how we are able to analyze sound frequency with precision.

### Inhibitory Responses

Various types of inhibitory interaction have been observed in central auditory structures. Noise, clicks and tones have been shown to inhibit the spontaneous activity of units. Inhibitory interactions between responses to tones and clicks, or between one tone and another have also been found. An interplay of inhibitory with excitatory influences has also been demonstrated in other ways. This has been shown for instance in the relation of stimulus intensity to strength of response. Although some units showed a greater response with increased stimulus intensity, others showed a weaker response, and yet others showed an increased response up to a certain optimum intensity, and then a decline as the stimulus intensity was further increased beyond this optimum. Such a decrease in responsiveness with increasing stimulus intensity is probably due to the addition of an inhibitory influence.

It appears that the inhibition of the spontaneous activity of a unit, or of its response to a sound stimulus, is synaptic in origin. It can occur at the level of the dorsal cochlear nucleus (Galambos and Davis, 1944; Galambos and Tasaki, reported by Tasaki, 1957) and the ventral cochlear nucleus (Moushegian et al., 1962) but in the cochlear nerve only very near the cochlear nucleus (Katsuki, 1961) where some cell bodies of second-order neurons are known to be located. Inhibitory effects have also been encountered at all higher levels of the auditory pathway including the auditory cortex (see, for instance, Thurlow et al., 1951; Galambos, 1952; Gross and Thurlow, 1951; Erulkar et al., 1956).

Inhibitory responses to tonal stimuli are of particular interest since they may underlie the mechanism of sharpening of frequency discrimination. It might be hoped that something analagous to lateral inhibition in the visual and somatosensory pathways could be demonstrated for audition also.

In some cases it has been possible to map inhibitory response areas to tonal stimuli by plotting the frequencies at which the spontaneous activity of a unit would be inhibited or at which the response of a unit to a click stimulus or to another tone would be inhibited. Sometimes such an inhibitory area was found to lie at one or the other side of the excitatory response area of the unit, but other units showed inhibitory response areas within their excitatory areas, or removed from them. The picture is not as orderly as that for lateral inhibition in the visual system. However, several investigators have reported that the tones producing the best masking were often in the same frequency region as those which activated the unit. It has also been observed that bands of effective suppressor frequencies were often encountered in the low frequency ranges.

Such neural events may underlie the perceptual phenomenon of auditory masking. If two tones differing in frequency are presented, one louder than the other, the weaker one may not be audible, especially if both are presented to the same ear. This effect can take place between tones of very different frequencies, though it is greatest when the two frequencies are close together. It has also been found that low frequencies are more effective at masking high frequencies than vice versa.

Inhibitory or occlusive interactions between responses to sounds presented to different ears have also been described at various levels. Such interactions occur as low down in the pathway as the superior olivary complex, which provides the first opportunity for such interaction to occur (Galambos et al., 1959). They may be important in the mechanism for auditory localization, which is discussed later.

## Intensity

The most frequent effects of increasing the intensity of a stimulus on the discharge of a unit are (a) a decrease in the latency of response; (b) an increase in the probability of response; (c) an increase in the number of spikes per response. However, those effects do not always occur (Galambos et al., 1952; Galambos et al., 1959; Erulkar et al., 1956; Galambos and Davis, 1943; Rose et al., 1963). Sometimes increasing stimulus intensity leads to an increase in the latency of response, sometimes to a decrease in the probability of response. Some units respond best at certain intensities and less well at both higher as well as lower intensities than the optima. It is apparent that inhibitory influences must often also play a role in determining the degree of response of a unit to a given stimulus. Some units have been reported in which there is a lack of correlation between stimulus intensity and number of spikes per response, or between stimulus intensity and response latency (Katsuki et al., 1959; Galambos et al., 1959).

When there is clearly an increase in the number of spikes per response correlated with stimulus intensity, such a relation is often found to be sigmoid. Katsuki et al. (1958, 1959, 1961) observed such a relation at all levels of the auditory pathway but reported that the curve relating stimulus intensity with discharge frequency was steep at the more peripheral levels and became flatter the more central the regions studied.

## Tonotopic Localization

By tonotopic localization is meant an arrangement of neural units such that different tones activate different places in the nervous system. Generally the term is applied where neighboring tones activate neighboring units. Many auditory nuclei do show a tendency to tonotopic localization. However, as seen in the preceding discussion of response areas, we should not think of a unit which is characterized as having a "best frequency" as being specifically sensitive to that frequency. We have seen that response areas are a very complex affair, and except at threshold intensities, units generally respond over quite a wide range of frequencies.

Rose et al. (1959) present convincing evidence that units in the cochlear nuclei are arranged in an orderly manner with respect to their characteristic frequencies (i.e., frequencies which activate the unit at lowest intensities). The authors divide the cochlear nuclei into three major groupings: the dorsal cochlear nucleus, the posteroventral nucleus and the anteroventral nucleus. (Although the ventral cochlear nucleus is not usually divided into two, anatomists had previously suggested this idea.) They demonstrated that in all three of these divisions the neurons are arranged in a dorsoventral sequence in general from high to low with respect to their characteristic frequencies. This finding is in accord with anatomical studies which showed that the cochlear fibers are arranged in an orderly manner and that fibers from different cochlear coils bifurcate in an orderly dorsoventral sequence.

Galambos, Schwartzkopf and Rupert (1959) were unable to find a clear ordering of best frequencies in any of the superior olivary nuclei. However, they did find evidence of a crude frequency segregation in the complex as a whole: nearly all units sensitive to tones below 1,000 cps. were located in the nucleus accessorius and the S-shaped segment, and units responding to high frequencies were located mainly in the trapezoid nucleus.

Katsuki *et al.* (1958) found evidence of at least gross tonotopic localization in the cellular part of the inferior colliculus. In its rostral area all elements investigated responded to high tones, and most elements lying caudally responded to tones below 2,000 cps. Rose *et al* (1963) also present

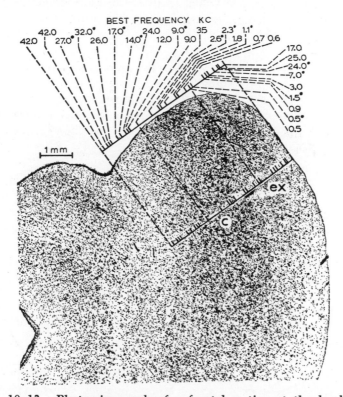

FIG. 10–13. Photomicrograph of a frontal section at the level of the inferior colliculus in cat 61–215. Nissl stain. A cell-sparse external nucleus (ex) and a cell-dense central nucleus (c) can be distinguished within the complex of the inferior colliculus at this level. A part of the electrode tract is visible to the left of the designation "ex." The solid black lines is a projection of the electrode track on the photograph. The track is assumed to be 0.5 mm. longer than is apparent from examination of histological sections. Bars indicate the depth of the successive points at which a single unit or a cluster of units was isolated by the electrode and a determination of best frequency made. Values marked by a dot indicate best frequencies of single neurons; other values show the upper limit of the effective frequency range which, for small clusters of units, is taken as an approximation of best frequency. Note that, neglecting a few irregularities, there is a sequence of best frequencies from high to low in the external nucleus and a sequence from low to high in the central nucleus. (From Rose, J. *et al.*, *J. Neurophysiol.* 26, 1963.)

evidence for tonotopic localization in the inferior colliculus, though their scheme does not coincide with that of Katsuki *et al.* (1958). They found that there is probably a sequence of best frequencies as the rim of the external nucleus of the inferior colliculus is tranversed in a ventral, oral and medial direction. They further demonstrated a consistent sequence of best frequencies arranged from low to high as the central nucleus is traversed (Figure 10–13).

Galambos (1952) failed to discover an orderly tonotopic organization in the pars principalis of the medial geniculate. Further, in a study by Rose and Woolsey (1958) it was concluded that each cross section of the pars principalis is probably connected with all cochlear turns.

## THE CORTICAL AREAS CONCERNED WITH AUDITION AND THEIR TONOTOPIC ORGANIZATION IN THE CAT

The auditory regions in the cortex of the cat may be divided on its cytoarchitectural characteristics into four main areas according to Rose (1949): AI, AII, EP and a dorsal fringe sector which he named SF or the

ssa—*anterior branch of suprasylvian*
ssp—*posterior branch of suprasylvian sulcus*
eca—*anterior ectosylvian sulcus*
ecp—*posterior ectosylvian sulcus*
pss—*pseudosylvian sulcus*

FIG. 10–14. Sulci on cortex of cat, important in discussion of hearing. Superimposed are cytoarchitectonic fields of auditory region according to Rose, 1949. (From Rasmussen, G. L. and Windle, W. F., *Neural Mechanisms of the Auditory and Vestibular Systems*, 1960; courtesy of Charles C. Thomas, Publisher, Springfield, Ill.)

suprasylvian fringe sector (Figure 10–14). Woolsey and Walzl (1942) showed that the basal turn of the cochlea projected to the anterior portion of AI and the apical turn to its posterior portion. However, in AII which lies just ventral to AI, the basal end of the cochlea projects to the posterior portion and the apical end to its anterior portion. As regards EP, it has been shown that there is an area responsive to stimulation of the basal cochlea (Downman, Woolsey and Lende, 1960) and that ventral to this area there is another, responsive to stimulation of the apex of the cochlea. There is also a frequency representation in the suprasylvian fringe sector. Woolsey (1961) reports that when the lateral bank of the suprasylvian sulcus and the adjoining lateral surface of the hemisphere were explored, a regular increase in represented frequency along the suprasylvian sulcus from the anterior to the caudal end was exhibited; this confirms the earlier less complete evidence from Hind (1953, 1960). Figure 10–15 illustrates these findings.

The question remains whether these cortical areas receive independent

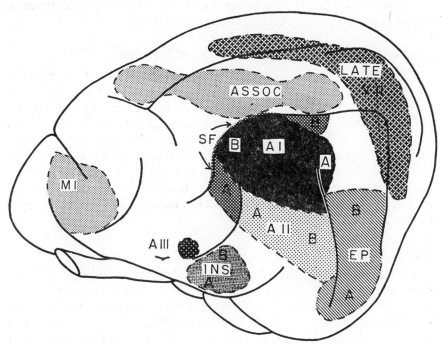

FIG. 10–15. Summary diagram showing four central areas with cochlea represented anteroposteriorly from apex (A) to (B) in the suprasylvian fringe sector (SF), from base to apex in AI; from apex to base in AII. In Ep, representation is base above, apex below. In insula (INS), evidence suggests base represented above, apex below. AIII is Tunturi's third auditory area. "Association" cortex (ASSOC) and precentral motor cortex gave responses to click with 15-msec latencies under chloralose. Visual area II (LATE) gave responses with 100-msec latency, also under chloralose. (From Rasmussen, G. L. and Windle, W. F., *Neural Mechanisms of the Auditory and Vestibular Systems*, 1960. Courtesy of Charles C. Thomas, Publisher, Springfield, Ill.)

input, or whether some areas are "secondary" or dependent on others. Kiang (1955) demonstrated not only that there was some dependence of EP on AI but also that AII and EP may be activated independently of AI. He found that when strychnine was applied to a point in AI, the frequency response curve for any point in ventral EP was similar to that for the point of strychnine application in AI. When strychnine was applied to a different point in AI, the frequency response curve from EP changed accordingly. He found this characteristic to be peculiar to EP and concluded that ventral EP receives projections from AI.

However, Kiang established that both AII and EP may be activated independently of AI by the following method. He isolated small patches of cortex by ablating all other auditory areas and found that normal surface positive responses persisted after a small area was isolated and disappeared when this area was undercut. This he found to be true for AI and AII and ventral EP, and he concluded that they all received primary afferent projections. Corroborative evidence comes from Downman *et al.* (1960) who report that after bilateral removal of AI, middle AII and EP could be activated by clicks and by cochlear nerve stimulation.

## Auditory Responses in the Second Somatic Area

Following a report by Tunturi (1945) on the dog that responses to auditory stimulation may be elicited in an area separate from those previously described, which lies partly in the second somatic area, a series of reports indicating that auditory stimuli also elicit responses in SII in the cat have appeared. Mickle and Ades (1952) found that the responses here to auditory as well as vestibular and somaesthetic stimuli were of such brief latency that they conclude that this is an example of a polysensory primary receiving area, in which correlation of messages from various modalities may be performed immediately without the messages having to be relayed further to a secondary area.

## The Insular Area

Pfaffmann and Woolsey (reported by Woolsey, 1961) obtained evidence that part of the insular cortex responded to auditory stimulation. Loeffler (1958) showed that the base and apex of the cochlea were differentially represented in this region (Figure 10–15). Desmedt and Mechelse (1959) found that responses may be elicited in this area to visual as well as to auditory stimuli and that an interaction occurs between such responses. They further present evidence that this area initiates an efferent control of incoming auditory stimuli (see below).

## Longer-Latency Responses

Longer-latency responses (about 15 msec.) to auditory stimulation are forthcoming from the suprasylvian and anterior lateral gyri and the precentral motor area. These areas are also responsive to visual and somatic stimuli (Buser and Borenstein, 1959). Late responses of latency 100 msec. to auditory stimuli may be obtained in the second visual area. No evidence of frequency representation has been found in these areas, which are also shown in Figure 10–15.

## Thalamo-Cortical Projections to the Main Auditory Areas

Some light is shed upon the organization of the auditory cortex by considering its connections. AI is connected to the pars principalis of the medial geniculate. Rose and Woolsey (1949) also conclude that it is connected to the pars magnocellularis. AII and EP are also separately connected to the pars principalis. There is also a projection from the posterior region of the pars principalis to the temporal and insular cortex. It also seems that AII, EP, the insular and temporal cortex are separately connected to the pars magnocellularis (Rose and Woolsey, 1949). However, Rose and Galambos (1952), who studied single-unit responses to clicks in the medial geniculate, were unable to find sufficient responsiveness in the pars magnocellularis to justify the conclusion that this was indeed a major auditory area.

## Cortical Areas Concerned with Audition in the Monkey

Studies on this problem using the monkey as experimental animal have been far fewer than those on the cat, partly because of the technical difficulties involved in reaching the cortical areas concerned, without injuring other parts of the cortex unduly. After studying degeneration in the monkey cortex following lesions in the medial geniculate, Poliak (1932) concluded that the cortical projection area for audition comprised most of the superior surface of the superior temporal gyrus. Le Gros Clark (1936) and Walker (1937), studying retrograde degeneration in the medial geniculate following cortical lesions, also delineated as auditory an area on the superior surface of the superior temporal gyrus. However, the area they mapped was smaller than that of Poliak and confined to the posterior section of this location. Ades and Felder (1942), studying click responses in the cortex, found a responsive area similarly located to those of Le Gros Clark and of Walker but somewhat larger, though not so large as that mapped by Poliak.

Later, Pribram et al. (1954) employed a different operative technique and so managed to avoid much of the damage which had been incurred in the course of previous experiments. They report responsiveness to clicks over a much wider area than had previously been considered auditory: the posterior supratemporal plane, the superior temporal gyrus, insula, and inferior parietal lobe.

## Tonotopic Localization in the Monkey

Walzl and Woolsey (Walzl, 1947) explored, in the macaque, cortical responses to stimulation of nerve fibers in the osseous spiral lamina. They found that stimulation of fibers in the basal coil of the cochlea caused responses in the posterior medial part of the auditory cortex. Stimulation of fibers at the apical turn caused responses in the anterior lateral part of the area. Licklider and Kryter (1942) studied responses in the auditory cortex of the macaque evoked by stimulation with tones of differing frequencies. Using the definition of the auditory area that was delineated by Ades and Felder, they report that the higher frequencies produced maximal responses in the posterior medial part of the region. The lower frequencies activated the anterolateral part of the area. Since the basal turn of the cochlea is concerned with high tone reception and the apical turn with low, this accords well with the findings of Walzl and Woolsey.

### LOCALIZATION OF SOUND IN SPACE

Psychophysical experiments on human subjects clearly indicate that the localization of sound in space is determined by an interaction of messages from the two ears. If two clicks of equal intensity are delivered simultaneously one to each ear, the observer hears only one sound located in the median plane. Increasing the intensity of one of these clicks causes the sound to be heard nearer the side of the louder click, and the more the intensity is increased, the further to that side the click is heard. Also if one of the clicks is delivered slightly before the other, the sound is heard nearer the side of the first click. Phase differences between two sounds also contribute to apparent localization.

Rosenzweig (1954) reports an interesting neurophysiological correlate of these findings. Using cats, he stimulated the two ears independently with clicks, varying the intensity and time of presentation systematically. He found that under those stimulus conditions in which a human observer hears a single sound at one side of the head, cortical activity in these cats is greater at the contralateral hemisphere (i.e., contralateral to the side at which a human observer would localize that sound). The further over to the side a human observer would hear a sound, the greater was the difference between the activity of the two hemispheres. When the stimulus conditions were such that a human observer would hear a sound in the median plane, the cortical activity was found to be equal at the two hemispheres. However, auditory localization is not performed by comparing the amounts of activity at the two hemispheres, since unilateral ablation of auditory cortex produces only a slight deficit in auditory localization (see below).

Evidence of binaural interaction at various lower centers may be considered to be related to auditory localization. Rosenzweig and Wyers (1955), recording from the inferior colliculi in cats, report that the responses to stimulation of both ears were smaller in amplitude than was the sum of responses to monaural stimulation of each ear. If one ear is stimulated slightly after the other, the response to the second stimulus is modified. Hind *et al.* (1963) describe complex interaction patterns between stimuli delivered to the two ears at the inferior colliculus. Rosenzweig and Sutton (1958) report a statistically significant interaction between paired clicks delivered one to each ear with short time intervals between them at the level of the lateral lemniscus.

Galambos, Schwartzkopf and Rupert (1959) present evidence that the superior olivary complex is concerned with sound localization. This is the earliest station in the auditory pathway in which individual nuclei receive input from both ears. They found that certain interaural time differences might alter the likelihood of a discharge of a unit, produce latency shifts, or suppress the discharge of a unit. The accessory nucleus was deemed by the authors to be of special importance in this regard. Anatomically, its cells display a striking symmetrical and equal innervation from both sides. A distinctively different slow wave appears at each area of the nucleus, depending on whether the click stimulus moves the eardrum inward or outward initially, or to which ear it is delivered. Furthermore, some of its cells show an invariant latency, may preserve time differences of .3 msec., or may show no response if both ears are stimulated with a slight time interval between them.

## THE EFFECT OF BRAIN LESIONS ON AUDITORY FUNCTIONS

## Localization of Sound in Space

Neff, Fisher, Diamond, and Yela (1956) and Neff and Diamond (1958) showed that bilateral, though not unilateral, ablations of AI, AII and EP in the cat leads to a severe deficit in the ability to localize sound in space. More recent studies (Neff, 1961) indicate that bilateral transection of the brachium of the inferior colliculus produces a complete loss in the ability to localize sound in space. Also, a slight deficit may result from unilateral cortical lesions which include AI, AII, EP, SII, IT and SS (suprasylvian gyrus); a small deficit has also been shown to result from unilateral transection of the brachium of the inferior colliculus. Small deficits were also noted to result from bilateral ablations of portions of the auditory cortex.

### Frequency Discrimination

After extensive bilateral lesions of the cortical auditory areas, cats can be shown still to be able to make frequency discriminations (Goldberg *et al.*, 1958; Goldberg and Neff, 1961a) provided adequate testing procedures are used. However, it is not known whether the difference threshold for frequency discrimination is altered by this procedure.

After bilateral section of the brachium of the inferior colliculus, cats are also able to perform frequency discriminations (Goldberg and Neff, 1961b). Under such conditions potentials are still evoked in the cortex by auditory stimuli (Galambos *et al.*, 1961). However, animals with bilateral sections of the brachium of the inferior colliculus which also extend medially (with the result that potentials are no longer evoked at the cortex by auditory stimuli) are unable to perform frequency discriminations. It appears that a medially placed pathway, running parallel to the classical afferent pathway, is of importance for frequency discrimination.

Such medially placed structures may also be important in the human case. Landau *et al.* (1960) report the case of a boy who died at age ten and at autopsy was found to have severe bilateral degeneration of the medial geniculate and auditory cortex. He had been studied intensively before death, and it was found that he could understand speech and carry out simple conversations, uttering the speech sounds correctly. It was therefore apparent that he could discriminate frequency as well as intensity of sound.

### Tonal Pattern Discrimination

Diamond and Neff (1957) found that when AI, AII, and EP were completely ablated, the ability to discriminate tonal patterns (i.e., the same tones arranged in a different order) was lost. Later, Goldberg, Diamond and Neff (1957) extirpated the temporal and insular cortex sparing SI, AII and EP and found a profound loss in ability to perform such tasks. Thus it seems that the ability to store the sequence of tonal events is lost by lesions in the auditory cortex.

### Absolute Intensity Threshold

A series of early experiments including a study by Kryter and Ades (1943) on the cat led to the conclusion that ablation of auditory cortical areas did not significantly affect absolute intensity threshold if a post-operative recovery time was allowed before testing. The above authors found that if in addition to the auditory cortices the medial geniculate bodies were destroyed, a loss of 40 db. to 50 db. resulted, which would only be termed a mild deafness.

### Discrimination of Intensity Differences

Another early series of experiments, including studies by Raab and Ades (1946) and Rosenzweig (1946), both on the cat, demonstrated that the ability to discriminate differences in intensity was not significantly affected by auditory cortical ablations. Raab and Ades showed that when the inferior colliculi were bilaterally ablated in addition, then DLs were increased. Oesterreich and Neff (reported by Neff, 1961) report little change to DLs after bilateral extirpation of all known auditory cortex. When, in addition, the inferior colliculi were ablated, a DL increase of 5 to 7 db. was noted. When the brachium of the inferior colliculus was sectioned bilaterally, DL changes of up to 10 db. were noted. Discriminations of large differences in intensity can still be performed after sections of the brachium of the inferior colliculus which extend medially so that potentials are no longer evoked in the cortex by acoustic stimuli.

## EFFERENT CONNECTIONS TO THE COCHLEA

The nerve endings at the hair cells in the cochlea are not only afferent, but also efferent. Such efferent fibers convey inhibitory messages to the hair cells. Their functional significance in hearing is at present only dimly understood. These efferent fibers have their origin in the superior olivary complex. Each ear receives an input of such fibers from the superior olivary complex on its own side and also from the superior olivary complex on the opposite side. Of the total of 500 efferent fibers to each cochlea, about 100 arise in the olivary complex on the same side, and the remainder cross the midline from the opposite side. Given that there are around 25,000 hair cells and the same number of afferent fibers (in the guinea pig), any efferent function exercised by these fibers must be relatively coarse.

Rasmussen (1946) first described this olivocochlear bundle also named the tract of Rasmussen. He found that it is composed of axons 3–5 m. in diameter (Rasmussen, 1960). Galambos (1956) was the first to demonstrate that suppression of auditory nerve activity was obtainable by the stimulation of the olivocochlear bundle. It has further been shown that such inhibitory action is not evoked by a single shock to the bundle, but needs at least four shocks, rising to a maximum at forty 30 msec. shocks (at 400 ps.) (Desmedt, 1962). The inhibitory effect on a click is dependent on the delay between the shocks to the bundle and time of arrival of the click, showing a fairly long decay to baseline after the maximum effect has been obtained (over 400 msec. after 42 shocks). Galambos (1956) found that stimulation at the rate of 25 to 30 ps. was ineffective, a slight effect appearing only at 40 ps.

Pfalz (1962) destroyed one cochlea and inserted microelectrodes into the consequently deafferented cochlear nucleus. He was able to observe a diminution of frequency of spontaneous firing in single neurons of the nucleus in response to acoustic stimulation of the contralateral ear. In half of the units studied there was some frequency at which the inhibitory effect on spontaneous firing of the unit was at a maximum and in the other half there was some frequency at which this inhibitory effect was at a minimum. However, the least intensity necessary to produce any inhibition at any frequency was 48 db. above threshold. These data on the guinea pig are in good correspondence with those of Fex (1962) on the decerebrate cat. However, Fex did not find units in which there was a frequency at which the inhibitory effect on spontaneous firing of the unit was at a minimum.

In addition, loci producing an inhibition of responsiveness in the cochlear nuclei have been found in the ventral nucleus of the lateral lemniscus, the ventral and anterior aspects of the inferior colliculus, and

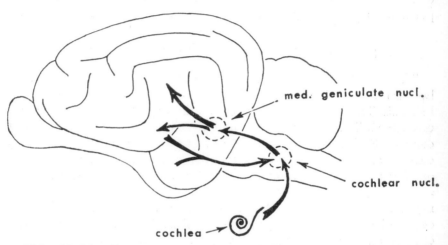

FIG. 10–16.    Diagram suggested tentatively by Desmedt to illustrate interplay of efferent and afferent pathways in the auditory system. (From Rasmussen, G. L. and Windle, W. F., *Neural Mechanisms of the Auditory and Vestibular Systems*, 1960; courtesy of Charles C. Thomas, Publisher, Springfield, Illinois.)

the mesial aspect of the medial geniculate (Desmedt, 1960). Though these areas are close to the ascending auditory pathway, they are not actually included in it. Stimulation of the mesencephalic reticular core did not in these experiments suppress the cochlear nuclear response to sound. Fibers of the descending pathway have been traced to the insular area of the auditory cortex (Figure 10–16).

However the functions of this efferent pathway remain obscure. Galambos (1960) performed several experiments to investigate the function of the olivocochlear bundle in freely moving cats. He taught cats a shock-avoidance response to a sound signal, and found that their thresholds for tones in the presence of masking noise so measured were unaffected by cutting the olivocochlear bundle. In other cats, electrodes were chronically implanted on the round window of each cochlea and the middle ear muscles cut on one side. Measurements were then taken of the $N_1$ response to clicks in the ear without its muscles (this providing a measure of the activity in the olivocochlea bundle). However no variation of this response was found to correlate with wakefulness, attentiveness, excitement or any other state. Such animals were also trained to expect a loud noise when a light appeared. No change of activity was detectable when the light alone was presented though it was anticipated that such activity would show itself if one efferent bundle had been active. This problem obviously awaits further investigation.

# 11

## VISION

In the study of vision we are concerned with the organism's response to light. Light is a form of electromagnetic radiation which may be viewed as consisting either of waves or of particles. As waves, light may be regarded as having a frequency, and since such waves travel at a certain speed, also a wavelength. When viewed as consisting of particles (quanta or photons), the energies of these particles depend on the wavelength of the light. Normally, light when it travels is treated as a continuous set of waves. However, when we deal with the emission or absorption of light, it is useful to consider light in terms of discrete particles.

The stimulation of the eye in vision is an instance of absorption of light. The eye in the dark is so sensitive that a retinal receptor, the rod, is excited by the absorption of one quantum of light, the smallest amount of light possible. However a single quantum cannot be seen, because vision depends on the pooled information from a few rods.

The fact that light consists of separate packets of energy, the number of which becomes very small at low intensities, assumes considerable importance when we consider vision in low illumination. First of all, at a given low intensity of illumination, the number of quanta reaching the eye fluctuates a great deal because of the random distribution in time of quanta. The absolute threshold of sensitivity of the eye must therefore fluctuate if only because of the physical nature of the stimulus. Secondly, the spatial distribution of quanta on the receptor mosaic of the eye will also vary considerably during illumination at low intensities. This will lead to an indistinctness of vision which again has physical as well as physiological or psychological origins.

Light may be regarded as the visible part of the spectrum of electromagnetic waves which stretch from gamma rays to bands at frequencies used for broadcasting. The visible part of this spectrum ranges from about 380 m$\mu$ (millimicrons or millionths of a millimeter) to about 760 m$\mu$.

Normal white light such as daylight contains a mixture of all such wavelengths. When these wavelengths are seen unmixed (for instance when they have been passed through a prism), the different wavelengths are seen as colors. The shortest wavelength is seen as violet; with increasing wavelengths, the appearance passes through blue to green then yellow and orange and finally to red. However, all wavelengths are not equally visible. Wavelengths taken from the extreme ranges of the spectrum require much higher energies to appear equally bright compared with wavelengths taken from the medium ranges. A similar function also holds for threshold intensities. Curves measuring such discrepancies in stimulating efficiency according to wavelength are called spectral sensitivity or luminosity curves (Figure 11-1).

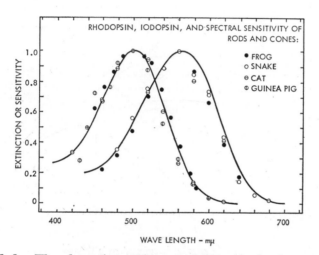

FIG. 11-1. The absorption spectra of chicken rhodopsin and iodopsin, measured by Wald, and photopic sensitivities of various animals as determined electrophysiological measurement, measured by Granit. (From Wald, G., *Handbook of Physiology*, 1960; by permission of the American Physiological Society.)

Besides varying in wavelength, light energy also varies in intensity or in the amplitude of its wave form. Though this is a clear and unitary concept, a variety of measures and terminologies to define intensity has grown up for various reasons, some practical, others historical. We shall discuss the units most frequently used. The intensity of a source of light is measured by comparing it with the intensity of a standard candle (a standardized candle with a flame one inch high). When light from such a standard candle falls on a surface one foot away and one foot square, the level of illumination is defined as one footcandle. (An alternative system uses meters instead of feet, and according to this system one meter-candle is the level of illumination thrown by a candle on a surface of one square meter, one meter away.) The amount of light reflected from an object, as distinct from that which is falling on it, is measured in millilamberts. One millilambert is the amount of light reflected from a perfectly diffusing and reflecting surface, one foot square, illuminated by 0.93 footcandle.

## THE EYE

The eye is roughly spherical in shape (Figure 11–2). It admits light through its transparent anterior surface, the cornea. This light then passes to the posterior surface of the eye, having been brought into focus by the optical apparatus. The image forming mechanism of the eye is not unlike that of a camera. Light rays are refracted or bent upon passing into the eye. As refraction of light takes place when it passes from a medium of one density into that of another, refraction begins to take place as soon as light

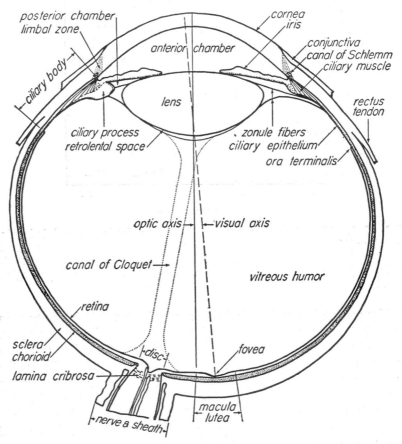

FIG. 11–2. Horizontal section of human eye. (From Walls, G. L., *The Vertebrate Eye.* Bloomfield Hills, Mich., Cranbrook Institute of Science, 1942.)

passes from air into the denser aqueous humor. (This is a fluid filling the anterior chamber of the eye in front of the lens.) More bending then takes place as the light passes into the denser substance of the lens, and then again as it passes into the vitreous humor behind the lens. In a simple camera, only the lens is responsible for light refraction.

Differential amounts of focusing (or accommodation) are necessary, depending on the distance of the object which is being viewed. In the eye, as in the camera, such differential focusing is brought about by changes in the lens. In the camera the lens is shifted in relation to the surface on which the image is formed. This is also the case in the eyes of some fish. However, in most vertebrate eyes, curvature of the lens is altered to produce the same results. Such alteration is accomplished by means of the ciliary muscles.

Another feature in which the eye resembles a camera is in the possession of an iris, which can be viewed as the analog of the diaphragm in the camera. The iris is a membrane resting on the outside of the lens. It controls pupillary diameter and thus the amount of light admitted through the lens. However, the range of diameter over which the pupil varies its size extends only from about 6.5 to 2.9 mm., while the range of intensities of light to which the eye is exposed is over a million to one. The iris therefore compensates only to a very limited extent for changes in illumination. This contribution of the pupil also helps to improve the depth of focus of the lens, and so the focusing ability at extreme ranges of distance of the object viewed. This is a principle familiar to amateur photographers. A demonstration of its use by the ocular apparatus can easily be obtained by asking a subject to look at a small object which is then brought slowly closer to his eye. It will be seen that as this is done the pupil begins to constrict.

Though for our purpose it is not necessary to review the optical mechanism of the eye in detail, it is important to mention the inversion which takes place in the eye during image formation. The eye resembles a pinhole camera in this respect. Points on the object being viewed are connected by straight lines (light rays) to corresponding points on the image being formed. All these lines must pass through a small aperture or pinhole between the object and the image. As a result there must occur a left-right, up-down inversion of the image relative to the object being viewed. Consequently, objects which are seen in the upper right quadrant of the visual field actually impinge on the lower left quadrant of the retina.

A perception of light can be evoked in a particular part of the retina by applying pressure on a point close to it on the surface of the eye. This is called a visual phosphene. The visual sensation is referred to a part of the visual field in accordance with the law of inversion stated above. For instance, deformation of the lower right part of the retina produces a visual sensation which appears to come from the upper left visual quadrant. That such a correlation between retinal locus and resulting appearance is unlearnt is shown by the fact that when such phosphenes can be evoked in the congenitally blind they are perceived to proceed from the same place as in normal subjects.

## The Retina

In the normal human eye the image is formed on the retina. This is a complex structure consisting of receptors and neural layers lining about 180° of the eye on its posterior surface. In the center of the retina lies the macula lutea (yellow spot). Within this central region there is a round depression, 1,500 $\mu$ in diameter, called the fovea centralis. This is the area which is used for vision of fine detail, and it is made up almost entirely of one class of visual receptive elements, the cones. The depression in the fovea centralis is due to the fact that blood vessels and nerve fibers run over the rest of the retina, whereas they bypass the fovea. Owing to a freak of development, the light sensitive elements in the retina are actually obscured by blood vessels and the neural connections to the light sensitive elements. These enter the eye through the optic disc, where consequently there is an interruption in the retina and the so-called "blind spot."

The elements which translate energy in the form of light into neural events lie closest to the posterior surface of the eye. There are two main types of such elements: the *rods* and the *cones*. Their differences will be discussed below. These elements contain pigments the state of which can be altered by light. The rods and cones make synaptic connections with *bipolar cells*. According to Vilter (1949), in the fovea, there are three bipolar cells for each cone, and it seems that each cone sends a message to three bipolar cells. The next synaptic contact in the retina is between the bipolar and *ganglion cells*. Here in the foveal region it seems that three bipolar cells converge on two ganglion cells.

The axons of the ganglion cells form the fibers of the optic tract. The rather favorable ratio of receptors to fibers leaving the retina holds only in the fovea and in the case of the cones. Out towards the periphery and in the case of the rods, convergence is extreme. Though there are about 125 million rods in the eye, only about one million myelinated fibers are to be found in the optic tract (Polyak, 1957). There is however a possibility that unmyelinated fibers also form the optic tract, and therefore the ratio of fibers to receptors may be much larger.

The connections described so far allow messages initiated by light to leave the retina. However there are two other types of connection. The first type enables influences to be carried laterally within the retina itself at two levels. At the end feet of the receptors there are *horizontal cells*, and between the bipolar and ganglion cell level there are laterally spreading *amacrine cells*. It is thought (Granit, 1962) that these laterally spreading plexiform layers are inhibitory in function. Indeed they would give an anatomical basis for the phenomena of contrast or lateral inhibition which is a pronounced feature in the visual system (see below). The second type of connection which has been postulated and about which there is some doubt (Granit, 1962) is represented by centrifugal fibers or fibers sending messages into the retina from other parts of the central nervous system.

## Rods and Cones

Though the distinction between rods and cones was originally made on the basis of shape, there seems to be in fact a considerable amount of overlap morphologically between the two types of receptor. Probably the best preliminary distinction between them can be made on functional grounds. The cones are used mainly when light is plentiful. They have developed in cases where high selectivity of information is at a premium. Rods, however, have developed to detect low levels of illumination. For instance, in the human eye, cones predominate in the fovea centralis which has a high capacity for color discrimination. However, rods predominate at the periphery which is much more sensitive to light after dark adaptation, but where color discrimination is absent. Similarly, diurnal animals have retinae composed mostly of cones, whereas nocturnal animals possess only rods.

It has lately been shown by direct measurement of pigments in individual cones (McNichol, 1964) that there are three kinds of cones distinguished from each other by the possession each of a different pigment. Each type of cone contains a pigment which breaks down most readily in light from a particular portion of the spectrum. The first type has its peak sensitivity at a wavelength of 447 m$\mu$ (blue-violet), the second type is maximally sensitive at 540 m$\mu$ (green), and the third at 577 m$\mu$ (yellow). This has been shown to be true of the macaque and also of man. This finding is important in the understanding of the basis of color vision (see below). The rods, on the other hand, contain a pigment, rhodopsin, with a peak of sensitivity close to 500 m$\mu$. The properties of the pigments to be found in the receptors determine many psychophysical results on vision as will be seen later.

## The Visual Pigments

Light must be absorbed in order to have any physical effect. In order for this to happen, light-absorbing substances or pigments must be present which are changed in some way when they absorb light. In the case of vision, this change must be such as to produce nervous excitation.

Visual pigments break down when they absorb light. Therefore, in order for visual functioning to be continuous, the change caused by light on the pigment must be reversible. Furthermore the change in the pigment which gives rise to neural excitation must be short-lasting or be quickly removed. Otherwise the eye could not detect rapid decreases of light.

There are four visual pigments known at present: rhodopsin and porphyropsin in rods, and iodopsin and cyanopsin in cones. Of these, probably rhodopsin and perhaps also iodopsin occur in the human visual apparatus. These four pigments have been shown to be combinations of two forms of retinene and two forms of opsin. Opsin is a protein, and retinene is a carotenoid closely related to vitamin A. Rhodopsin, when it absorbs light, passes into retinene$_1$ via some intermediates and rod opsin. Retinene$_1$ may then be modified into vitamin A$_1$, or it may recombine with opsin to form rhodopsin again. If retinene$_1$ is modified into vitamin A$_1$, retinene$_1$ can be resynthesized from this vitamin. Retinene$_1$ and opsin will then form rhodopsin again. There are therefore two processes whereby rhodopsin is regenerated: a fast one from retinene$_1$ and opsin and a slow one ultimately from vitamin A$_1$ and opsin.

A similar process occurs in the case of the other visual pigments. Rhodopsin and iodopsin (a cone pigment extracted from the retinae of chickens) are both composed of retinene$_1$, and differ only in the protein to which this retinene is attached. Rhodopsin contains a protein called rod opsin, whereas iodopsin contains a protein called cone opsin. There is a similar relation in the case of porphyropsin and cyanopsin. Porphyropsin is contained in the rods of vertebrates which spawn in fresh water, such as certain fishes and amphibia. Cyanopsin is found in the cones of the Greek tortoise and the tench (a freshwater fish). Instead of containing retinene, these two pigments contain a closely similar carotenoid, retinene$_2$. Porphyropsin is formed by retinene$_2$ and rod opsin, whereas cyanopsin is composed of retinene$_2$ and cone opsin. Though the chemistry of the four naturally occurring photopigments at present known is well understood, it is not yet clear how the dissociation of such pigments into their components by light produces neural excitation.

Measurements have been made of the rates at which monochromatic lights decompose the visual pigments, and of how much they are absorbed by such pigments. In the case of rhodopsin there is a striking parallel between the sensitivity of the human dark-adapted eye to various portions of the visible spectrum and the amount of light in these same portions absorbed by this pigment. Of the other pigments, iodopsin, the cone pigment extracted from the chicken retina, comes fairly close to the sensitivity of the human light-adapted eye, though its peak of sensitivity is displaced towards the longer wavelengths. The slight chemical differences present in these various pigments produce differences in their absorption spectra.

## DARK ADAPTATION

One consequence of the properties of photosensitive pigments on vision relates to dark adaptation. It was suggested by Hecht (1937) that the amount of unbleached rhodopsin present in rods was regulated by the rate at which it was being bleached by light and also by the rate at which it was being resynthesized by the eye. Therefore if the amount of light falling on the retina was sharply cut down, there would be an increase in the amount of unbleached rhodopsin in the rods because the average length of time that a resynthesized rhodopsin molecule would stay unbleached would be longer. Further, the larger the number of unbleached rhodopsin molecules,

FIG. 11–3. Comparison of dark adaptation curves of normal and rod monochromat subject. The dots indicate rate of regeneration of rhodopsin of both subjects. This rate of regeneration is the same for both subjects as the dots do not divide into two populations. (From Rushton, W. A. H., "Visual Pigments in Man," *Scientific American*, 207, 12, November, 1962. © by Scientific American, Inc. All rights reserved.)

the greater the chance that a quantum of light on entering the eye would strike an unbleached molecule. Now when a quantum of light is absorbed by an unbleached molecule, energy is released which will in its turn contribute to the stimulation of the neural receptor, and so to a visual sensation. Thus the less light there is, the more sensitive to light the eye becomes.

We should expect from the above that the increase in light sensitivity of the eye when it is placed in the dark should parallel the resynthesis of visual pigments by the eye. That such is the case can be seen from Figure 11–3. The way this evidence was obtained is most ingenious. Rushton (1962) has been able to determine the rate of resynthesis of rhodopsin in the intact eye by measuring how much light shone into the eye is reflected from it. Since less light is reflected when rhodopsin is unbleached, one can determine the rate at which rhodopsin is resynthesized while at the same time taking reports of sensation from the subject. The subject whose curve of increasing sensitivity and rhodopsin resynthesis is illustrated in Figure 11–3 was chosen by Rushton because he was a "rod monochromat." In a "rod monochromat" the cones do not function; consequently, foveal vision is almost absent, acuity is poor, and there is total color blindness. On the other hand the properties of such an eye are not complicated by the

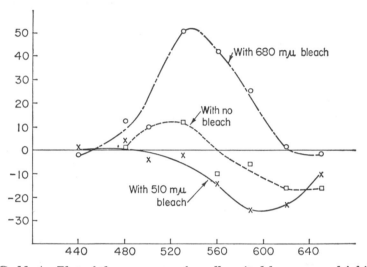

FIG. 11–4. Plot of the responses of a cell excited by green and inhibited by red to various monochromatic lights. Conditions indicated on curves. (From De Valois, R. L., *Contributions to Sensory Physiology*, W. D. Neff (Ed.). New York: Academic Press Inc., 1965.)

presence of cones so there should be a direct match between the properties of rhodopsin and behavioral response. It can be seen from Figure 11–4 that this is the case.

In the normal eye, cones are also present so we should expect dark adaptation to be a function of the resynthesis of the cone pigments as well as of rhodopsin. It appears that the cone pigments do not ever become as light sensitive as does rhodopsin, however long we stay in the dark. On the other hand, using the above method, Rushton has measured the rate at which cone pigments are resynthesized in the eye and he found that this rate is very much faster than that of resynthesis of rhodopsin. This is in agreement with Wald's (1959) measurement of the rate of synthesis of cone and rod pigments in solution. We should therefore expect if we compare the rod monochromat with the normal subject that the normal will initially adapt more quickly as his cone pigments resynthesize but will soon hit a temporary ceiling of sensitivity as the concentration of cone pigment quickly reaches its maximum. After a while the slower but eventually more sensitive rhodopsin will resynthesize to the point where the rods, or rhodopsin containing elements, become as sensitive as the cones, while still not reaching their own point of maximum sensitivity. As the rods become even more sensitive, the sensitivity of the normal eye begins to increase again to a final plateau. That this is the case can be seen from curves of dark adaptation (Figure 11-3) in the normal subject. As was mentioned above, rods predominate in the visual periphery, and as a result we should expect the same type of curve from the periphery of the normal eye as that to be found in the monochromat. This is also the case.

As we explained above, the various visual pigments are each maximally sensitive in a different part of the spectrum. When they are all taken together the cone pigments are most sensitive towards the red end of the spectrum, whereas rhodopsin is most efficient in the blue part of the spectrum. This accounts for the common observation that blue and green objects appear to be much brighter in relation to yellow and red objects in dusk than in daylight. This phenomenon is known as the Purkinje shift. Furthermore, because of the insensitivity of rhodopsin to the red end of the spectrum, dark adaptation (resynthesis of rhodopsin) can take place unhindered also if we are placed in deep red light, though we are not actually in the dark.

This insensitivity of rhodopsin to deep red light is put to interesting use by the Bronx Zoo. At this zoo, small nocturnal mammals with all rod retinae are placed in deep red light which they cannot see during the day and in white light at night. In this way their activity cycle is reversed. Since they are active during the day, they can be viewed as such by their human observers whose cone pigments are sensitive to the longer wavelengths. In zoos where this is not done such animals are almost invariably asleep when visitors are admitted.

It appears from various measurements (Rushton, 1962; Wald, 1959) that the bleaching of very small amounts of rhodopsin leads to a very large decrease in sensitivity in the dark-adapted human subject. According to Wald (1959), visual sensitivity is reduced 8.5 times by the bleaching of only 0.006 percent of rhodopsin, whereas sensitivity is reduced 3,300 times by the bleaching of 0.06 percent of rhodopsin. It appears that it is the logarithm of sensitivity which varies with the concentration of rhodopsin. To explain this, Wald has suggested the theory that rhodopsin resides in a large number of compartments within the rod. Each compartment contains a large number of rhodopsin molecules, but only the bleaching of the first molecule within each compartment produces excitation, even though the other molecules in the compartment continue to absorb light. In this way, a high state of light adaptation can be produced by the bleaching of a very small quantity of rhodopsin. The observed logarithmic relation would be generated by such a system.

## COLOR AND BRIGHTNESS

As we have described above, there are various types of receptors in the eye, differentiated on the basis of the pigment they contain. These receptors feed into a second stage, the bipolar cells which in turn feed into ganglion cells. There are also two layers corresponding to the junction zones between these cells which provide means of horizontal interaction. Such an anatomical picture suggests that there may be interesting recombination of the information from the receptor layer. More direct evidence from electrophysiological recording confirms such a notion. Two main types of combination of the basic information supplied by the receptor cells have been discovered. The first type consists of combinations of like sign, and the second type of combinations of opposite sign. In the first category, signals from receptor cells converge onto a ganglion cell, and in some cases each signal excites the cell, and in other cases each signal inhibits it. In the second category, the ganglion cell is excited by input from one class of receptor and inhibited by input from another. It will be seen that the like-sign channel conveys information about overall brightness regardless of color and the unlike-sign channel carries information about color almost regardless of intensity.

Evidence concerning these two types of channel was first discovered in the retinae of certain fishes by Svaetichin (see Svaetichin and MacNichol, 1958). Recording with micropipettes, Svaetichin found a negative resting potential in the retina which increased with the intensity of light, regardless of wavelength. However, some wavelengths were more effective in producing a change than others. Another type of potential, however, changed from negative to positive as the illuminating wavelength shifted from the blue end to the red end of the spectrum. Both these potentials Svaetichin called S-potentials. They are not spike potentials but steady potentials, and it is unclear from which structures they originate. Some of the potentials which reverse sign have their highest sensitivity in the red and green regions (one corresponding to the peak of negativity and the other corresponding to the peak of positivity). Another type has its two peaks in the blue and yellow regions of the spectrum. Perhaps at the ganglion cell level these graded or steady potentials are translated into the usual type of spike potential, or the inhibition of spike activity, as the case may be. In higher forms, such information is then carried probably without much change to the cells in the lateral geniculate, in which the axons of the ganglion cells (the optic nerve) mainly terminate. It is most profitable to consider the activity as it appears at the level of the lateral geniculate, because this has been excellently investigated by DeValois (1965) in the macaque monkey. DeValois and his collaborators have shown by careful psychophysical procedures that the visual system of the macaque and man are virtually identical. That is why their neural recording from the macaque has most relevance for color vision as we understand it. Let us first consider the evidence from cells combining signals of like sign.

## Like-Sign Summators

These cells have also been called broad-band cells. They are functionally similar to the retinal ganglion cells described by Granit (1962) which he calls dominators.

Using microelectrodes, DeValois was able to demonstrate the existence of cells in the lateral geniculate of the macaque, which reacted in the same way qualitatively to all wavelengths in the visible spectrum. Some cells would react by inhibition, others by excitation. The cells showed the same sensitivity to different parts of the visible spectrum as did the whole monkey in behavioral tests. It seems therefore that these cells carry brightness (luminosity) information.

From the overall sensitivity of these cells it is often possible to see to what receptors they are linked at the periphery. Some have a sensitivity curve which corresponds to that of rods. Others show a rod curve at low intensities and yet at higher intensities the luminosity curve characteristic of daylight vision. Thus the Purkinje shift can be seen in a single cell. This indicates that these cells are indirectly connected both to rods and cones. Other cells in this class show curves which are like some of the curves for two cone pigments added together.

## Opposite-Sign Summators

These are cells on which converge inputs, some of which excite and some of which inhibit ongoing activity. These inputs come from receptor cells with different sensitivities, i.e., the blue, green, and yellow cones. Good examples of these have been demonstrated among ganglion cells in the retina of goldfish (Wagner et al., 1960). When an excitatory input from a receptor arrives, such a cell fires at the onset of the light stimulus. If on the other hand the stimulating light excites a receptor which sends inhibitory messages to the ganglion cell, inhibition of spontaneous activity occurs and the ganglion cell fires when the stimulating light is switched off. (This is known as post-inhibitory rebound and occurs commonly in units of the nervous system.) When the stimulating light is of an intermediate wavelength, such as to affect both those receptors which excite the cell and those which inhibit it, then the ganglion cell fires both on the "on" and on the "off" of the stimulating light. To test the correctness of this interpretation of the linkage of receptors with these ganglion cells, experiments were done to bleach out selectively the pigment belonging to one of the receptors thought to be linked to a given ganglion cell. When this was done and the receptor inhibiting the cell had been thus desensitized, an "on" response could be obtained by almost any wavelength in the spectrum. Clearly the inhibitory process had been inactivated, and it could not cancel out the excitatory process anywhere in the spectrum. The ganglion cells studied were connected to receptor processes most sensitive in the red region of the spectrum and in the green region.

Similar results have been obtained by DeValois (1965) in the lateral geniculate of the macaque (Figure 11–4). Most of the cells found here were excited by green and inhibited by red or vice versa. Other cells responded in a similar way to blue and yellow. Further combinations were also identified, some cells for instance being inhibited by colors at both ends of the spectrum but excited by colors in the middle ranges. It was found that the relative excitation or inhibition of a particular cell is determined by the proportions in which the receptor cells indirectly connected to it are excited by the incident light. The pigments producing the excitation in each receptor cell (such as the green and yellow cones) have greatly overlapping sensitivities which in fact only differ slightly over most of the spectrum. The visual mechanism adopts a good stratagem by processing the information in such a way that the excitation which is common to both type of receptor cancels out and that which is not common is registered. (A similar principle is used in the differential amplifier which is employed in neurophysiological recording.) Consequently, there is a great sharpening of the signal concerning color, which now corresponds to the difference between the two curves. However (as in the case of the differential amplifier) such a scheme of cancellation produces a difficulty. The cancellation obtained tends to differ depending on the absolute as well as the relative magnitudes of the signals which are summed. This is because it is difficult to adjust such a device so that both channels respond to an increase in the signal (in this case light) according to precisely the same function. One channel may register the same increase of light intensity with a slightly smaller increase in firing rate than the other. In this case a wavelength which produces perfect cancellation at one intensity (since here the two channels are equally excited) may fail to do so at another intensity, and cancellation at the second intensity will instead occur at a different wavelength. Because of this there should be expected a shift in the peak of excitation in a lateral geniculate cell as the intensity of a stimulating light is raised. DeValois (1965) has noted that such a shift of peak sensitivity in the cells of the lateral geniculate does indeed occur and that it is highly similar to the change in color which is perceived with increasing intensity by the human observer. This is known as the Bezold-Brücke effect, and the neurophysiological data presented above explain it in a very satisfying manner.

It should also be noted that in an arrangement where two curves cancel with regard to their common sensitivity, the peaks of sensitivity of the two initial curves are shifted away from each other. Thus the peak of sensitivity of the deep yellow pigment at the cones is effectively shifted at the lateral geniculate into the red. Similarly the green pigment is shifted towards the blue when it is linked with the deep yellow. For the same reason a linkage of the green and blue cones in an opposite-sign summator would lead to a shift of the green curve into a maximum in the yellow region and some shift of the blue towards even shorter wavelengths. In this way three primary pigments would give rise to four basic colors.

There are some other phenomena of color vision which the physiological data presented so far also explain. It has been known for a long time that any three colors (such that no one of them could be matched by a mixture of the other two) could be mixed by a separate adjustment of their intensities to match any single color. Three colors conforming to the above properties are called primaries, and one set of such primaries is red, green, and blue. The fact that no less than three different primaries are needed to produce a match implies that there are at least three channels which convey information about a single color, and also that probably there are only three. This is the basis of the Young-Helmholtz three-color theory. Now that it has been possible to show that there are three types of cones each with a maximal sensitivity to a different wavelength, we see that the three-channel hypothesis is right.

On the other hand we can also see that a regrouping of the three channels takes place as the nervous system takes the information from the three types of receptor and recombines it. This recombination in which the basic three channels are made to oppose or cancel each other in various ways generates another set of phenomena which could not be explained in a very straightforward way by a simple three-channel theory. Many phenomena suggest the existence of two specially related pairs of colors, red and green on one hand and blue and yellow on the other. These are called complementaries. Together such complementaries cancel out, that is they make white or gray. Secondly, a color leaves its complementary as an afterimage. Also, yellow and blue are seen much further into the periphery of vision than red and green, and the fields within which the two pairs of colors can be seen are almost coextensive for the two colors of each pair. Such observations led Hering (1874) to formulate his opponent-process theory, which has been developed by Hurvich and Jameson (1957).

It can readily be seen that the phenomena described above fit readily into the neurophysiological picture of two main types of opposite-sign summators, the red-green and blue-yellow.

## Color Blindness

Color blindness is a generic term for a large number of different conditions in which color discrimination is abnormal. Such abnormalities are observed in 8.2 percent of the male population and 0.4 percent of the female (Marriott, 1962). Before more direct information was obtained, these conditions were intensively studied in the hope that they might shed some light on the mechanism of color vision. In a way, color blindness may be regarded as a lesion made by nature, and lesions are studied to obtain evidence on the working of the intact organisms. However, it has been impossible to make any unique interpretation of the color-blindness symptoms prior to knowledge of how the mechanism works anyhow, based on more direct types of evidence.

Color blindness may be divided into three main groups: dichromatism, monochromatism, and anomalous trichromatism. Monochromats can match any color simply by adjusting the intensity of any other color. Their condition is normally due to a complete absence of cone function. There are also rare cases where cone function is present, and these could be due to an absence of opposite-sign summators. Dichromats can match any colored light with two colors, one from the red and the other from the blue end of the spectrum. One type of dichromat, the protanope, is completely unable to see light at the deep red end of the spectrum. According to Rushton (1962) who made measurements of the light reflected from the retina of protanopes, the cone pigment most sensitive in the red region is missing in this condition. On the other hand, deuteranopes, another class of dichromat, have, according to Rushton (1962), a different cone pigment missing which is most sensitive in the green region. Both deuteranopes and protanopes confuse reds, yellows, and greens. The third class of dichromat, the tritanope, confuses shades of blue with green and also pink with orange. From reports of subjects who are color-blind in one eye and normal in the other (Graham and Hsia, 1958; Judd, 1948), reds, yellows and greens appear as yellow and the rest of the spectrum as blue in the case of both a protanope and a deuteranope. The anomalous trichromats, classified into protans, deutans, or tritans, are seemingly intermediate between respectively the protanopes, deuteranopes, and tritanopes on one hand and the normal on the other. They are perhaps to be regarded as having a weakly developed aspect of their color mechanism, rather than a complete absence of such an aspect.

## SPATIAL INTERACTIONS

So far some account has been given of how the eye processes information from light falling on it without much regard for the spatial arrangement of such light. However, the eye functions not only to detect light and its differences in wavelength but also to interpret information about the relative spatial distribution of patches of light on the retina.

The general picture which emerges from recording studies from ganglion cells or their axons (composing the optic nerve) is as follows: First, each ganglion cell receives excitation upon stimulation of a small area in the retina. Second, it is inhibited by stimulation of the region surrounding the small area from which it receives excitation. In some cases, the situation is reversed, and the ganglion cell is inhibited by stimulation of a small retinal area and excited by stimulation of a field surrounding this small area. This has been shown by Kuffler (1953) in the cat's light-adapted eye. He placed a microelectrode in a ganglion cell and recorded activity in this cell as he moved a small exploring light spot on the retina. When the light was shone within about ½ mm. of the ganglion cell, the cell gave a burst of spikes. When the light was placed about 1 mm. away and switched on, there was no response; instead, the ganglion cell gave a burst of spikes when the light was switched off. In an intermediate zone, the cell discharged both when the light was switched off and when it was switched on. It is probable that when a cell fires at the offset of a stimulus it is being inhibited or partly inhibited by the presence of such a stimulus. So it seems that the cell recorded from was being excited by impulses from receptor cells within a central area and inhibited by impulses from those outside the area.

However, this organization of the retina only occurs in the light-adapted eye. Barlow, Fitzhugh and Kuffler (1957) found that in the dark-adapted eye of the cat the outer zone of opposite sign was lost. In the case of the cells whose surround produced an off response when it was illuminated, this no longer happened in the dark-adapted state. Only the response to a light being switched on in the center of the field remained. This would indicate that during dark adaptation there is not only a change due to the visual pigments being in an altered state, but also a neural reorganization whose mechanism is at present obscure.

## LATERAL INHIBITION

The results quoted in the preceding section on the light-adapted eye suggest that not only does excitation over small areas of the retina summate but that inhibition of one excited area by another also takes place when larger distances are involved. This sideways spread of inhibition is called lateral inhibition and has been studied in a quantitative manner by Hartline (1949) the eye of Limulus, the horseshoe crab. This animal has a compound eye and the different elements can be separately illuminated. It can be shown that if two such elements are stimulated by two lights of different intensity, one inhibits the other in proportion to their relative rates of discharge. The more active an element, the greater the inhibition it exerts. The amount of inhibition decreases and the threshold which inhibition must reach to be effective increases with distance from the element exerting such inhibition. Elements exert such inhibition upon each other. It follows from this that if there are two neighboring regions (consisting of a large number of elements), one of which is excited and the other not, the elements in the excited region will inhibit each other. However, those elements in the excited region which are closest to the unexcited region will be least inhibited because of the absence of excited neighbors at least on one side. Therefore there will be most excitation at the border of the two regions. Such a mechanism has been postulated to be the basis of contrast phenomena (Hartline, 1949) and also of figural aftereffects (Deutsch, 1963). Similar interactions have been shown to occur in the eye of the cat (Kuffler, 1953).

More complex interactions underlying the responses of retinal ganglion cells have also been found. Hartline (1940) observed that movement of a light spot was particularly effective in eliciting responses in single optic fibers in the frog. Even more remarkable are the observations of Barlow and Hill (1963) in the rabbit and Maturana and Frank (1963) in the pigeon. There are ganglion cells in the retina that respond not only to moving stimuli, but also only to stimuli moving in a particular direction.

## THE TECTAL LOBES OR COLLICULI OF THE FROG

That the retina possesses within it a remarkable capacity for perceptual analysis has been shown in the frog by Maturana et al. (1960). Instead of using spots of light, they used the kinds of stimuli that the frog has to distinguish in its natural environment in order to catch its food, flies, and escape predators. Microelectrode recordings were taken from the terminations of optic nerve fibers in the tectum, which receives most of the output from the retinae in the frog. The first kind of fiber Maturana described produces a burst of activity when an edge, lighter or darker than the background, is moved across a small area of the retina. If the edge stops moving within this area, the neural response persists though at a lower frequency. When the illumination is switched off, the response disappears. When the light is switched on again, the response reappears. Further if an edge is introduced during darkness, a neural response also appears when the light is switched on again. Wide variations in illumination do not affect the characteristic responses described above. The second kind of fiber signals the occurrence of a curved edge in a small area of the retina, reacting best to small dark spots. Though these fibers will continue to signal the presence of such spots if they had been moved into a particular area and then made stationary such a signal will cease if the general illumination is turned off and then on again. Nor will a signal be given if such spots are introduced into the area during a period of darkness which is then followed by general illumination. However, wide variations in general illumination do not change its responsiveness to the effective stimuli, dark spots. A third class of cells responds only to a moving edge and never when such an edge is stationary. In the fourth class of cells, activity is evoked by a general dimming of the illumination, whereas in the fifth a steady activity signals the general level of the illumination, increasing as illumination decreases. These results emphasize the value of teleological thinking in the experimental analysis of biological systems. The experiments were undertaken, as is explained by Maturana et al., by considering the function of the frog's eye and its biological purpose.

## SPATIAL RESPONSES IN THE HIGHER VISUAL CENTERS

Each retina may be pictured as being divided by a vertical line drawn through the fovea. The half of the retina thus established which is closer to the nose is called the nasal hemiretina; the other half, the temporal hemiretina. The fibers from the nasal hemiretina cross the midline at the optic chiasm, whereas those from the temporal hemiretina continue without crossing. In consequence, the fibers from the nasal hemiretina in one eye and those from the temporal hemiretina in the other eye proceed to the same hemisphere (Figure 11–5). The left nasal hemiretina and the right temporal hemiretina both receive light from the left half of the visual field. It follows that objects in the left half of the visual field are

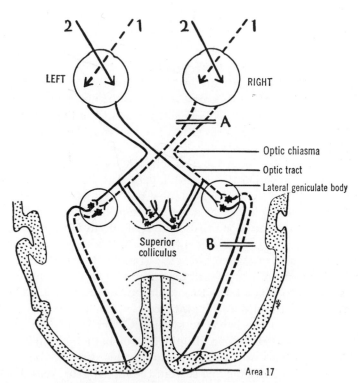

FIG. 11–5. The visual pathways. Arrows numbered 1 indicate the light from objects in the right visual fields (when looking straight ahead) reaches the left halves of the retinae. The reverse is true for the opposite visual fields. The collaterals from the visual path (to the superior colliculi for reflexes) are really separate fibers and not branches of true visual fibers. Cutting the optic nerve at A causes complete blindness in that eye. A lesion at B, however, causes blindness in the left half of each field of vision (arrows numbered 2). (From Gardner, E., *Fundamentals of Neurology*, 4th ed. (Philadelphia: W. B. Saunders Company, 1963.)

represented by messages going to the right hemisphere, whereas those in the right visual field find their destination in the left hemisphere (see Figure 11–5). This is true in man. As we descend the phylogenetic scale, there is an increasing tendency for the fibers in each optic nerve to cross to the opposite hemisphere.

The most important visual pathway in man passes to the lateral geniculate nucleus (LGN). The LGN is made up of six layers of cells separated by layers of fibers. The fibers from the nasal hemiretina of the opposite side terminate in cell layers 1, 4 and 6. The fibers from the ipsilateral temporal hemiretina end in the other layers. No significant interaction at the LGN between the inputs from the two eyes has been demonstrated either from anatomical or electrophysiological evidence.

Axons of the ganglion cells of the retina terminate in boutons on cell bodies in the LGN. These cell bodies send axons to the fourth layer of the striate cortex. In the monkey LGN (Glees and Le Gros Clark, 1941), there are no terminations on the same cell from more than one axon coming from the retina. Instead each axon sprays out into five or six branches which then each terminate on a single geniculate cell. In such a way there is divergence, but no convergence or overlap. In the cat, however, in line with its lower visual acuity (Glees, 1941), there is definite overlap which could lead to the pooling of information from several fibers coming from the retina. There are also so-called association cells in the LGN, with short axons which terminate in dense arborizations. Such cells could be the basis of lateral interaction, perhaps of an inhibitory kind, between the various channels passing through the LGN. Hubel and Wiesel (1961) working on the cat were able to show that a geniculate cell behaves in much the same way as the retinal ganglion cells which feed into it. LGN cells tend to have roughly circular peripheral receptive fields. These consist first of a central region, circular in shape, a discrete stimulus to which excites the cell (the "on" response). This is surrounded by a larger field again roughly circular, a stimulus to which tends to inhibit the "on" response, and which excites the cell when the stimulus is switched off (the "off" response). The one difference between the behavior of the LGN cells and the ganglion cells of the retina is that diffuse illumination of both the "on" and the "off" regions simultaneously produces no response in the LGN cells, whereas some "on" activity may be seen in the retinal ganglion cells. This implies that there is a more precise balancing out of the excitatory and inhibitory influences on a cell at the level of the LGN. As was seen with the ganglion cells of the retina, not only are there cells, the centers of whose receptive fields produce excitation and the peripheries of which produce inhibition but there are also cells with receptive fields the centers of which exercise an inhibitory influence, whereas the peripheries produce excitation. It should also be mentioned at this point that adjacent points in the LGN are stimulated by neighboring points on the retina. Such an orderly projection is preserved when we reach the destination of the axons of the LGN cells in the cortex. A disproportionately large part of the LGN projection is occupied by the central part of the retina.

The axons from the LGN reach the posterior portion of the cortex by the geniculocalcarine tract. The area of cortex receiving these projections is also known as the striate (or striped) area. In the gray matter of the cerebral cortex there are two white laminations of myelinated nerve fibers which lie parallel to the surface of the cortex. These two laminations appear as white bands where the cortex is sectioned and are called the inner and outer lines of Baillarger. In the striate cortex only the outer line or band is visible, but it is more conspicuous than elsewhere. It is here called the line of Gennari and gives this portion of the cortex its striped appearance. In man, most of the visual area as defined by the projection of fibers from the LGN is buried in the depths of the calcarine fissure, the deep cleft separating the two hemispheres in their occipital portion. Fibers representing the center of the retina or the macula are mapped at the more posterior end of the fissure, close to the exterior. This macular region of the retina occupies a disproportionately large part of such a map.

Electrophysiological studies have shown however that there are three maps of the retina in the cortex which lie adjacent to each other. These are known as Areas I, II, and III. The existence of the first two has been shown in the cat, rabbit, and monkey (Thompson, Woolsey and Talbot, 1950; Hubel, 1963). The third has been described by Hubel and Wiesel (1965) in the cat. The second and third representations are not in the striate area but adjacent to it (Figure 11–6).

Microelectrode studies (Hubel and Wiesel, 1962) have revealed a most remarkable organization amongst cortical cells subserving vision. Instead of finding the type of cell whose receptive field is circular and composed of two concentric regions one of which tends to inhibit and the other excite, they have found fields divided by straight lines. Cells here also are excited by stimuli falling on one small region of the retina and inhibited by stimuli impinging on a neighboring region. However, the shape of the boundaries between any such two regions is in the form of a straight line and one of the two fields is not necessarily within the other (as it is at the level of the retinal ganglion cells and the LGN).

There are in fact two main types of receptive field at the cortex. The first is composed of a narrow central strip (which may be excitatory or inhibitory) divided by two straight lines from two flanking fields. These flanking fields are inhibitory if the central strip is excitatory, and excitatory if the central strip is inhibitory. Such fields when they have an "on" center produce their highest discharge to a visual stimulus consisting of a narrow strip and coinciding exactly with the position of the "on" center. If the stimulus encroaches on the "off" portion of the field, reduction in firing takes place as might be expected. The second type of field is composed of an "on" area divided on only one side by a straight line from an "off" area. Exact superimposition of an edge along the boundary of the receptive field

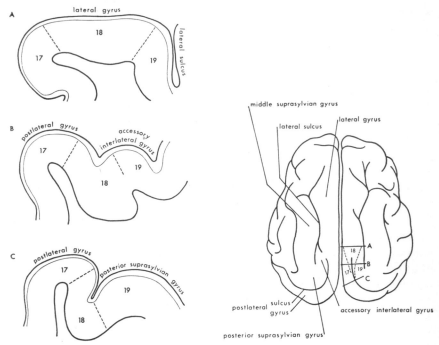

FIG. 11–6. Composite diagram showing coronal sections at three antero-posterior levels through visual areas *I*, *II*, and *III* (or *17*, *18*, and *19*). Boundaries are based on several criteria, including histology as studied in Nissl- and myelin-stained sections, distribution of projections from area 17 to nonstriate visual cortex by the silver-degeneration technique and physiological recordings. (From Hubel, D. H., and Wiesel, T. N., *J. Neurophysiol.* **28**, 1965.)

produces the largest effect. The balancing between the excitatory and inhibitory parts of the field is such that these cells do not respond to changes in diffuse illumination.

As the width of the central strip in many of the receptive fields of these cells resembles in size the width of the central regions of the receptive fields of LGN cells, Hubel and Wiesel believe that each cortical cell receives projections from a set of LGN cells and that these LGN cells have receptive fields which taken together form a straight line.

A further complication is introduced by the fact that at least 12 directions of such strip or boundary detecting cells have been found. This means that different cells are most sensitive to different slants or directions of lines, if these are directly superimposed on a specific retinal locus. The cells just described have been called "simple" cells by Hubel and Wiesel because they respond only to stimulation at a specific locus. Another class of cells they termed "complex." In spite of displaying complete specificity with regard to the orientation of lines or edges by which they will be activated, they will respond to such lines located anywhere within a certain small portion of the visual field. It appears that they are linked to the output of a large number of simple cells all responding to lines of the same orientation.

In this way complex cells respond to the orientation of a line, independent of specific locus. Complex and simple cells have also been found in the cortex which respond only to lines or edges which move. Some are sensitive not only to a particular direction of movement but also to its speed.

Whereas little or no binocular interaction occurs at the level of the LGN, Hubel and Wiesel (1962) reported that 84 percent of the units in the cortex responded to stimulation from corresponding points on the two retinae, and this could very well be an underestimate. If the two stimuli on the two corresponding points were the same, their effects summed. If the excitatory part of the field was stimulated in one eye and the inhibitory portion in the other, the effects tended to cancel. The responses obtained from the cell to stimulation of the two eyes were not always equal; one eye would produce a stronger response than the other.

An interesting aspect of the functional organization of the orientation-sensitive cells, both simple and complex, is that they are arranged in columns with each column at right angles to the surface of the cortex. Each column has in it cells, both simple and complex, sensitive only to one orientation. The various cells in the column, however, are not from only one point on the retina; they are simply from the same neighborhood.

Hubel and Wiesel (1965) reported the discovery of further kinds of cells in the visual cortex. So far the cells we have described come from Visual Area I. There are, as we have seen, at least two other areas in the cat in which there is a topographical map of the retina—Visual II and Visual III (Figure 11-6). Recording from these areas, Hubel and Wiesel found what they term hypercomplex cells and hypercomplex cells of higher order. Hypercomplex cells are of various kinds. Some give a maximal response to a line in one particular orientation, but only if the end of the line does not extend past a particular point. If the line is progressively extended past this point, the response diminishes and then ceases altogether. In another kind of cell, extending a line in either or both directions abolishes the response. It is as if two or more simple cells described above were all connected to another cell, one connection being excitatory and the others inhibitory. Still other hypercomplex cells give their maximal response to two precisely positioned boundaries at right angles to each other, the response varying as a function of the angle between the two boundaries. The amount of firing from this last class of cells could serve as the basis of recognition of angle, irrespective of rotation. This ability is probably basic to shape recognition (Figure 11-7).

Hypercomplex cells of higher order are found mainly in Visual Area III. These mostly stand in a similar relation to hypercomplex cells as simple

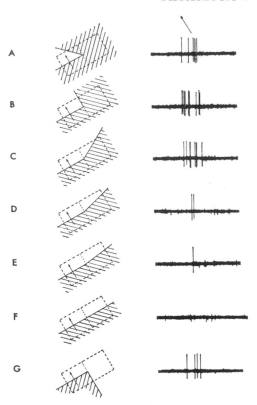

FIG. 11–7. Stimulation of a cell with two intersecting edges across its retinal receptive field as shown on left of the figure. The response as seen on the right varies as a function of the angle between the two intersecting edges. (From Hubel, D. H., and Wiesel, T. N., *J. Neurophysiol.* 28, 1965.)

cells stand to complex cells. They may signal the ends of lines of a certain orientation anywhere within a given region of the retina. There are also other cells classified by Hubel and Wiesel in this category. These are sensitive to lines in a particular orientation and ending at a particular point and also to lines at right angles to them. McCollough (1965) has shown some interesting perceptual consequences of the existence of orientation-specific edge detectors which presumably occur also in the human visual system. Observers were shown alternating fields of orange-vertical and blue-horizontal stripes. After such an exposure a test pattern consisting of black-vertical stripes appeared blue, green and black-horizontal stripes appeared orange. If the field was tilted 45°, the colored afterimage disappeared. If the inspection of the colored stripes was made with one eye, no colored afterimage was seen with the other. This experiment then demonstrates the presence of edge detectors in the human visual system and further that some or all of these edge receptors are specific to color. Because the afterimage shows no "interocular" transfer, the experiment also shows that such edge detectors function at a stage in the visual pathway before the inputs from the two eyes have converged.

## TEMPORAL FACTORS IN VISION

The eye cannot follow changes in illumination which occur above a certain rate. For instance, if the interval between light flashes is too short, these flashes are not seen as separate. Practical interest attaches to this property of the eye because it is the basis of the cinema and television industries.

The properties of the eye in reacting to the temporal characteristics of stimulation are probably best considered by starting with the initiation of neural impulses at the retina. Any limitation in the ability to follow rapid changes there, is bound to be a limitation imposed on the whole of the

FIG. 11–8. Variation of the critical time $\tau$ as a function of the logarithm of luminance. (GK) represents the results of Graham and Kemp (in millilamberts). (Kel) indicates the results of Keller (in trolands). (From Pieron, H., *Contributions to Sensory Physiology*, W. D. Neff (Ed.), New York: Academic Press Inc., 1965.)

visual system. If no signal reporting a change arises peripherally, then the visual system has no information that such a visual change has occurred, whatever the changes in the physical stimulus. Therefore, if we find that the limitations of our visual capacities determined behaviorally coincide with the limitations in the speed of the photochemical responses on the retina, the behavioral data is adequately explained.

When light reaches the retina, no neural activity leaves the retina for 20 to 70 msec. This is known as retinal lag, and it is shorter for bright lights and longer for dim lights. Related to this is a certain period known as the critical time, or $\tau$, over which the light stimulus is averaged by the eye. The same number of photons, however, distributed in time within a certain brief period produces the same visual sensation. This is known as Bloch's law and is a special case of the Bunsen-Roscoe law. (This states that the product of intensity of stimulus and its total time is constant $[i \times t = k]$.) The length of the critical time decreases with increasing intensity of the stimulating light (Figure 11–8). Though most of the evidence relating to the critical time, $\tau$, has been obtained through psychophysical methods. Grusser and Kapp (1958) obtained a value of $\tau$ of 25 msec. recording action potentials from ganglion cells in the cat's retina. Whatever the spacing of the same two flashes within this critical time of 25 msec., the same number of action potentials was recorded. As this time is close to what would be expected from results from psychophysical data (Piéron, 1965), it seems that the averaging over a certain small interval of time which has been described above is a characteristic of the visual process before, or at, the ganglion cell level.

The eye's ability to distinguish steady from intermittent stimulation (flicker) has been extensively studied by behavioral methods. Various general relationships have emerged at the psychophysical level. It is approximately true that flicker fusion frequency (the frequency at which flicker becomes indistinguishable from a steady light) rises as the logarithm of the intensity of stimulating light. This is called the Ferry-Porter law. More accurate measurement shows that the curve relating stimulus intensity to fusion frequency is divided into two parts with a kink in the middle. The steeper rise at higher intensities is attributable to the cones.

On the neural side a suggested limitation on the rate at which flicker can be perceived lies in the frequency at which the optic tract discharges at a given level of steady illumination. One might argue that flicker can only be detected by successively more frequent and less frequent groupings of action potentials. This cannot occur unless the rate of neural discharge at a given level of intensity is much higher than the rate of flicker imposed on the eye. However, as we saw above, there are ganglion cells which respond with a discharge only at the "on" and others only at the "off" of illumination. Such elements might therefore signal intermittency without the limitation which has just been described.

But the limitation on the perception of rate of flicker occurs before we reach the optic nerve. Studies on ganglion cells in the retina of the cat have been undertaken by Enroth (1952, 1953), and Grusser and Rabelo (1958), and Reidemeister and Grusser (1959). From such studies it seems that the fusion point of flicker is determined chiefly by the averaging of stimulation over the critical time, $\tau$, which occurs before the message from the retina is translated into action potentials at the ganglion cell level. Discharges, indistinguishable from those in response to steady illumination, occur in ganglion cells at rates close to those expected from the critical time, $\tau$, as measured by Grusser and Kapp (1958). Ganglion cells of the "on-off" variety (discharging when illumination comes on and goes off) produce a response indistinguishable from their discharge under steady illumination at a frequency of about 35 flashes per second. Slightly lower rates are necessary for "on" and "off" types of ganglion cells to produce a discharge such as that which is given to steady illumination. Measurements were taken at a similar intensity as that used in the experiment of Grusser and Kapp who used double flashes. Given a critical time, $\tau$, of 25 msec., over which perfect averaging takes place, we would expect a rate of 40 flashes per second to be indistinguishable from a steady light.

There is another interesting phenomenon associated with intermittent stimulation: the Brücke phenomenon, discovered in 1864. When flicker occurs at about 10 per second, and while it is clearly perceived as flicker, the flickering light appears brighter than a steady light and brighter than other flicker. Such a brightness enhancement seems to have its origin before, or at, the level of the ganglion cells in the retina. Grusser and Creutzfeldt (1957) have shown a similar enhancement of activity in the ganglion cells of the retina in the cat.

## Eye Movements and the Visual Image

Because visual adaptation is rapid, frequent changes in illumination are necessary for the continuous functioning of elements of the visual system. Ditchburn and Ginsborg (1952) and Ratliff (1952), by the use of ingenious optical systems, were able to compensate for the movements of the eye and so to stablize the image thrown on the retina. Under such conditions, the image fades out within a few seconds. Normal vision can be maintained only by making the image move across the retina or by introducing flicker (Cornsweet, 1956). Such fading is normally counteracted by small rapid eye movements. However, considerable fading can occur in spite of small eye movements even under conditions of voluntary fixation. A black bar on a white ground will tend to fade if steadily fixated for about a minute, as the reader can readily observe, and the whole visual field will even become obscured, as observed by Aubert (1865). In the periphery, disappearance is even more rapid. This is called the Troxler (1804) phenomenon.

### VISUAL ACUITY

Visual acuity, or the capacity to resolve or discriminate fine detail, depends on (a) the configuration and illumination of the stimulus, (b) where on the retina such detail falls, and (c) whether the retina is stationary with regard to the object being viewed, or in motion. Because of the difference which the configuration of the stimulus makes, that is, what kind of detail we are interested in resolving, three main tests of acuity have been adopted though other tests would give yet different results. In the first type of test, acuity is measured by the minimum separable. Here we determine how small a white gap between two black lines or blocks can be made before such lines or blocks are seen as one. Under good conditions of illumination the gap that can be seen corresponds well with the diameter of a single cone as estimated by Polyak (1941). This subtends about 24″ (seconds) of visual angle at the center of the fovea. As illumination decreases so does acuity. One obvious reason for low acuity at low intensities is that the total number of light quanta striking the retina from the region of the gap may be below threshold for vision. Increasing the size of the gap increases the number of quanta reflected from the gap and so a larger gap becomes visible (Pirenne, 1962). Further, at low intensities, rods will detect light when it is below the cone threshold. Consequently, the observer is forced to use regions of the retina outside the fovea centralis, where rods occur. Not only does each of these receptors subtend a larger visual angle, but also it is probable that excitation from many rods converges on a single fiber. Hence illumination is averaged over a larger area and detail is thereby lost.

Even under optimum conditions of illumination, acuity may be considerably worse than the diameter of a single cone. This can be due to defects of the image-forming mechanism. It has often been pointed out that even the best the eye is capable of in the matter of bringing a line half a minute of arc into focus still leaves a considerable blurring of the image on the retina. The illumination from such a narrow strip will to a large extent be distributed over a few cones. However, the important thing to consider here is the gradient of illumination formed by the image. If the disparity in the amount of light falling on one or more receptors compared with neighboring receptors is greater than the differential threshold for brightness, a change of illumination, and so a gap should be seen. It is true that the gap may be seen as wider than it actually is, but the test of acuity is whether it can be seen, not whether it can be seen as the correct size.

A similar argument can be applied to the second measure of acuity, the minimum visible. In this test, a fine black line is superimposed on a white ground. Acuity here is measured by the minimum width of such a line which can be seen. Using such a measurement one can detect a line whose width subtends an angle of $1''$ (second), which is much smaller than the diameter of a single cone. This may be explained on the same lines as above. Provided the image of the line decreases the illumination on a row of cones, however large or numerous they may be, by more than the differential threshold for brightness, the line will be reported as seen.

It is of interest to note that acuity is better when the eye is not moving, as might be expected. This has been shown by Riggs et al. (1953) and Ratliff (1952) who concluded: "It has also been demonstrated that the relatively large changes in the position of the eye as a result of the rapid tremor are a hindrance to monocular acuity." This finding is in contradistinction to the fact that if the image remains fixed on the retina fading occurs, with a consequent loss of acuity (Riggs et al., 1953).

A third test of acuity determines the smallest misalinement of two lines. Starting with a single long vertical line, one of the two halves is shifted parallel to itself. The smallest deviation from the continuation of the line which can be detected is called a measure of vernier acuity. Optimal values are of the order of $5''-10''$ (seconds) of arc, deteriorating if the two lines are shortened. This judgment probably depends on our ability to extrapolate the course of a line.

## CEREBRAL LESIONS AND VISION

Total destruction of the visual cortex in man appears to produce total blindness (Teuber, 1961). In the monkey, after such a loss, differences in the total amount of light reaching the eye may still be reacted to, but pattern vision is absent (Kluver, 1942). Similarly, pattern vision is destroyed in the cat and rat (Teuber, 1961). An exception to this has been reported by Doty (1961). Apparently, if the striate cortex is destroyed in kittens, they will as adults perform normally in tests of shape discrimination.

In animals, destruction of the striate cortex leads to a loss of retention of habits based on the discrimination of visual intensity. However, such habits may be relearned. The explanation of such an apparent memory loss is obscure. There are many possibilities. One is that the animal relearns by using another part of its neural apparatus which is still intact, perhaps by reacting on the basis of different cues. This first possibility is supported by the observations of Kluver (1942) and Bauer and Cooper (1964). Kluver found that monkeys with lesions of the striate area can no longer make discriminations on the basis of brightness (luminous flux per unit area) but are still capable of distinguishing on the basis of total luminous flux. That is, the monkey can still perceive the total amount of light reaching the eye, but can no longer discriminate between its arrival on different parts of the retina. It is therefore possible for the lesioned monkey to relearn a task (originally learned on the basis, say, of pattern) on the basis of differences in total luminous flux between the discriminanda. Bauer and Cooper have shown that rats with translucent plastic cups over their eyes show good retention of a light-dark discrimination after striate area removal. This contrasts with the poor retention of such a habit after striate removal by a group which learned the habit with unobstructed vision. The wearing of plastic cups over the eyes would force learning on the basis of luminous flux before striate area removal.

It is interesting to note in this connection that rats with removal of the striate area can still learn logically complex visual tasks, provided that the original visual discrimination remains within their capacity. Bauer and Cooper (1964) were able to train rats with striate lesions to go left when the lights were off and right when they were on. The same task with black and white cards instead of lights, proved insuperable to the lesioned rats.

A second possibility is that a so-called generalization decrement has occurred. It is possible to produce a "memory loss" in a perfectly normal rat simply by altering an aspect of the total training situation which is seemingly irrelevant to such a discrimination. Yet a third explanation could be that the stimuli to be discriminated still impinge on the animal but that they have altered in appearance to the animal as a result of the lesion. This notion is supported by an experiment of Thompson (1960), who ablated the striate cortex in two stages, which would be expected to make the transition from one kind of appearance to another more gradual. Under these conditions he found good postoperative retention of the habit.

The fact that animals can relearn (or retain) a visual intensity discrimination after destruction of the striate cortex and subsequent degeneration of the LGN means that other parts of the central nervous system besides the LGN and striate cortex receive fibers from the optic tract. Two such areas are known. The first is the superior colliculus, and the second, the pretectal area.

In the cat at least there is a good point-to-point projection of the retina to the colliculi (Apter, 1945). Blake (1959) has found that pattern discrimination in this animal is grossly impaired after lesions of this area. In man, these structures are credited with a role in the control of eye movement. The pretectal area, on the other hand, seems concerned with the light reflex of the pupil. It therefore seems that other portions of the nervous system besides the pathway to the LGN and striate cortex can subserve visual function. However, though discrimination of the total amount of light is possible, the differential threshold for such a discrimination is sharply raised.

Partial lesions of the striate area in man produce scotomata or regions of the visual field in which normal object vision is absent. However, it seems that when figures are exposed so that there is a continuity of contour between the part of the figure exposed outside and inside the scotoma, such figures can be "completed" (Teuber, 1961). Parts of the figure which would not be seen within the scotoma if they were presented alone seem to be in some sense visible when they are connected to parts of the figure falling on an area outside the scotoma where vision is normally possible. However, impairment of vision as a result of brain lesion does not manifest itself only as a scotoma. There may be areas of the visual field where objects can be seen, but only as long as other objects are not present in less impaired parts of the visual field. They may either become less distinct ("obscuration") or disappear altogether ("extinction") (Bender, 1952). When the object in the less impaired part of the field is removed, the object in the more impaired part of the field reappears again. Similar phenomena occur in the somatosensory system (see Chapter 9).

Two other types of visual sensory deficit appear after brain lesions. The first are associated with injuries causing scotomata; the second with any brain injury at all. The first kind of change may be exhibited by parts of the visual field where object vision appears normal. Contours fade more rapidly, flicker fusion thresholds are reduced, dark adaptation is impaired as is perception of real and apparent movement. The second type of visual change is linked with lesions anywhere whether in the striate cortex or not. The patient finds it hard to detect figures which are imbedded in other shapes. In animals such as the rat and the monkey it seems that only small islands of striate cortex need be spaced when lesions are made, to preserve the ability to discriminate patterns (Lashley, 1939; Harlow, 1939; and Settlage, 1939). However, it is not known whether there are more subtle deficits, as those found in human patients, in the remaining parts of the visual field.

We may ask if the striate area of the cortex is the only one needed for the processing of visual information. In the rat, Lashley found that any lesion, provided it spared the visual cortex, did not interfere with visual

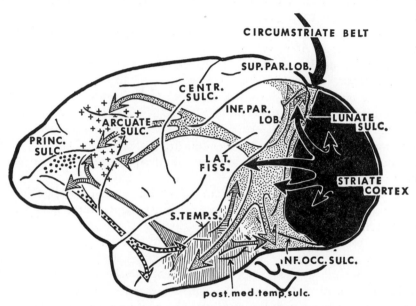

FIG. 11–9. Diagrammatic representation of some of the corticocortical fiber connections, observed by Kuypers *et al.* (From Kuypers, H. G. T. M., *et al.*, *Experimental Neurology.* New York: Academic Press Inc., 1965.)

discriminative capacity. However, in the cat, Myers (1956) and Sperry (1958) found that increasing ablation of areas other than the visual cortex produces increasing visual deficit. Evidence from human head injuries also suggests strongly that other areas of the cortex are involved in visual perception. Injuries to the posterior parts of the parietal lobe and adjoining occipital cortex cause a syndrome known as visual disorientation (Holmes, 1918). Many aspects of the perception of space are disturbed. The patient finds it difficult to estimate the distance of objects away from him and is also unable to estimate length and size. Objects, though seen, are not reacted to (visual inattention). It may be that such symptoms are not due to a destruction of the parietal cortex, but instead to interruption of tracts which connect the striate area with a part of the cortex of the temporal lobe, an area of which appears to subserve visual functions.

The role of the temporal lobe in visual function can be discerned in some of the symptoms of the Kluver-Bucy syndrome (see Chapter 7). Following the bilateral removal of the temporal lobes in the monkey there is found, among other symptoms, a visual agnosia. That is, the animal does not seem to recognize objects even though it can see them.

It is mainly the lesion of the inferotemporal or ventral temporal cortex which produces the visual deficit which has been noted (Mishkin, 1954). The connections between the striate area and this area are transcortical. Monkeys with lesions of the inferotemporal area seem to show a disproportionate difficulty with visual discriminations requiring a considerable degree of abstraction.

Through an ingenious combination of behavioral and surgical techniques, Mishkin (in press) was able to show that the inferotemporal region in the monkey was connected to the striate area on both sides via a belt of cortex, surrounding the striate area, termed by Kuypers *et al.* (1965) "a circumstriate cortical belt." This belt comprises the parastriate and preoccipital areas, analogous to Visual Areas II and III in the cat (Figure 11-6; Figure 11-9) and corresponds to Areas 18 and 19 in Brodmann's classification. This circumstriate belt sends fibers to the inferior part of the temporal lobe and to the frontal lobe around the arcuate sulcus. The inferior part of the temporal lobe sends fibers back to parts of the circumstriate belt and to the lateral and ventrolateral surface of the frontal lobe. Finally, the frontal lobes send fibers to the inferior part of the temporal lobe.

## CENTRIFUGAL EFFECTS IN THE VISUAL SYSTEM

It has been suggested that there are pathways leading to the retina in such a way as to influence its activity. The anatomical evidence for such pathways is difficult to assess. Walter (1958) in one of the more recent studies confirms the existence of fibers running into the retina (because not all fibers in the optic tract degenerate when the retina is removed). However, whether such fibers are directly connected to the visual system is in doubt, because at least some of these centrifugal fibers run to blood vessels in the retina. Granit (1955) has studied the problem by using electrophysiological techniques. He stimulated the brain stem while placing microelectrodes close to ganglion cells in the retina. He was able to show that brain stem stimulation could inhibit and excite single ganglion cells, and he attempted to argue (1962) that the observed effects could not have been due to vascular changes.

Evidence for centrifugal effects at higher levels of the visual system is less equivocal. There is evidence for instance that the striate area of the cortex sends impulses back to the lateral geniculate (Niemer and Jimenez-Castellanos, 1950). Further, in mammals there is an increase in development of the projection from the visual cortex to the tectum (Crosby and

Henderson, 1948) as we ascend the phylogenetic scale. This development goes hand in hand with a decrease in importance of the superior colliculi. This suggests that the cortex assumes increased control over eye movements.

## Visual Afferents to the Brain Stem

Activity due to strong visual stimulation is not only relayed to areas with a specific visual function, such as the lateral geniculate, but also to large areas of the brain stem. Though the anatomical basis for this is obscure, evoked potentials with long latencies (45–25 msec.) have been recorded in the brain stem in response to a strong light flash by Ingvar and Hunter (1955). The long latencies recorded imply that such effects are carried either by very thin fibers or across a large number of synapses.

# ·12

# TASTE AND SMELL

## TASTE

The sense of taste plays an important part in the selection of substances to eat or drink. It is important to the organism not only in food selection, but also in the regulation of the amount eaten or drunk. These roles are discussed in detail in the chapter on hunger and thirst. They way that taste enters into the determination of behavior is chiefly discussed in those chapters. Here we shall be concerned mainly with the physiological modus operandi of this sensory avenue.

Taste is concerned with the detection of chemical substances in solution. As a result, most experiments on taste are concerned with the qualitative and quantitative variation of solutions. The quantitative aspect of solutions is measured in terms of the weight of a substance as a proportion of the solvent, which is usually distilled water. One method where the solution is described in percentage terms is to describe as a 2 percent saline solution a mixture of two grams of salt and enough water to make up a 100 cc. of solution. Similarly, a 15 percent concentration of glucose consists of 15 grams of glucose in distilled water to make up 100 cc. of solution. Another method of specifying the strength of solution used is in terms of molarity, i.e., the number of molecules that is added to a fixed amount of solvent, but, of course, only indirectly. A solution of mole is prepared by placing the molecular weight of a substance in grams in distilled water to make up a 100 cc. of solution. The molecular weight times grams of a substance is the mass of $6.023 \times 10^{23}$ molecules. Therefore two solutions of different substances (both of the strength of one mole) contain the same number of molecules. To obtain a solution of 0.1 mole, one tenth of the molecular weight in grams is placed in water to make up a 100 cc. of solution.

As in the case of colors, all tastes can be regarded as the mixture of a few basic qualities. In the case of taste there are four: salt, sweet, sour, and bitter. Agreement on this has come about because it has been shown that any taste can be matched by a mixture of these four qualities. In such experiments one must be careful to exclude "tastes" which are really odors, or which arise through the stimulation of free nerve endings of the trigeminal nerve in the oral cavity to produce "hot" tastes (as those of some spices) or through the direct stimulation of cold receptors to produce "cool" tastes (as that of menthol). That such "tastes" are numerous can be surmised from the fact that people without a sense of taste are frequently unaware of their handicap as long as their sense of smell is intact (Moncrieff, 1951).

A second reason for belief in the four basic taste qualities is that it is possible to affect the perception of these four qualities separately, or to differing degrees, the order depending, say, on the kind of drug painted on the tongue. For instance, gymnemic acid produces a temporary inability to taste sweet-tasting substances. Our confidence in the inference that salt, sweet, sour, and bitter are the basic taste qualities is further increased by the results of electrophysiological investigation to be described below (p. 364).

## The Organs of Taste

The organs of taste are called taste buds. In fish these buds may be distributed over large parts of the body surface. However, in man, as in mammals generally, they lie mainly on the tongue. These organs each consist of 10 to 15 taste cells, together with other cells. These other cells have been thought by some to be sustaining cells. However, it has been suggested that these sustaining cells are in reality old or aged taste cells, which are no longer innervated (Figure 12–1).

Each taste cell has a set of fine hairlike structures projecting through pores onto the surface of the tongue. These structures are about 4 microns in length and about 0.2 microns in diameter. Most of the taste buds are placed in the circumvallate, foliate, and fungiform papillae. In man, the taste buds at the tip of the tongue are more sensitive to sweet substances, and those at the back of the tongue are more responsive to bitter substances. There are also taste buds in the larynx and pharynx.

## Mode of Stimulation of the Taste Receptors

It seems likely that it is the tiny hairs or microvilli which project through the taste pores to the surface of the tongue that are the structures actually stimulated by taste solutions. Each microvillus is surrounded by a single thickness of membrane of about 80 Å. This membrane is probably made up of oriented protein and phospholipid. It seems that such a membrane has on it a number of receptor sites which combine with the taste solution in a highly specific way. Beidler (1954) has argued that such

FIG. 12–1. A drawing of the ultrastructure and organization of the taste buds in the foliate papilla of the rabbit. (From Lorenzo, A. J. D., *Olfaction and Taste*, Zotterman, Y. [Ed.], 1963. Courtesy of the Pergamon Press.)

a combination involves a physical rather than a chemical reaction. Van de Waals forces, hydrogen bonding, dipole-dipole interactions, and ionic forces have been suggested as producing the interaction between receptor site and the adsorbed substance. Evidence that the reaction involved in stimulating a taste receptor is not chemical but physical is provided by Dethier and Arab (1958). These workers stimulated the tip of the chemosensory hair of the blowfly with sugar and showed that a change of temperature of 0–35° C did not affect the efficiency of stimulation, as it would in the case of most chemical reactions. If the whole cell or animal were altered in temperature, then, of course, it might be expected on the other grounds that the response of the whole system would be affected. By using the tip of the chemosensory hair alone, such an alteration was avoided.

The stimulating particle probably produces a change in the configura-

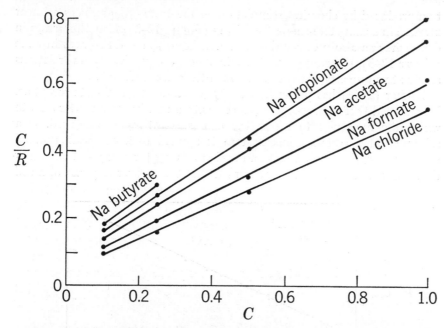

FIG. 12–2. The ratio of the molar concentration of the stimulus and the magnitude of the integrated response of the taste receptors is plotted against the molar concentration of the stimulus. The ratio of the molar concentration of the stimulus and the magnitude of the receptor potential plotted against molar concentration also produces a straight line. (Reprinted from Beidler, L. M., in *Sensory Communication*, Walter Rosenblith (Ed.), by permission of The M.I.T. Press, Cambridge, Mass. Copyright 1961, The M.I.T. Press.)

tion of a macromolecule at the receptor site when it is bound to it. Such a change may form a hole which allows potassium to leak out of the cell (Beidler, 1963). In this way, a part of the receptor cell becomes depolarized, and the depolarization spreads electrotonically to the site on the cell at which the spike impulse is generated. Browne and Hodgson (1962) have shown that in the blowfly chemoreceptor, an impulse can be initiated less than 4 msec. after the application of the stimulus. This is similar to the latency of response to an electrical stimulus with an anodal pulse in mammalian receptors of 5 to 7 msec. found by Pfaffmann (1941). But the latency to chemical stimulation in mammalian preparations is about 35 to 40 msec.

In the case of the mammalian receptor cell, the work of Kimura and Beidler (1961) suggested that the site of spike initiation is not on the taste cell itself. It seems as if the depolarization of the taste cell is transmitted either chemically or electrically to the nerve fiber with which the taste cell is in intimate contact. A spike impulse is first initiated on the nerve fiber which innervates the taste cell. An increase in the amount of depolarization produced by chemical stimulation of the taste cell produces a linear increase in steady-state single fiber firing (Figure 12–2). Equal increases in depolarization also produce the same number of j.n.d. differences in taste (Figure 12–3), showing that, in this instance, the psychophysical relations are due to a property of the transducer at the cell membrane.

Beidler (1954) has proposed a theory of stimulation of taste receptors. He assumed that each receptor is a cell with a number of receptor sites to which the molecules to which the cell is sensitive are adsorbed. If a substance at a certain concentration is applied to a cell with unfilled receptor sites, then only a certain number of receptor sites will be filled at that concentration. He further assumed that the highest response of a cell

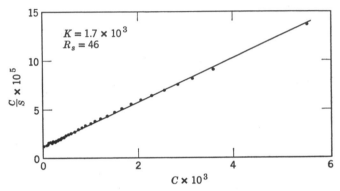

FIG. 12–3. The ratio of the molar concentration of the stimulus and the number of consecutive taste j.n.d.'s ($\triangle S$) for man is plotted against the molar concentration of the stimulus. (Data from Lemberger, 1908.)

occurs when all the receptor sites are filled. He thus arrived at the fundamental taste equation:

$$\frac{C}{R} = \frac{C}{R_s} + \frac{1}{KR_s}$$

where $C$ is the concentration of the stimulus; $R$ the magnitude of response; $R_s$, the magnitude of maximum response; and $K$, the equilibrium constant. All these parameters can be directly measured except for $K$. However, if the theory is correct, then when the ratio of the concentration stimulus and the magnitude of receptoral response is plotted against the concentration of the stimulus, a straight line should be obtained. That this is so can be seen from Figure 12–2.

The equilibrium constants which Beidler has calculated from these and similar results are low. From these and other experiments, he concluded that the process of taste stimulation is not an enzymatic reaction but a physical process of adsorption to proteins. Though this theory was originally proposed by Beidler to account for the taste of salts, he has found it applicable, with certain complications, to the case of acids, sugars, and bitter substances.

Of interest is the fact that the taste equation proposed by Beidler has been applied by him to psychophysical data. Assuming that a j.n.d. of taste represents an equal increment of response of the taste receptor to the stimulating substance, then the concentration divided by the cumulative number of j.n.d.'s plotted against the concentration should yield a straight line (Figure 12–3).

TOUCH

0.5M NaC1

DIST. WATER

15% SUCROSE

0.04% SACCHARINE

0.02M QUININE

0.2M ACETIC ACID

FIG. 12–4. Integrated electrical responses of the whole chorda tympani of man to sapid solutions poured on the tongue. Note that water depressed the spontaneous afferent activity. Time in seconds. (From Diamant, H., *et al.*, *Olfaction and Taste*, Zotterman, Y. [Ed.], 1963. Courtesy of Pergamon Press.)

It is probable that the basic taste stimuli all have specialized receptor sites associated with them. Sourness is clearly associated with acids, the hydrogen ion being an important determinant of sour taste. The positive and negative ions of salts in solution produce a salty taste. (Though common salt [NaCl] is the only salt which has a pure salty taste, it is somewhat paradoxical that weak solutions of it taste sweet.) The physical bases of sweetness and bitterness are obscure. It has also been shown that in certain species, water leads to an increase of activity in certain fibers. However, in the rat, and probably man (Diamant *et al.*, 1963), water leads only to a decrement in firing in the salt fibers (Figure 12–4).

## Specificity of Taste Cells

There are various kinds of receptor sites, each adsorbing different substances. A specific type of receptor site can adsorb different kinds of ions or molecules with different binding energies and different stimulating efficiencies. Further, it seems that different types of sites coexist on the same cell. It is possible to measure the amount of depolarization of a taste cell when taste solutions are applied by penetrating the cell membrane with a microelectrode. Kimura and Beidler (1961) have been able to show by this means that a taste cell is normally sensitive to salt, sucrose, hydrochloric acid, and quinine, and so on, in varying combinations. A table showing some of the sensitivities of two single taste cells is Table 12–1.

### TABLE 12–1
#### Response in Millivolts of the Hamster Taste Receptor
#### to Basic Stimuli of Four Taste Qualities

| Taste Receptor | 0.1 M NaCl | 0.1 M Sucrose | 0.02 M Quinine | 0.01 M HCl |
|---|---|---|---|---|
| 1 | 10.5 | 2 | 4.5 | — |
| 2 | 8.5 | 2 | 7.5 | 0 |
| 3 | 9 | 1 | 4.5 | — |
| 4 | 11.5 | 5 | 8 | 22.5 |
| 5 | 10 | 6.5 | 9 | 12.5 |
| 6 | 6.5 | 1.5 | 5 | — |
| 7 | 9.5 | 2.5 | 7 | 9 |
| 8 | 14 | 0 | 5 | 14 |

K. Kimura and L. M. Beidler, *J. Cell, and Comp. Physiol.* 58.

## Innervation of Taste Cells

De Lorenzo's (1963) electron microscope studies show the way taste cells are innervated (Figure 12–1). Under each taste bud are seen myelinated fibers from 1 to 6 $\mu$ in diameter. On their way towards the taste bud, they lose their myelin sheath. The unmyelinated fibers, upon entering the taste bud, establish synaptic contiguity with the taste cells. Two types of nerve fibers appear to terminate on the taste cell. The larger type (0.5 to 1.0 $\mu$ in diameter) appears always to terminate on one receptor cell only. However, De Lorenzo is not sure whether the smaller fibers are not branches of the larger fibers. Further, one cell may be doubly innervated. Recordings of single fibers also show that specific responding to a basic quality such as "sweet" is rare. This of course might be expected, as receptor cells themselves are rarely specific, and because a single nerve fiber appears to be joined to more than one receptor cell. Work on single fibers has been reported by Pfaffmann (1955), Fishman (1957), and Cohen *et al.* (1955).

Fishman (1957) pointed out certain difficulties in interpreting the sensitivity profiles of taste fibers which have a lower threshold to quinine than to salt. However, the maximum rate of responding obtainable with quinine will be very low, whereas the maximum rate attainable with salt will be much higher. Presumably such properties can be explained if we assume that there are receptor sites of two types on the same receptor cell. If there are only a few "bitter" sites with a high sensitivity and a large number of "salt" sites with a lower sensitivity, we would obtain the relationship Fishman found. He argued that such relations make it difficult to classify any one fiber. If it is grouped according to threshold, it might be classified as bitter, but salty if suprathreshold levels of rate of discharge are considered. Fishman's observations suggest a possible explanation for alterations in certain tastes such as that of salt, at low intensities, when salt tastes sweet. Sweet receptor cells may have on them salt sites of low threshold which saturate at low intensities. Consequently, at low concentrations of salt, most of the discharge comes from units whose firing is normally interpreted as signaling the presence of sugars. The same rate of discharge would occur from these receptors if sugar were applied to them.

The problem of innervation of receptor cells is complicated in the case of taste, because taste receptors are constantly dying and being replaced by new cells. Beidler (1963) stated that quantitative data show that the taste cells of the rat have a life-span of three to five days. Mature taste cells do not appear to undergo division. Instead, taste cells are replaced by epithelial cells which move into the taste buds where they become innervated and are transformed into taste cells. As they age, they move inward into the taste bud and are replaced by fresh epithelial cells migrating inwards into the taste bud. However, it seems that the innervation of the taste cell does not remain with it as the cell migrates, so that each cell on its journey inward into the taste bud will send signals down a succession of fibers. In order that a fiber innervating the receptors should send the same information irrespective of the receptor cell connected to it, we must assume that each innervating taste fiber determines the quality of the receptor sites located on the cell to which it becomes attached. When innervation from the taste nerves to the tongue is removed, all taste buds quickly disappear. As the nerve regenerates, differentiation of the cells again occurs, and the taste buds reform from the epithelial cells. This shows that the nerve is capable of modifying the characteristics of the cells with which it comes in contact. (It has, however, also been reported that some branches of the fibers innervating the taste buds end in the epithelium surrounding the taste buds [Kolmer, 1927]; such fibers may be responsible for the mechanical and temperature sensitivity seen in many single taste fibers.)

## The Gustatory Pathway

The taste buds in the fungiform papillae of the anterior two thirds of the tongue send messages to the central nervous system via the lingual and chorda tympani nerves. These are branches of the seventh cranial nerve (facial nerve and nervus intermedius) (Figure 12–5). The cells of origin of this nerve lie in the geniculate ganglion. The taste buds in the circumvallate and foliate papillae of the posterior third of the tongue are connected to the central nervous system via the ninth cranial or glossopharyngeal nerve. The cells of origin of this nerve are in the petrosal ganglion. The taste buds in the larynx and pharynx are supplied by the vagus or tenth cranial nerve, probably by way of the internal laryngeal nerve. The cells of origin of this nerve lie in the nodose ganglion. All the diverse peripheral connections turn into the tractus solitarius and the nucleus of the tractus

FIG. 12–5.  Diagram to illustrate the gustatory pathways and their regions of termination in the dorsal thalamus and the cerebral cortex. The general visceral afferent fibers and their central relationships are also shown. (From Ranson, S. W., and Clark, S. L., *The Anatomy of the Nervous System*. Philadelphia: W. B. Saunders Company, 1959.)

solitarius (called nucleus parasolitarius where well developed) in the medulla. Electrophysiological studies of the tractus and nucleus of the tractus solitarius have been carried out by Pfaffmann *et al.* (1961), and Makous *et al.* (1963). Similar characteristics of response to those obtained more peripherally were seen. There was a wide range of responsiveness to chemical stimuli, and the threshold to stimulation was also similar. Some of the results obtained are illustrated by Figure 12–6. There are also wide variations in the reactivity of units, similar to those found in the periphery. Further, Makous *et al.* (1963) reported that out of 21 taste units tested, 13 responded to mechanical stimulation of the tongue. Also, out of 24 taste units tested, 21 responded to tap water if it was cold (9–12° C). However, the firing frequency of such nongustatory responding appears small compared with the responses to taste stimuli. Similar results are reported by Pfaffmann *et al.* (1961). Responses to mechanical and temperature stimuli occur even in the chorda tympani taste fibers (Pfaffmann, 1941; and Fishman, 1957). From the medulla, the taste pathway ascends via the medial lemniscus to the thalamus.

FIG. 12–6. The action potential frequency of a single taste unit to chemical and thermal stimulation of the tongue. The axis, "Water temp. °C," refers only to the curve labelled "Water." The average level of activity to distilled water is plotted as a horizontal dashed line parallel to the *x* axis. (From Makous, W., *et al.*, *Olfaction and Taste*, Zotterman, Y. [Ed.], 1963. Courtesy of Pergamon Press.)

Not only do taste units show mechanical sensitivity, but there is a great deal of intermingling of gustatory and somesthetic units at all levels of the nervous system, as if the gustatory sensitivity of the tongue were treated more or less as another modality of the somesthetic system, much like cold or mechanoreception. This picture is only partially correct, however, as some segregation of the taste modality has taken place. However, even where such segregation occurs, as on the cortex of the rat, it occurs inside the somatic sensory face area. Cohen *et al.* (1957) and Landgren (1957) reported that gustatory, tactile and thermal units were all intermingled in the somatic sensory tongue area of the cat.

In the thalamus, the relay intermediate between the nucleus of the tractus solitarius and the cortex, Frommer (1961), Frommer and Pfaffmann (1961), Pfaffmann, Erickson *et al.* (1961) showed that the area for taste was not coextensive with other modalities in the rat. This area is the ventral part of the nucleus ventralis of the thalamus at its medial tip. The responses to taste stimuli found in this area resemble those found in the chorda tympani nerve and the medullary relay. A somewhat similar separation has been shown to exist at the thalamic level in the monkey (e.g., Benjamin, 1963).

It has been shown (Ables and Benjamin, 1960; Oakley and Pfaffmann, 1962) that removal of this thalamic area produces a marked reduction in "preference" of various solutions such as salt and sugar. Besides establishing an anatomical point, such results also show that the overdrinking of such solutions is due to their taste.

In the rat, the taste area in the thalamus projects to the somatic sensory face area. Bilateral removal of this area produces impairment of taste discrimination (Benjamin and Pfaffmann, 1955; Benjamin and Akert, 1959). Further, removal of all the rest of the neocortex while the taste area was spared left discrimination normal. However, it is to be remembered that removal of the cortical area also causes degeneration of the thalamic taste relay. Benjamin (1955a, 1955b) found that removal of the cortical taste area alone did not alter the aversion threshold to quinine when the animal was under high drive and drinking was restricted to an hour. The threshold was the same as that of normal animals under high or low drive. However, if more extensive lesions of the cortex were made, an elevation of threshold manifested itself. If, on the other hand, the animals with a lesion only of the taste area were tested under low drive, when drinking was ad libitum, an increased threshold to quinine was shown. This interesting result is at present difficult to interpret.

In the rabbit, Bremer (1923) has shown that taste deficit is caused by the ablation of cortical areas concerned with mastication. Ruch and Patton (1946) have shown that discrete lesions of the para-insular cortex deep in the sylvian fissure in chimpanzees and monkeys produce gustatory impairment. Penfield and Rasmussen (1950) reported that stimulation of this region in patients elicits reports of taste sensations. A diagram of the gustatory pathways appears in Figure 12–5.

## Temporal Characteristics of Stimulation

When a taste stimulus is applied to a taste receptor, a steady change in receptor potential occurs. No rapid initial increment followed by a decrement is observed. This rapid increment followed by a decrement is found when recording is done from single taste fibers, which suggests that the initial overshoot and its subsidence originate at the site where the action potentials are generated.

It seems, from the experiments of Krakauer and Dallenbach (1937), that complete adaptation measured by behavioral methods is rather fast, ranging from 1.5 to 3 minutes. However, electrophysiological data, at least in the case of salt (Beidler, 1963), do not show such a process of adaptation to occur peripherally, though it does so subjectively. Beidler (1957) stated that neural activity consequent to salt stimulation drops somewhat during the two seconds after the stimulus has been applied and then remains at a steady level when monovalent salts such as NaCl are used. However, such a lack of peripheral adaptation as contrasted with subjective adaptation occurs in monovalent salts only. When divalent salts such as $CaCl_2$ are used, complete adaptation slowly occurs. It is to be noted that the same receptor cells respond both to NaCl and $CaCl_2$.

A further fact of great interest in this regard is that there is very little cross-adaptation between NaCl and $CaCl_2$ at the peripheral neural level. Adaptation to calcium chloride can be complete and yet the response to sodium chloride be almost undiminished. In line with this is the finding of Hahn (1949), on the subjective level, that no cross-adaptation occurs between a sample of 24 inorganic salts. However, in the case of sour, adaptation by one acid transfers to the sour taste of other acids, while for bitter and sweet cross-adaptation occurs only between some stimuli.

Hahn's results on adaptation show that the threshold for salt after adaptation finally reaches a value just above the concentration of the adapting stimulus. McBurney and Pfaffmann (quoted as Pfaffmann, 1963) measured such an effect at saline concentrations close to threshold (Figure 12–7). They were able to establish clearly that saliva normally acts as an important adapting stimulus, greatly elevating the absolute threshold.

Pfaffmann reported that when adaptation to the salt solutions occurred, there was no salt sensation even for the strongest concentrations used. Pfaffmann concluded a process of central adaptation must occur.

McBurney and Pfaffmann's result is interesting because it enables us to reconcile results obtained by electrophysiological means with data obtained by psychophysical methods on man. Changes in taste threshold when salt deprivation or changes in fluid intake occur have been reported

FIG. 12–7. The relation between adapting solution on the tongue and threshold. Each point shows the threshold obtained on one experimental determination; solid dots for adaptation to water or salt, open circles where the tongue is adapted to saliva with a Na+ composition shown on the abscissa as determined by flame photometry. (From Pfaffmann, C., *Olfaction and Taste*, Zotterman, Y. [Ed.], 1963. Courtesy of Pergamon Press.)

from psychophysical studies by de Wardener and Herxheimer (1957) and Yensen (1959). However, electrophysiological studies of neural responses in sodium-deprived rats have consistently failed to show any differences in sensitivity to NaCl. Pfaffmann (1963) explained this discrepancy by pointing out that during electrophysiological studies the rat's tongue is constantly rinsed with distilled water. If we assume no change in the sensitivity of the receptor, but merely changes in the constitution of the saliva in the psychophysical tests, then changes in the saliva causing differential levels of adaptation will bring about variations in threshold. It is to be expected that the constitution of saliva would change sufficiently in human subjects depending on their physiological state to produce the observed discrepancy.

Though the NaCl threshold rises above the saline solution to which the tongue is adapted, this does not mean that solutions below such a threshold are tasteless. They are tasteless in the immediate vicinity of the adapting stimulus. Distilled water after the tongue is adapted to a saline solution tastes bitter or sour (Bartoshuk, McBurney, and Pfaffmann).

Another interesting effect emerges from these findings on adaptation. McBurney (1963) asked his subjects to rate the magnitude of sensation irrespective of quality after adaptation to various NaCl solutions. He found that the magnitude of taste sensation was lowest around the solution to which adaptation had taken place (Figure 12–8). Solutions above the adapting solution were rated as increasing in saltiness, those

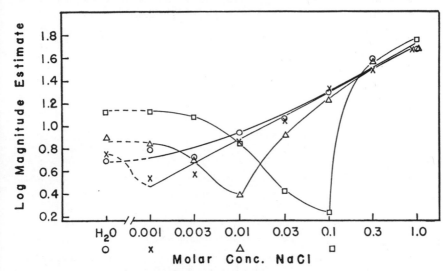

FIG. 12–8. Plot of estimate of magnitude of sensation of NaCl solutions after preadaptation to various salt solutions. Curve obtained after preadaptation with $H_2O$ marked $o$; with 0.001 molar conc. NaCl marked $x$; with 0.01 molar conc. NaCl marked △; with 0.1 molar conc. marked □. (Courtesy of McBurney.)

below as increasing in sourness or bitterness. Further, adaptation to higher concentrations of NaCl did not simply make the tongue less sensitive to NaCl by a constant amount or fraction. It can be seen from the curves (Figure 12–8) that when there is adaptation to the 0.1 concentration, the 0.3 concentration is judged as intense as when there is adaptation to distilled water. As a result there is a marked deviation from a simple power function when a 0.1 adapting solution is used. (It can be seen that when a 0.001 molar concentration of NaCl is used, a straight line is obtained when the logarithm of the concentration is plotted against the logarithm of the magnitude estimate. This indicates that the two magnitudes are related according to a simple power law.) If there was some kind of overall decrement in sensitivity due to adaptation, then a solution of 0.3 molar after an adapting stimulus of 0.1 molar should taste equally strong as a solution of 0.003 molar after an adapting stimulus of 0.001 molar. But this, or anything like it, is not the case. Instead 0.3 molar tastes as strong whether the adapting stimulus was 0.1 or 0.001 molar in concentration. In other modalities it has been shown that the difference threshold is smallest around the adapting value.

SMELL

The sense of smell is probably one of the most important sensory avenues for many mammals. Though it appears to have declined in importance in the primates, olfaction still plays a large part in food selection and in the maintenance of a clean environment. The effective stimuli to the sense of smell are molecules of volatile substances. To be smelled, substances must be airborne and in a finely divided state. Such substances are brought in proximity with the sensory surface by breathing or sniffing. To this end, the olfactory receptor surface, or olfactory mucosa, lies in the upper portion of the nasal cavity. In man the sensitive surface occupies about 2.5 cm² in each nostril. This sensitive surface is not in the direct flow of the inspired air. Consequently the air carrying odorous particles reaches the sensitive surface by eddying. The magnitude of such eddying is increased by sniffing. Adrian (1956) reported that different compounds tend selectively to stimulate different parts of the sensory surface. Etheral smells in weak concentration usually stimulate the anterior parts of the receptor surface, whereas heavy oils have their maximum effect on the posterior parts.

In the case of smell, the functions of sensory cell and nerve cell are not separate, as is the case in taste. The sensory element in olfaction is the specialized dendrite of a bipolar neuron. The cell body of this neuron is about 5 to 10 $\mu$ in diameter (Figure 12–9). Below the nucleus the cell narrows to form the olfactory nerve fiber, about 0.2 $\mu$ in diameter, which runs directly to the olfactory bulb, which is a part of the central nervous system. The receptor cells are cylindrical in shape and are wedged between sustaining or sustentacular cells of a similar shape. Most of the receptor cell is entirely surrounded by the sustentacular cells. However, the dendrite of the receptor cells juts out at the surface above the surrounding sustentacular cells. This bare end, called the olfactory rod, has on its end 6 to 12 fine hairlike structures or cilia, probably about 100 $\mu$ in length and about 0.1 to 0.2 $\mu$ in diameter. It would seem that it is this exposed part of the neuron which comes in contact and reacts to the molecules of odorous substances. The function of the cilia is presumably to increase the surface area of the receptive cell. In the rabbit there are 100 million cells in the olfactory area with a density of about 125,000 receptor cells per square millimeter. Each receptor cell is separately connected via its own axon directly to the olfactory bulb.

## Single Receptor Cell Recordings

Recently, Gesteland et al. (1963) reported that they were able to record from single receptor units in the olfactory mucosa of the frog. They found

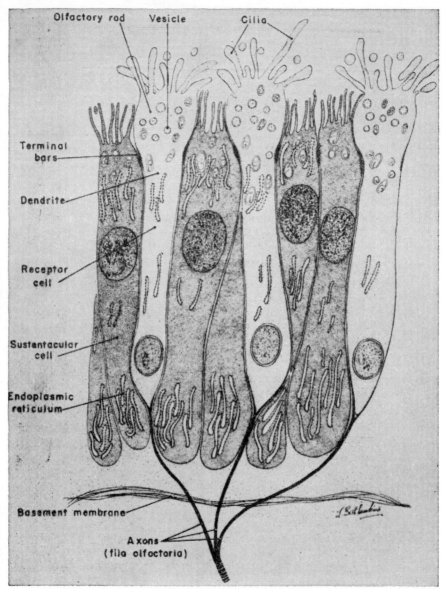

Olfactory rod    Vesicle      Cilia

Terminal
bars

Dendrite

Receptor
cell

Sustentacular
cell

Endoplasmic
reticulum

Basement membrane

Axons
(fila olfactoria)

FIG. 12–9. Schematic drawing of the olfactory mucosa showing the relationships of the various cell types based upon DeLorenzo's observations with the electron microscope. (From DeLorenzo, A. J. D., *Olfaction and Taste*, Zotterman, Y. [Ed.], 1963. Courtesy of Pergamon Press.)

that the action potential is long in duration (3 to 5 msec.) from extracellular recording sites near the axon hillock. The maximum repetition rate of neural discharge is 20 per second and is seen only rarely. A common rate of response to a stimulus is from 1 to 5 per second. The resting rate of discharge is extremely low.

## TABLE 12–2

| Stimulus | Cells Sampled | Cells Responding |
|---|---|---|
| n-Amyl Alcohol | 25 | 14 |
| Musk Xylene | 38 | 20 |
| Benzaldehyde | 36 | 19 |
| Benzyl Acetate | 12 | 6 |
| Geraniol | 18 | 9 |
| Benzonitrite | 22 | 11 |
| Pyridine | 32 | 15 |
| Indole | 19 | 9 |
| Camphor | 32 | 14 |
| Methyl Salicylate | 18 | 8 |
| Butyric Acid | 30 | 13 |
| Linalool | 14 | 6 |
| Pinene | 7 | 3 |
| n-Butanol | 47 | 19 |
| c-Hexanol | 20 | 8 |
| Nitrobenzene | 42 | 16 |
| Triethylamine | 14 | 5 |
| Ethyl Butyrate | 31 | 10 |
| Mercaptoacetic Acid | 19 | 6 |
| Valeric Acid | 13 | 4 |
| Limonene | 17 | 5 |
| Coumarin | 22 | 6 |
| Carbon Disulfide | 28 | 7 |
| Cinnamaldehyde | 25 | 6 |
| Methyl Anthranilate | 6 | 1 |
| Salicylaldehyde | 21 | 3 |

The stimuli used in various experiments by Gesteland *et al.* (1963), the number of cells on which each was tried, and the number of those which responded with an increase in discharge rate are tabulated here. Weak and strong responses are lumped together. (From Gesteland, R. C. *et al.*, *Olfaction and Taste.* Zotterman, Y. [Ed.] 1963. Courtesy of Pergamon Press.)

Each receptor shows selectivity to groups of odors. Each responds strongly to some odors, weakly to others, and to some not at all. The tabulation shows the proportions of cells sensitive to the various stimuli used. From an analysis of the sensitivities of the receptor cells sampled, it was possible to suggest a grouping of the receptors:

|  | *Sensitive to—* | *Less sensitive to—* |
|---|---|---|
| Group 1 | Limonene (lemon)<br>Camphor (moth repellent)<br>Pinene (carrot seed turpentine) | Carbon disulphide (rotten egg) |
| 2 | Coumarin (new mown hay)<br>Musk (heavy putrid) | |

3  Butyric acid (rancid butter)
   Valeric acid (rancid butter)
   Mercaptoacetic acid (offensive odor)
   Cyclohexanol (peppermint-like)

4  Benzaldehyde (bitter almond)
   Nitrobenzene (crude bitter almond)
   Benzonitrite (bitter almond)
   Musk (heavy putrid)
   Amyl alcohol (flowery fragrant)

5  Pyridine (burnt)
   Musk (heavy putrid odor)
   Cinnamaldehyde (cinnamon)
   N-butanol (glue solvent)

6  Musk (heavy putrid odor)            Benzaldehyde (bitter almond)
                                       Nitrobenzene (bitter almond)

7  Pyridine (burnt)

8  Butanol (glue solvent)
   Ethyl butyrate (pineapple)
   Amyl alcohol (flowery fragrant)
   Geraniol (geranium)

Gesteland and co-workers are of the opinion that there are other rarer groups also. From their results on single neuron stimulation, they believe that there are different types of receptor sites, distributed over each receptor cell. Different groups of cells could differ by having different ratios of receptor types on them. In this way, the receptoral scheme in smell seems to be like that seen in taste, except that there seems to be a larger number of special receptor sites.

## Mode of Stimulation of Olfactory Receptors

In the previous section we saw how olfactory stimuli are placed in different qualitative classes by the stimulation of different types of specific receptors. Before this experimental work was done it had been suggested that qualitative differences in smell were due to spatial or temporal patterns of a homogeneous population of receptor cells. The question to be asked now is related to the previous problem. What general kind of interaction occurs between the stimulating molecule and the receptor cell? Though many different theories have been suggested, based on radiation or chemical interaction, they have not received much support. An interesting approach to this problem of the physical process producing receptor excitation has been made by Jones (1955). He measured the absolute threshold for a large number of substances, calculating the relative number of molecules necessary to produce a sensation for each substance. He then attempted to correlate the stimulating efficiency of the various substances with various physical properties such as their water solubility, vapor pressure, dipole moment, and standard free energy of formation. He discovered that vapor pressure had a very high correlation with stimulating efficiency in terms of the number of molecules necessary to reach absolute threshold. The results are plotted in Figure 12–10. As in general, substances of lower vapor pressure are more readily adsorbed, he concluded that the most likely physical process involved in excitation of the receptors

FIG. 12–10. $Log_{10}$ of the undiluted vapor pressures plotted against median thresholds. (From Nowell Jones, 1955; permission of *J. Psych.* 40.)

is the adsorption of molecules on the receptor surface. In this way, the mechanism of receptor excitation in smell would be similar to that in taste.

If the mechanism of stimulation of olfactory receptors is analogous to that proposed for taste, then we should expect various loci on the membrane of the receptor cell selectively to adsorb molecules as a result of certain highly specific properties such as a particular shape. Depending on further properties of the adsorbed molecule, a change in the permeability to ions of the membrane at the receptor site results when the molecule has been adsorbed. This results in a lowering of the electrical potential across the cell membrane. In the case of the smell receptor if the lowering of the potential is sufficiently drastic, then as this change spreads electrotonically across the membrane of the cell, it reaches a region on the membrane at which an action potential is generated. This action potential is then propagated along the cell and its axon. Ottoson (1963) argued that the part of the membrane producing the initial alteration in potential does not also produce the action potential. He has measured this initial depolarization of the cell membrane from the surface of the epithelium (Ottoson, 1956) and has found that it is not affected by antidromic stimulation of the olfactory nerve, which shows that the action potential is not conducted to this region. He quoted examples on impulse initiation in the lobster's stretch receptors (Edwards and Ottoson, 1958), in spinal motorneurons (Coombs, etc., 1957), and the giant cells of Aplysia (Tauc, 1962) where the cell body does not participate in the production of impulses and suggested that olfactory receptor neurons are similar.

The characteristics of the change in potential when odors strike the olfactory mucosa are of considerable interest. Ottoson (1956) was the first to detect such changes by recording with large electrodes from the surface of a very large number of receptors simultaneously. When a prolonged odorous puff is passed over the frog's mucosa, after an initial decline of electrical activity little adaptation takes place. This is in agreement with the observations of Adrian (1950) on the secondary neurons in the olfactory bulb of the rabbit. This lack of adaptation shown by electrophysiological methods at more or less peripheral loci is at variance with the rapid adaptation to smells as it occurs in our perception. We very soon fail to be able to smell an odor when we are continuously exposed to it. To explain this discrepancy, Adrian (1950) suggested that the signals from the receptors are suppressed by the intrinsic activity in the olfactory bulb. Work on efferent control of the olfactory bulb (see section below) suggested that such signals may be inhibited by efferent fibers reaching the olfactory bulb from other points in the central nervous system.

Ottoson has been able to measure the relation between the increase of the potential at the mucosa and stimulus strength. By plotting the amplitude of potential against the logarithm of stimulus strength, a curve of increasing slope is obtained. This means that a larger proportionate increase of stimulus is needed at lower intensities to produce the same absolute change in amplitude of potential than at higher intensities. At higher intensities a smaller proportionate change will produce the same absolute change. Let us assume that when we discriminate different intensities of the same odor, a discriminable difference is always the same absolute difference between potentials. For instance, we could assume that we can detect a difference between any two levels of an odor whenever the difference between the potentials to which they give rise is more than a tenth of a millivolt. If this reasonable assumption is made, then there is good qualitative agreement between Ottoson's result and the results of psychophysical experiments. According to Zigler and Holway (1935), a much larger proportionate increase at low intensities of odor is necessary to produce a noticeable difference than at high. That is, $\Delta I/I$ decreases as $I$ increases. It would therefore seem that the psychophysical law as applied to the case of smell reflects some property of the membrane covering the end of the olfactory receptor cell.

One of the noteworthy features of the olfactory receptor is its extreme sensitivity. De Vries and Stuiver (1961) have calculated that the largest estimate of mercaptan molecules necessary to stimulate a receptor cell is 6 and that at the most 40 receptor cells have to be stimulated to produce a sensation. Neuhaus (1955) showed that olfactory receptors in dogs could react to a single molecule of fatty acids.

## Theories of Olfactory Quality

There have been many suggestions about the physical properties to which the receptor is sensitive. Most of the theories proposed so far are not capable of encompassing more than a small proportion of the evidence and many have conclusive evidence against them. These have been well reviewed by Jones and Jones (1953).

There have also been a number of attempted classifications of odors (Zwaardemaker, 1925; Henning, 1924; Crocker and Henderson, 1927). However, it is not even clear how many of the smells thus classified actually represent stimulation of olfactory receptors, rather than taste receptors giving rise to sweet or sour "smells," or of free nerve endings belonging to the trigimineal nerve, capable of reacting to chemical stimuli giving rise to pungent "smells" or of cold fibers stimulated by certain substances, such as menthol, giving rise to fresh "smells." Such classifications may be descriptively useful, but it is dubious whether they shed any great insight on the mechanism of olfaction.

Factor analysis has been applied in a preliminary but promising manner to the problem of basic olfactory qualities by Jones (1957). He obtained recognition thresholds for 20 substances on a large number of subjects. From the intercorrelations of these thresholds, he was able to conclude that individual differences in thresholds are systematic, that there are many varieties of receptor, and that his results corresponded to no existing scheme of odor classification.

The theory which has so far received the strongest measure of experimental support is in its outline due to the Roman poet, the Epicurean Lucretius. He believed that different substances gave off molecules of different shapes and sizes. These then entered pores of different shapes and sizes in the palate and accordingly were perceived as different odors. This stereochemical theory of odor was restated in modern times by Moncrieff (1951). Molecules of various odorants by virtue of their shape and size were thought of as fitting into different shaped receptor sites on the surface of the receptor membrane. Amoore (1964) has made this theory more specific by working out the shapes and sizes of such receptor sites. He postulates seven varieties of receptor site (Amoore *et al.*, 1964). These according to him correspond to seven primary odors:

camphoraceous (like moth repellent), musky (like angelica root oil or heavy putrid odor), floral (like roses), pepperminty, ethereal (like dry-cleaning fluid), pungent (like vinegar), and putrid (like bad eggs). The pungent molecules stimulate not because of their shape but because they are positively charged. Similarly, putrid molecules stimulate because they are positively charged. It is claimed that from these seven primary odors it is possible to match any other known odor. Because of their shape, some molecules will fit into more than one type of receptor site, and this is held to account for mixed odors. It has further proved possible to predict the odor of a new compound from its shape and to modify it in a predicted direction by changing the shape. Molecules of the same shape but belonging to different chemical substances were found to have the same odor; quite different chemicals of the same overall molecular shape were quite often indistinguishable.

## Central Connections

The receptor cells send their axons directly to the central nervous system and there is no interconnection between the receptor cells at the peripheral level. The axons penetrate the cribriform plate of the ethmoid bone to end in the olfactory bulb (Figure 12–11). The axons from the anterior and dorsal parts of the olfactory mucosa connect to the anterior part of the olfactory bulb, and those from the ventral and posterior parts project to the posterior part of the bulb. Each of these axons belonging to the receptor cells then passes into a glomerulus and ends there. It does not branch until it passes into the glomerulus. The glomerulus is a spherical bush of dendrites belonging to the tufted mitral and external granular cells lying more deeply in the olfactory bulb (Allison, 1953). It is interesting to note that the connection between the receptor cells and the mitral and tufted cells is of an unusual type. The axon of the receptor cell connects to the dendrites of the mitral and tufted cells (axo-dendritic connection) instead of connecting directly with the cell body (axosomatic connection) which is the usual arrangement found in the higher vertebrates. The axo-dendritic mode of connection is typical of the nervous system of invertebrates and lower vertebrates and is considered to be less rapid and efficient in the transmission of impulses. It is also to be noted that the sense of smell possesses another primitive feature inasmuch as the functions of receptor cell and conductive neurons are combined. This is different from the case of taste and again resembles the sensory arrangement to be found in invertebrates (for instance the blowfly, Dethier and Arab, 1958).

The axons of the mitral cells (the dendrites of which the receptor cells connect in the glomeruli) form the lateral olfactory tract, which flows into the primary olfactory cortex. It should also be noted that as well as possessing dendrites which meet the incoming fibers in the glomerulus,

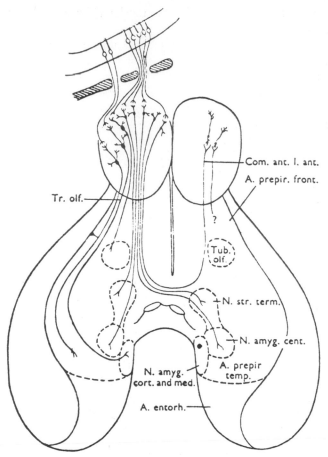

FIG. 12–11.   Diagrammatic representation of the secondary olfactory pathways in the mammalian brain: a.prepir.fr(ont), frontal part of the prepiriform area; a.prepir.temp. temporal part of the prepiriform area; a.entorh, entorhinal area; n.amyg.cent. central amygdaloid nucleus; n.amyg. cort. cortical amygdaloid nucleus; n.amyg.med. medial amygdaloid nucleus; tr. olf. olfactory tract; tub.olf. olfactory tubercle; com.ant.l.ant. commissure anterior lateralis anterior; N.str.term. nucleus of the stria terminalis. (From Allison, A. C., 1953; courtesy of *Biological Reviews* 28.)

each mitral cell has accessory dendrites which lie close to the dendrites of other mitral cells in the external plexiform layer. This is also true of the tufted cells. Further, both the mitral and tufted cells divide their axons into two as these axons pass out of the olfactory bulb. One branch runs out. The other branch of the axon doubles back (and is therefore called recurrent collateral) to end on the accessory dendrites of its own class in the olfactory bulb. The axons of the tufted cells pass into the anterior commissure and run into the contralateral olfactory bulb. There they form synaptic connections with granule cells. The axons of the granule cells extend towards the surface to end on the accessory dendrites of mutual and tufted cells. Each glomerulus in the rabbit has 26,000 axons from receptor cells ending in it. From each glomerulus, information runs through 24 mitral cells to higher olfactory centers, and through 68 tufted cells to the contralateral olfactory bulb. There are about 60,000 mitral cells in each olfactory bulb of the rabbit. It seems likely that axons from receptor cells of similar sensitivity to specific odors collect on the same glomerulus and that mitral cells in different regions of the olfactory bulb tend to respond selectively to different odors (Adrian, 1953; Mozell and Pfaffmann, 1953). Using small electrodes to record from the layer of mitral cells in the rabbit's olfactory bulb, Adrian (1953, 1956) reported that such cells are differentially sensitive to odorous stimuli. He stated that mitral cells can be divided into at least four or five groups, depending on their peak sensitivity:

Group 1. Aromatic compounds (benzol, toluol) (lighter fluid, dry-cleaning fluid)
   2. Esters of fatty acids (amyl and ethyl acetate) (fruity)
   3. Paraffin hydrocarbons (pentane and homologues) (gasoline)
   4. Terpenes (limonene, cedar oil, eucalyptus) (lemon, etc.)
   5. Sulphur compounds (mercaptan, $H_2S$) (foul, rotten eggs)

A slow potential change, paralleling that recorded from the olfactory mucosa, can be recorded from the olfactory bulb. This is thought to arise from the glomeruli and to represent a summed dendritic potential. Superimposed on this slowly rising bulb potential are a series of faster rhythmic waves. Some interesting observations on this phenomenon have been made by Moulton (1963) on unanesthetised rabbits with chronically implanted electrodes. He reported that occasionally low-amplitude asynchronous waves in the range of 75 to 90 cps. could be recorded from the bulb even when the rabbit was breathing filtered air. When an odor was introduced, high-amplitude sinusoidal waves appeared in the record varying from 50 to 85 cps. Spike discharges recorded from the bulb did not always coincide with the rhythmic activity.

The spoke discharges recorded by Moulton did not show any regular relation to the strength of the presented odor, as repeated presentation of the odor brought about habituation. When he paired shock with a previously habituated odor, enhancement of the response appeared, though quantitative relations still remained inconsistent. This suggests some relation to states of arousal or attention of the amplitude of response. The effect of various attentional states on activity in peripheral sensory structures is discussed further in Chapter 5.

## Efferent Influences on the Olfactory Bulb

Cajal (1911) and Cragg (1962) have shown that a very large number of centrifugal connections end in the olfactory bulb. These end on the granule cells of the bulb, some arising in the prepyriform cortex. It has been shown by Kerr and Hagbarth (1955) and Hagbarth and Kerr (1954) that both the resting and induced activity of the olfactory bulb may be modified by stimulation of the prepyriform cortex, amygdaloid nucleus, olfactory tubercle and anterior commissure. Kerr (1960) demonstrated the inhibition of induced waves in one bulb by strong olfactory stimulation of the contralateral bulb. Efferent effects have also been described by Yamamoto and Iwama (1961) and Walsh (1959). Moulton (1963) described the effect of severing the efferent fibers to one bulb and its connections with the opposite bulb. This was done by a lesion to the anterior olfactory areas through which run efferent fibers to the bulb (Cragg, 1962) and to the anterior commissure, through which run the fibers from the opposite bulb. A better correlation between input to the bulb and recorded output was obtained on the side with no efferent input. There also appeared a larger and more regular response. Whereas diminution of response with repeated presentation of the same stimulus occurred in the side whose efferent input was intact, no such diminution was observed on the contralateral side. Kerr and Hagbarth (1955) obtained similar phenomena in cats and could not decide whether the depression of activity represents some form of desynchronization such as occurs on activation in the cortex, or a true inhibition of activity in the olfactory bulb.

## Connections of the Olfactory Bulb with Other Areas*

Direct connections of the mitral cells in the olfactory bulb with the rest of the nervous system are made via the lateral olfactory tract. This terminates ipsilaterally in the olfactory tubercle parts of the prepyriform cortex and the cortical and medial groups of the amygdaloid nuclei. The tufted cells are connected via the anterior limb of the anterior commissure in the nucleus of the stria terminalis and the central amygdaloid nucleus. They are also connected to the granule cells in the contralateral olfactory bulb. The olfactory tubercle, the cortical, medial and central amygdaloid nuclei, and the nucleus of the stria terminalis receive connexions from nonolfactory areas also. It is therefore difficult to know whether their efferent connexions have a specifically olfactory function or whether they themselves have such a function. The only area which is specifically olfactory is the prepyriform cortex, according to Allison (1953). When the prepyriform cortex is electrically stimulated in the dog, spikes can be recorded 3 msec. later in the ventrolateral portion of the prefrontal area and from no other area (Allen, 1943b). The agranular insular cortex is considered by Allison (1953) to be equivalent to the area described by Allen. Allison (1953) found that in the rabbit, degeneration of fibers

* See Figure 12–11.

passing into the agranular insular cortex occurs after destruction of the prepyriform area. Ablation of this prefrontal area has been shown by Allen (1940, 1941) to yield a behavioral deficit. He found that this area is necessary for conditioned differential response to olfactory stimuli and impairs other olfactory learning to some extent. The differential conditioned response which was so severely affected meant in effect that the dog had to learn to decide in 7 seconds whether to jerk its foreleg when it smelled cloves and not to jerk it when it smelled asafetida. In a control experiment Allen (1943a) found that the same lesion had no effect on the learning of the same habit to auditory, cutaneous and visual stimuli, thus ruling out an interpretation of the result in terms of general intellectual impairment. Other lesions designed to test the extent of the brain areas necessary for olfactory discrimination have yielded negative results. Swann (1934, 1935) designed a test in which a rat had to dig through wood shavings scented either with oil of anise or creosote to obtain food. That is to say the rat had to discriminate between two paths leading to food on the basis of odor. However, lesions of the septum, amygdaloid complex, pyriform lobes, hyppocampus, fimbria, fornix, and habenula had no effect on the discrimination. Brown and Ghiselli (1938) also failed to observe any effect on olfactory discrimination after a variety of subcortical lesions, as did Lashley and Sperry (1943) who severed the cortical radiations coming up from the anterior group of thalamic nuclei.

Traditionally, the rhinencephalon as a whole used to be credited with olfactory function. This view has not been substantiated by recent evidence. Though it is possible to record from a large number of structures events initiated by stimulating the olfactory bulb, it is not clear at present how many of these are concerned with smell in any direct manner.

## Behavioral Phenomena

Perhaps the most important and difficult problem in research on olfaction concern the method of stimulation. Various instruments and procedures have been designed to ensure the delivery of a known and uniform amount of odorous substance to the sensory surface. The difficulties inherent in this have been ably reviewed by Wenzel (1948). Zwaardemaker (1925) designed an instrument called an olfactometer. This consists of an outer tube, the inner surface of which is impregnated with the substance to be tested, and an inner tube of glass. This inner tube fits into the outer tube, and is slid into it to varying extents. The further it is slipped in, the less of the odorous surface is exposed when the subject sniffs the free end of the inner tube. In this way, some gradiation of odorous intensity is achieved. Instead of relying on the sniffing power of the nose, it is possible to attach a pump to the tubes in such a way that air is blown into the nostril for a fixed amount of time. A further refinement of technique has been introduced by Elsberg and Levy (1935), called the blast injection method. In this technique, varying amounts of air are forced into a bottle with an odorous substance in it. As a consequence, varying amounts of pressure build up and are then suddenly released into the nostrils of the subject. However, this technique has been brought into question by Jerome (1942), Wenzel (1949) and Jones (1953). The differences in threshold found cannot be related to the concentration of odorous substance but rather on pressure. To overcome these difficulties, Wenzel (1955) introduced a technique in which threshold measurements are taken during normal breathing with satisfactory reliability. The whole head is placed in a plastic box with the face and hair covered leaving access

FIG. 12–12. Diagram of the essential portions of the Olfactometer de signed by Nowell Jones. (From Nowell Jones, 1954; courtesy of the *Amer. J. Psych.* 67.)

only to the nostrils. Then a stream of air to which various amounts of odor can be added is blown into the box.

An olfactometer which gives a close control over the duration, volume, pressure, and temperature of the stimulus and which permits specification of dilution of odorant has been designed by Jones (1954). It is illustrated in Figure 12–12 (Jones, 1954). Basically it consists of a syringe (*B*) which may be filled with differing proportions of pure air and a certain dilution of the odor to be tested. What proportions of the odorant and air are sucked into the syringe by withdrawing the plunger is controlled by turning the three-way stopcock at *C*. Air is taken in from a purified source (not shown in the diagram) which connects separately to the stopcock and to the bottles of odorant at *A*. When the syringe is full, the odorant mixture is delivered into the subject's nose through the nosepiece at *D* by switching on the electric motor at *F*. This engages the toothed rack (*E*) to drive the plunger of the syringe (*B*). A stop is mounted at *H* to ensure that the plunger travels through the same distance every time the subject is stimulated. A blast of 40 cc. is delivered to the subject in 0.8 sec.

It has already been mentioned that complete adaptation to an odor, as shown by subjective reports, does occur. Zwaardemaker (1925) has shown that the rate of elevation of absolute threshold is higher with stronger stimuli. Not only do odors diminish with perceived intensity, but there are some which also change qualitatively as adaptation proceeds. Presumably rates of adaptation to various components differ. Adaptation is to a certain extent specific. Thresholds for oil of clove and eucalyptus and for ether are elevated by previous exposure to camphor. However, adaptation to benzaldehyde leaves the threshold for these odors relatively unaltered. Such relationships presumably reflect differences in the receptor sites occupied by different odorous molecules. However, as can be seen from the case of taste, this is not necessarily so. It is also possible to produce a new odor by mixing odors. Also an odor may be rendered imperceptible by the presence of another, a phenomenon analogous to that of auditory masking. The physiological bases of these observations are at present obscure.

# 13

## MOTOR SYSTEM

### Ian P. Howard

In any logical account of the motor system, each step assumes a knowledge of what is to follow. This is because the various parts of the system are interdependent and are involved in closed control loops. For purposes of exposition (and experimental analysis) these control loops must be broken into, but for a final understanding their integrity must be restored. The student is thus asked to read through this account more than once. Things which are not understood at the first reading, because they anticipate facts explained later, should become clear on subsequent readings.

## MUSCULAR CONTRACTION

Muscle, together with its associated skeletal structures, is a machine converting chemical energy into mechanical energy. There are two main types of muscle; striated muscle, and smooth muscle. All skeletal muscles, that is muscles attached to tendons and bones, are striated, but a few striated muscles are not skeletal; for instance, muscles in the iris and heart. Most striated muscles are under voluntary control and are often called voluntary muscles on this account. Smooth or unstriated muscle is never skeletal and is normally not under voluntary control.

There are about 400 skeletal muscles in the human body, comprising almost one half of its total weight. There are about 250 million muscle fibers or cellular units supplied by about half a million myelinated nerve fibers. Thus many muscle fibers are supplied by one efferent nerve fiber, and any such group of muscle fibers is known as a *motor unit*. Motor units vary in size in different parts of the body; those muscles involved in fine, precise movements have smaller motor units than those involved in cruder movements. The muscle fibers belonging to any one unit are scattered at random in a particular muscle. Contiguous muscle fibers are bound together by connective tissue into bundles. Many bundles go to make up a skeletal muscle. Each end of a skeletal muscle is attached by a tendon to a bone in such a way that contraction of the muscle causes movement at a joint.

Each striated muscle fiber consists of a mass of parallel *myofibrils*, each 1 to 2 $\mu$ thick. Each fibril shows cross striations when viewed under a microscope and the fibrils are so arranged that their patterns of striation are in step. The pattern of striations repeats down the length of the fibrils, and each unit or segment of the pattern is bounded by highly refractive bands, between which stretch parallel molecular *filaments*. These filaments are therefore parallel to the direction of the muscle fibrils and fibers. Thicker filaments composed largely of *myosin* are interleaved with thinner and longer filaments composed largely of another muscle protein, *actin*.

The contraction of the muscle involves a contraction of the myofibrils. The contraction of the fibrils is caused by the myosin and actin molecular filaments sliding past each other, presumably because of obliquely acting forces between them. Neither the myosin filaments nor the actin filaments are contractile—it may be seen under the electron microscope that the length of the filaments does not alter. Contraction consists of an increased overlapping of the two sets of filaments. For further details of this theory of muscular contraction see H. E. Huxley (1956).

An older view (Fulton, 1955) was that contraction involves an alteration in the length of the actin and myosin chain molecules by a process of "molecular folding." This is now known to be wrong, but perhaps the obliquely acting forces between the actin and myosin filaments do involve "molecular folding."

Something is known about the biochemical processes by which energy is made available for the contractile process. However, a discussion of these processes is beyond the scope of this book. The student is referred to Fulton (1955) and British Medical Bulletin (1956).

## Smooth Muscle

Smooth, unstriated muscle is innervated by the unmyelinated nerves of the autonomic nervous system, and is not, in any obvious way, organized into motor units. It typically lines body cavities, such as the bladder, uterus, intestine, and blood vessels. Many smooth muscles contract rhythmically even in the absence of nerve impulses. Smooth muscle, like striated muscle, contains myofibrils and the same muscle proteins, actin and myosin; however the myofibril segments of smooth muscle are not aligned with each other, which accounts for its smooth unstriated appearance. This lack of alignment is probably due to the fact that smooth muscle fibrils do not have to pull in concert against a skeletal member, but rather in all directions over a sheet of contractile tissue so as to control the volume of the body cavity of which they form the lining.

## The Neuromuscular Junction

Figure 13–1 is a diagramatic representation of a neuromuscular junction on a striated muscle fiber. It shows one dendritic terminal bouton in close proximity to the motor endplate of a muscle fiber. The motor endplate is a very specialized part of the muscle membrane. The nerve impulse stimulates the release of acetylcholine in the synaptic junction. Acetylcho-

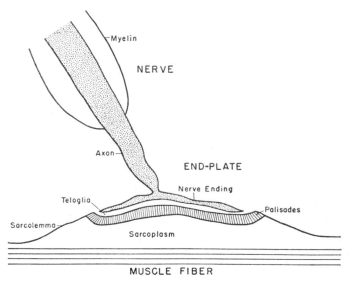

FIG. 13–1.  Diagram of end-plate region. (Adapted by Couteaux from Acheson, G., *Fed. Proc.*, 1948, 7; 447.)

line is known as a transmitter, and acts by increasing the permeability of the muscle membrane to sodium and potassium ions. This leads to a transient "puncture" of the end-plate membrane, which causes its resting potential to drop and a wave of depolarization to spread over the muscle membrane. The mechanism by which this membrane potential is conducted is similar to that by which the action potential in a nerve axon is conducted (see p. 451). It quickly spreads to all parts of the fiber, to each fibril, and finally to each actin and myosin filament.

When the nerve impulse has ceased, the acetylcholine must be removed rapidly, or the muscle would continue to contract. An enzyme, acetylcholinesterase is responsible for the breakdown of the transmitter. Poisons are known, for instance, physostigmine, which combine with the acetylcholinesterase and prevent it from working. Small amounts of such poisons are sufficient to cause rapid death consequent upon the permanent contracture of all the muscles of the body. Other poisons, for instance curare, interfere with the action of acetylcholine and produce muscle paralysis. These drugs are useful in the experimental analysis of muscular function, as well as clinically. There are several diseases, some of which are inherited, for instance, family periodic paralysis and myasthenia gravis which affect the processes of neuro-muscular transmission (see Brain, 1952).

## Mechanical Aspects of Muscular Contraction

Contracting muscle is subject to certain internal physical restraints which impede its free movement, quite apart from any external load which may be imposed. These restraints are: the inertia due to the muscle's mass, the internal friction, the muscle's elasticity, and the extent of any damping. Each of these restraints affects contraction in a different way.

Inertia is a function of mass and is a measure of the extent to which the moving part resists any change in velocity. According to classical mechanics, the force required to move a body is equal to the product of its mass and acceleration. Thus the mass or inertia of a limb affects its movement only when it is required to change its speed of movement.

Friction resists change of position, and is especially high when a limb moves from rest, but may be regarded as a constant when movement has started.

Elasticity is a measure of the force which is required to extend the muscle at any particular length. It increases as a function of length and tends to restore the muscle to its original length. Resting muscles are always under some elastic tension, so that elasticity would facilitate muscular contraction except that every striated muscle is balanced by its antagonist which resists its contraction. The elastic forces which arise when a muscle is stretched have two components: the first is due to the elasticity of the tendons and other elastic elements in series with the muscle fibers, the other is due to the active contraction of fully innervated muscle in response to the stimulus of stretching (the stretch or myotatic reflex). The physical elasticity is practically independent of the rate at which the muscle is stretched and is only dependent on the amount of stretch, at least up to the point of injury. The active elastic component is a complex function of many factors and depends on the integrity of a complete reflex arc.

Damping is a measure of the forces which resist movement in proportion to the velocity of movement. One form of damping is a consequence of the viscosity of the tissues. A second form of damping is provided by the adaptation of the reflex arcs which control the muscle's contraction. This topic will be mentioned again.

These are the basic properties of muscle which determine the way a muscle will contract to a given stimulus, assuming there is no external load.

Figure 13–2 may help to clarify these matters. The relative spatial arrangement of the inertial, frictional, elastic, and damping elements is important. For instance, the elastic element A in Figure 13–2 is "outside" the inertial mass and damping; on release of tension, this part of the system will contract rapidly, as it will not have to move a mass or overcome damping. The elastic element B is "inside" the inertial and damping elements, and will therefore contract only slowly. Both types of elasticity are present in muscle. The relative positions of other elements are equally important. In practice, they are distributed, though not evenly, throughout

EXTERNAL LOAD

↑ FORCE

FRICTION

ELASTIC ELEMENT B

MASS –INERTIA

DAMPING VANE

ELASTIC ELEMENT A

VISCOUS FLUID

FIG. 13–2. A diagrammatic representation of the mechanical elements of muscle.

each muscle. Such mechanical models are a useful aid to understanding but give only an approximation to the actual state of affairs. In reality the elements we have discussed do not function independently; a change in one brings about a change in another. In other words, living systems are *nonlinear*.

The behavior of muscle under different conditions of external load will now be considered. If a muscle is stimulated by a brief electric shock it responds with a "*twitch*." If the stimulus is repeated, even before the first response has died away, the muscle will again contract. With high-frequency stimulation, the individual twitches fuse into a smooth, continuous contraction or *tetanus*. If a muscle is anchored to a rigid tension-measuring device it will be unable to shorten when stimulated, but the tension developed will increase with the strength of the stimulus. The muscle is said to be contracting *isometrically*. On the other hand, if it is attached to a light lever which records movement rather than tension, the muscle will shorten at constant tension and is said to be contracting *isotonically*. The tension developed in isometric contraction is a function of the extent to which the muscle is initially stretched and is a maximum when the muscle is as long as it is in the resting limb. In the body, the maximum tension is also a function of the number of muscle fibers arranged in parallel, but a balance is struck between the need for strong "in-parallel" muscles and the need for "in-series" muscles which have a greater range of shortening. When muscle under isometric tension is suddenly released, there is a rapid shortening due to the endogenous elasticity of the tissues, followed by a slower shortening due to active contraction.

Under isotonic contraction, the muscle takes time to shorten to its full extent. This *latent* period is a function of the tension against which the muscle has to pull; when there is no external load, the speed of contraction is maximal and is determined by the muscle's internal mass, friction, elasticity, and damping constants. At the other extreme, when the muscle contracts isometrically, its speed of shortening is zero. The velocity varies enormously between different muscles in the body and between different species. Striated (voluntary) muscle is, on the whole, faster than unstriated (involuntary) muscle. The wing muscles of insects contract in less than 1 msec.; they are the most rapidly contracting of all muscles. At the other extreme, the unstriated circular muscle of the column of the sea-anemone, *Metridium senile*, requires five or six minutes for a single "twitch." For further details on this subject see Wilkie (1956).

## The Gradation of Muscular Contraction

In the intact animal, the gradation of the strength of muscular contraction in a particular muscle is controlled by the number of motor units which are stimulated, and by the frequency of the efferent neural discharge. Records of the changes in electrical potential which accompany muscular contraction (electromyography) have revealed that more units are recruited with increased muscular tension, and that the neural discharge rate to a single motor unit varies from about 5 to 50 per second, as the strength of contraction increases, although contraction rarely involves complete tetanus. It used to be thought that the individual muscle fibers obey the all-or-none law; that is, that they contract fully, or not at all. It is now known that fatigue, drugs, and disease may modify the strength of contraction of a fiber, even though the nerve impulses remain constant (Merton, 1956). The $\gamma$-fiber system is an also important mechanism for controlling the strength of muscular contraction (see p. 394).

Muscular contraction must not only be graded in strength, but also smooth and balanced in operation. At the cellular level, all the fibrils in a particular muscle fiber and all fibril segments receive impulses practically simultaneously, for each fiber receives many terminal boutons from any single neuron, and the action potential spreads quickly over the fiber membranes. The muscle fibers comprising a motor unit are scattered throughout the whole muscle, and they also contract simultaneously, because they are supplied by the same neuron. However, the different motor units do not fire in synchrony, but those units that are firing at any time are evenly and randomly spread throughout the muscle. It is rare for all the units to fire together; they fire in rotation like the cylinders of a car engine. The final effect is that the contraction is smoothed, just as the running of the car engine is smoothed by the out-of-step firing of the cylinders. If the firings were not well distributed at any one time, one end of the muscle would contract before or more than the other end, or one side would contract before the other side; the movement would be off balance. It is the random distribution of the fibers comprising each motor unit that ensures this balance of the contractile process. Muscle is indeed a well-designed machine.

## Muscular Fatigue

Muscular fatigue has been attributed at different times to the central nervous system, the neuromuscular junction, the action-potential which triggers the fibrils, and the contractile process itself. Merton (1956) convincingly demonstrated that muscular fatigue (as distinct from boredom) is due to a failure of the contractile process itself. He showed that there is no falling off of the muscle action potential in a fully fatigued muscle, so that muscle fatigue is not due to blockage at the central nervous system or the neuromuscular junction. He also showed, contrary to an earlier belief, that it is not possible to contract a muscle by stimulating the fibrils directly, after the muscle has been fully fatigued by voluntary effort. This rules out the action-potential-to-fibril trigger mechanism as the cause of fatigue, and the only possibility left is that fatigue occurs in the final contractile process, perhaps because of the exhaustion of a biochemical process. In support of this conclusion it was found that cutting off the blood supply to a fatigued limb prevented recovery and induced rapid fatigue in an unfatigued muscle.

### THE RECEPTOR SYSTEMS OF MUSCLES AND JOINTS

## Muscle Spindles and Golgi Tendon Organs

Muscle spindles are the receptors for the afferent discharge from muscles. Tendon organs, named Golgi tendon organs after their discoverer, are receptors for the afferent discharge from tendons. The detailed histology of the spindles was described in the eighteen nineties by Ruffini. At the same time Sherrington established the function of spindles as receptor end organs. A detailed knowledge of the function of muscle spindles and tendon organs had to wait until modern electrophysiological techniques were available for recording from single afferent neurons.

Figure 13–3 shows the structure and innervation of the muscle spindle and tendon organ; their detailed histology is given in Barker (1962) and Lissman (1950).

Muscle spindles are specialized muscle fibers interspersed among the ordinary muscle fibers in most if not all muscles of the body. Each spindle consists of a central or equatorial region containing receptor endings and two elongated ends or poles containing contractile elements known as *intrafusal fibers*. The receptor endings are protected by a lymph-filled capsule which surrounds the equatorial region.

FIG. 13–3.  Schematic diagram of the structure and innervation of skeletal muscle. (From Barker, D., *Zoology and Medical Science*, 1963. Courtesy of the University of Durham Press.)

The receptor endings are of two kinds: primary endings which usually have an *annulo-spiral* structure, and secondary endings which usually have a *flower spray* structure. The primary endings are innervated by large, fast-conducting, low-threshold afferents; the secondary endings by smaller, higher-threshold fibers.

The primary endings have a low-frequency, resting discharge, which ceases during muscular contraction. This so-called "pause" demonstrates that the muscle spindles are in parallel (in line abreast) with the muscle fibers; when the muscle contracts, tension is taken off the spindles by the muscle fibers and the end organs cease firing until the slack in the spindles is taken up by the active contraction of the muscle fibers within the spindles.

The discharge from primary spindle endings is approximately proportional to the amount of stretch applied to the passive muscle, but adaptation is rapid and therefore the maximum discharge reached will depend as much on the rate at which the muscle is stretched as on the absolute tension.

Spindle afferents feed into the spinal cord by way of the sensory dorsal roots. They initiate the local, monosynaptic stretch reflex (see p. 402) and feed into tracts which ascend to the cerebellum, but not to the cerebral cortex.

The tendon organs have a higher threshold to external stretch and do not show any resting discharge. Therefore, spindles produce a greater discharge than tendon organs at lower tensions, but as the tension increases, more and more tendon organs start to discharge. Tendon organs discharge during muscular contraction when the spindles show their pause, that is, they behave as if they are in series (in tandem) with the contracting muscle fibers, and anatomical evidence supports this conclusion. They respond to the total tension in the muscle, whether this be produced by active contraction or by passive stretch.

The tendon organ afferents go by way of the sensory dorsal roots into the spinal cord. They initiate the clasp-knife reflex as described on page 404 and like the large afferents from muscle spindles ascend in the dorsal cerebellar tracts to the cerebellum, but do not reach the cerebral cortex by any direct route, if at all. It is for this reason that muscle spindles and tendon organs are not regarded as sense organs.

## The Gamma Fiber System

Each muscle spindle contains several contractile muscle fibers (*intrafusal fibers*). The efferent nerve fibers which supply the intrafusal muscle fibers are known as *gamma* ($\gamma$) *fibers*. They are smaller than the main motor efferents or *alpha* ($\alpha$) *fibers*. A single "$\gamma$" fiber innervates several spindles, and a single spindle receives branches from several "$\gamma$" efferents.

In normal muscular contraction the spindle muscle fibers may contract before the main extrafusal muscles. This spindle contraction produces very little tension in the muscle, but it induces afferent discharges from the spindle receptor end organs which reflexly facilitate contraction of the main muscles; a process known as *proprioceptive recruitment*. When the extrafusal muscle fibers have "caught up" with the contracted spindles, the tension in the spindle is relieved and facilitation of muscular contraction ceases. The spindle receptors, in effect, signal the difference in length between muscle and spindle fibers (Eldred, Granit, and Merton, 1953). Hyde and Gellhorn (1949) were still able to elicit muscular contractions from the gastronemius muscle of a cat after sectioning the afferent fibers from the muscle spindles, although the response was weaker than with intact afferents. Variations in the strength of the electrical stimulus applied to the motor cortex still affected the strength of the muscular contraction, showing that gradations in muscle responses can be independent of proprioceptive recruitment. Conditioned motor responses have been found to survive limb deafferentation (Knapp, Taub, and Berman, 1959), although not without some change in the pattern of the response (Gorska and Jankowska, 1963).

## Cerebellar and Brainstem Control of Muscle Spindles and the Control of Servo-oscillation

Granit and his coworkers, in an extensive series of experiments, found that the "γ"-system could be both activated or inhibited by stimulating either the anterior cerebellum or the diencephalic reticular formation, and that only in the presence of the anterior lobe of the cerebellum does "γ"-firing facilitate muscle contraction. Reflex activity, however, survives removal of the cerebellum, and the conclusion is that in this case the direct "α"-system is used to initiate muscle contraction without facilitation by "γ"-outflow. In the intact animal, either system is available; the direct "α" system is probably used for ballistic and well-practiced movements, and the indirect "γ"-leading system for exploratory movements. The cerebellum apparently controls whether the "γ"-leading system or the direct system is used.

Any control system which, like the spindle control system, depends upon negative feedback is potentially unstable. This is because the error signal takes time to generate a corrective response, which therefore has its effect after the limb has moved beyond the target position. A second correction has to be applied in the opposite direction which also results in overshooting, and soon the limb oscillates about the target position. In order to compensate for this oscillation, the reflex control system must have an output determined by both position error (length misalignment) and the rate of change of muscle length. This latter information enables the system to anticipate the future position of the limb, and adjust the corrective signal accordingly. We have already mentioned that damping is a rate-dependent function, and therefore damping in any one of its forms should be able to provide the necessary rate-of-movement information. Purely mechanical damping is provided by the viscosity of the muscle tissues and joints. Damping is also provided by sensory adaptation in spindle receptors, which attenuates the muscle to spindle length misalignment signal. Damping is also provided by inhibitory control from the tendon organs. The cerebellum also probably helps to control this rate-dependent adjustment by timing "γ" outflow in relation to the "α" outflow. After cerebellar ablation, cats art ataxic (see p. 412), and although they recover to some extent, they are never again normal (Higgins and Glaser, 1964). Tremor due to cerebellar disease in man (see p. 412) may represent a disturbance of the same system.

To summarize, the prime function of the "γ" system (i.e., fibers and intrafusal fibers) is to prevent the muscle spindles from becoming flaccid during muscular contraction; the spindles are kept in trim and their threshold maintained at a usable level. The "$\gamma$" system also serves to initiate or at least facilitate voluntary contraction by the process of "$\gamma$"-leading, and contributes to the stability of muscular control. See Granit (1955) for further details.

## Antidromic Control

We have already discussed how muscular contraction is inhibited by the release of tension in the spindles, and by increased discharge from Golgi tendon organs. But muscular contraction is also reflexly inhibited by activity generated in nerve fibers known as recurrent collateral or anti-dromic fibers which branch from motor axons and run back via the ventral horns into the motoneuron pools of the spinal cord. This system was described by Renshaw (1941) and is known as the *Renshaw loop*. Not only are the active motoneurons inhibited by these antidromic discharges, but inactive motoneurons are also inhibited. The reflex involves one synapse, but its latency is shorter than that of the spindle-initiated stretch reflex, and the two reflexes are distinguishable on this basis. These mechanisms of "$\gamma$"-leading and antidromic inhibition have an important bearing on the problems of the normal and pathological reflex control of movement, and in particular the knee jerk and stretch reflex. For details see Granit (1955) and Hammond, Merton, and Sutton (1956).

## Receptors in the Joint Capsule and Skin

The articular surfaces of free-moving or diarthrodial joints are lined with cartilaginous material and a limiting synovial membrane. The synovial fluid is secreted into the joint and lubricates it. Ligaments bind the joint to form the joint capsule (for further details of joint physiology, see Gardner, 1950). The ligaments of mammalian joints are well provided with sensory endings. The receptors in the skin surrounding the joint may be considered to be joint receptors also.

The afferents from joint receptors (and skin receptors) are known to project via the dorsal root into the spinal cord and up to the thalamus and sensory cortex. They are therefore truly sensory. The discharge patterns of the various neurons, both in the nerve and at the cortex, show a range of types. Most neurons show an initial, high, transient discharge followed by a slowly adapting discharge when the joint is held at a particular angle. Some units are active at any joint position, others are maximally active at small joint angles, and others are maximally active at large joint angles. Some pairs of spatially related cortical cells are reciprocally related; one cell being active as the joint moves in one direction, and the other being active when the joint moves in the other direction. For references and details see Rose and Mountcastle (1959).

## KINESTHESIS

Kinesthesis is best understood as a behavioral term. It includes the discrimination of the positions of body parts, the discrimination of movement, and the amplitude of movement of body parts, both passively and actively produced. Visual and auditory information is assumed to be absent. Afferents from muscles and tendons do not reach the cortex and are therefore probably not directly involved in kinesthesis. Afferents from joints and skin, and the pattern of motor innervation are almost certainly involved in kinesthetic judgments. We define kinesthesis, therefore, as the discrimination of the positions and movements of body parts based on information other than visual, auditory, or verbal.

There are many types of kinesthetic judgment. The main ones are set out in Table 13–1; they will be discussed in that order.

### TABLE 13–1
#### A Classification of Types of Kinesthetic Judgment

| | |
|---|---|
| Passive Movement | Threshold of movement |
| | Judgment of position (indication of when previous position is regained) |
| | Threshold of direction of movement |
| | Accuracy of direction judgments |
| | Judgment of amplitude of movement |
| | Judgment of speed of movement |
| Active Movement | Steadiness and fineness of movement |
| | Judgment of position |
| | Accuracy of direction of movement |
| | Accuracy of amplitude of movement |
| | Accuracy of pressure production |
| | Accuracy of speed of movement |

## Kinesthesis in Passive Movement

The basic measure of kinesthetic sensitivity is the threshold of passive movement. Like all other thresholds it varies with the conditions; the speed of movement, the position of the limb, and the type of joint are important variables. A value as low as 0.2° has been found for the arm moving at 0.3° per second (Goldscheider, 1889; Cleghorn and Darcus, 1952). Movement through larger angles is necessary before the direction as well as the presence of movement is detected. Proximal joints are more sensitive than distal ones. No reliable figures exist to indicate the accuracy with which people can judge the position, direction, amplitude or speed of passively moved limbs.

## Kinesthesis in the Active Movements

Active movements can be produced which are finer than the passive threshold, but the steadiness and fineness of control of active movements depend upon the limb use, fatigue, and the health of the system. There are various ways of studying the active position sense of a limb: (1) The blindfolded subject may be asked to place a limb in a given position and then to regain the same position after the limb has been displaced. (2) The blindfolded subject may be asked to bring the two index fingers together, or to duplicate the position of one limb by its partner. Cohen (1958) used the first method and found that his subjects could reduplicate a position of their extended arm to a mean accuracy of 3.3 cm. This error is the sum of the inaccuracy in the registration of the initial position and of the inaccuracy of the reproductive movement. If it is assumed that the accuracy of a single movement is half this, it follows that over 1,000 positions of the extended arm are discriminable in this way. The second method, in which the index fingers are brought together, constitutes a well-known clinical test of kinesthetic-motor sensitivity.

There seem to be no data on the accuracy with which directions of movement may be discriminated.

The ability to estimate an amplitude or extent of movement may be studied by two methods: (1) The subject may be asked to move a limb through a given distance and then to duplicate the movement. (2) The subject may be asked to run his finger between two stops and then to estimate whether subsequently executed movements between stops are the same. Kramer and Moskiewicz (1901) used the first method and found a tendency for the arm to move a shorter distance in the reproduction than in the initial movement. This is a time-order error which contaminates the method insofar as measurements of kinesthetic sensitivity are concerned. Breternitz (1934) used the second method and found that accuracy varied with the joint used, and the distance moved.

For a discussion of the judgment of pressure, the student is referred to Provins (1957). A related topic is that of weight judgment.

Having discussed the various types of kinesthetic judgment, we shall now enquire into the sensory and motor mechanisms involved.

## Sensory and Motor Conditions for Kinesthesis

On the sensory side, kinesthesis in any or all of its forms may depend upon the muscle-spindle and tendon receptors and/or the joint receptors. Tactile receptors may also be involved. On the motor side, active-movement kinesthesis may depend upon the motor-outflow information reaching whatever centers are involved in kinesthetic judgments. In order to study each of these factors, the others must be removed. The techniques for leaving each component are shown in Table 13–2 together with a statement of the types of judgment possible in each case.

The muscle spindles and tendon organs are considered together, as there is no known technique for separating them. The eye and the tongue contain no joint receptors, and when the conjunctiva or skin is anesthetized, these organs provide a means of studying muscle-tendon receptors. Irvine and Ludvigh (1936) showed that a surface anesthetized eye has no kinesthetic sense of any kind when passively moved, although they found

TABLE 13–2

**Procedures for Isolating Sensory and Motor Components of Kinesthesis and the Known Judgments Possible in Each Case**

| Receptors Left Active | Procedures | Known Types of Judgment Possible |
|---|---|---|
| Spindle-tendon receptors | Passive movement of tongue, eye, or joint with anesthetized capsule. | No passive kinesthesis. |
| | Direct stimulation of motor neurons. | No information available. |
| Joint receptors | Passive movement with severed tendons. | No information available. |
| Motor outflow | Active movements with anesthesia of all afferents. | No passive kinesthesis. Active appreciation of amplitude of movement as long as the limb is not loaded. |

that the position and extent of movement of the surface anesthetized eyes may be judged when they are moved actively. It would seem therefore that spindle-tendon receptors are not sufficient to indicate the position or movement of the passively moved eye. However, the pattern of discharge from spindle-tendon receptors is not the same for passive movement as it is for active movement, and it is possible that these organs play a role in the appreciation of active eye movements. Whatever the role of spindle-tendon organs in eye muscles, they may be involved, along with other receptors, in the appreciation of passive and active movement in jointed limbs. There are no reliable data for the tongue.

The second procedure for isolating the effects of spindle-tendon receptors is to anesthetize the joint capsule of a limb joint. Anesthesia may be induced by electric currents, drugs, or cutting off the blood supply to the joint capsule, leaving the muscles intact. This procedure has a long history, and the results are controversial, but it may fairly be concluded that the appreciation of passive movement in all its forms is either absent or severely impaired by joint anesthesia; which suggests that the joints contain the receptors necessary for passive kinesthesis (see Provins, 1958, for details).

Active movements of specified extent are still accurately executed when the joint capsule is anesthetized, although the position of the limb when at rest cannot be judged. Either the motor outflow or the active spindle-tendon discharge, or both, are responsible for this active kinesthesis.

An experiment which Lashley carried out in 1917 suggests that the motor outflow is involved in normal active kinesthesis. He observed a patient with loss of afference from the leg joints and muscles due to a bullet wound in the spinal cord, and found that although the patient had no passive kinesthesis, he could move his legs through specified distances as accurately as a normal subject. This latter ability in the patient, but not in the normal subject, was lost when the leg had to pull against a spring. This suggests that either the spindle-tendon organs or the joint receptors compensate for load changes when judgments of the extent of active movements are made with varying resistances to the movement. Theoretically, either or both types of receptor could serve this function, but the experiments to decide which have not been done. One possible experiment would be to test whether the ability to move through a given distance with varying load is possible in a limb in which the joint has been anesthetized. If this ability were intact under these circumstances, it would demonstrate that the spindle-tendon organs serve to compensate for load changes; it would not of course prove that the joint receptors cannot do the same thing. Nobody has been able to study the role of spindle-tendon organs when both the joint receptors and motor outflow are absent. One way of doing this would be to anesthetize a joint, stimulate the motor nerve directly, and ask the blindfolded subject to estimate the extent of the resulting movement and position of the limb.

Very rapid movements such as those involved in piano playing may be complete before there has been time for muscle spindle or capsule receptor activity to have any effect. It has been shown that the reaction time for kinesthetic feedback is 160 msec. (Vince, 1948). Ballistic movements must therefore be wholly under the control of the motor outflow. Such a dead-reckoning system works well for well-practiced movements when the resistance encountered is normal. Part of the business of learning a motor skill is the building up of central motor programs which may when required produce accurate, rapid sequences of movements without the need for feedback from peripheral receptors.

In conclusion, it may be said that joint receptors are necessary and spindle-tendon organs are not sufficient for passive kinesthesis. Whether spindle-tendon receptors are involved in active kinesthesis is not known. Active movements of given extent are possible in the absence of all afferents, as long as the limb is not loaded. But whether load compensation is a function of the joint receptors or the spindle-tendon receptors is not known.

## THE SPINAL CORD AND REFLEX ACTIVITY

## The Structure of the Cord

The spinal cord of man is an extension of the central nervous system extending from the brain to about half way down the back. It is about as thick as a fountain pen and has the consistency of jelly. Such a delicate structure needs protection. This is afforded by two enveloping membranes, the dura mater and the pia mater, and the spongy, shock-absorbing arachnoid which is contained between them. The protecting structures are known as the *meninges* and cover the whole central nervous system. The spinal cord and meninges lie inside the bony vertebrae of the spine. A central canal continuous with the cerebral ventricles runs the length of the cord carrying spinocerebral fluid which also surrounds the cord. Deep folds, or sulci, penetrate the cord, one from the dorsal surface and one from the ventral surface.

Between each pair of vertebrae, on each side, a pair of spinal nerves emerges to innervate the muscles and sense organs of the body segment. The dorsal (posterior) root of each pair is the sensory nerve, and the ventral (anterior) root of each pair is the motor nerve. This separation of sensory (afferent) and motor (efferent) nerves was first described by Charles Bell and François Magendie in the first half of the eighteenth century. It became known as the *Bell-Magendie law*, and was one of the first scientifically based observations on the functions of the nervous system. It is now known that there are some afferent fibers in the ventral root, but the Bell-Magendie law is still regarded as an important generalization.

The central grey core of the cord contains synapses and neuron cell bodies; the outer white regions contain parallel, longitudinal bundles of myelinated axons interspersed with a feltwork of neuroglia cells which probably serve to maintain the metabolic functions of the nerve cells proper. The grey matter extends in the directions of the four roots to form the four horns. Incoming and outgoing fibers run in the horns from or towards their appropriate root. The six bundles of white matter are known as funiculi: two dorsal (posterior), two ventral (anterior), and two lateral. Each funiculus contains smaller regions known as *fasciculi* and *tracts* which carry axons up and down the cord. Axons running across the cord traverse the *commissure* of the grey matter. The axons in the white matter nearest the grey matter (fasciculi proprii) run a short distance before reentering the grey matter; the axons further out run longer distances to or from the brain stem.

## General Properties of Reflex Activity

On entering the dorsal root, the neurons from the various somesthetic sensory end organs split into many branches, some of which ascend without synapse in the spinal cord (see Chapter 9). Others ascend or descend for some little distance before each of them synapses either in the dorsal or the ventral horn. The postsynaptic fibers have one of several destinations: (1) Some run out to ipsilateral (same side) or contralateral (opposite side) motor roots without synapsing further, and mediate so-called *monosynaptic reflexes*. (2) Others synapse again with ipsilateral or contralateral motor neurons in the same segment of the cord. The latter are known as *internuncial neurons*, mediating *segmental reflexes*. Some internuncial neurons send off collateral branches which synapse with other internuncial neurons to form closed chains or loops round which discharges may reverberate. (3) Others run in the fasciculi proprii and reenter the ventral horns of other segments to synapse with ipsilateral or

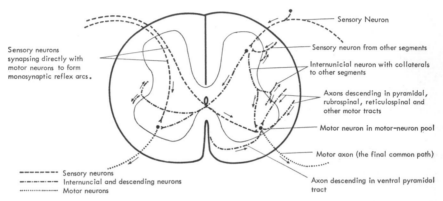

FIG. 13–4. Transverse section of spinal cord showing fibre tracts involved in spinal reflexes.

contralateral motor neurons. These internuncial neurons mediate *intersegmental reflexes*. (4) Others enter one or other of the *spinal somesthetic pathways* in the funiculi, and ascend to the brain stem, thalamus, cerebellum, or cerebral cortex. Stimulation of any one afferent somesthetic neuron may initiate activity in all these separate routes.

On the motor side, each motor axon which leaves by the ventral root originates in the ventral horn from a large cell body upon which may converge as many as 1,400 dentrites from many different sensory neurons, from internuncial neurons, and from neurons which have descended in the motor tracts from higher centers (see Figure 13–4). A group of motor neurons belonging to a particular muscle is known as a *motoneuron pool*.

Granit and Eccles have distinguished between *tonic* and *phasic motor units*; the tonic units show long afterdischarge to a single shock stimulus, and the phasic units a short afterdischarge. This distinction is not always clear however.

It should be obvious from the above description of the ramifications of afferent discharges in the dorsal horn and of the convergence in the ventral horn, that reflex arcs, as individual and separate circuits, do not exist. They are convenient abstractions for the purpose of analysis. Each afferent neuron is in structural synaptic contact, directly or indirectly, with all the neurons of the central nervous system (spinal cord and brain). Inhibitory barriers prevent an impulse in a neuron firing off the entire system. These barriers may be broken down locally with drugs such as strychnine, and when this is done, any disturbance fires off a large part of the system. Reflexes are functional routes in this inhibitory matrix of synapses. Discharges along these routes are not separate from each other, but interact, sometimes facilitating each other and summating their effects, and at other times inhibiting each other.

Once a motor axon has been fired, nothing can normally prevent the muscle from contracting, and there is no normal way in which the muscle can be made to contract except by discharges arriving along those motoneurons which supply it. Any given muscle may take part at different times in many reflexes, yet all these reflexes must finally funnel their impulses through the same motor axons. This common part of the system is therefore called the *final common path*.

If two reflexes which share a final common path are stimulated at the same time, they may be allied and summate, or they may be antagonistic when one will be inhibited by the other. The stretch reflex and the extensor thrust reflex (see later) are allied and summate to support the animal against gravity. If two antagonistic reflexes occur at the same time, they must compete for the final common path. Generally one of them gains a *total victory* over the other. Which one does so, depends upon the relative strength and the relative importance of each of the two reflexes. For instance, nociceptive reflexes, that is those which involve withdrawal from painful stimuli, would normally have precedence over the scratch reflex. If antagonistic reflexes take command over the final common path in rhythmic succession, the resulting pattern is known as *successive induction*. Walking is an example of such a mechanism.

Other reflexes may be antagonistic—not because they share a final common path but because they are functionally incompatible. For instance, the hindlimb scratch reflex is incompatible with the forelimb withdrawal reflex, because the animal would lose its balance if both responses occurred together.

Reflexes do not occur in vacuo, but against an ever-present pattern of postural reflexes and voluntary movements. Nor do reflex responses necessarily remain constant over time; they show fatigue and are influenced by higher centers and hence by learning.

If several stimuli occur in succession, the activity which they engender may summate to give a larger response than any of the stimuli would have evoked separately. Stimuli which individually are at a subthreshold (subliminal) level may converge at one time or in quick succession upon a single motor neuron to produce a discharge. This *summation* is thought to occur at the spinal synapse of the motoneuron; any activity there sets up a *central excitatory state*, which if sufficiently intense, discharges the motor axon. If the central excitatory state is subliminal it diminishes to zero in a period of about 10 to 20 msec.

Each reflex has a characteristic *latency*, which is the time delay between the application of the stimulus and the arrival of action potentials at the muscle. The latency of the receptor end organ, the afferent and efferent conduction times, and the central synaptic delays and conduction time all contribute to the overall latency of the reflex. The weaker the applied stimulus, the longer is the latent period.

Reflex muscular contractions are often rhythmical, for instance the scratch reflex. They often outlive the stimulus, when they are said to show an *afterdischarge* or rebound which may be due to continuing activity in internuncial closed chains.

Antagonistic muscles work as a pair, when one contracts, the other is reflexly inhibited so as to allow the limb to move. This is known as *reciprocal innervation*. In some reflex patterns, such as the startle pattern which occurs in response to a loud noise, agonists and antagonists contract together, but the functional significance of this response is obscure.

## Segmental Reflexes

The segmental reflexes are known as *myotatic, autogenetic, or myogenic reflexes*. They are a response of a muscle to stimuli arising in that same muscle or its antagonist. The *stretch reflex* is a myotatic reflex invoked by pulling on the tendon of a muscle or, in the intact animal, by pushing against a limb. It serves to compensate for changes in external load which limbs may encounter, particularly those limbs which support the animal against gravity. The afferent signals which trigger the reflex arise in the muscle-spindle receptors and travel to the dorsal horn of the cord in large myelinated fibers. These fibers synapse directly with motor neurons, both ipsilaterally and contralaterally. Internuncial neurons are not involved; the reflex is *monosynaptic*. The response is limited to the stimulated muscle and to its antagonist; the neural response to the ipsilateral muscle facilitates contraction, that to the contralateral muscle inhibits contraction.

The "tendon jerk," an example of which is the knee jerk produced by a tap on the patellar tendon, is related to the stretch reflex.

If an increasing pressure is applied to the limb of an animal, a pressure will be reached when the resistance to movement of the limb suddenly collapses. This is the *lengthening or "clasp-knife" reflex*. It too is a monosynaptic, myotatic reflex. The sudden onset of the reflex occurs when the tension in the tendon reaches the threshold of the tendon receptors. As soon as this happens, the discharge from these receptors inhibits the opposing stretch reflex arising from the lower-threshold spindle receptors, and the extensor muscles relax. Tension on the tendon is thus relieved, and the stretch reflex again takes command until the external pressure on the limb builds up once again to produce a second clasp-knife reflex. A succession of shortening reactions thus occurs as pressure is applied to a limb. The shortening reaction is presumably a safety device protecting the limb from the effects of too much tension.

*Cutaneous reflexes* are segmental reflexes triggered off by stimuli applied to the skin. One example is the *extensor thrust* of the leg elicited by pressure on the feet. It serves to maintain the animal in a standing posture. It is a two-synapse reflex involving internuncial cells in the spinal cord. Most stimuli applied to the skin induce ipsilateral reflex flexion and contralateral extension. The extensor thrust is an exception to this rule.

*The Babinski reflex* is another example of a cutaneous reflex. This occurs in young children and often in sleeping or diseased adults and is a useful clinical sign. It consists of the turning up of the great toe in response to a scratch on the sole of the foot, and probably serves a withdrawal function. A further interesting segmental cutaneous reflex is the *grasp reflex*, which is an automatic grasping induced by an object touching the palm of the hand. Infants and brain-damaged patients may show this reflex; the patient may be unable to let go of whatever he is holding. It enables the young mammal to cling to its mother.

## Intersegmental and Suprasegmental Reflexes

Intersegmental reflexes are those in which the stimulus is applied to receptors in one segment of the body and the response occurs in another. Internuncial neurons running in the fasciculi proprii form the link between the segments. The *scratch reflex* in the dog is a well-known intersegmental reflex. The receptors lie in the skin on the back and sides of the animal; the response is a rhythmic scratching movement by the hindlimb.

Suprasegmental reflexes depend on centers in the brain stem or higher centers. Breathing involves a complex of suprasegmental reflexes coordinated in the medulla. Eye reflexes, swallowing, and other reflexes in the head are suprasegmental. Postural reflexes are suprasegmental and in view of their behavioral importance, they will be discussed in a separate section.

For further reading on reflex activity see Sherrington's *Integrative Action of the Nervous System* (1947) and Denny-Brown *et al.* (1938).

### THE PYRAMIDAL SYSTEM

The pyramidal tracts are thought to be the main pathways involved in the voluntary control of movement. In man, about 40 percent of the fibers in these tracts originate in the so-called *percentral motor areas* in the cerebral cortex (see p. 492). The rest originate largely in the prefrontal and parietal lobes of the cerebral cortex. The large pyramid-shaped *Betz cells* of the precentral motor areas together contribute about 30,000 large axons to the pyramidal tracts, but account for only about 3 percent of the total number of fibers in the tracts. About 40 percent of all the fibers in the tracts are unmyelinated, and most of those that are myelinated are very small.

The tracts descend on each side in the white matter of the cortex, making up part of the internal capsule (see Figure 13–5). The two halves descend and form the peduncle in the ventral midline region of the upper brainstem. Most of the fibers decussate or cross to the opposite side at this level to form the lateral pyramids or lateral corticospinal tracts; the undecussated fibers continue as the ventral pyramids or ventral cortico-

FIG. 13–5. A diagrammatic represenation of the pyramidal pathways. (Adapted from Elliot, H. C., *Textbook of Neuroanatomy*, 1963; courtesy of Pitman Medical Publishing Co., London.)

spinal tracts. The bundles of decussating fibers form a pyramid-shaped structure, from which the pyramidal system derives its name. The fibers which supply the motor nuclei of the head muscles depart from the main tract at the level of the pons. Collateral branches in the brainstem feed into the extrapyramidal system (see next section).

The axons of the spinal pyramidal tracts are the longest in the body. In primates, some of these axons terminate directly in motoneurons in the ventral horns, but most of them terminate in internuncial neurons. Their influence on motoneurons is studied by recording the effect which pyramidal stimulation has upon monosynaptic reflex pathways. This influence is invariably facilitatory. A small percentage of the fibers in the pyramidal tracts are afferent fibers ascending to the cortex, but their function is not known.

Electrical stimulation of the motor cortex excites extrapyramidal as well as pyramidal pathways, and for this reason, cortical stimulation elicits muscular contractions even after pyramidectomy. The contribution of the pyramids may be studied by electrical stimulation at lower levels, where the pyramids are uncontaminated by extrapyramidal fibers. The movements elicited show great variability, apparently because of the internuncial neurons which are interposed between the pyramidal axons and the motoneurons, and perhaps because of varying spread of the electric stimulus to neighboring structures.

In primates, unilateral pyramidectomy leads to contralateral paresis or plegia involving the musculature from the neck down. The paretic muscles are hypotonic, weak, and incapable of executing fine skilled movements. Skin reflexes are weak or absent. No clear cases of pyramidectomy are known in man; any damage involves extrapyramidal tracts as well, and the symptoms are those of spasticity (see next section).

## THE EXTRAPYRAMIDAL SYSTEM

Central motor control mechanisms other than the pyramidal system and the cerebellum are known as the extrapyramidal system. Lower vertebrates have no pyramidal system and their only motor centers are those structures which are homologous with the extrapyramidal subcortical nuclei. The extrapyramidal nuclei receive connections from the precentral motor cortex (Brodmann's area 4) as well as from other cortical areas, and the distinction between the two systems at the cortical level is obscure.

The main subcortical nuclei comprising the extrapyramidal system are the following:

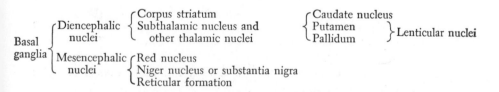

The nuclei comprising the corpus striatum surround the halves of the internal capsule—the massive V-shaped bundles which contain the fibers going to and from the cortex. The putamen and pallidum (globus pallidus) are tucked into the V of the capsule and are therefore lens-shaped —hence their name, "lenticular nuclei." The subthalamic nucleus is situated under the thalamus in the diencephalon or subcortical forebrain. The red and niger nuclei are bilateral structures near the midline in the midbrain or mesencephalon. The reticular formation extends in the midline down the medulla.

Each of these nuclei have connections, directly or indirectly, with each other and with the cerebellum, thalamus, and cortex. The spinal outflow from the system takes its origin from the red nucleus and the reticular formation as the rubrospinal and reticulospinal tracts respectively.

## Clinical Extrapyramidal Syndromes

Damage to the extrapyramidal system in man leads to one of two syndromes; hyperkinetic-dystonia or *spasticity* on the one hand, and hypokinetic Parkinson's disease on the other.

Spasticity is characterized by hyperactive stretch reflexes, that is, by reflexes released from central inhibitory influences which normally arise in the extrapyramidal system (Magoun and Rhines, 1947). The commonest cause of the disease is injury to the central nervous system at birth. The manifestations vary depending on which part of the system is damaged.

Damage to the putamen and caudate nucleus leads to the *choreic syndrome*; involving irregular, rapid, involuntary jerky movements and impairment of voluntary movement. The same syndrome may also arise from damage to the cerebral cortex and subthalamus. Damage to the straitum, but particularly the pallidum, leads to the *athetoid syndrome*, involving involuntary, spasmodic, worm-like movements, especially of the peripheral limb segments. These movements are slower than the choreic movements; the joints become fixed in abnormal postures, and voluntary movements are again impaired. Damage to the subthalamic nucleus of one side leads to contralateral *hemiballismus*, involving violent tossing movements of the limbs, so violent sometimes that the patient falls down; the limbs can hardly be moved voluntarily. Damage to the reticular formation leads to *myoclonus*, involving arrhythmic contractions of single muscles or muscle groups. The consequences of damage to the red nucleus are very variable and may be any or all of the syndromes so far mentioned.

The *hypokinetic Parkinsonian syndrome* arises from damage to the substantia nigra; it does not involve spontaneous, large involuntary movements, but rather stiffness of the limbs and fine tremor when the limbs are at rest, the so-called *tremor at rest*. For more details of these clinical conditions see Benda (1952).

## The Functional Significance of the Extrapyramidal System

Only recently have experimental physiological procedures confirmed information derived from clincial observation. Some of the experiments on the effects of stimulating extrapyramidal structures in the diencephalon are discussed in the section on righting reflexes.

The extrapyramidal system functions along with the cerebellum in controlling movements. The red nucleus receives fibers from the cerebellum and relays them to the motor cortex which in turn connects to the cerebellum via the pons, thus completing a feedback loop. Fibers also descend to the motoneurons of the cord from the red nucleus, influencing movements of the limbs, which in turn induce activity in muscle afferents and perhaps vestibular afferents which feed back to the cerebellum and cortex, completing another control circuit. These two examples, among many, serve to demonstrate the functional integrity of the whole motor and motor-afferent system, including the vestibular system. The γ-efferent system too must not be forgotten for the role it plays in initiating and controlling movements.

Voluntary movement involves the setting up of a central spatial-temporal template of the required action, presumably in the cortex initially. Corresponding instructions are fed into cerebellar, extrapyramidal, and spinal centers where they are translated into effective discharge patterns to the motoneurons after being integrated by these centers into the on-going reflex and postural-background activity in the body's musculature. Feedback from proprioceptors, exteroceptors, and the vestibular apparatus informs the cerebellum and motor cortex whether the movements have been executed as planned. If this *re-afferent* copy does not correspond to the central pattern corrective impulses are discharged after due allowance has been made for the time delays in the system. Many subroutines are stored in the system at various levels: as reflex patterns in the spinal cord and brain stem, as postural stereotypes in the vestibular, cerebellar, and extrapyramidal systems, and as complex movement "templates" in the neocerebellum. The cortex is thus relieved of the necessity of controlling the innate routines and well-learned skills, and is free to devote itself to the mastery of new patterns of movement, which in practice means the adaptation of subroutines into new movement sequences. For a fuller discussion of the extrapyramidal system see Jung and Hassler (1960).

## THE CEREBELLUM

### Structure and Connections

The cerebellum is a large convoluted part of the central nervous system consisting of many nuclei and fiber masses. It sits above the fourth ventricle and is connected to the rest of the nervous system by six large peduncles or stalks, three on each side. The cerebellum has two principal subdivisions.

1. The flocculo-nodular lobe is the most primitive part. It is situated at the base of the cerebellum immediately above the fourth ventricle. Its position makes it difficult to approach, and for this reason, experimental studies have been hampered. The component structures have remained relatively undeveloped in higher mammals. It is the only part which has direct two-way connections with the vestibular nerve and nuclei.

2. The corpus cerebelli, or cerebellar cortex, is particularly well-developed in higher mammals, and its development has paralleled that of the cerebral cortex. It is divided into an anterior or paleocerebellar lobe and a posterior

or neocerebellar lobe (Larsell, 1960). The cortex is highly convoluted into folia, and consists mainly of white matter covered with three layers of grey matter: a superficial molecular layer, a Purkinje cell layer, and a deep granular layer. Incoming impulses arrive in the so-called mossy fibers which synapse profusely with the complex dendritic endings of the granular cells of the granular layer. Outgoing fibers originate entirely in the massive Purkinje cells. The granular cells send ascending and intricately bifurcating axons into the outer molecular layer where they envelop denditic expansions from the Purkinje cells. The Purkinje cell dendrites are also enveloped by dendrites from "star cells" and "basket cells" in the molecular layer (see Figure 13-6).

The incoming mossy fibers deliver impulses from many sources: from the spinal cord via dorsal and ventral spinocerebellar tracts, from the cerebral cortex via pontine nuclei, from the reticular formation and basal ganglia, and from the vestibular system.

**FIG. 13-6.** Schematic representation of neuronal arrangement in a transverse and longitudinal section of a cerebellar folium.

The Purkinje cell axons run into the cerebellar white matter and terminate largely in grey nuclear masses in the white matter (fastigii, globosus, emboliformis, and dentate nucleus). From these nuclei arise the main outflow from the cerebellum (Jansen and Brodal, 1954).

Changes in electrical potential at the cerebellar surface may be evoked by stimulation of the vestibular apparatus, muscle spindles, and tendon, joint, cutaneous, visual, and auditory receptors as well as by artificial stimulation of the sensory and motor areas of the cerebral cortex (Adrian, 1943, Brookhart, 1960). Each sensory end organ evokes potentials in a particular part of the cerebral cortex according to its location in the body. In other words, the cerebellum is *topographically organized*. This topographical organization has an approximate point-to-point correspondence with the topographial organization of the sensory-motor cerebral cortex. Cerebellar cortical tracts run via the red nucleus and thalamus, and a corticocerebellar tract runs via nuclei in the pons.

Even in the absence of external stimulation, the cerebellar cortex maintains a rhythmic, asynchronous discharge with a frequency of 150 to 250 oscillations per second. This rhythmic activity originates in the Purkinje cells, and is particularly vulnerable to anesthesia and the effects of drugs (Dow, 1938). One may conclude that incoming influences exert their effects by altering the rate of discharge of the Purkinje cells; increasing it or decreasing the basic frequency, rather than initiating activity in otherwise quiescent cells. The basic rhythmic activity is continually being modified by impulses from very diverse sources. This continual flow of information into the cerebellum from all sensory and motor systems which are concerned with reflex and voluntary sensory-motor coordination clearly means that the cerebellum has a central role in sensory-motor coordination. The cerebellum has no direct access to the spinal cord, and cannot therefore influence motor neurons directly. Its influence is funneled through brain stem nuclei, including the red nuclei, the vestibular nuclei, the reticular formation, and basal ganglia, and through the motor areas of the cerebral cortex.

## The Functions of the Cerebellum

Stimulation of the anterior or the posterior lobe with high-frequency (over 40 cps.) impulses leads to a depression of muscular tonus (hypotonus) through the body. If decerebrate rigidity is present (see p. 423), stimulation of the anterior lobe promptly inhibits it. Part at least of this hypotonus must be a consequence of the inhibition of the gamma system which follows from cerebellar stimulation (see p. 395). Stimulation of the anterior lobe with lower frequency impulses leads to facilitation of muscular tonus or hypertonus (Terzuolo and Terzian, 1953). This hypertonus is coupled with, and will to some extent be caused by, augmented gamma-fiber activity, although Granit (1955) considered that both gamma and alpha motor neurons are directly influenced by cerebellar activity.

Stimulation of the posterior lobe produces conjugate deviation of the eyes. But the main effects of stimulating the posterior lobe are the inhibition and facilitation of voluntary motor activity. This control is mediated by impulses from the cerebellum acting on the cerebral motor cortex and extrapyramidal system (basal ganglia, and reticular formation).

One may conclude from present-day physiological evidence that the anterior lobe of the cerebellum is concerned with the control of the distribution of tonus in reflex activity, both spatially in the various muscles, and temporally in the sequence of movements. This control is over both postural reflexes and other reflexes, and is funneled via the rubrospinal and reticulospinal tracts.

The posterior lobe or neocerebellum also controls reflex activity, but is mainly concerned with the spatial and temporal organization of voluntary motor activity or skills. Its influences are funneled through the motor cortex and pyramidal system as well as through brain stem nuclei of the extrapyramidal system. Voluntary activity can only take place against a background of reflex and particularly postural reflex activity. It is the integration of voluntary activity into the pattern of reflex and postural adjustments which is the function of the neocerebellum. The physiological evidence upon which the above conclusions are based was obtained for the most part from decerebrate animals (see Brookhart, 1960, for further details). Caution must be exercised in applying the results to man. However, the conclusions from anatomical and electrophysiological evidence are confirmed by evidence from extirpation experiments in animals, and by clinical evidence in man.

Holmes (1922) classified the disorders of motility due to cerebellar disease in man. The following are the principal effects:

1. *Muscular Hypotonia.* In cerebellar hypotonia, the muscles are flaccid and show a diminished resistance to passive movement. If a hypotonic limb is shaken passively, the terminal segments of the limb flop about loosely on their joints. If the lesion is confined to one cerebellar hemisphere, the hypotonia is confined to the same side of the body. Cerebellar hypotonia probably depends upon (*a*) depression of vestibular centers which normally facilitate tonus, (*b*) decreased gamma fiber activity, and (*c*) direct depression of alpha motor activity.

2. *Disturbances of Posture.* With a unilateral lesion, the affected side often sags; the weight of the body is put on the unaffected leg, and the head is turned to that side. The patient may be unable to stand, and tends to fall towards the affected side. If he is able to walk he veers to the affected side.

3. *Cerebellar Ataxia.* Voluntary movements are disturbed or ataxic. They are weak, easily fatigued, and show a long reaction time. They are *dysmetric*, that is, their range is poorly controlled, and the harmonious synthesis of movements at different joints and of different limbs is lost. This last disorder is also called *asynergia*. Reaching movements oscillate about their target. This *"intention tremor"* is especially evident in skills involving finely controlled movements of the fingers. If a patient is asked to hold his forearm against an applied pressure, his arm jerks in an uncontrolled ballistic movement when the applied pressure is released. Normally such uncontrolled *rebound* would be controlled by the reflex contraction of antagonistic muscles. In the early phases after cerebellar damage, the eyes may show a skew deviation. Spontaneous nystagmus is common, especially when the eyes are deviated towards the side of a unilateral lesion.

In lower mammals, cerebellar ablation commonly leads to overactivity of extensor muscles; if the animal attempts to stand, the forceful extension of the forelimbs often throws the animal onto its back. There is some recovery from these symptoms after a time. Primates show little of this overactivity, which is due primarily to a release of vestibular impulses from cerebellar inhibitory control (Bach and Magoun, 1947; De Vito, Brusa, and Arduini, 1956), but probably also to enhanced gamma fiber outflow and direct facilitation of alpha motor outflow.

## THE VESTIBULAR APPARATUS

In mammals, the vestibular apparatus is a set of sense organs in the bony labyrinths of the inner ear. These sense organs, like the auditory cochlea, with which they are associated, contain a sensory epithelium covered with sensitive hair cells which cause neural discharges when displaced. The cochlea is "tuned in" to high-frequency vibrations, whereas the organs of the vestibular apparatus are "tuned in" to very low-frequency mechanical disturbances produced by accelerations of the head. This selectivity of response is largely due to the mechanical resonant properties of the structural components of the sense organs rather than to the end organs (sensory receptor cells) themselves.

There are three main components of the vestibular system: the three

FIG. 13–7. Diagram of the inner ear, showing the semicircular canals, utricle, saccule, and cochlea, together with the nerves innervating them. (After Hardy, M., 1934, *Anat. Rec.* 59. 412.)

canals, the utricle, and the sacculus. The function of the sacculus is unknown and will not be discussed further.

The anatomical arrangement of the vestibular organs and cochlea are shown in Figure 13–7. All these organs are suspended in perilymph fluid. The internal cavities of the organs are linked together, and filled with endolymph fluid.

The utricles are often called static receptors because one of their functions is to indicate the position of the head in relation to gravity, and the canals are often called dynamic receptors because they indicate rotary acceleration. This is a false distinction. The canals, as a triplet, are sensitive

FIG. 13–8. Schematic drawing of one half of a crista ampullaris, showing innervation of its epithelium. Thick nerve fibers forming nerve calyces round type I hair cells at the summit of the crista; medium caliber fibers innervating type I hair cells on the slope of the crista; medium caliber and fine nerve fibers forming a nerve plexus innervating hair cells of type II. The sensory hairs pass from the hair cells into fine canals in the cupula, which is separated from the epithelium by a narrow subcupular space. (From Wersäll, 1956, *Acta oto-laryngol*, suppl. 126.)

to both the direction of rotary acceleration and its amount; and similarly, the utricles are sensitive to both the direction of linear acceleration and its amount. The distinction between them is that the canals respond to rotary acceleration and the utricles respond to linear acceleration. Gravity is one form of linear acceleration; in relativity theory we may be regarded as accelerating away from the center of the earth at 22 feet per second per second. Our dynamically neutral state is the state of free fall achieved only by cosmonauts for any length of time. In this state we are weightless and our utricles are not stimulated.

## The Vestibular Canals

In man, the canals lie in planes approximately at right angles to each other. Each canal has a contralateral parallel partner with which it forms a

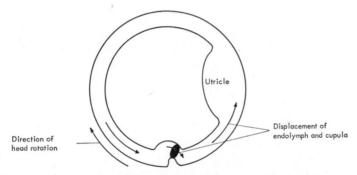

FIG. 13–9. Schematic diagram of a vestibular canal showing the complete fluid circuit. The arrows depict the consequences of a clockwise rotation of the head in the plane of the canal.

synergic pair. In spite of the fact that the three canals share a common cavity in the utricle, each one functions independently of the others, as if each one were a complete and independent fluid circuit. Their usual name "semicircular canals" is therefore misleading.

At one point in each canal, near its junction with the utricle, is a swelling or *ampulla* which contains the sensory epithelium or *crista ampullaris*. The structure of a crista is shown in Figure 13–8. It is a ridge of epithelium protruding into the cavity or lumen of the ampulla, and carrying many multiciliated sensory cells interspersed with structural cells. The cilia of all the cells project into a common gelatinous mass or *cupula* reaching to the far side of the ampulla which is arched at this point so that the cupula may swing from side to side like a swinging door (see Figure 13–9). In each sensory cell, the cilia membranes are continuous with the cell membrane. A resting potential of about 160 millivolts exists across the membrane; the cell interior is negative with respect to the outside. The whole structure is thus a charged "condenser."

Each sensory cell synapses with a sensory neuron. The neurons gather together to form the vestibular branch of the eighth or acoustic cranial nerve.

Mach and other early theorists did not realize that the cupula seals the lumen of the ampulla, and consequently thought that the endolymph flowed over the cristae. In 1931, Steinhausen observed the true functioning of the cupula in a living fish by injecting india ink into the endolymph. Modern electrophysiological methods enable microelectrodes to explore both the resting membrane potential and the discharge patterns conse- quent upon stimulation. The results of these investigations have given rise to the following account of the functioning of the canals.

Consider the right horizontal canal. When the head is rotated to the right in the plane of the canal, the inertia of the endolymph causes it to lag behind and flow to the left relative to the walls of the canal. The cupula is consequently deflected towards the utricle. The cilia are deflected which results in a decrease in the resting membrane potential (depolarization). The mechanism of this depolarization is not understood, but it causes an increase in the frequency of firing in the sensory neurons. In the same way a rotation of the head to the left is accompanied by an outward deflection of the cupula, an increase in the resting potential (hyperpolarization), and a decrease in the frequency of the afferent discharge. The end organ is thus bidirectional, although the sensory membrane as a whole is more sensitive to depolarization than to hyperpolarization at least in lower animals. This asymmetry of function is known as *Ewald's law of vestibular directional preponderance* (see Lowenstein, 1956 and Gernandt, 1959, for further physiological details).

Steinhausen described the behavior of the cupula by the well-known differential equation for the torsion pendulum:

$$I\ddot{\xi} + \Pi\dot{\xi} + \Delta\xi = 0$$

where   $I$ = moment of inertia of the cupula.
   $\Pi$ = moment of friction at unit angular velocity.
   $\Delta$ = directional momentum at unit angle.
   $\xi$ = angular deviation of the endolymph.
   $\dot{\xi}$ = angular velocity of the endolymph.
   $\ddot{\xi}$ = angular acceleration of the endolymph.

Experimental findings have confirmed that within limits this equation adequately describes the behavior of the end organ. However, as we shall see, the formula only partially accounts for the behavioral consequences of rotations of the body.

During a period of rotation at *constant angular velocity*, the endolymph catches up with the canal walls, the cupula returns to its resting position, and the discharge ceases. If the body is now brought to rest, the deceleration displaces the cupula in the opposite direction. It takes about 30 seconds before it regains its central position, and during this recovery period the subject will behave as if he is still decelerating. He will fall to one side, his eyes will move nystagmically, and he will experience turning sensations and nausea.

If an acceleration is followed immediately by a deceleration, the two opposed deflections of the cupula cancel out leaving no residual deflection and no aftereffects. If a *steady rate of acceleration* is continued for several minutes, the subject will report that the rotation is stopping, even though the cupula remains deflected. It is not known whether this adaptation effect depends on a peripheral or central process (Ek, Jongkees, and Klijn, 1960).

Determinations of the threshold of angular acceleration have been made with a variety of methods—a recent determination gave $0.5°/\sec^2$ (Groen and Jongkees, 1948). For short time intervals, the product of the acceleration and the time required to reach threshold is constant; for instance, shorter times of application require greater accelerations to reach threshold. This relationship is analogous to Bloch's law in vision (see p. 349).

## The Utricles

The utricle or statolith organ is a sac at the junction of the three vestibular canals. It contains a sensory organ—*the macula*—which responds to the extent and direction of linear acceleration, including the linear acceleration due to gravity. Organs sensitive to position with respect to gravity are very old in the evolutionary scale. They are represented in every animal phylum, and are known as statocysts in invertebrates. One of the neatest ways of studying their function is provided by the crayfish's habit of using its pincers to replace grains of sand in its statocyst after every moult. These grains serve to stimulate the statocyst as the crayfish moves about. If iron filings are the only small particles available, the crayfish will place these in its statocyst cavity, and will then alter its orientation in response to the movements of a magnet. See Lowenstein (1950, and 1956) for details of the comparative aspects of otolith functioning.

The mammalian utricle is filled with endolymph which has nearly the same specific gravity as water. The macula consists of an epithelium of ciliated sensory cells covered by a gelatinous substance containing calcium carbonate particles or *otoconia*. The specific gravity of the otoconia is greater than that of the surrounding endolymph, so that the heavy otoconia are displaced by changes in the extent or direction of linear acceleration. When the head is erect, the macula is in an approximately horizontal position, and the sensory hairs are vertical with the otoconia lying on top of them.

Trincker (1962) recorded the potential changes inside the macula of the guinea pig and found that only shearing forces produced by tangential displacements of the hair cells are effective in producing neural responses.

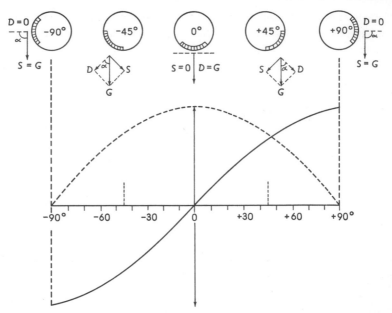

FIG. 13–10. Stimulation of the macular sensory epithelium by shearing force, and the characteristic curve representing information input. Above: schematic drawings of the utricle, with its macula and statolithic membrane, undergoing tilting in both directions around the horizontal rostro-occipital axis of the head. Forces on the sensory epithelium represented as vector parallelograms. G, gravity; S, shearing force (the component of gravity, acting tangentially on the epithelium); D, pressure (or tension), the component, acting vertically on the macula. In a normal position S = 0; at 90°, D = 0. Below: the relationship of shearing force (continuous line) and pressure (broken line) to degree of inclination (abscissa); shearing gives a sine-relationship, while pressure gives the cosine. (From Trincker, 1962, *S.E.B. Symposium*, 294.)

Pressure or tension applied at right angles to the macula epitheluim has no effect. A shearing-force mechanism produces a utricular response that is a sine function of the angle of tilt, whereas a tension mechanism would produce a response that is a cosine function of tilt (see Figure 13–10). Trincker was able to demonstrate the sine function in actual recordings from the tilting macula of the guinea pig. Wing (1963) has not been able to record any consistent potential changes in the mammalian vestibular ganglion in response to head tilt, and suggested that the utricle is largely vestigial in higher mammals, where vision and kinesthesis are dominant in maintaining balance.

## Labyrinthine Pathways

The vestibular part of the eighth nerve on each side passes to four *vestibular nuclei*, which sit astride the cerebellar peduncle. The vestibular nuclei on each side of the head are connected together directly as well as by fibers running through the reticular formation. Othr fibers from the vestibular nuclei form the *medial longitudinal fasciculus* which ascends to the oculomotor centers of the brain stem to mediate the vestibular nystagmus reflex. Other fibers descend into the spinal cord as the vestibulospinal tract which terminates in motoneuron pools in the cord and mediates vestibulospinal reflexes. Some fibers pass directly to the cerebellum and reticular system. Although doubted for a long time, it is now established that the vestibular apparatus projects via the thalamus to the cerebral cortex, principally to the contralateral superior ectosylvian fissure.

## The Behavioral Consequences of Labyrinthine Stimulation

The foregoing account of the complex ramifications of the vestibular afferents throughout the central nervous system suggests that the behavioral consequences of vestibular stimulation are equally complex. At the same time, the paucity of cortical projections suggests that these behavioral consequences are largely at the unconscious, reflex level. When a person rotates about his body axis the eyes execute a series of slow movements in the opposite direction to the rotation alternating with quick return sweeps. This pattern of eye movements is known as *vestibular nystagmus* and may be elicited in a horizontal, vertical or frontal plane (torsional nystagmus), depending upon which of the three canals is in the plane of rotation of the body.

The speed of the slow phase is roughly proportional to the speed of rotation for moderate speeds and clearly serves to retain, as far as possible, a stationary image of the visible world on the retina. The quick phase is mediated by brain stem centers, and is not controlled by proprioceptive impulses from the eyes. The whole reflex occurs in the dark and is therefore not dependent on vision, although when the eyes are open, the nystagmus is more nicely geared to the speed at which the retinal image moves. It is thought that, although the vestibular apparatus initiates the nystagmus, optokinetic or visually induced nystagmus takes command when the eyes are open (Dodge, 1923). An illusion of visual movement accompanies postrotational nystagmus, especially when only a single point of light is visible. This illusory movement has been called the *oculogyral illusion* (Graybiel and Hupp, 1946) and it may outlast the nystagmus, so that the movement of the eyes is not the only cause of the illusion (Guedry, Collins, and Sheffey, 1961).

An absence of postrotational nystagmus has often been taken to signify defective labyrinths although it is often not present in normal subjects. A rotating chair in which people may be tested in this way is known as a Bárány chair. A vast clinical literature has grown up on the basis of this and similar tests. If the duration of postrotational nystagmus is plotted as a function of the logarithm of the rate of deceleration (cupula deflection), a straight-line function known as a *cupulogram* is obtained (Ek, Jongkees, and Klijn, 1960). The duration of postrotational nystagmus would logically seem to represent the time which the cupula takes to return to equilibrium and the slope of the cupulogram would seem to represent the rate of this recovery. However, the cupulogram slope changes with practice, and there is no evidence that a change in the rate of cupula recovery is responsible for this change. As an example of the effects of practice on the cupulogram, look at Figure 13–11 and compare the averaged cupulograms from ordinary people with the averaged cupulogram from practised aviators. The slope of the cupulogram from the experienced aviators is less than normal, reflecting a high degree of cortical suppression of vestibular

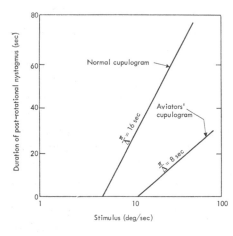

FIG. 13–11. A normal cupulogram compared with that of the average cupulogram of 18 experienced aviators. (Adapted from Groen, 1960, *Acta oto-laryngol.* p. 60.)

aftereffects; an obviously desirable accomplishment in aviators. For further details of cupulometry see Cawthorne, Dix and Hallpike (1956).

The decline with practice of postrotational nystagmus and other postrotational effects is known as *vestibular habituation*. The mechanism of vestibular habituation is not understood, although it presumably depends on central factors. It is well established that drowsiness and lack of attention speed up vestibular habituation (Collins, 1962) and that arousal restores postrotational nystagmus, although not to its pre-habituation level. It may be concluded that habituation depends upon a reduction of arousal, but not entirely on this factor. Habituation is especially marked when the eyes are open and probably the most important factor in habituation under these conditions is an increased stabilization of the eye by visual fixation. It may be supposed that postrotational phenomena are normally habituated to some extent because of the rotations to which people are continually subjected. If this is so, newborn infants should manifest an unusually low threshold for, and an extra long duration of postrotational nystagmus. This seems to be the case (Groen, 1963), although the child's poorly developed mechanism of visual fixation is also a probable contributory factor, and the infant like the adult, must be kept alert in order that the nystagmus may be elicited.

The central adaptive control of the effects of angular and linear accelerations is further illustrated by the well-known acclimatization to the movements of a ship. It is as if the person learns to anticipate each movement by producing a central "copy" of the particular sequence and by partialing this out from the afferent signals as they come in. When one returns to land the firm ground seems to pitch and roll, because the partialing-out process persists for hours or even days.

## Effects of Loss of Labyrinthine Function

Unilateral loss of vestibular function is followed by a period of acute discomfort. The patient is unable to move his head without feeling distressed, nauseated, and disoriented; the skin is pallid, pulse rate is high, and vomiting is frequent. He has nystagmus and falls to the undamaged side. These symptoms subside after some days or weeks, presumably because of a change in the way in which the central nervous system makes use of an asymmetrical vestibular input.

A patient with bilateral vestibular loss shows none of the nausea, distress, or nystagmus symptoms. He is unable to stand steadily upright with eyes closed, and he is likely to swim downwards instead of upwards when submerged in water. Some recovery of stability takes place, especially in man, who is able to rely on proprioceptive and visual signals.

## Motion Sickness

Motion sickness is a state that develops in animals and humans when they are subjected to accelerations over which they have no control. It manifests itself in nausea, vomiting, and distress.

The literature on this subject was reviewed recently by Chinn and Smith (1955), and Loftus (1963). There is abundant evidence that the vestibular apparatus is implicated in the etiology of motion sickness. Bilateral labyrinthectomy or sectioning of the vestibular-cerebellar tracts in animals and man renders the subject immune to motion sickness. Caloric or electrical stimulation of the vestibular apparatus induces motion sickness. Modern evidence suggests that both canal and utricular stimulation may be involved. Low-frequency, high-amplitude oscillations seem to be more effective than high-frequency, low-amplitude oscillations. However, the most potent stimulus seems to arise when there is a complex series of changes in the amplitude and direction of both linear and rotary acceleration. Even if the person is subjected to a simple sinusiodal rotation or swing, complex forces will act on his head every time he moves it. These forces arise through interaction between the forces produced by the movements of the swing and those produced by the movement of the head. If the head is strapped in one position, motion sickness symptoms are much reduced (Johnson and Taylor, 1961). Most people adapt to sickness-inducing conditions after a time. For instance, Graybiel, Clark, and Zarriello (1960) observed volunteers living in a slowly rotating room for many days. The initial distress and incapacity gradually diminished.

Thus complex stimulation of the vestibular apparatus is the main etiological factor in motion sickness. However, the fact that adaptation takes place demonstrates that central factors are also important.

Summarizing our knowledge about the vestibular apparatus, it may be concluded that the differential equation for the torsion pendulum adequately describes the behavior of the peripheral organ. However, central factors modify the effects which the afferent discharge has on behavior, and probably the afferent discharge itself. This is a typical situation; behavioral mechanisms are "layered," and the top control layers must be stripped away to reveal the simpler mechanisms which are ultimately describable in terms of differential equations. An experimental psychologist must understand the basic physiology and physics of peripheral mechanisms, and no physiologist should ignore the complex nonlinear central mechanisms. The study of vestibular mechanisms is a field where important contributions have been made both by physiologists and physicists working on peripheral mechanisms (Mach, Ewald, Groen, Jongkees, etc.) and by psychologists working on the central mechanisms (Dodge, Dunlap, Mowrer, Graybiel, etc.).

## POSTURAL REFLEXES

There are two main types of postural reflexes. The first type—the tonic reflexes—are concerned with the control of the attitude of parts of the body in relation to each other but not in relation to gravity. The second type—the righting reflexes—maintain the body in a constant orientation to gravity. Many of the segmental reflexes discussed in the last section, such as the stretch reflex and crossed extensor reflex, are tonic postural reflexes. The suprasegmental reflexes will be discussed in this section.

Magnus, while working in Sherrington's laboratory in Liverpool, noticed that the distribution of tonus in the body of a decerebrate cat is affected when its head is passively moved about. He went on to study postural reflexes over the next fourteen years with his co-workers, Rademaker, de Klejn, and others in the University of Utrecht. His classic work, *Körperstellung*, appeared in 1924; an English summary is contained in the Cameron Prize Lectures of 1926. In man, postural reflexes are overlaid by complex learned motor response patterns; the young child, however, does not possess a functional cerebral cortex, and may therefore exhibit postural reflexes in their primitive form. This work has been thoroughly reviewed by Peiper (1963).

## Tonic Reflexes of the Decerebrate Animal

When the brain stem is sectioned just above the vestibular nuclei, the extensor muscles throughout the body go into continuous spasm, resulting in a rigid extension of the limbs. This postural pattern is known as *decerebrate rigidity* and is due to the release of vestibular tonic centers from control by extrapyramidal centers.

When the head of such a decerebrate preparation is placed in different positions, the distribution of tonus in the whole body musculature is changed. Two reflexes are involved in this response: (1) a *tonic neck reflex*

FIG. 13–12. Asymmetrical neck tonic reflex (fencing position) in an infant girl age 2 months 9 days. (Drawn from a photograph in Peiper, 1963, p. 157).

resulting from stimulation of neck-muscle receptors, and (2) a *tonic labyrinthine reflex* resulting from stimulation of the utricles.

In order to study the tonic neck reflex in isolation from the tonic labyrinthine reflex, the labyrinths must be removed. Under these circumstances, rotation of the head causes extension of the fore and hind limbs on that side towards which the jaw is rotated ("jaw limbs"), and relaxation of the limbs on the side towards which the back of the head is rotated ("skull limbs"). Inclination of the head towards one shoulder causes extension of the jaw limbs and relaxation of the skull limbs. Lowering or dorsiflexion of the head causes an extension of the forelimbs and relaxation of the hind limbs. Elevation or ventro-flexion of the head causes flexion of the forelimbs and extension of the hind limbs.

Tonic neck reflexes occur in many human infants during the first six months of life, before the cerebral cortex has gained control over the lower reflex centers. Figure 13–12 shows the typical reflex pattern induced by a sideways head position in a newborn infant; it is known as the "fencing position" for obvious reasons.

In order to study tonic labyrinthine reflexes in isolation from the tonic neck reflexes, the head is immobilized in relation to the body by a plaster jacket, or the tonic neck reflex outflow is interrupted by cutting the first three cervical roots of the spinal cord.

When such a preparation is moved into different positions in relation to gravity the extensor tonus changes in the same way in all four limbs. The tonus is maximal when the animal is in the supine position and the otoliths are pulling down on the macular epithelium; tonus is minimal when the animal is in the prone position and the otoliths are pressing on the macular epithelium. In other positions extensor tonus is intermeate.

In the presence of both neck and labyrinthine reflexes the pattern of tonus in the body represents the algebraic sum of their effects. For example, if the head of a prone, decerebrate cat is flexed ventrally, the forelimbs will relax under the influence of both reflexes, but the hind limbs may not change, as they are influenced in opposite directions by the two reflexes.

These attitudinal reflexes last as long as the head is held in a certain position, and it is for this reason that they are called "tonic." They may be seen in the active behavior of intact animals. For example, a cat when reaching for food on the ground lowers the head which causes the forelimbs to relax. When a cat reaches up, the head elevates and the forelimbs extend but the hind limbs do not change markedly in their position. These reflex tonic attitudes are not easy to detect in intact primates, but may be seen in decerebrate preparations and in clinical conditions in humans.

## Righting Reflexes

The reflexes discussed so far may be elicited in a decerebrate animal where the section is made just rostral (towards the head) to the vestibular nuclei. If the section is more rostral and leaves the midbrain and thalamus intact, the preparation is known as a *thalamic preparation*. The animal no longer manifests the extensor contracture of decerebrate rigidity and is able to restore itself to an upright posture when disturbed.

Five groups of reflexes which cooperate in righting responses were identified by Magnus. In order to demonstrate any one of these components the animal must first of all be placed in such a state that none of them is active. This so-called "zero condition" is fulfilled if a thalamic animal, after bilateral labyrinthectomy, is suspended freely out of contact with any surface. In lower animals, which do not have optic-righting reflexes, it is not necessary to cover the eyes; in higher mammals, this is necessary.

## The Labyrinthine-Righting Reflexes

All blindfolded, thalamic mammals with intact labyrinths show the labyrinthine-righting reflexes. If the animal is held by the pelvis, its head remains in the upright position as far as possible, no matter how the pelvis is moved (see Figure 13–13). These reflex head movements depend upon

FIG. 13–13. Head down suspension of a thalamus preparation of a rabbit. The head does not follow gravity, but is brought into normal position in space by the labyrinthine righting reflex. (Sketch by Peiper after Magnus, 1924.)

the utricle and perhaps also the sacculus, and are therefore absent in labyrinthectomized animals (see Figure 13–14). They are only faintly demonstrable in the neonate human, but develop during the first year of life. They enable the growing infant to lift his head and later to sit up and stand.

FIG. 13–14. (a) Rabbit without labyrinths; (b) intact rabbit in suspended lateral position. In the animal without labyrinths the head responds to gravity; in the intact animal the labyrinthine righting reflex raises the head to normal position. (Sketch by Peiper after Rademaker, 1926.)

## The Neck-Righting Reflexes

The neck-righting reflexes orient the body in relation to the head. If the body is tilted, the head regains the upright position by the action of the vestibular-righting reflexes, consequently the neck becomes twisted which evokes the neck-righting reflexes which in turn cause the thorax and then the lower parts of the body to be brought back into line with the upright head.

### Body-Righting Reflexes

If a labyrinthectomized animal is held freely in the lateral position and lowered onto a surface, it immediately brings its head into a normal position with regard to the surface. The asymmetric stimulation of the touch receptors in the skin evokes this reflex. If the tactile stimulation on each side of the body is made symmetrical by pushing a board against the animal, the head will return under the influence of the neck-righting reflex to the lateral position. If the head of the animal is held firmly in the lateral position as the animal is lowered onto a surface, its body will right itself. This reflex is also induced by the asymmetrical stimulation of the skin, and it occurs in spite of the opposing neck-tonic reflex which tends to keep the body in line with the laterally placed head.

### Optic-Righting Reflexes

In intact higher mammals, such as cats, dogs, and primates, the orientation of the head is controlled largely by vision. If an animal with labyrinths removed but otherwise intact is freely suspended in the air, its head remains disoriented until the eyes are opened and the animal fixates on something in the environment.

All these reflexes normally work together to maintain the upright posture of the unconstrained intact animal. The head always leads; if the animal is disoriented, the head is first restored to the vertical position through the mediation of visual-, vestibular-, and tactile-righting reflexes. The thorax is then brought into line with the head through the mediation of neck-righting reflexes and tactile body-righting reflexes. Finally the hindquarters and legs are brought into line by spinal and tactile-righting reflexes. This sequence of events is called a chain reflex and may be seen in the way a cat rights its body when falling. This chain reflex may also be demonstrated in infant humans.

## The Central Control of Postural Reflexes

The way in which postural motor patterns are organized by the central nervous system has been studied by Hess (1957) and his co-workers in Zürich. They found that electrical stimulation delivered by fine electrodes embedded in the diencephalic region of an otherwise intact cat induces reproducible attitudinal responses of the head, or head and body. A head-lowering-legs-flexing response is induced by stimulation of the posterior commissure. An opposed response is induced by stimulation in a zone over the posterior hypothalamus, or in the rubrospinal tract. The head rotates in response to stimulation of the thalamus or subthalamus—the direction of turning depending on the exact site of stimulation. Head turning is induced by stimulation of the lateral thalamus. All but this last response show rhythmic activity synchronous with low-frequency stimulation.

The various head responses produced by diencephalic stimulation are similar to the postrotational vestibular reflex head movements induced by the various vestibular canals. Hess concluded that the normal mode of stimulation of these diencephalic centers was from the vestibular canals, via the cerebellum and brachium conjunctivum. He also traced routes from the sensory tracts of the body and head, namely the spinothalamic and trigeminal tracts, which presumably carry information regarding the relative position of body parts to these diencephalic centers.

A further set of responses from the diencephalon were observed which involved lifting of the forelimbs and perhaps the whole side of the body. That these were not related to nociceptive (pain) reflexes was evident from the calm demeanor of the animal. Hess concluded that these responses correspond to postural reflexes under the control of proprioception, such as the crossed extensor reflex.

These results do not prove that basic motor patterns are controlled solely by central processes irrespective of proprioceptive inputs. There has been a long dispute about the relative importance of central and proprioceptive factors in the control of basic motor response patterns. On the one hand the *chain reflex theory* holds that rhythmical motor patterns such as walking result from the successive interaction of proprioceptive and tactile reflexes. On the other hand, claims have been made that walking movements may occur in limbs in which all sensory nerves have been cut. However, Gray (1950) suggests that walking movements in a deafferented limb depend on the integrity of sensory nerves in other limbs. The most recent evidence is that walking and other movements are possible even with complete deafferentation of the body (Taub, 1965).

## The Maintenance of the Postural Vertical

In order to study the ability of a person to judge when his body is in an upright position, it is usual to seat the blindfolded subject in a chair which can be tilted. In the absence of visual information, a person is able to set his body to the vertical to within one degree. However, many factors upset his judgment, such as the degree to which he was initially tilted before being allowed to restore himself to the vertical, the direction of the initial tilt, the speed of return to the vertical, and the duration of delay in the tilted position. For details of experimental work on these factors see Howard and Templeton (1966).

Other work has been concerned with the sensory modalities involved in setting the seated body to the vertical. These modalities could include vision, touch, kinesthesis, and the labyrinths. Garten (1920) tested subjects with defective inner ears and found that they could accurately set their bodies to the vertical in a tilting chair. He concluded that the labyrinths are not important for this ability. He found also that the performance of normal subjects was affected by complete immersion in water, although anesthetizing the skin areas which were in contact with the chair (by cooling the buttocks) had no effect on performance. He concluded that kinesthesis must therefore be the crucial modality for this ability. This conclusion is not valid. If a person is able to use any one modality to set his body to the vertical, removing one as Garten did would not affect accuracy even though each modality could be important when it alone is present. However, it seems that tactile stimulation of the skin is not an essential factor in the ability to set the body to the vertical, at least for the seated person.

Some recent evidence has been put forward in support of Garten's suggestion that the labyrinths are not essential for body orientation. Thetford and Guedry (1952) studied five subjects with unilateral labyrinth loss, under a variety of conditions on the tilting chair. They performed just as well as normal subjects. This was probably because the subjects had become adapted to the asymmetrical vestibular input. One cannot conclude from these experiments that vestibular stimulation is unimportant for setting the body to the vertical in normal people. Errors have been found to be greater when the head of a normal subject is held upright than when it is fixed in the median plane of the body (Fleishman, 1953; Solley, 1960). Only in the latter condition is the utricle brought into action, which suggests that normal subjects do use their utricles in judging the orientation of their bodies.

The influence of the visual frame on the setting of the body to the vertical has been studied by Passy (1950). The subjects adjusted themselves to the vertical in the tilting chair from an initial tilt of 45° with the frame tilted to various angles up to 20° to either side. The constant error in the direction of the frame tilt was found to increase as the tilt of the frame was increased, particularly when the frame was tilted to the same side as the body. The maximum effect of the tilted frame on the constant error was, however, only 2°. The subjects at all times set their bodies much nearer to the true vertical than to the position of the visual frame.

The method of using a passive, seated subject for studying the ability to set the body to the vertical has little relevance to man's capacity to maintain a vertical posture in conditions where he is free to move actively. In a real life situation, the usual task is that of maintaining body balance while standing or moving about.

It has already been pointed out that people with defective labyrinths are able to largely compensate for their disability, even when their eyes are closed. The most important modality for the maintenance of upright posture is undoubtedly proprioception. The joint-capsule receptors in proximal joints, particularly the hip joints, are very sensitive to body sway. It is apparent from studies of the electromyographic activity of the antigravity muscles that control of posture is not by steady contraction of these muscles but rather by intermittent correction of balance. If one stands on one leg with eyes closed, the intermittent nature of posture adjustment is apparent (see Eldred, 1960, for further details).

The extent of the body sway when the eyes are closed is affected by many factors: age, the height and weight of the body, drugs, and suggestion. The sway amplitude is easily measured; such a measure is known as the *sway test*. It is used in the diagnosis of disorders of the proprioceptive system, as a test of drunkenness, and a test of suggestibility or hypnotizability (see Edwards, 1942).

## MOTOR AREAS OF THE CEREBRAL CORTEX

Fritsch and Hitzig reported in 1870 that electrical stimulation of certain areas of the dog's cerebral cortex produced movements of parts of the body. This was the first demonstration that motor functions are localized in the cerebral cortex. Similar motor areas were reported in primates by Leyton and Sherrington in 1917, and in humans by Penfield and Rasmussen in 1950. The so-called classical motor area from which these responses were elicited is situated in Brodmann's area 4 just in front of the central sulcus in the precentral gyrus. It forms a strip extending from deep in the longitudinal fissure down into the lateral fissure. Figure 13–15 shows the distribution of the body parts which are maximally aroused by stimulation of given loci in the motor strip.

Although motor responses are most readily elicited from the classical motor area, this is not the only part of the cortex to produce motor responses when stimulated artificially; motor responses may be elicited from the neighboring postcentral gyrus which is normally considered to be the somesthetic area (see p. 262), and from so-called secondary motor areas in the frontal and parietal lobes.

In addition, cortical centers for eye movements exist in the occipital and frontal lobes; and centers producing autonomic motor responses, such as hair erection, changes in heart beat, etc., exist in the frontal and temporal lobes.

Stimulation of other widespread areas of the cortex may cause any ongoing motor activity to be suppressed. These so-called suppressor areas are not localized as was once thought; whether a particular area excites or suppresses depends to some extent upon the nature of the electrical stimulation applied.

The precise muscle group responding to stimulation of any particular locus of the precentral motor cortex depends upon the strength and frequency of the stimulus and the nature of the preceding stimulation (Murphy and Gellhorn, 1945; Liddell and Phillips, 1950). Furthermore,

Ward (1938, 1952) showed that stimulation of a particular locus of the motor cortex of an unanesthetized cat brought a limb to a particular final position whatever the initial position of the limb, although the final position was affected by the position of the head. Any one locus of the motor cortex must therefore send impulses to many spinal motor neurons, and the particular response elicited at any time must depend upon the postural state of the body, that is, on kinesthetic feedback and the background activity in spinal, vestibular, cerebellar, extrapyramidal, and

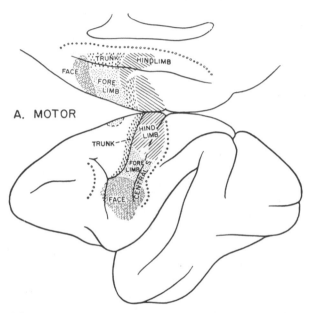

**FIG. 13–15.** Diagrammatic represenation of the precentral motor areas in the brain of the monkey showing the topographical localization of body areas.

cortical motor centers. Even so, under the right conditions of stimulation, precisely localized muscular responses may be elicited (Chang, Ruch, and Ward, 1947).

It is an interesting fact that patients undergoing brain surgery report that the movements induced by stimulation of the motor cortex occur as if "someone were pulling the strings." That is, the patients do not feel they are making the movements themselves.

Removal of area 4 results in a general flaccid paralysis, from which considerable recovery takes place. Presumably other motor areas take over the functions of area 4 to some extent. However, if the spinal cord is damaged, the loss of motor function is more severe and permanent although more localized. Destruction of motor neurons of the final common path produces irreversible and complete paralysis of particular muscles, which subsequently atrophy.

Relative paralyses of motor function which result from lesions in the pyramidal system are known as *plegias*. A plegia occurs on the side contralateral to the lesion when the lesion is rostral to the decussation. When affecting the whole of one side of the body, the plegia is known as a *hemiplegia*; when affecting the upper or lower part of the body, it is known as a *paraplegia*.

Damage to any part of the motor system, including the pyramidal and extrapyramidal systems, and cerebellum, produces incoordination of movement in certain muscles. Any such loss of muscular control is known as *ataxia*.

Damage to cortical motor areas outside area 4, particularly damage to area 6, is usually accompanied by what is known as *apraxia*. An apraxic patient is able to move his limbs normally in simple tasks, but is unable to plan and execute complex learned skills. The motor system itself is intact but cannot be marshaled adequately into spatial-temporal patterns. Apraxias may be more or less specific to one type of skill; *agraphia* is an inability to write; dressing apraxia is an inability to carry out the manipulations involved in getting dressed.

Such disturbances of higher motor functions cannot be considered in isolation from defects in related abilities. For instance, motor incoordination will result from disorders of the *body scheme*; that is, the frame of reference in terms of which the positions and movements of body parts are judged and acted upon. Body scheme disorders are associated with damage to the parietal lobes (see Critchley, 1953). A defect in the ability to comprehend the spatial relationships of objects, which may also arise through parietal lobe damage, could affect motor coordination when an attempt is made to manipulate objects. It is impossible to specify any one center that is solely concerned in the control of a complex skill; a motor skill is the end product of the complex interaction of many sub-systems, and may suffer through damage to any one sub-system. At the same time, the nervous system, especially that of higher mammals, is adept at compensating for localized damage, either by recovery or by substituting alternative means of control.

## VISUAL-MOTOR COORDINATION

One of the main tasks of voluntary movements is the control of the movement of limbs in relation to visible objects. There are several experimental approaches to this problem of visual-motor coordination.

1. The surgical rearrangement of nerve to muscle connections, sensory inputs, or tendon to bone insertions.

2. The displacement of the optical array entering the eyes and the study of the subsequent adaptation of visual-motor coordination.

3. The rearing of animals under restricted conditions of growth.

4. The study of human skills under a variety of stimulus conditions. Typical of this approach is the use of the pursuit rotor.

A few remarks will be made about each of these procedures.

## Surgical Rearrangement

The nerves of amphibians, especially young ones, may be readily transplanted so that they innervate atypical muscles (Sperry, 1945). For instance, the nerves to an agonist and antagonist in the forelimb of the frog may be transposed. When this is done, and the animal has regained the use of the limb, it is found that this limb walks backwards relative to the other limbs; the same muscles contract in the same sequence as before, even though the resulting movements are maladjustive. The frog never learns to walk normally. In other words, it is the muscle itself which decides how it is to contract, and not the nerves innervating the muscle. Each muscle of the body must somehow instruct the central nervous system to make central patterns of synaptic connections so that that muscle will contract in a way determined by the type of muscle it is. Weiss (1941, 1950) summarized this state of affairs by saying that "muscles have names," and this theory has become known as the myotypic theory of muscular control. It is not known how the muscles instruct the nervous system to make appropriate central connections.

Not only muscles determine central neural connections; sense organs apparently do the same. For instance, if an extra cornea is grafted onto the cheek of a frog and allowed to become innervated by a branch of the trigeminal nerve, it will cause a blink of the normal eyes when touched. The grafted cornea has somehow instructed the trigeminal branch to make those central motor connections appropriate to that other branch of the trigeminal nerve which normally innervates the cornea. This type of rearrangement of central connections works only within the field of any one peripheral nerve. For instance, it is not possible to make the auditory nerve act like an optic nerve by grafting the retina into the place of the cochlea.

Tendons may be easily regrafted onto atypical bones. Lower animals never learn to adapt their behavior to such a rearrangement. Tendons are sometimes regrafted in human patients, and a considerable degree of relearning takes place. This modifiability is presumably related to the development of the motor cortex in man.

## The Displacement of the Optical Array

If wedge prisms are worn which displace the optical array to one side, reaching movements toward visible objects are disturbed. The human subject readily adapts his movements to a visual displacement if he is informed of his errors. On moving the prisms, accuracy is again disturbed for a while. This type of visual-motor adaptation is normally specific to the particular arm used in training but is not specific to the particular eye which is open during training. However, if training consists of moving the eyes until they are fixated on an immobile finger which remains unseen until the end of the movement, the training is not specific to the hand used. The rule seems to be that the training is specific to whichever part of the body is required to change its normal movement during training.

Von Holst and Mittelstedt (1950) concluded from their observations on insects and fish that the important thing in visual-motor coordination is the relationship between self-produced movements of the body or parts of the body and changes in the pattern of stimulation of the sense organs which these movements produce. Such changes in sensory stimulation consequent upon self-produced movement were called *"re-afference."* Changes in sensory stimulation produced solely by changes in the external world were called *"ex-afference."* An animal capable of orientating itself must be capable of distinguishing between re-afferent and ex-afferent stimulation. It does this by disregarding the changes in sensory stimulation which a given pattern of muscular innervation normally produces. This theory has something in common with Helmholtz's theory of unconscious inference.

Held (1962) has recently applied this theory to the case of visual-motor adaptation to prisms. His basic procedure was to compare the effectiveness of self-produced movement with that of passive movement in the adaptation of visual-motor coordination to a displaced visual input in adult human subjects. Only the self-produced movement led to any adaptation, and Held concluded that re-afference is necessary for adaptation. However, it has been demonstrated by others that under appropriate conditions visual-motor adaptation may occur without self-produced movement during training (see Howard and Templeton, 1966) though not as effectively as with self-produced movement.

## Restricted Rearing

Held and Hein (1963) have recently claimed that for kittens at least re-afferent experience is essential for the development of visual-motor skills such as the blink response, paw placing, and avoidance of the visual cliff. This conclusion, however, may be questioned because the control group of kittens which were denied reafferent experience were also denied many types of exafferent stimulation which may have been sufficient for the development of the skills mentioned.

There is a general difficulty with all experiments involving early deprivation; the procedures may not merely prevent the development of the relevant motor abilities but may cause the degeneration of control mechanisms which were originally present.

## The Pursuit Rotor

A pursuit rotor consists of a drum rotating past a slit so that the subject sees a track sweeping from side to side in a predetermined sequence. The subject's task is to keep a stylus on the track. Such a task may be used to study temporal factors in visual-motor control. Reaction time sets a limit to the accuracy with which abrupt changes in the track may be followed, and an artificial delay in the visual display of the position of the stylus leads to severe deterioration of performance. However, if the movements of the track are repetitive, the subject may learn to anticipate rapid changes and thereby overcome the limitations imposed by his reaction time or display delays.

A great variety of visual-motor tasks have been studied; peg-board assembly, aiming, steadiness, etc. The correlations between performance scores on such tasks is notoriously low, human motor abilities are highly specific. See Bilodeau, 1966, for further details of this topic.

### EYE MOVEMENTS

Eye movements are the fastest, most accurate, and most complex in the body. They therefore merit special mention.

FIG. 13–16. Origins and insertions of the extraocular muscles. (From Cogan, D. G., *Neurology of the Ocular Muscles*, 1956; courtesy of Charles C. Thomas, Publisher, Springfield, Ill.)

## The Extraocular Muscles

The extraocular, or extrinsic, eye muscles control the position of each eye in its socket. Each eye has three pairs of muscles, the medial and lateral recti, the superior and inferior recti, and the superior and inferior oblique. Their positions in relation to the orbit are shown in Figure 13–16.

The extraocular muscles are controlled by nuclei in the upper brain stem. There are important neural connections between these nuclei and the cerebellum, vestibular apparatus, and superior colliculi. There are also two important eye-movement centers in the cerebral cortex: the occipital and preoccipital areas, on the one hand, and the frontal-lobe eye fields on the other. Consistent patterns of eye movements are observed when loci within these cortical areas are electrically stimulated (for details see Bender, 1965).

Movements of each eye considered separately are known as *ductions*. Rotations of an eye about the visual axis are known as *torsions*. A movement of one eye is normally accompanied by a movement of the other; a fact known as *Hering's law of equal innervations*. Movements of the eyes in the same direction are known as *versions or conjugate movements*; movements in opposite directions are known as *vergences or disjunctive movements*. For details of the geometry of eye movements see Helmholtz (1925, Vol. 3, p. 37), Fry (1945, 1947a, 1947b), and Howard and Templeton (1966).

When a person fixates a small visible target, his eyes show low-amplitude, involuntary movements, sometimes referred to as physiological nystagmus. These movements are discussed in Chapter 11.

## The Functions of Eye Movements

The conditions under which the eyes move are classified in Table 13–3. If an animal is to decode the information received by the retinae the

TABLE 13–3

Functional Classification of Eye Movements

| General Type | Specific Type |
|---|---|
| Maintaining constant position of retinal image | Optokinetic nystagmus vestibular and proprioceptive reflexes. Foveal pursuit movements (in foveate eye only). |
| Fixation changes | Voluntary changes of fixation (foveate eyes only). |
| Movements serving stereopsis | Versions and vergences. Only in eyes with corresponding projections (hemidecussation). |

images must be kept still for some time, in spite of movements of the animal's head. Therefore, eye movements evolved in the first place to maintain retinal images in the same position, and in lower animals they still serve no other function (Walls, 1962).

The simplest way of compensating for movements of the head is for the eyes to reflexly follow any consequent movement of the retinal images. This reflex is present in all vertebrates, and may be demonstrated by moving a series of stripes in one direction across the field of view of the stationary animal. In response, the eyes move conjugately and rhythmically; slow, smooth movements in pursuit of the moving stimuli alternate with quick return sweeps. The whole involuntary rhythmic to-and-fro oculomotor response is known as *optokinetic nystagmus*, or OKN.

It is difficult, if not impossible, to consciously inhibit OKN unless there is a stationary object upon which the gaze may be anchored. It is also impossible to move the eyes smoothly without the aid of a moving target.

OKN has been found to persist for some time after the lights are put out. Attempts have been made to ascribe the movement aftereffect to this optokinetic after-nystagmus. However, movement aftereffects may be induced in several directions at the same time, and this fact excludes optokinetic after-nystagmus as the sole cause.

The study of OKN has practical uses, for example, it has been used for the objective determination of acuity, as a test for malingering blindness, and as a test of eye dominance. Its use for the diagnosis of lesions of the central nervous system is a subject of some debate (see Howard and Templeton, 1966, for a fuller account of optokinetic nystagmus).

Even when the eyes are closed, they still automatically move saccadically behind the closed eyelids in response to rotation of the head. The slow phase still approximately compensates for the movement of the head. The semicircular canals of the vestibular system are responsible for generating the signal for this so-called *vestibular nystagmus*. When the head is rotated with eyes open, the optokinetic nystagmus and vestibular nystagmus reinforce each other.

When the head is held in a tilted position, the normally vertical retinal meridian tends to remain vertical; that is, the eyes tort about the visual axis up to a maximum of about six degrees. This reflex is known as *countertorsion* and the signals for it arise in the utricles.

All these compensatory reflex eye movements are involuntary and very primitive. They occur even in animals whose eyes have no fovea. In animals whose eyes do have a fovea, *foveal pursuit movements* may occur in response to movements of a small part of the field of view. They serve to maintain the object which is fixated, on the area of clearest vision. If only one object in the field of view moves, that object tends to be fixated and pursued. If more than one object moves, factors of vividness, size, speed, etc., determine which is pursued. All the types of eye movement mentioned so far are concerned with keeping the retinal images stable on the retinae.

The second class of eye movements (see Table 13–3) are the changes of fixation which occur in foveate eyes in response to objects which attract the attention in the periphery. They serve to bring such objects into the area of clearest vision, and always involve both eyes, even if one of them is covered. Once the visual axis has centered on the new object, it is maintained there by the pursuit phase of vestibular and optokinetic nystagmus. When an eye changes its fixation, it does so with a single, rapid, and remarkably accurate saccadic movement. This movement is initiated after a latent period of between 0.12 and 0.18 seconds, after the first appearance of the new fixation light. A typical velocity time curve for a 20° saccade is shown in Figure 13–17.

Westheimer (1954) concluded that saccadic movements "are brought about merely by a change in torque which the extraocular muscles are applying to the eyeball, the latter coming to rest in a position representing an equilibrium of the forces applied." The movements are triggered off as a unit by the central nervous system, proprioceptive and visual feedback are not involved. Saccadic eye movements are thus controlled by a "dead-reckoning" system stabilized by the pattern of reciprocal innervation in the muscles, viscous damping, and resistances. A differential equation similar to that shown on p. 416 for the cupula has been applied with some success by Westheimer, although the system is not altogether linear. The eyes can

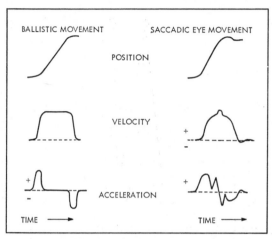

FIG. 13–17. Schematic diagram of position, velocity, and acceleration changes during a hypothetical ballistic movement (left) and a typical saccadic eye movement (right). (From Westheimer, G., *Archives of Ophthalmology*, 1954, 52. By permission of the editor and author.)

develop a dead-reckoning system to a high order of accuracy because the load which the eyeball has to move is nearly constant, unlike the situation in skeletal muscles.

In reading, the eyes move in a series of saccadic jerks interspersed with fixation pauses. Over 90 percent of the total time is taken up by the fixation pauses; the duration of any particular pause is governed by the nature of the material at that point. A skilled reader makes few backward or regressive movements, and makes shorter pauses. See Tinker (1951) for further details about eye movements and reading.

The final class of eye movements is that which involves the simultaneous movement of both eyes. These are the *conjugate versions* and *disjunctive vergences*. They are the last type to evolve, and occur in those animals with a large, overlapping binocular visual field. These movements serve to keep similar images on corresponding parts of each retina; if this were not done, things would be seen double. Corresponding parts are parts which project to equivalent points in the visual cortex. Hemidecussation (see p. 343) of the optic nerve fibers is a prerequisite for the development of projection correspondence, although not all animals which have incomplete decussation have binocular stereoscopic vision (Walls, 1962).

When the point of fixation changes to a target which is at a different distance as well as in a different direction, a complex sequence of movements is necessary. A schematic representation of these movements is shown in Figure 13–18. This figure describes data from actual eye-

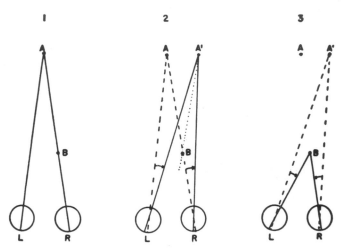

FIG. 13–18. Schematic diagrams illustrating sequence of movements in changing fixation from A to B. 1, binocular fixation of A; 2, conjugate lateral movement without change of convergence to A¹, so that bisector of angle of convergence passed through B; 3, convergence movement from A¹ to B. Steps 2 and 3 are to some extent superimposed; but, in view of their time characteristics, they are easily distinguished.

(From Westheimer, G., and Mitchell, A. M., *Archives of Ophthalmology,* 1956, 55. By permission of the editor and author.)

movement records (Westheimer and Mitchell, 1956). The conjugate and convergence movements involved are entirely separate responses, and occur in sequence, not at the same time. The two eyes first move to a new direction of conjugate lateral gaze so that the bisector of the angle of convergence passes through the new fixation point. A convergence movement then occurs bringing the two lines of sight to intersect in the new fixation point. The two eyes always move together, as Hering's law of equal innervations demands. In the example given, if the left eye had merely changed its direction of gaze until its visual axis intersected the new fixation point, the right eye would not have had to move. The whole movement would have been much simpler, but Hering's law would have been violated. The reason for this pattern of movements is probably that the repertoire of "programmes" for saccadic eye movements in the central nervous system need not be so extensive if the movements obey Hering's law of equal innervations.

Hering's law does not hold for slow pursuit movements. Such movements do not depend upon set programs, but are guided by visual feedback. Therefore, the need to economize on a central repertoire does not apply.

The eyes may be released from the fusional reflex, for example by having the subject look into a stereoscope and fixate one eye on a vertical line, and the other on a horizontal line. When this is done, it is often found that the angle of vergence differs from that normally associated with corresponding targets at that distance. The extent of this difference is known as *phoria*. If this tendency to imbalance is so strong that the fusional reflex cannot overcome it, the person has a squint or *strabismus*. In order to avoid double vision, one eye of a strabismic person usually becomes suppressed or *amblyopic* when both eyes are open, but sometimes a new functional correspondence is set up between the two eyes, that is, there is a shift in the relative directional space values of one eye.

Vergence movements also occur in conjunction with changes in accommodation. This fact may be demonstrated by moving a fixation target down the visual axis of one eye and feeling the movements of the corneal bulge of the other eye under its closed lid. The open eye does not move but merely changes its accommodation or focus. It must, therefore, be the change in focus which is related to the reflex vergence response of the closed eye. The vergence movements are not triggered by the accommodative response; both responses are triggered off simultaneously by the central nervous system which responds in this double way whenever a change of accommodation is called for. In fact, it is a triple response, for the pupil diameter changes also. For further details see the review in Volume 3 of Davson (1962).

## Eye Movements and the Stability of the Visible World

If an observer moves his eyes when viewing a stationary object he will normally report that the object remains stationary in spite of the movement of the retinal images. If the object is moving, the observer is able to judge its speed even when his eyes move so as to cancel out the movement of the retinal images. These achievements imply that the observer takes account (not necessarily consciously) of movements of his eyes as well as of the images on his retinae in making judgments about movements in the visible world.

Signals regarding eye position and movements could be derived from muscle-spindles and tactile receptors in the extraocular muscles and membranes, and/or from the central outflow to the eye muscles. The following evidence suggests that the motor outflow is the main source of eye-movement signals available to the center or mechanism in the central nervous system responsible for judgments of visual direction.

1. When the eyeball is moved passively by the finger, a stationary visible object is reported to move. Passive movement of the eyeball must stimulate muscle spindles in the extraocular muscles, and if the afferent inflow from these spindles were the crucial information that the visual direction mechanism required, the world would be reported as stationary when the eye is moved passively. What is lacking with passive movements is the motor outflow from the eye movement centers. It must be concluded that the visual direction center is informed of the voluntary motor outflow. However, the motor outflow involved in *involuntary* eye movements such as nystagmus, apparently does not reach the visual direction center, for during these movements the visible world is reported to move. In these cases the muscle-spindle feedback is no different to that in voluntary eye movements, and if this feedback were sufficient to indicate eye movements to the direction center, the visible world would be reported to be stable during these movements as well as during voluntary movements.

2. If the eye muscles are paralyzed, any attempt to move the eyes results in an apparent movement of the stationary visible world in the same direction as the attempted movement. In this case, the motor-outflow information reaches the visual direction center but is not accompanied by the expected movement of the retinal images. The situation is one which would normally arise if the visible world were to move with the eyes, and this is what the observer reports.

3. If an afterimage is formed, and the eyes are closed and moved voluntarily, the afterimage is reported to move with the eyes. Motor-outflow information is again not accompanied by the usual movement of the retinal image. If an eye is moved passively, the after image is reported to be stationary. In this case there is neither outflow information nor retinal-image motion.

All this evidence supports the theory that the visual movement center is informed about the voluntary motor outflow to the eye muscles rather than about any feedback from those muscles. The ability to judge seen movements depends on the interplay of information from the centers which are responsible for the voluntary (but not involuntary) control of eye movements and information from the visual centers indicating image movements on the retinae. When the movement of the retinal images which results from voluntary eye movements has such speed and direction as normally accompany that motor outflow, the visible world is judged to be stationary. If the retinal-image movement is more than this, the world is judged to be moving in the opposite direction to the eyes, and if it is less, it is judged to be moving in the same direction.

The visible world appears stable, not only when the eyes move, but also when the head moves. In this case, proprioceptive inputs from the neck muscles probably play an important role.

These relationships are not immutable. If spectacles are worn which reverse the optical array from left to right, the visible world appears to move with the head at twice the speed at which the head moves. This is due to the reversal of head parallax by the spectacles. After a few days, a subject reports that the instability diminishes. Eventually the visible world regains its apparent stability when the head moves. When the spectacles are removed, the visible world is again judged to be unstable until the subject adapts back to the normal situation (Kohler, 1951; Taylor, 1962).

# 14

## NEURONAL PHYSIOLOGY

### C. I. Howarth

### The Neuron

In recent times there has been no doubt that the functional unit of the nervous system is the individual nerve cell. (For a summary of the arguments which lead to this conclusion, see Cajal, 1954.) These functional nerve cells are called neurons and can be identified under the microscope by their structure. Figure 14–1 shows a selection of representative nerve cells from different parts of the nervous system. The histological investigation of the structure of the nerve cell preceded by a considerable period the development of techniques for investigating their activity.

Early ideas about the functioning of the nerve cell were developed from behavioral work on simple reflexes, notably by Sherrington and his school who worked largely on the spinal reflexes of decerebrate preparations. Their method of investigation was to stimulate sensory nerves either with a normal sensory stimulus or by electrical stimulation of the nerve itself, and then to measure the strength of the reflex twitch which developed, usually in one of the limbs. They investigated the relationship between the strength of the reflex response and the intensity and timing of the stimulus, and also investigated the effects of giving more than one stimulus at a time. Their main findings were as follows (Creed *et al.*, 1932; Sherrington, 1906; Fulton, 1943).

1. As the intensity of the stimulus increased, the strength of the reflex response increased while its latency decreased.

2. If a simple stimulus was just below threshold for evoking a response, a second stimulus immediately following it would sum with it to produce a reflex response. The size of the reflex response was usually greatest when the two subliminal stimuli were given simultaneously and decreased as the time interval between them was increased (Figure 14–2).

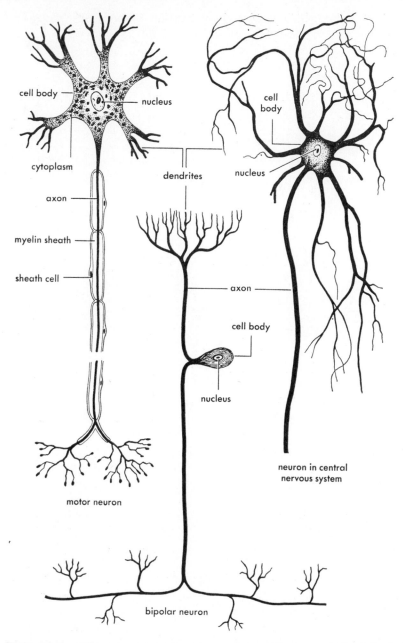

FIG. 14–1. Three neurons of common types. The one at the left shows the myelin sheath formed from sheath cell membranes rolled several layers thick around the axon proper. Many neurons are much longer, relative to the diameter of axon and cell body, and many have much thinner myelin sheaths or only a single cell membrane surrounding the axon. Within nerve trunks outside of the central nervous system even the nonmyelinated axons lie inside sheath cells. (From Griffin, D. R., *Animal Structure and Function*. New York: Holt, Rinehart and Winston, 1962.)

3. A stimulus which produced contraction of one muscle would in general produce a relaxation of the antagonistic muscles (i.e., those muscles which tend to move the limb in an opposite direction). The first is attributed to the excitatory effect of the stimulus, and the second to its inhibitory effect.

4. If two stimuli each separately produced a response which affected the same muscles in the same way, then the effect of both stimuli together was greater than the effect of either alone. In some cases, particularly when the stimuli were intense, the effect of the two together was less than the arithmetical sum of the two separate effects. In other cases, particularly when the stimuli were weak, the effect of the two together was greater than the arithmetical sum of the two separate effects.

5. If two stimuli produced effects in opposite directions, i.e., were

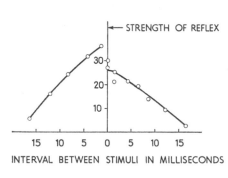

FIG. 14–2. Reflex responses of a muscle (*tibialis anticus*) to two stimuli (each one of which is just threshold) at various intervals to two nerves (med. gastroc. n. and lat. gastroc. n.) Abscissae—stimulus interval in msec.; ordinates—tension in grams. To right of zero, lat. gastroc. n. is stimulated first; to left of zero, med. gastroc n. first. Curve shows relation of stimulus intervals to resulting tension. (From Creed, R. S., et al., 1932, *Reflex Activity of the Spinal Cord*; courtesy of Clarendon Press, Oxford.)

antagonistic, then the two together produced an effect which was less than the effect of either alone. In general, the stimulus producing the greater response overcame the weaker, although there were many exceptions to this rule. Some reflexes which seem to have greater biological importance are, in Sherrington's term, prepotent and tend to overcome antagonistic reflexes even when the latter are of greater strength. Also a reflex which has been in operation for some time can be overcome more easily than a reflex which is stimulated for the first time.

To explain these characteristics of reflex behavior Sherrington developed some simple theories of nervous action which have since been largely confirmed by more direct investigations made possible by improved physiological techniques. Sherrington made use of the concept of the neuron in developing his theory of nervous activity, although no records of the activity of neurons existed at that time. He argued that nervous activity was passed from one neuron to another through the synapse. (Sherrington coined this word for the functional connection between one neuron and another.) This activity must finally be transmitted to the muscles via the motor neurons, and since many kinds of activity are mediated by the same muscles and by the same motor neurons, there must be a great deal of "convergence" of sensory and other neurons onto this "final common path." The exact nature of this convergence must determine the effect of combined stimuli.

Sherrington's model of the interaction of neurons is shown in Figure 14–3. Each incoming neuron connects with several other neurons in a particular neuron pool. Some of these will be affected to a threshold level, and others

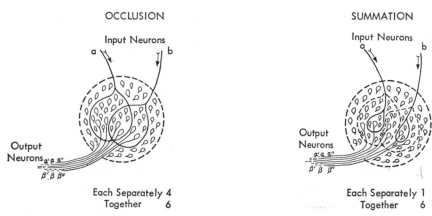

FIG. 14–3. Sherrington's model of neural interaction.

The dotted circles indicate the populations of neurons subliminally stimulated by each input neuron. The solid circles indicate the populations of neurons effectively stimulated by each input neuron. Neurons within the subliminal fringe of each input neuron are effectively stimulated by the summation of the two subthreshold effects.

Whether the effect for two simultaneous stimuli is more or less the sum of the effects of each separately is determined by the relative numbers of neurons subliminally or supraliminally excited by each stimulus, and the amount of overlap of the two populations. (Adapted from Creed, R. S., *et al.*, 1932, *Reflex Activity of the Spinal Cord*; courtesy of Clarendon Press, Oxford.)

only subliminally. The stronger the incoming signal the greater the proportion stimulated above threshold. If the incoming signal is too weak, it may be inadequate by itself to produce any activity in the neurons in the pool. The subthreshold effects of two stimuli may, however, be enough to excite some neurons in the pool when they are combined. At a slightly higher intensity each alone may excite a few neurons which are likely not to be the same ones. Still more neurons will be excited by the combined effect of the two incoming signals, so that the combined effect of the two will be greater than the sum of the effects of each alone. At a higher intensity still, each incoming signal excites practically all the neurons in the pool, many of them being excited by both ("convergence"). In this case the combined effect of the two incoming signals will be less than the sum of each separately.

To account for the temporal characteristics of excitation and inhibition, Sherrington postulated a central excitatory state (c.e.s.) and a central inhibitory state (c.i.s.). Both were thought of as active persisting states in a pool of neurons which could combine algebraically—the c.e.s. having a positive sign and the c.i.s. having a negative sign. The output from a pool of neurons is determined by the positive result of the combined c.e.s. and c.i.s. Figure 14–3 shows the different modes of excitatory interaction. One can fairly easily extrapolate to the possible interactions of c.i.s. alone, or c.e.s. and c.i.s. combined. Figure 14–4 shows the temporal characteristics of the c.e.s. and c.i.s. for two spinal reflexes.

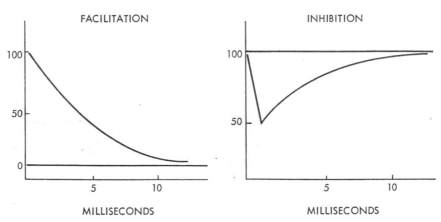

FIG. 14–4. The stimuli in these experiments were two short electrical stimuli to the sensory nerves, at different intervals (msec) between them. Natural stimuli prolong the time relations because of the long latency of the sense organs. (From Lloyd, *J. Neurophys.* 9, 1946.)

Modern methods of electrical recording reveal a great deal about the signals which are transmitted by the neurons and the nature of the c.e.s. and c.i.s.

## The Nerve Spike

The modern era of neurophysiology began when sensitive thermionic tube amplifiers were developed in the 1920's. These enabled the very fast low-voltage activity of the neurons to be recorded. A still further advance came with the development of the cathode ray oscilloscope, which gives a recording system with as fast a response as the electronic tube amplifiers. Figure 14–5 shows diagrammatically a typical modern apparatus for recording the activity of single nerves.

The unit of neural activity is the nerve spike. This unit is a transient change in voltage of about 60 mv. and lasting for about 0.4–2 msec. A continuously stimulated nerve will typically produce a train of these nerve spikes which travel at a constant rate away from the point of stimulation. Nervous conduction always involves spike activity, and the spike always has the same essential characteristics, whether recorded from simple nerve fibers or from a nerve trunk, from sensory or from motor nerves. The amplitude of the spike potential is astonishingly constant for a given nerve.

If a single short stimulus produces a single spike, a second similar stimulus will not produce a second spike unless there is a time interval of 0.4–2 msec. between the stimuli.

The second stimulus at short intervals produces no second spike. At slightly longer intervals a small second spike is produced, and at still longer intervals a full-sized second spike develops. This experiment may seem to

FIG. 14–5. Apparatus for recording the activity of single nerves.

contradict what has just been said about the constant amplitude of the spike. But in this case the small second spike travels more slowly along the axon than the larger first spike. In this way the interval between the two increases and at the same time the amplitude of the second spike increases until it equals the amplitude of the first spike. It then travels at the same speed as the first so that the time interval between them now remains constant.

If the intensity of the second stimulus is increased, a second spike can be evoked at shorter intervals, but for intervals of the order of 1 msec. no second spike can be produced, no matter how intense the second stimulus. This interval, within which no second spike can develop, is called the absolute refractory period. The larger interval within which a second spike can be produced, provided a strong enough stimulus is used, is called the relative refractory period. Preceding or following the relative refractory period there may be a short interval when the second spike may be more easily evoked than the first. This is known as the supernormal phase, but it is not found in all nerves. These phases of changing excitability following the nerve spike show a very close correlation with the form of the electrical activity in the nerve just after the spike. Recent work with microelectrodes placed within the nerve cell has made it possible to understand these correlations.

## Microelectrical Recordings

In the 1940's a number of techniques were developed for inserting electrodes into nerve cells (see Eccles, 1953). The first involved pushing electrodes down inside the cut end of a very large diameter axon. Later, workers made use of very fine electrodes which were pushed through the intact membrane of a nerve cell. In the latter case the electrodes could be inserted into the cell body or into the axon. In all these studies it has been found that the nerve membrane has a charge across it of about 60 mv., being negative on the inside. Effective stimuli decrease this voltage. When the membrane has been depolarized by a sufficient amount (usually to about 40 mv.), a spike potential develops. Following the spike, the original membrane potential is restored more or less rapidly. If the membrane stays relatively depolarized for a short time following the spike, then a smaller stimulus is needed to depolarize it to the threshold for a second spike. If it becomes relatively hyperpolarized, then a larger stimulus is needed to produce the threshold depolarization. The relative constancy of the threshold depolarization, coupled with the form of the membrane potential following the spike, provides at least a preliminary explanation of the relative refractory period and the supernormal phase. Figure 14–6 shows a

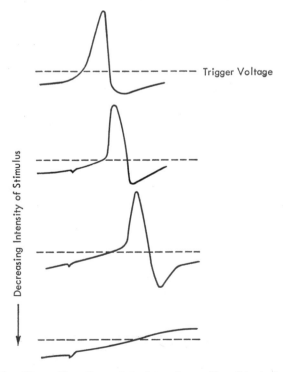

FIG. 14–6. Recording from interior of a cell subjected to increasing stimuli. (From Eccles, R. M., 1957; courtesy of The Johns Hopkins Press, Baltimore, Md.)

typical microelectrode recording from the interior of a cell which was subject to successively stronger and stronger stimuli. The depolarization took place more rapidly to the stronger stimuli, and so the trigger voltage was reached more quickly.

## The Resting Membrane Potential

The chemical composition of the axoplasm in the interior of the nerve cell is very different from the chemical composition of the tissue fluids which surround it. The membrane potential is developed because of the different concentrations of positive and negative ions on either side of the membrane. (An ion is an atom or molecule which has gained or lost electrons so as to acquire a net electrical charge. Such ions have complete electron shells and so are relatively inert chemically. However, their high electrical charge combined with their small size causes them to attract strongly other ions (as in a salt crystal) or molecules with a strong electrical dipole. In solution in water the ions tend to be surrounded by a relatively permanently attached shell of water molecules, attracted to the ions because of their strong electrical dipoles.)

The resting membrane is relatively permeable to the positive potassium ions which are found in their greatest concentration in the axoplasm. It may also be relatively permeable to the negative chloride ions which are found in the surrounding tissue fluid. The membrane is relatively impermeable to the positive sodium ions which are in their greatest concentration in the tissue fluid and also the very large negative ions which are found in the axoplasm (Figure 14–7). The net positive charge on the

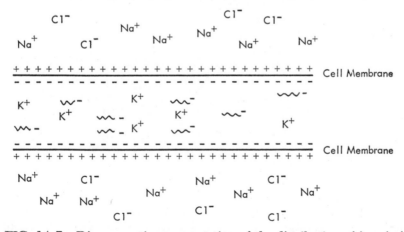

FIG. 14–7. Diagrammatic representation of the distribution of ions inside and outside a nerve cell. The cell membrane has a net positive charge in the outside largely because of an excess of positive sodium ions ($Na^+$) in the surrounding fluid and of negative organic ions (〜-) on the inside. Positive potassium ions ($K^+$) are in excess inside the cell and negative chloride ions ($Cl^-$) outside the cell, as a passive consequence of the distribution of the other two.

outside of the membrane is due to the distribution of these ions which will not pass through the membrane. The other ions will tend to pass through the membrane in such a way as to neutralize the charge developed across it by the ions to which it is impermeable. It seems likely that the presence of potassium ions in high concentration inside the membrane and of chloride in high concentration on the outside is a passive consequence of the distribution of the impermeable ions. Since potassium and chloride ions exist in such high concentrations on one side of the membrane to which they are freely permeable, they will tend to diffuse across the membrane towards the area of lower concentration. A state of equilibrium is achieved in which the diffusion gradient is opposed by the electrical gradient. Such an equilibrium is known as a Donnan equilibrium. The relationship between the electrical gradient and the concentration gradient should, under these conditions, be given by the Nernst equation:

$$Er = \frac{RT}{-F} \log_e \frac{(Ki)}{(Ko)} = \frac{RT}{F} \log_e \frac{(Clo)}{(Cli)},$$

Where $Er$ is the membrane voltage, $Ki$ and $Ko$ are the potassium concentrations inside and outside, and $Cli$ and $Clo$ are the chloride concentrations inside and outside the membrane, $T$ is the absolute temperature, $R = 8.2$ joules per mol-degree abs.; and $F = 96,500$ coulombs per mol.

The differences in concentration of most ions between the inside and outside of the membrane can be accounted for simply as a consequence of the difference in potential between the exterior and interior of the cell. For instance in the case of the negatively charged chloride ions these tend to be driven out of the electrically negative interior of the cell (because negative charges repel each other). On the other hand, such a tendency to expulsion is countered by the opposite tendency to diffuse back into the cell. The negativity inside the cell of 70 mv. coming into balance with this tendency to diffuse is sufficient to produce the difference which is observed between the concentration of the chloride ion inside and outside the cell. On the other hand, some additional factor besides such a balance is needed to explain the difference in concentration between the interior and the exterior of the cell in the case of the sodium and potassium ions; thus an active process in which the cell expends energy to transfer ions has been postulated. It has been called the "sodium pump."

The membrane potential is largely maintained by such an uneven distribution of the impermeable sodium ions, and there is a great deal of evidence that the distribution of sodium across the membrane is largely determined by an active process (the "sodium pump") which is clearly dependent upon metabolic energy for its operation. If a nerve is deprived of oxygen then the concentration of sodium in the interior of the nerve cell slowly increases and the membrane potential decreases. The same result has been obtained by squeezing out the contents of a giant squid axon and replacing them by various electrolytes. When the axon is filled with isotonic potassium solution, the membrane has a normal potential and is normally excitable. If on the other hand it is filled with sodium solution, the membrane potential falls to zero and the membrane becomes inexcitable (Baker, Hodgkin, and Shaw, 1961).

## Ionic Fluxes during the Nerve Spike

The nerve spike causes a sudden reversal of the membrane potential. The cause of this reversal is revealed by experiments which measure the resistance of the membrane. Coincident with the spike is a sudden decrease in the membrane impedance (resistance to alternating electrical current; Cole and Curtis, 1939) which is primarily due to the membrane becoming momentarily permeable to sodium ions (Hodgkin and Huxley, 1952). The detailed mechanism of the spike activity was investigated by Hodgkin and Huxley by the use of a voltage clamp. They inserted a core electrode 7 mm. into the cut end of a giant nerve fiber taken from a squid. Outside the axon was an external electrode. By means of an electronic feedback device they were able to "clamp" the membrane voltage at any desired value. They then measured the strength and direction of the current which had to be applied to preserve the voltage at a particular value. The applied current is the exact inverse of the currents developing naturally in the membrane under these conditions. Hyperpolarizing the membrane requires very little current to maintain the voltage. The resistance of the membrane remains high. A much smaller amount of depolarization produces a transient flow of current in such a direction as to cause a further depolarization. The voltage clamp has, therefore, to reverse the direction of its applied current for about 2 msec. in order to prevent the depolarization from increasing beyond the set value. After 2 msecs. the applied current again reverses, so that it is now again in the direction one would expect in order to maintain the depolarization. The spontaneous initial flow of current is produced by a very great lowering of the membrane's resistance to sodium ions, which flow rapidly across the membrane under the influence of the electrical and concentration gradient. It is this sudden inward flow of the positive sodium ions which produces the reversal of the membrane potential at the moment of the spike activity. When the sodium in the surrounding medium is replaced by chlorine, a large positive organic ion to which the membrane is impermeable, the transient inward flow fails to develop and the voltage clamp does not need to reverse the direction of the applied current. Instead there is a slow decrease in the membrane resistance which is due to an increased permeability to potassium ions which in the absence of the clamp would produce a net outward flow of current. The outward flow of potassium is almost certainly responsible for the fast recovery of the membrane potential to almost its initial value. The outward flow of potassium cancels, after a short delay, the effect of the inward flow of sodium. That sodium and potassium are largely responsible for the electrical activity of the nerve spike has been demonstrated by using radioactive traces, which show that spike activity produces a transfer of sodium and potassium across the membrane, but not of the other ions (Keynes, 1951; Eccles, 1957).

## Normal Synaptic Activity

### The Synapse

As has been stated above the nerve spike travels along a nerve fiber from the point at which it has been initiated. When the nerve spike reaches the end of the nerve fiber along which it is traveling, the spike normally reaches a synapse, or a structure which enables the signal from one neuron to be transferred to another closely neighboring neuron. The nerve fiber which carries impulses to other neurons is generally the axon. This ends in a multitude of small structures called synaptic knobs. These knobs are in close contact with the cell body and dendrites of a neighboring neuron, separated only by a gap of about 20 millimicrons, called the synaptic cleft. Each knob can be seen under the electron microscope to contain a large number of small round sacs, called synaptic vesicles. It is thought that each of these synaptic vesicles contain minute quantities of transmitter substance and that when a nerve spike arrives some of these sacs rupture, thus releasing the transmitter substance. This substance then diffuses across the synaptic cleft, altering the permeability of the membrane of the neighboring neuron to selected group of ions. In this way depolarization may occur at an excitatory synapse, and hyperpolarization at an inhibitory synapse, because of the different transmitter substances released.

### Excitatory Reactions

It has already been mentioned that the nerve membrane merely has to be depolarized to a threshold value for the nerve spike activity to be triggered. By placing microelectrodes within the nerve cell body it has been possible to record the activity of normal synapses (see summary by Eccles, 1957, 1965). Figure 14–8 shows the kind of record which is obtained from a spinal motoneuron when a small amount of excitation is produced by a weak stimulus to the appropriate sensory nerve. This activity is clearly very different from the nerve spike. It is of a much smaller voltage. It is relatively slow, and its voltage varies with the intensity of the stimulus. It is the result of normal synaptic activity and has been labeled an excitatory postsynaptic potential (e.p.s.p.). It is due to synaptic activity producing a small amount of depolarization of the membrane, the amount of depolarization probably determined by the number of nerve spikes reaching the synaptic knob from the presynaptic fiber. There is some evidence that the

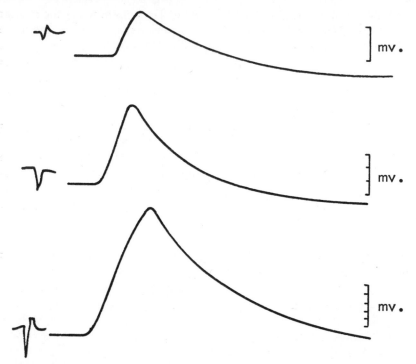

FIG. 14–8. E.p.s.p. to increasing intensities of presynaptic volleys. From Eccles R. M., 1957; courtesy of The Johns Hopkins Press, Baltimore, Maryland.)

e.p.s.p.'s are quantized, in that there is a minimum size for the e.p.s.p. and that large e.p.s.p.'s are the sum of many quantal e.p.s.p.'s. Simple spatial summation of e.p.s.p.'s can also be demonstrated by stimulating two different sensory nerves which probably act on different synapses in the same motoneuron. Temporal summation can also be demonstrated very simply. These potentials are called excitatory potentials because they depolarize the nerve membrane. When they depolarize the membrane to a threshold degree, they produce spike activity in the same way as an applied electrical stimulus will elsewhere. In fact, Figure 14–6 was obtained from a motoneuron stimulated in this way. The slowly rising potentials are e.p.s.p.'s of progressively increasing amplitude.

It seems clear that the e.p.s.p. can be identified with Sherrington's central excitatory state and that experiments on the e.p.s.p.'s have dramatically confirmed many of the properties of the central excitatory state which Sherrington had postulated on the basis of very indirect evidence. The summation of e.p.s.p.'s provides an obvious explanation of the summation of reflex effects. The time course of the e.p.s.p. agrees very closely with the time course of the central excitatory state postulated by Sherrington. The effect of varying the interval between two stimuli is accounted for by the observed decay time of the e.p.s.p. while the shorter latency with more intense stimulation is explicable in terms of the more rapid rise of the larger e.p.s.p.'s towards the threshold for spike activity. Temporal summation of e.p.s.p.'s evoked by successive spikes at a synapse can account for the longer latencies observed to prolonged low-intensity stimulation.

Even when temporal summation is invoked, it is difficult to account for some of the prolonged effects observed in spinal reflexes. Sometimes the reflex effect may be prolonged long after the termination of the stimulus. This is called the "afterdischarge" and is usually explained in terms of the activity in complex neuronal circuits which may be circular and so self-reexciting.

## Inhibitory Reactions

In some preparations, potentials resembling the e.p.s.p. but of opposite electrical sign have been observed (Figure 14–9a). They produce a transient

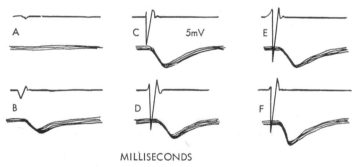

MILLISECONDS

FIG. 14–9a. Inhibitory postsynaptic potentials recorded in a biceps-semitendinosus motoneuron in the spinal cord of a cat, when a stimulus is applied to a sensory nerve from an antagonistic muscle, the quadriceps. The upper trace shows the afferent nerve activity recorded at the dorsal root. The lower curve shows the i.p.s.p. recorded simultaneously from a microelectrode in the motoneuron cell body. (From Coombs, Eccles, and Fatt, 1955; courtesy of *J. Physiol.*)

increase in the membrane potential and are clearly associated with inhibition. The simplest hypothesis about their activity is to assume that these i.p.s.p.'s (inhibitory postsynaptic potentials) are the equivalent of Sherrington's central inhibitory state and that they interact algebraically with the e.p.s.p.'s, the negative voltage of the i.p.s.p. canceling the positive voltage of the e.p.s.p. It has been shown that such interactions do in fact occur (Figure 14–9b). However, the effect of the inhibitory synapse has been shown to be greater than would be expected from a simple summation of the positive and negative e.p.s.p.'s and i.p.s.p.'s. Coombs, Eccles and Fatt (1955) compared the time course of inhibition as measured by the techniques shown in Figure 14–4 with the time course predicted from the assumption of simple summation of e.p.s.p. and i.p.s.p. measured. This comparison shows that there is a greater inhibitory effect at short intervals between the excitatory and inhibitory stimuli than would be expected from the simple summation hypothesis, but at larger intervals the simple summation hypothesis is adequate to account for all the inhibition

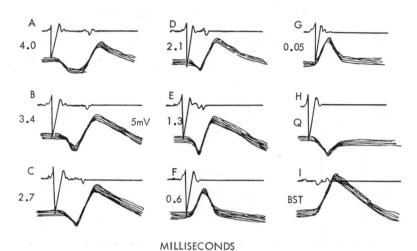

MILLISECONDS

FIG. 14–9b. The interaction of e.p.s.p. and i.p.s.p. in a biceps semi-tendinosus motoneuron. The upper trace shows afferent volleys recorded at the dorsal root for stimuli to quadriceps and biceps semitendinosus sensory nerves. The lower trace shows the interaction of i.p.s.p. and e.p.s.p. recorded with a microelectrode in the motoneuron cell body. The intervals in milli-seconds between the volleys is marked on each trace. (From Coombs, Eccles, and Fatt, 1955; courtesy of J. Physiol.)

which occurs. Figure 14–10 shows the experimental comparison by Araki, Eccles and Ito (1960) of the time course of inhibition and of the e.p.s.p. in the same preparation.

This discrepancy is explicable in terms of the ionic theory of excitation and inhibition developed by Eccles and others. We have already seen that the depolarization of nerve membrane during spike activity is due to a flow of positive sodium ions to the inside of the membrane, while the subsequent recovery of the membrane voltage is due to the flow of positive potassium ions to the outside. It is therefore not surprising to find evidence indicating that the e.p.s.p.'s are due to a small amount of ionic sodium leaking across the subsynaptic membrane and producing a local depolariza-tion of the cell membrane. These depolarizations of the membrane, which are insufficient to trigger off a spike potential, are not propagated along the membrane in the way that the spike potential is, they can have effects at a distance from their origin, but these effects decrease with distance from the origin. Similarly, the i.p.s.p.'s appear to be due to local hyperpolarization produced by a local flow of potassium ions to the outside of the membrane. This flow of positive ions occurs against the electrical gradient of the membrane potential. Eccles has suggested (1957, 1965) that since the hydrated potassium ion is smaller than the hydrated sodium ion, the difference between the excitatory and inhibitory effects at a subsynaptic membrane is simply due to differences in the size of the holes through

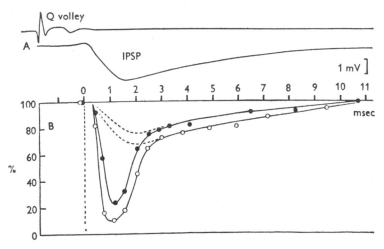

FIG. 14–10.  Reflex inhibition curves and i.p.s.p. in the same preparation from Araki, Eccles and Ito, 1960. In *B* the ordinate shows the percentage size of the reflex spike recorded from a ventral root in the cat. The response was produced by a standard stimulus to an afferent nerve from the biceps semitendinosus muscle delivered at various times after a similar stimulus to an afferent nerve from the quadriceps muscle, which is antagonistic to the semitendinosus. *A* shows the time course of an i.p.s.p. recorded in a ventral horn cell and the dotted line in B shows that part of the inhibitory effect which can be attributed directly to the hyperpolarizing effect of the i.p.s.p. (By courtesy of *J. Physiol.*, 1960.)

which the ions can pass. If at an excitatory subsynaptic site the permeability of the membrane were increased by the appearance of a number of relatively large holes in the membrane, then both sodium and potassium ions could pass through. But in this case more sodium would pass from outside to inside, assisted by the electrical gradient across the membrane, than potassium from inside to outside against the electrical gradient. Thus the net effect would be one of depolarization. If at the inhibitory sites there is an increase in permeability due to the appearance of smaller holes in the membrane, which are large enough to let through the potassium ions but not the sodium ions, then diffusion of potassium ions from the inside to the outside of the membrane will depolarize the membrane. If this concept of inhibition is correct we would expect there to be a limit to the degree of hyperpolarization which can occur at the subsynaptic membrane, because hyperpolarization increases the electrical gradient across the membrane and so increases the resistance to the passage of more positive potassium ions to the outside. In fact, as Eccles has shown (Coombs, Eccles, and Fatt, 1955) hyperpolarization of the membrane can cause the i.p.s.p. to reverse its sign so that the inhibitory synapse produces a depolarization rather than a hyperpolarization of the membrane. Because of this effect the amount of potassium flowing outward will be greater at such a site if the membrane is depolarized by excitatory action at adjacent sites. Hence the inhibitory effect of an inhibitory site should be greater than one would expect from the amount of hyperpolarization produced in the absence of any excitatory effect. By assuming that the i.p.s.p. is due to a transient increase in the permeability of the membrane to potassium, producing hyperpolarization which persists for a short time after the permeability returns to normal, we have a complete and satisfying explanation of the data shown in Figure 14–10. The excess of inhibitory effect at short intervals is due to the increased, but selective, permeability at the inhibitory subsynaptic membrane.

In the previous discussion we have ignored the question of what happens to the chloride ions in the subsynaptic membrane. This is because the evidence concerning chloride is less satisfactory than the evidence concerning sodium and potassium. Eccles' original hypothesis supposed that chloride is freely passed by both inhibitory and excitatory membranes and that since it will tend to hyperpolarize the membrane, its action is similar to that of potassium. Recent evidence, however, indicates that the excitatory membrane is relatively impermeable to chloride (Takeuchi and Takeuchi, 1960), while the inhibitory membrane is relatively permeable to it (Araki, Ito and Oscarson, 1961).

## The Nature of Synaptic Transmission

There has in the past been some dispute about the physical nature of synaptic transmission, whether it was due to a direct electrical influence of the presynaptic spike activity on the synaptic membrane or to the release of a chemical "transmitter" by the presynaptic membrane by the presynaptic spike activity which then diffused across to the subsynaptic membrane. The evidence now points solidly to the latter mechanism (see Eccles, 1953, 1957; and Nachmansohn, 1959). Perhaps the most direct evidence against the electrical theory of transmission was obtained by Bullock and Hagiwara (1956), who recorded from intracellular electrodes simultaneously in the presynaptic and postsynaptic regions of the giant synapse of the squid *Loligo*. They found that the depolarization of the postsynaptic membrane does not begin until the presynaptic spike potential is almost completely finished. The delay at the synapse is most easily explained in terms of the time taken for a transmitter substance to diffuse across the gap between the synaptic knob and the subsynaptic membrane.

A great deal more is now known about the chemistry of these transmitter substances, notably acetylcholine, which has been shown to be involved in transmission across the neuromuscular junction, in sympathetic and in parasympathetic ganglia, and which is present at many other sites in the peripheral and central nervous system. These transmitter substances act on the subsynaptic membrane to produce the e.p.s.p.s. and i.p.s.p.s. They are probably synthesized within the presynaptic nerve fiber, are released when a nerve spike reaches the synapse, diffuse across the space between the pre- and postsynaptic membranes, and are then destroyed by the action of an enzyme so that their activity lasts only a short time. Possibly the decomposition products then migrate back to the presynaptic fiber and are resynthesized into the transmitter substance. A number of drugs are known which interfere with this cycle. For example curare is known to prevent transmission at the neuromuscular junction by blocking the sites on the synaptic membrane which receive acetylcholine. Strychnine and tetanus toxin appear to have a similar action at inhibitory synapses. Other drugs may have their effect by interfering with the breakdown or resynthesis of the transmitter or by preventing the release of the transmitter from the presynaptic membrane. Dale (1935) proposed that the transmitter substance released by a nerve was the same at all its synapses. This hypothesis has received some support; for example, the $\alpha$ motoneurons of the spinal chord whose axons make synaptic connection with the muscle fibers of skeletal muscle, also make synaptic connection, via branching collateral fibers, with the small Renshaw cells within the spinal cord. The evidence that acetylcholine is the transmitter at the neuromuscular junction is now overwhelming. It has also been found that anticholinesterases, which prevent the enzymatic breakdown of acetylcholine, greatly prolong the discharge of the Renshaw cells, so it appears likely that acetylcholine is the transmitter here also. Dale suggested that no nerve can have an excitatory and inhibitory action since, he supposed, the synaptic effect of a transmitter was characteristic of the chemical nature of the transmitter rather than the nature of the subsynaptic membrane. There seems to be no a priori reason to expect this to be the case, and, in fact, examples have been found recently, in invertebrates, where the same transmitter has both excitatory and inhibitory effects. Terzuolo and Bullock (1958) investigated the activity of the extrinsic inhibitory axon of the cardiac ganglion of the lobster and found that it could produce depolarization of some cells in the ganglion and hyperpolarization of others. Apparently the same cell made direct synaptic connection with each neuron and so was having opposite effects on different cells. There is, as yet, no indication that this sort of thing occurs in vertebrates, where there is considerable evidence that inhibition is the function of specialized cells, probably small internuncial neurons. There has been some controversy about this recently. Lloyd and Wilson (1945) maintained that the existence of monosynaptic inhibitory effects proved that the same sensory fiber must be having both excitatory and inhibitory effects. Eccles (1961 and elsewhere) has maintained with some heat that there are no monosynaptic inhibitory effects, and has supported this assertion by showing that the latencies of i.p.s.p.'s produced by an afferent volley were about 1 msec. longer than the latencies of the e.p.s.p.'s in different cells but produced by the same afferent volley (Eccles, Fatt, and Landgren, 1956). This was attributed to the extra delay introduced by the excitation passing through an extra synapse to an inhibitory internuncial neuron. Lloyd and Wilson (1959) answered this argument by proposing that the i.p.s.p. was not the cause of inhibition but an unimportant aftereffect of inhibition, occurring about 1 msec. after the inhibitory process. Eccles (1961) and Frank and Fuortes (1961) have disagreed emphatically with Lloyd and Wilson's hypothesis. The recent work of Araki, Eccles, and Ito (1960) has shown that the onset inhibition recorded directly is within 0.1 msec. of the onset of the i.p.s.p.'s recorded in the same preparation (Figure 14–12).

There is some evidence that in a chain of neurons the successive neurons produce different transmitter substances. For example, in the optic pathway it appears that the bipolar cells release acetylcholine, the ganglion cells do not, while there is evidence that the synapses in the lateral geniculate also release acetylcholine. Such an alternation of transmitter substance possibly prevents self-stimulation at a synapse. Further evidence for alternation of transmitter substance is provided by the finding that myanesin selectively depresses polysynaptic reflexes but has no effect on monosynaptic reflexes. This suggests that the internuncials in a polysynaptic reflex have a different transmitter substance from the primary sensory fibers. Strychnine has a complementary action to myanesin, since it potentiates polysynaptic reflexes, but has little effect on monosynaptic reflexes (Eccles, 1957). Strychnine has been shown to block the action of inhibitory transmitters so that alternation of transmitter mechanisms may occur for the inhibitory fibers also.

Evidence that a nerve cell may be stimulated by its own transmitter substance is provided by the evidence for presynaptic inhibition (see section on presynaptic inhibition).

## Quantization of the Synaptic Mechanism

Fatt and Katz (1952) showed that at the neuromuscular junction, even in the absence of efferent spike activity, there were transient depolarizations of the postsynaptic membrane. These were attributed to the release of acetylcholine by a chance process possibly related to Brownian motion. Acetylcholine is thought to be present in the muscle end plate (the equivalent of the synaptic knob for this function) in the form of minute vesicles containing the acetylcholine in solution. These vesicles are so small that they must undergo vigorous Brownian Motion, and the accidental release of acetylcholine at the neuromuscular junction seems not unlikely.

## Presynaptic Inhibition

Frank and Fuortes (1957) found a reduction in the effectiveness of stimuli to muscle sensory fibers in exciting $\alpha$ motoneurons in the spinal cord of the cat when sensory fibers from antagonistic fibers were also stimulated. The time course of this inhibition was considerably longer than that shown in Figures 14–4 and 14–10, having its maximum effect about 10 msec. after the beginning of the inhibitory stimulus. Moreover it did not correlate with any observable change in the excitability of the postsynaptic cell or with the production of any observable i.p.s.p.s. Frank and Fuortes called this "remote" inhibition and suggested it could be due either to inhibitory synapses on the ends of the dendrites of the $va$ motoneurons which were so far from the recording electrode that their direct effect could not be recorded, or that it could be due to a reduction in the effectiveness of the afferent impulses at a presynaptic level. Eccles (Eccles, Eccles, and Magni, 1961; Eccles, Magni, and Willis, 1962) has found impressive evidence for the latter mechanism. Under certain conditions stimulation of muscle afferents will produce a dorsal root reflex, i.e., antidromic firing of other afferent fibers. The time course of this dorsal root reflex is the same as that of Fuortes' "remote" inhibition, and conditions which favor the one also favor the other (cooling of the spinal cord and stimulation of flexor rather than extensor afferents). Moreover, they both correlate with the appearance of an oriented d.c. potential in the spinal cord whose orientation is best explained in terms of depolarization of the terminal branches of the afferent fibers within the cord. On the basis of this evidence Eccles has suggested that there is a second mechanism of inhibition which he has renamed presynaptic inhibition. If it is supposed that the afferent fibers make synaptic connections with the terminal branches of other afferent fibers, and that they produce depolarization of the subsynaptic membrane, then the correlation of the inhibition with the dorsal root reflex is explained. The depolarization may become enough to trigger off spike activity which will be conducted antidromically and appear as the dorsal root reflex. If the depolarization is not sufficient to trigger off spike activity, its effect will be to reduce the amplitude of afferent spikes when they reach the depolarized terminal branch. It is a plausible hypothesis that these smaller spikes should release less transmitter substance than the normal size spikes.

Hubbard and Willis (1962) have shown that direct artificial depolarization of the afferent nerve branches has an inhibitory effect, and Gray (1962) has observed structures in the spinal cord of the cat which could be small synapses overlaying the large synaptic knobs which are in contact with the ventral horn cells. Lundberg and Voorhoeve (1961) have observed what appears to be presynaptic inhibition in the spinal cord as a result of stimulation of the sensorimotor cortex, so that presynaptic inhibition may not be restricted to reciprocal inhibition of afferent fibers in the spinal cord, but may be a widely used mechanism throughout the nervous system.

## The Origin of the Spike Potential in Normal Synaptic Activity and the Maintenance of Sustained Discharges

Normal e.p.s.p.'s have time constants of the order of 1–10 msec. Longer time constants have been observed, however, in the giant ganglion cells of Aplysia and in the Renshaw cells of the mammalian spinal cord. Recently, different time constants have been found for e.p.s.p.'s within the same cell. Brookhardt and Fatiga (1960) and Fatiga and Brookhardt (1960) found that the e.p.s.p.'s in the frog motoneuron had different time constants according to whether they were evoked by stimulation of the dorsal roots or by stimulation of the lateral column within the spinal cord. It seems likely that the synapses concerned were at different sites on the cell soma or on the dendrites. Since the nerve spike probably does not reach the dendrites, a fairly steady depolarization could be maintained at subsynaptic sites on the dendrites.

It has been suggested that in some dendrites at least something like nerve spike activity can occur. Lorente de Nó thought that such dendritic spikes might not be completely self-maintaining and might decrease in amplitude as they travel along the dendrites. Spencer and Kandel (1961) found evidence for possible dendritic spikes in hippocampal neurons, and, of course, in many nerve cells the distinction between dendrites and axons seems rather arbitrary (see Figure 14–1).

Whether or not the spike invades the dendrites, there is some evidence that in normal synaptic activation the nerve spike is triggered off first in the axon hillock, not in the membrane of the soma (Eccles, 1957). Nerve spikes recorded from electrodes in the soma of the spinal motoneurons have a slightly different shape from those recorded from the axon itself. They always have a slight notch in the rising phase of the spike. It is suggested that the initial rise is due to the spike activity at the axon hillock and that the later sharp rise is due to the spike activity in the cell soma and dendrites. The chief evidence for this comes from the effect of hyperpolarization on the antidromically evoked spike. At normal membrane potentials there is a full-sized spike with a notch in the rising phase, but when the cell is hyperpolarized only a small spike is observed, whose amplitude corresponds to the height of the notch on the normal spike. It is suggested (Eccles, 1955) that the small spike occurs at the axon hillock and that the spike does not propagate to the soma or the dendrites under these conditions, because of the hyperpolarized state of the membrane. The lower threshold of the axon hillock may be due to the relative absence of synaptic knob in the region of the cell.

Because the normally evoked spike has the same shape as the antidromically evoked spike, it seems likely that the synaptic activity triggers off the spike at the axon hillock and that it then propagates backwards into the cell body as well as orthodromically along the axon. Edwards and Ottoson (1958) have shown by direct recording that the spike potential in the lobster stretch receptor originates at some distance from the cell body.

It is clear that the nerve cell itself is capable of quite complex integrative activity. The mammalian motoneuron whose cell body is only about 70 $\mu$ across with dendrites up to 1mm. (1,000 $\mu$) long may have as many as 100 synaptic connections on it coming from a very large number of afferent fibers and ascending and descending fibers in the spinal cord. Some neurons may act as simple summators of the excitatory and inhibitory influences acting upon them. But in other cells the interaction may be much more complex.

A great deal of new evidence concerning the integrative activity of single cells has come from work on invertebrates where in a number of cases ganglia containing small numbers of comparatively large cells have proved particularly easy to work on. Vertebrate nerve cells may not have such complex activity as these invertebrate cells but there is no good reason, except lack of evidence, to suppose that they have not. Bullock (1959) and Horridge (1963) have summarized a great deal of the vertebrate and invertebrate work on single neuron preparations, and Bullock has described the present situation as a "quiet revolution in our concepts of how nerve cells act alone and in concert." Unfortunately this quiet revolution has not resulted in a new ordering of the subject but has, instead, revealed new orders of complexity which still remain to be explored. The new complexity consists largely in the discovery of local differences within single cells. The classification of cellular potentials suggested by Bullock is shown in Figure 14–11. In any cell many of these potentials may be simultaneously present. We have as yet very little quantitative data on their interaction. In addition, there may be changes in the state of the cell not revealed by the potentials. One example of this has already been dealt with in the account of inhibition produced by increased permeability of the cell membrane. Another example is facilitation, where successive impulses arriving at a synapse may produce successively larger e.p.s.p.'s, or diminution, where the reverse occurs. Neither effect correlates with a change in the membrane potential. If one adds to these effects the possibility of presynaptic inhibition, the theoretically possible but as yet unobserved presynaptic facilitation, and nonsynaptic interaction between nerve cells, it is clear that even in relation to the interaction of a small number of nerve cells, we have very little quantitative information. Concerning the interaction of large numbers of nerve cells, we have no information at all because of the technical difficulty of the problem.

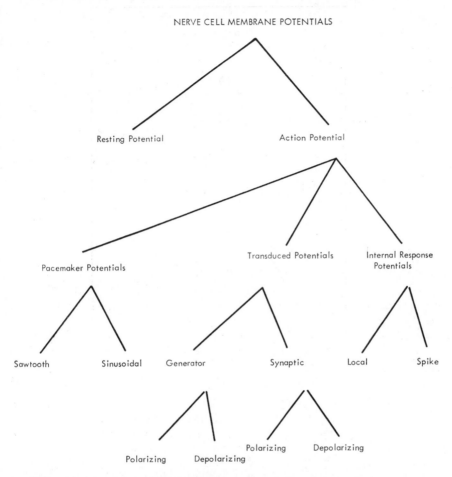

NERVE CELL MEMBRANE POTENTIALS

**FIG. 14–11. Nerve cell membrane potentials. (From Bullock, T. H., "Neuron Doctrine and Electrophysiology," *Science*, 129, 1959.)**

## INPUT-OUTPUT RELATIONS IN SIMPLE SYNAPTIC SYSTEMS

The complexity of the interactive mechanisms revealed in the previous section may produce an extreme variety and complexity of possible modes of interaction between cells. Unfortunately we have very little direct information concerning the input-output relations of single cells or groups of cells.

One piece of evidence comes from records from gross electrodes in the lateral geniculate (Bishop and McLeod, 1954). An electric shock applied to the optic nerve produces a synchronous volley of impulses which reach the lateral geniculate simultaneously and produce a sharp positive deflection recorded from the gross electrode on the optic tract or in the lateral

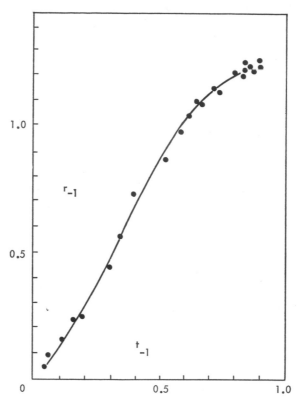

FIG. 14–12.   The amplitude, in millivolts, of the postsynaptic $r_1$ spike plotted against that of the presynaptic $t_1$ spike, the strength of shock to the optic nerve being varied and all other conditions held constant. (From Bishop, P., and McLeod, *J. Neurophysiol.* 17, 1954.)

geniculate. The electrode on the optic tract records only a single deflection, but the electrode in the lateral geniculate records two deflections with peaks separated by about 0.4 msec. The second deflection is probably the synchronized postsynaptic spikes appearing after the usual synaptic delay. Bishop and McLeod measured the relationship between the amplitude of the pre- and postsynaptic spikes. An almost linear relationship was found (Figure 14–12). Since only a single spike was evoked in each fiber, the data are relevant only to spatial interaction at the lateral geniculate. The very simple relationship found may not be characteristic of other synaptic systems, since the amount of spatial interaction in the lateral geniculate may be unusually small.

There seems no direct evidence concerning the relationship between the frequency of spike impulses reaching a synapse and the frequency of postsynaptic spikes. There is, however, some indirect evidence suggesting that the relationship may normally approach linearity. Hodgkin (1948) has shown that there is a linear relationship between the depolarization of the cell membrane and the frequency of nerve spikes generated. We also know that each spike will produce an e.p.s.p. of about the same amplitude and that these will summate. So, provided the spikes are not separated by too great a time, there should be a linear relationship between the frequency of spikes and the amount of depolarization. An argument of this type is probably behind Rushton's assumption (1961) that excitatory interactions are linear.

There is a great deal of very elegant and quantitative work on inhibitory interactions in the eye of limulus polyphemus, the horseshoe crab

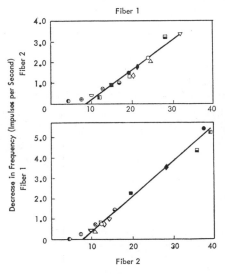

FIG. 14–13. Mutual inhibition of two receptor units in Limulus polyphemus. In each graph the magnitude of the inhibitory action (decrease in frequency of impulse discharge) exerted on one of the ommatidia is plotted on ordinate as a function of the degree of concurrent activity frequency of the other abscissa. The different points were obtained by using various intensities of illumination on ommatidia 1 and 2, in various combinations. The data for points designated by the same symbol were obtained simultaneously. (From Hartline and Ratliff, *J. gen. physiol.*, 1957; by permission of the Rockefeller University Press.)

(Hartline and Ratliff, 1957, 1958; Hartline, Ratliff and Miller, 1961), and on the inhibitory interactions of the Renshaw cells in the spinal cord with the α motoneurons of the ventral horn in the cat (Granit, 1961). In both cases the interaction appears to be almost linear. Granit's experiment is conceptually simpler. The Renshaw cells are stimulated by branching collaterals of the α motoneurons within the spinal cord. They have an inhibitory action of adjacent α motoneurons within the central horn. Their normal action is probably to reduce the total α motoneuron response to afferent or centripetal stimulation. They can be stimulated independently of an afferent stimulation by antidromic stimulation of the α motoneurons at the ventral root. Granit recorded the activity of a single fiber at one ventral root to varying degrees of afferent stimulation. He then recorded the activity produced by the same stimulation when the cell was inhibited by a standard stimulus to an adjacent ventral root and investigated the relationship between the normal frequency and the reduced frequency resulting from the standard amount of inhibition. The results could be fitted fairly well by the equation

$$fi = fu - c \, ,$$

where $fi$ is the frequency when inhibited, $fu$ the uninhibited frequency, and $c$ a constant.

Hartline and co-workers have obtained even better data from a more complex system (Figure 14–13). Limulus has a faceted eye with each ommatidium sending a fiber to the optic lobes in the crab brain. Hartline records from a single fiber and measures its frequency of firing as a function of light intensity when the appropriate ommatidium alone is stimulated (or a small number of ommatidia around the appropriate one). If a small group of adjacent ommatidia are now simultaneously stimulated, it is found that the response of the first fiber is reduced by the inhibitory action of the adjacent ommatidia. The situation is complicated by the fact that the first group of ommatidia also inhibit the second, so that to describe the mutual interaction of single sensory cells in the Limulus eye, Hartline has to set up sets of simultaneous equations such as

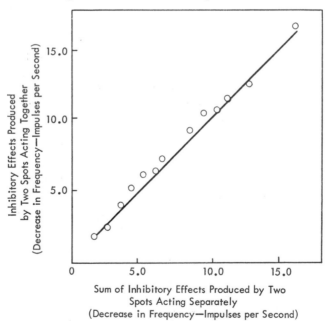

FIG. 14–14. The summation of inhibitory effects produced by steady illumination, at various intensities, of two widely separated groups of receptors. The sum of the inhibitory effects on a test receptor (steadily illuminated at a fixed intensity) produced by each group acting separately is plotted as abscissa; the effect produced by the two groups of receptors acting simultaneously is plotted as ordinate. (From Hartline and Ratliff, *J. gen. physiol.*, 1958; by permission of the Rockefeller University Press.)

$$r_1 = e_1 - K_{1,2} \{ r_2 - r^\circ_{1,2}$$

$$r_2 = e_1 - K_{2,1} \{ r_1 - r^\circ_{2,1}$$

where $r_1$ and $r_2$ are the simultaneous frequencies of two fibers whose ommatidia are close enough to inhibit each other and which are being separately stimulated, $e_1$ and $e_2$ are the frequencies with which each would fire if stimulated separately, $K_{1,2}$, $K_{2,1}$ are constants expressing the degree of mutual interaction, while $r^\circ_{1,2}$ and $r_{2,1}$ are constants indicating that the inhibitory effect has a threshold so that when, for example, $r_2$ is less than $r^\circ_{1,2}$ the second fiber will have no inhibitory action on the first. Hartline has been able to show that these equations represent very accurately the behavior of this particular system with the proviso that the expression in the brackets can only take positive values. Negative values are equivalent to zero since no inhibition then occurs. Hartline has also shown that a number of the consequences which might be expected to result from the activity of such a system, do in fact occur. Such a mechanism produces spatial contrast and the enlargement of activity at the edge of a patterned stimulus. And if a third ommatidium is stimulated this may inhibit the second fiber to a greater degree than it inhibits the first fiber, so that stimulation of the third ommatidium may actually increase the rate at which the first fiber fires by releasing it from the inhibition exerted by the second. Hartline has compared this to the disinhibition which is observed in the interaction of spinal reflexes. Hartline and Ratliff have also shown that when ommatidia which are far enough apart to have no mutual inhibitory effect, their inhibitory effects on an intermediate ommatidium show simple linear summation (Figure 14-14).

# 15

# THE NERVOUS SYSTEM

The nervous system is generally subdivided into three main portions:
(1) *the central nervous system* comprising the brain and spinal cord; (2)
*the peripheral nervous system* comprising the cranial and spinal nerves;
and (3) *the autonomic nervous system* comprising the autonomic nerves
and ganglia.

## THE PERIPHERAL NERVOUS SYSTEM

There are generally considered to be twelve pairs of cranial nerves which
are attached to the brain at irregular intervals. These are highly specific in
organization and function, and their anatomical arrangements are described where relevant in other portions of the book (Figure 15–1).

Thirty-one pairs of spinal nerves originate from the spinal cord. These
consist of eight pairs of cervical spinal nerves, twelve pairs of thoracic
nerves, five pairs of lumbar nerves, five pairs of sacral nerves, and one pair
of coccygeal nerves (Figure 15–2).

Each spinal nerve is made of the union of two nerve roots passing out of
the spinal cord. The first is the ventral root, which carries efferent fibers.
The second is the dorsal root, which is composed of afferent fibers. (There
are some exceptions to this functional division.) Just before the dorsal and
ventral roots unite there is an enlargement or swelling on the dorsal root
called the dorsal ganglion. This contains the cells of origin of the dorsal
root fibers. The cells of origin of the ventral root fibers lie in the ventral
horn of the grey matter of the spinal cord (Figure 15–3).

Each spinal nerve makes its exit from the vertebral canal by means of an
opening between the vertebrae (intervertebral foramen). It then branches
into dorsal and ventral rami. Many of the spinal nerves enter into
complicated plexuses where they intermingle considerably. As a result, the
regions supplied by the peripheral nerves arising from these plexuses do not
correspond to the regions supplied by the spinal nerves entering the

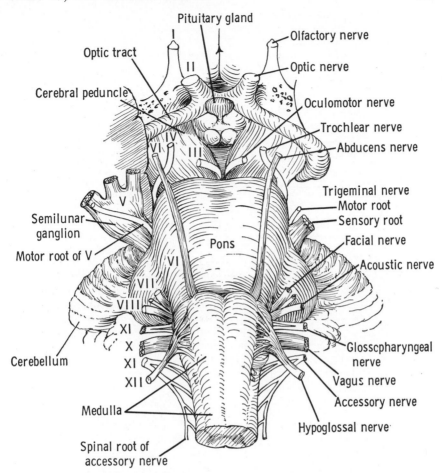

**FIG. 15–1.** Emergence of cranial nerves from the brain. View from base of brain. Note the position of the medulla, pons, and pituitary gland. (From Chusid, J. G., and McDonald, J. J., *Correlative Neuroanatomy*, 12th ed., Lange Medical Publications 1964.)

plexuses. That is, one spinal nerve may contribute to several peripheral nerves and one peripheral nerve may distribute fibers derived from several spinal nerves. There is also considerable overlap between the areas supplied both by the spinal nerves and by the peripheral nerves.

## THE AUTONOMIC NERVOUS SYSTEM

The outflows of the somatic and autonomic nervous systems may be distinguished on the basis of the types of effector organ which they innervate. Whereas the somatic outflow is distributed to striated muscle, the autonomic outflow innervates the smooth muscle of the viscera and blood vessels, cardiac muscle, and glands.

FIG. 15–2. The origin of the spinal nerves in the spinal cord. C1-8 = cervical spinal nerves; T1-12 = thoracic nerves; L1-5 = lumbar nerves; S1-5 = sacral nerves; Coc. 1 = coccygeal nerve. The associated vertebrae are marked in Roman numerals. (From Haymaker, W., and Woodhall, *Peripheral Nerve Injuries*, Philadelphia: W. B. Saunders Company, 1953.)

Further distinctions between somatic and autonomic outflows are generally made on the basis of function. For instance, the somatic outflow is more under voluntary control than is the autonomic outflow. We find it easier to control the movements of our limbs than to control our heart rate, respirating, or body temperature, for example. Of course, this is only true as a general statement. A further distinction often made is that whereas the somatic nervous system is concerned with regulating external environment, the autonomic nervous system regulates our internal environ-

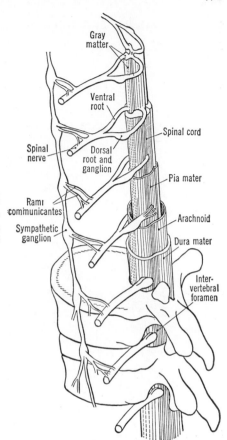

FIG. 15–3.  The spinal cord and associated structures. (From Gardner, E. Q., *Fundamentals of Neurology*, 4th ed. Philadelphia: W. B. Saunders Company, 1963.)

ment. Autonomic outflow regulates body temperature, blood pressure, heart rate, respiration, digestive function, and so on, thus maintaining constancy in our internal environment. However, exceptions could again be found to this general distinction.

The outflow of the autonomic nervous system has its own anatomical arrangement, as described below. One characteristic which distinguishes it from the somatic outflow concerns the location of the ultimate neuron. Somatic motor neurons always have their cell bodies located inside the central nervous system. In the autonomic system (with the exception of the innervation of the adrenal medulla) the cell bodies of the ultimate neurons are located outside the central nervous system. Another interesting difference between the two outflows is that if autonomic effector organs are completely denervated they will usually not degenerate, but will continue to function autonomously. In contrast, striated muscle will atrophy after denervation.

## The Sympathetic and Parasympathetic Divisions of the Autonomic Nervous System

The autonomic nervous system has traditionally been classified into two divisions (Figures 15–4 and 15–5). The first has been named the

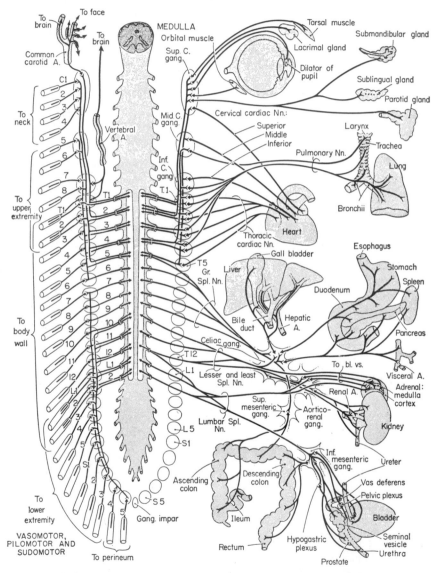

**FIG. 15–4.** Diagram to illustrate the sympathetic division of the autonomic nervous system. On the left side of the spinal cord is shown the innervation of the blood vessels, sweat glands and pilomotor muscles. On the right is shown the innervation of the various viscera. (Reprinted with permission of the Macmillan Company from *Correlative Anatomy of the Nervous System*, by Crosby, Humphrey and Lauer. Copyright 1962 by the Macmillan Company.)

sympathetic or thoracicolumbar division, and the second the parasympathetic or craniosacral division. This classification has been made on several grounds. First, the two divisions originate in different portions of the central nervous system. Second, the sympathetic outflow is much more diffuse than the parasympathetic outflow. This is apparent first from the anatomical arrangements of the two systems, described below. Second, the sympathetic outflow innervates the adrenal medulla, which discharges epinephrine and norepinephrine into the blood stream. These substances

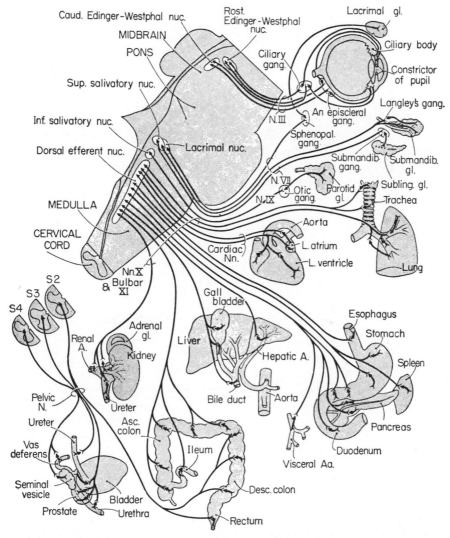

FIG. 15–5.  The parasympathetic division of the autonomic system as it innervates the various viscera. (Reprinted with permission of The Macmillan Company from *Correlative Anatomy of the Nervous System* by Crosby, Humphrey and Lauer. Copyright 1962 by the Macmillan Company.)

are the sympathetic transmitter substances, and so such a release has the general effect of a diffuse sympathetic activation.

Figures 15–4 and 15–5 provide a summary of the sympathetic and parasympathetic outflows and their functions. It will be noted that some of the autonomic effector organs are innervated only by sympathetic fibers. Others are acted on by both sympathetic and parasympathetic influences. In the latter case the two influences often have antagonistic actions. For instance sympathetic influences accelerate the heart and parasympathetic influences decelerate it. Again, in some cases sympathetic activation causes vasodilation and parasympathetic activation causes vasoconstriction. However, the two influences may act synergistically. For instance both sympathetic and parasympathetic influences stimulate secretion of the salivary gland, but the secretions stimulated by the two pathways differ in viscosity.

Two points may be made concerning these contrasting effects. First, it appears that the sympathetic system is activated in states of emergency to mobilize body resources for such events as flight or fighting. Thus an animal under stress has dilated pupils, increased blood pressure, deepened respiration, it sweats, its hair stands on end—all of these are sympathetic effects. In contrast, parasympathetic functions such as occur in the digestive tract are inhibited. On this basis the general statement has been made that sympathetic activities predominate in states of stress, and parasympathetic activities in states of quiescence. But again this is a very general statement, to which exceptions may be found. Another function of this system of antagonistic innervation is that it can provide a very sensitive regulatory device, based on the two sets of tonic discharges impinging on the same effector organ.

## Anatomical Organization

Autonomic outflow originates from *preganglionic neurons*. In the brain stem these are located in the nuclei of cranial nerves III, VII, IX and X. Those in the spinal cord form a long column in the intermediolateral part of the grey matter. The small myelinated preganglionic fibers (axons of preganglionic neurons) leave the central nervous system by way of their corresponding cranial nerve or ventral root. They synapse with *postganglionic neurons*, located in ganglia outside the central nervous system. The unmyelinated postganglionic fibers (axons of postganglionic neurons) project to autonomic effectors.

## Location of Autonomic Ganglia

Two long nerve trunks extend one on each side of the vertebral column. These are known as the *sympathetic chains* or *trunks*, and they consist of sympathetic ganglia and fibers joining them (Figure 15–3). There are 21 or

22 sympathetic ganglia in each chain. Sympathetic ganglia are also located elsewhere in the body. The parasympathetic ganglia are not arranged in trunks, but are located in or near the effector organs which they innervate.

## Sympathetic Outflow

Sympathetic preganglionic neurons are located in the thoracic and upper lumbar spinal segments. Their axons leave the spinal cord via the ventral roots, and enter the corresponding spinal nerves. However, they leave these nerves via the *white rami communicantes* to enter the sympathetic trunks. Here a preganglionic fiber may pass up or down the trunk and then synapse with postganglionic neurons. In this case it would connect with postganglionic neurons located in several ganglia. It has been calculated that preganglionic fibers from a single white ramus may activate as many as eight ganglia. Alternatively a preganglionic fiber may pass without synapse through the sympathetic trunk into a splanchnic nerve to reach other ganglia. Some preganglionic fibers in the splanchnic nerve directly innervate the adrenal medulla, without the intervention of postganglionic neurons.

Postganglionic fibers originating in ganglia of the sympathetic trunk pass through the *grey rami communicantes* to enter their corresponding spinal nerves. Running in these nerves they reach the skin and subcutaneous tissue, and these innervate blood vessels, sweat glands, and smooth muscle of hair follicles. Some postganglionic fibers arising in the cervical and thoracic ganglia are distributed to structures in the thoracic cavity and the head.

Postganglionic neurons located in other sympathetic ganglia send fibers to various organs, as shown in Figure 15–4.

## Parasympathetic Outflow

The parasympathetic outflow may be divided into two portions: the cranial and the sacral. The preganglionic neurons of the cranial division are located in the nuclei of cranial nerves III, VII, IX, and X in the brain stem. Fibers arising therefrom proceed in these nerves and synapse with postganglionic neurons located close to or actually in visceral effectors in the thorax, abdomen, and head. The preganglionic neurons of the sacral division are located in the second, third, and fourth spinal segments. Their fibers leave the nervous system via the appropriate ventral roots and run in the pelvic nerves to synapse with postganglionic neurons located in ganglia close to or actually in the autonomic effector organs which they innervate. These include the bladder, colon, rectum, and blood supply to the genitalia. In contrast with the sympathetic system, interconnections between ganglia in the parasympathetic system are very few, so that parasympathetic outflow is more discrete (Figure 15–5).

## Directions in the Brain

Anatomists have developed a terminology to enable them to refer to directions in the brain. We shall first describe this terminology as it is applied to infrahuman forms. Structures toward the front of the head are called anterior; those toward the tail posterior or caudal. Those toward the top of the head are called dorsal or superior; those toward the base, ventral or inferior. This is because in most animals dorsal (literally, belonging to the back) structures are in fact higher or superior to ventral (literally, belonging to the belly). In the human case the nomenclature is often kept, as if man had not adopted upright posture and consequently bent the top of his nervous system through 90°. Structures at the base of the human brain are often called ventral (even though in terms of direction with regard to the rest of the body they should be called caudal).

Further as the central nervous system is symmetrical about a midline or a plane, structures closer to the plane about which symmetry occurs are called medial, and those away from such a plane, lateral. The plane about which the nervous system is symmetrical is called the median plane. Any plane parallel to the median plane is a sagittal (Latin sagitta, arrow) plane. A coronal or frontal plane divides the brain in such a way that all points on one side of it are anterior to those on the other. A horizontal plane divides the brain so that all points on one side of it are superior to the points on the other side of such a plane. Such planes have to be specified especially in the case of sections or cuts through the nervous system.

## THE CENTRAL NERVOUS SYSTEM

## Development of the Central Nervous System in the Human Embryo

At one stage of embryonic development a neural tube is formed, and it is from this that the mature nervous system is derived. The brain is formed from one part of the tube and the spinal cord from the rest. Together they form the central nervous system (Figure 15–6).

Three enlargements develop in the portion of the tube which constitutes the brain. These are: (a) the forebrain or prosencephalon, (b) the midbrain or mesencephalon, and (c) the hindbrain or rhombencephalon. Later the forebrain itself subdivides into two enlargements: (i) the endbrain or telencephalon, and (ii) the interbrain or diencephalon.

With further development, from the telencephalon are derived the cerebral cortex, the corpora striata and the rhinencephalon. From the diencephalon are derived the thalamus, epithalamus, and hypothalamus.

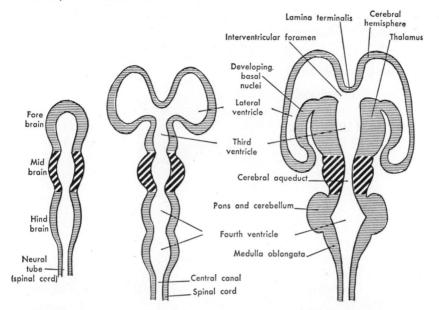

FIG. 15–6. Diagram of three- and five-vesicle stage in the development of the brain, with early development of the cerebral hemispheres. (From Gardner, E. Q., *Fundamentals of Neurology*, 4th ed. Philadelphia: W. B. Saunders Company, 1963.)

The corpora quadrigemina and crura cerebri develop from the mesencephalon, and the cerebellum, pons, and medulla are finally derived from the rhombencephalon.

## Gross Anatomy of the Brain

### The Brain Ventricles

The brain ventricles are derived from the cavity of the embryonic neural tube. They are filled with cerebrospinal fluid, which also circulates around the subarachnoid space surrounding the brain.

Running through the caudal portion of the medulla is a prolongation of the central canal of the spinal cord. This ultimately broadens into the diamond-shaped *fourth ventricle,* and this is continuous with the relatively small *cerebral aqueduct* which runs through the mesencephalon. The cerebral aqueduct opens into the *third ventricle,* a narrow cleft which runs through the diencephalon. This communicates through the interventricular foramina with the *lateral ventricles* of the cerebral hemispheres. The walls and roof of the fourth ventricle contain the lateral and median apertures, through which cerebrospinal fluid circulates to the subarachnoid space (Figure 15–7).

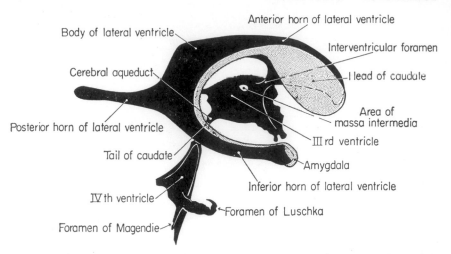

FIG. 15–7. The brain ventricles with caudate nucleus and amygdala. (Reprinted with permission of The Macmillan Company from *Correlative Anatomy of the Nervous System* by Crosby, Humphrey and Lauer. Copyright, 1962, by the Macmillan Company.)

## The Spinal Cord

The central nervous system consists of the brain and the spinal cord. We shall begin with a description of the spinal cord. This structure is most relevant to the subject matter on motor function and somesthetic mechanisms, for through it run pathways which produce movement in most of the body, and also pathways which convey sensory information from most of the body. Further, in the spinal cord itself, some of the information about the state of the body is applied to the pathways producing movement.

The spinal cord is deemed to begin at the foramen magnum (Latin—large opening) at the base of the skull. It passes through a segmented hollow tube of bone called the vertebral column. The segments of this tube are called vertebrae. These vertebrae are divided into four groups: seven cervical (neck) vertebrae, twelve thoracic (chest) vertebrae, five lumbar (lower back) vertebrae, and the sacral vertebrae, fused into a single bone, at the end of the spinal column. The spinal cord, however, only extends just beyond the first lumbar vertebra (see Figure 15-2) though separate nerve trunks and roots of spinal nerves continue to run through the vertebral column. This collection of nerves at the bottom of the spinal column is called cauda equina (Latin—horse's tail) from its appearance. There are openings between the vertebrae from which pass the spinal nerves.

The spinal cord itself retains much the same arrangement throughout its length. It consists of two portions: the butterfly shaped gray matter,

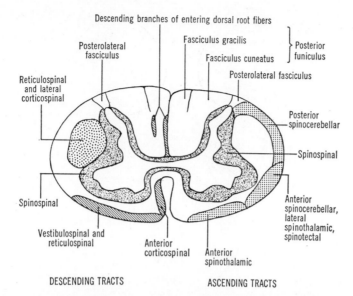

Descending branches of entering dorsal root fibers

Posterolateral
fasciculus

Fasciculus gracilis

Fasciculus cuneatus

Posterior
funiculus

Posterolateral fasciculus

Reticulospinal
and lateral
corticospinal

Posterior
spinocerebellar

Spinospinal

Spinospinal

Anterior
spinocerebellar,
lateral
spinothalamic,
spinotectal

Vestibulospinal and
reticulospinal

Anterior
corticospinal

Anterior
spinothalamic

DESCENDING TRACTS          ASCENDING TRACTS

**FIG. 15–8.** The main tracts of the spinal cord. Only afferent ascending tracts are shown on the right; only efferent descending tracts are shown on the left. (From Gardner, E. Q., *Fundamentals of Neurology*, 4th ed. Philadelphia: W. B. Saunders Company, 1963.)

containing mostly cell bodies, surrounded by the second component, the white matter, made up of nerve fibers. Out of the gray matter emerge on one side the ventral roots and on the other side the dorsal roots. The tracts tional significance is dealt with in the chapters on somesthesis and motor function. There are local enlargements in the amount of gray and white matter in the spinal cord where the nerve supply to the limbs leaves the composing the white matter are illustrated in Figure 15–8. Their func- cord, namely in the cervical and lumbosacral regions. This leads to a local enlargement of the diameter of the whole cord.

## The Brain

### The Hindbrain

The hindbrain consists of the medulla oblongata, pons and cerebellum.

*The Medulla.* As the cranial cavity is entered through the foramen magnum we reach the region known as the medulla. Here there is a gradual rearrangement of the structures seen in the spinal cord together with an addition of other structures, such as some of the nuclei of the cranial nerves (Figure 15–9).

The cells of origin of the sensory components of cranial nerves lie outside the main neural column; this arrangement is similar to that found

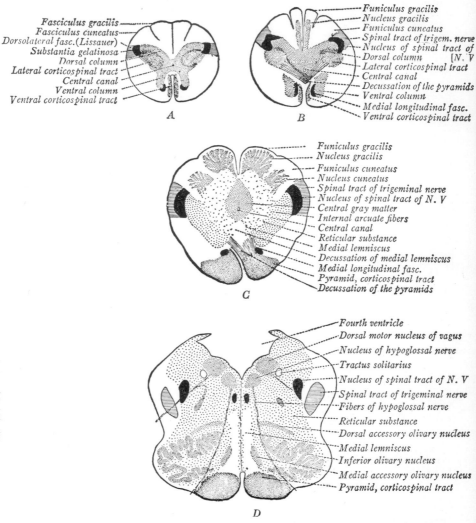

FIG. 15–9. Diagrammatic cross sections to show the relation of the structures in the medulla oblongata to those in the spinal cord: A, First cervical segment of spinal cord; B, medulla oblongata, level of decussation of pyramids; C, medulla oblongata, level of decussation of medial lemniscus; D, medulla oblongata, level of olive. (From Ranson, S. W., and Clark, S. L., *The Anatomy of the Nervous System*. Philadelphia: W. B. Saunders Company, 1959.)

in the dorsal roots and their ganglia. The ganglia found at the bulbar (adjectival form of the medulla) level belong to the trigeminal, facial, glossopharyngeal, vagus, cochlear, and vestibular nerves. On the sensory side, the fibers from the cells in these external ganglia of origin pass out to the periphery and also into the medulla where they form synaptic connections with the cell bodies of sensory fibers of the second order.

These aggregations of cell bodies and their afferent connections form various sensory nuclei within the medulla. From these second order sensory neurons connection is made to motor neurons (forming motor nuclei) which then pass out of the central nervous system to form the efferent components of the cranial nerves. Connections are also made by the second order sensory neurons to centers higher in the nervous system. The spatial arrangement of these tracts and nuclei of these cranial nerves is illustrated in Figures 15–1 and 15–9.

An important change which takes place in the medulla, as mentioned above, lies in the gradual rearrangement of the components of the spinal cord as it passes upwards. This is due mainly to two developments. First, the fibers in the ventral corticospinal tract and the lateral corticospinal tract come together to form one large corticospinal tract called the pyramids (Figure 15–9) which occupies the ventral and medial portion of the medulla. To do this the lateral corticospinal tracts cross over from one side of the medulla across the midline to the other. This crossing is known as the decussation of the pyramids. In crossing over the fibers also swing towards the ventral portion of the medulla (Figure 15–9). The second change which modifies the appearance of the medulla as it passes upward is the termination of the fibers of the gracile and cuneate fasciculi. The fibers of these fasciculi end in the nucleus gracilis and nucleus cuneatus, and synapse there with the cell bodies and dendrites of neurons whose axons pass upwards and are known as internal arcuate fibers. These fibers cross the midline to the opposite side in what is known as the decussation of the lemniscus. They then pass upwards to the thalamus in a fiber tract called the medial lemniscus. At about the level where the medial lemniscus appears there is found a set of prominent landmarks known as the olivary nuclei. The inferior olivary nucleus looks like a heavily crumpled gray band enclosing a tract known as the hilus of the olivary nucleus. Close to it is placed the medial accessory olivary nucleus.

A somewhat less conspicuous though very important occupant of this area is the reticular formation. This is a region consisting of mingled white and gray matter, occupying the spaces between the better defined structures in the pons and the medulla. In it are included the lateral reticular nucleus, the reticular nucleus of the pontine tegmentum, the paramedian reticular nucleus, the large-celled or gigantocellular reticular nucleus, the caudal reticular nucleus of the pons, and the oral reticular nucleus of the pons which extends up to the midbrain. Less conspicuous are the small-celled reticular nucleus and the ventral reticular nucleus (Figure 5–6, Chapter 5).

The reticular formation sends fibers to the anterior portions of the spinal cord, and to many parts of the brain. There are also systems of fibers connecting the various parts of the reticular formation. On the afferent side there is input from the main sensory pathways and from many brain structures (see Chapter 10). This region is considered important for a variety of functions, and there is particular interest in its role in arousal and attention.

*The Pons.* The pons is composed of two parts: the dorsal or tegmental part and the ventral or basilar portion. The dorsal part is a direct continuation of the medulla. The ventral part is composed of three types of structure. The first consists of longitudinal fibers, that is, fibers passing parallel to the main axis of the nervous system. Some of these are corticospinal fibers which pass through the pons (and in the medulla become the pyramids), and yet others, called corticopontile fibers end in the pons. The corticopontile fibers and collaterals from the corticospinal fibers make synaptic connections with the second set of structures in the pons, the nuclei pontis. These nuclei of gray matter in their turn contain cell bodies whose fibers form the third structure in the ventral pons. These fibers run at right angles to the main axis of the nervous system, and the majority cross the midline to collect at the level of the pons in the large middle cerebellar peduncle which curves upward to enter the cerebellum, in company with the ventral spinocerebellar tract (Figure 15–10).

There are two other peduncles connecting the cerebellum to the rest of the nervous system: the inferior cerebellar peduncle and the superior cerebellar peduncle. The first consists of ascending fibers of the dorsal spinocerebellar tract, the olivocerebellar tract from the inferior olivary nuclei, and dorsal and ventral external arcuate fibers arising from cuneate, arcuate, and lateral reticular nuclei. The second, or superior cerebellar peduncle, consists of efferent fibers to the red nucleus and the thalamus (Figure 15–10).

The dorsal or tegmental part of the pons contains the dorsal and ventral cochlear nuclei. In these end the fibers of the cochlear nerve. Most of the fibers from the cochlear nuclei cross the reticular formation to and in the superior olivary complex, which may be divided into five main nuclear masses (see chapter on hearing). Some fibers arising in the cochlear nuclei end in the reticular formation, others travel to the ipsilateral superior olivary complex, and others join the tract of the lateral lemniscus. The tract of the lateral lemniscus arises mainly in the superior olivary complex. Also, efferent fibers from this complex run to back the ipsilateral and contralateral cochleae.

In this portion of the pons are to be found also the nuclei of the vestibular nerve at the floor of the fourth ventricle. These nuclei contribute a large proportion of the fibers in the medial longitudinal fasciculus, which is especially concerned with the reflex control of the head and eyes. The pons further contains the motor nucleus of the facial nerve, the nucleus of the abducens nerve, and the nuclei of the trigeminal nerve. The medial lemniscus (carrying somatosensory fibers to the thalamus) also runs through the pons.

*The Cerebellum.* The cerebellum is an entirely separate structure,

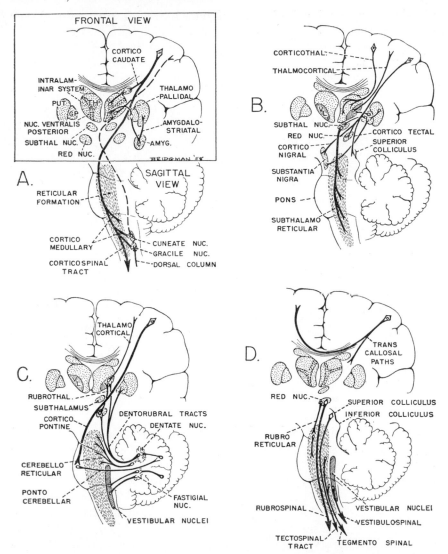

FIG. 15–10. A scheme of major corticosubcortical interrelations. In each figure the cerebral hemisphere has been drawn in coronal section and the brain stem in sagittal view. A: Arrangement of the primary sensory pathway (dashed) and the corticospinal, corticomedullary, corticostriated and amygdalo-striated pathways. B: Major corticothalamic, corticorubral, corticonigral and rubroreticular connections. C: Corticopontocerebellar, Cerebelloreticular, cere-bellovestibular and cerebellorubrothalamic paths. D: Origin of the main subcortical motor influences descending to spinal levels. (From Terzuolo and Adey, 1960, *Handbook of Physiology*, Vol. II, by permission of the American Physiological Society.)

already adequately described in the chapter on motor function, and only connected to the pons by structures described above.

### The Midbrain

The ventral portion of the midbrain is similar in certain features to the pons (Figure 15–11). At the base are the cerebral peduncles. The outermost layers of these are occupied by a large plate of efferent fibers called the basis or pes pedunculi, which continue into the pons. Above this we observe a new feature, the substantia nigra, which divides the region of the efferent tracts from the rest of the mesencephalon. It consists largely of cells whose axons are sent into the structure just dorsal to it, the mesencephalic tegmentum. This is continuous with the reticular formation of the pons, being similar in structure. As in the case of the reticular

Lamina quadrigemina
Cerebral aqueduct
Central gray stratum
Tegmentum
Basis pedunculi
Substantia nigra

FIG. 15–11. Schematic cross section of the human mesencephalon. (From Ranson, S. W., and Clark, S. L., *The Anatomy of the Nervous System*. Philadelphia: W. B. Saunders Company, 1959.)

formation of the pons and medulla, the midbrain has many nuclei and fiber tracts imbedded in it. Among the nuclei may be mentioned the ventral and dorsal tegmental nuclei. These receive fibers from the mammillary body (see below) via the mammillo-tegmental tract.

The most conspicuous fiber tract coursing through the tegmentum is the superior cerebellar peduncle. This decussates within the tegmentum, and soon after crossing the midline it reaches the red nucleus (nucleus ruber) and mostly ends within it. (However, some fibers from the superior cerebellar peduncle reach the ventral part of the thalamus.) Fibers from the red nucleus pass down to the medulla and to the spinal column to form the rubrospinal tract, and some pass back to the cerebellum and reticular formation. The fibers descending from the red nuclei to the bulbar and spinal levels cross the midline to form the ventral tegmental decussation otherwise known as the decussation of Forel.

Moving upward and towards the midline we come to the central gray stratum, surrounding the cerebral aqueduct. The central gray stratum contains the nuclei of the oculomotor and trochlear nerves and the mesencephalic root of the trigeminal nerve. Going still further up (dorsal) we come to the roof of the midbrain or the mesencephalic tectum. Here lie the corpora quadrigemina. These are two pairs of bodies, the superior colliculi and the inferior colliculi. Most of the fibers of the lateral lemniscus run to the inferior colliculus fibers from which form a part of the brachium of the inferior colliculus, running to the medial geniculate body. The majority of the afferent fibers to the superior colliculi come from the optic tract. Fibers arising from the superior colliculi sweep around the central gray stratum then to form the dorsal tegmental decussation of Meynert and then pass downward as the tectobulbar and tectospinal tracts.

# The Diencephalon

The diencephalon connects the cerebral hemispheres with the mesencephalon. The thalamus, epithalamus, subthalamus, and hypothalamus are classified together as parts of the diencephalon. (The retinae and the optic nerves are embryologically a part of this portion of the central nervous tissue.)

## The Subthalamus

The subthalamus forms a zone of connection between the dorsal thalamus and the mesencephalic tegmentum. Certain of the structures of the mesencephalon continue into it. These are the red nucleus, substantia nigra, and the reticular formation of the mesencephalon. (This last is called the zona incerta in the mesencephalon.) Lateral to the subthalamus lies the internal capsule as it reforms into the basis pedunculi. The internal capsule consists partly of a sheet of fibers (enveloping much of the thalamus) which stream downward from the motor cortex on their way to the pons and the spinal cord and partly of fibers running from various portions of the thalamus to the cortex. Medial and rostral to the subthalamus is the hypothalamus. The subthalamus includes the subthalamic nucleus (or corpus luysii) whose connections are more elaborately described in the chapter on motor function. Some connecting bundles may be seen in the fields on Forel (divided into three parts H, $H_1$, and $H_2$). These are the fasciculus lenticularis from the internal division of the globus pallidus, and the ansa lenticularis also from the globus pallidus. These bundles are joined by some others and collect together to form the thalamic fasciculus, which then runs to the anterior ventral nucleus of the thalamus.

## The Hypothalamus

The hypothalamus is one of the most essential structures in the brain. It plays a very important role in the regulation of many functions, including body temperature, water balance, hormone level, sleep and wakefulness, cardiovascular adjustments, eating and drinking, sexual activity and emotion. Detailed descriptions of its role in several of these functions are given elsewhere in the book.

The hypothalamus lies on the ventral surface of the brain close to the third ventricle and ventral to the thalamus and subthalamus. Its anterior border is rostral to the optic chiasm, and its posterior border caudal to the mammillary bodies, which appear on the surface of the brain as two rounded bodies (mammillaris, Latin—of breast). Anterior to this lies the tuber cinereum, which as its Latin name betokens is an ashen or gray excrescence, to which is attached the infundibulum (Latin—funnel, so named for its shape). This forms the connection between the hypothalamus and the hypophysis, whose functions are discussed in the section on the endocrine system (Figure 15–12).

FIG. 15–12.  Diagram showing relative positions in sagittal plane of hypothalamic nuclei in typical mammalian brain, and their relation to fornix, stria habenularis and fasciculus retroflexus. A, anterior commissure; Ch, optic chiasma; Hyp, hypophysis; 1, lateral preoptic nucleus (permeated by the medial forebrain bundle); 2, medial preoptic nucleus; 3, paraventricular nucleus; 4, anterior hypothalamic area; 5, suprachiasmatic nucleus; 6, supraoptic nucleus; 7, dorsomedial hypothalamic nucleus; 8, ventromedial hypothalamic nucleus; 9, posterior hypothalamic nucleus; 10, medial mammillary nucleus; 11, lateral mammillary nucleus; 12, premammillary nucleus; 13, supramammillary nucleus; 14, interpeduncular nucleus (a mesencephalic element in which the fasciculus retroflexus terminates); 17, fornix; 18, fasciculus retroflexus of Meynert (habenulopeduncular tract). (From Le Gros Clark et al., The Hypothalamus. London: Oliver and Boyd, 1938.)

Various cell groupings can be discerned in the hypothalamus. In the anterior (or supraoptic) region are the preoptic, supraoptic and paraventricular nuclei. In the middle or tuberal region there are the dorsomedial and ventromedial hypothalamic nuclei. In the posterior or mammillary region are the medial and lateral mammillary nuclei and the nucleus intercalatus.

The hypothalamus is also composed of large fiber tracts. Some of the most important afferent tracts are the medial forebrain bundle which runs in a rostro-caudal direction, the fornix connecting the hippocampus with the mammillary nuclei, the stria terminalis connecting the amygdaloid nuclei with the anterior region of the hypothalamus, and the mammillary peduncle through which fibers arising from spinal and tegmental structures reach the lateral mammillary nucleus.

On the efferent side, the supraopticohypophyseal tract arises from the supraoptic nucleus and courses through the infundibulum into the neural lobe of the hypophysis. Fibers from the tuber cinereum and the paraventricular nucleus also end there. It is to be stressed that innervation from the hypothalamus reaches only one division of the hypophysis, namely the neurohypophysis (sometimes referred to as the posterior hypophysis). This produces oxytocin and a vasopressor antidiuretic agent. The adenohypophysis (or anterior pituitary) is devoid of innervation by the hypothalamus, being instead controlled by secretions from the hypothalamus (as described in the section on the endocrines). There are three other major efferent tracts: the mammillothalamic tract of Vicq d'Azyr, which joins the medial mammillary nucleus to the anterior thalamic nuclei; the mammillotegmental tract, which connects the medial mammillary nucleus to the mesencephalon; and the dorsal longitudinal fasciculus, which interconnects a large number of structures in the thalamic and hypothalamic nuclei, mesencephalon, pons, and medulla.

### The Thalamus

The thalamus lies under the lateral ventricle and on the side of the third ventricle. It is divided by the internal medullary lamina (a vertical sheath of white matter) into lateral and medial masses. Anteriorly this internal lamina divides to enclose the anterior nuclei (a third group) of the thalamus (Figure 5–7, Chapter 5, and Figure 15–13).

The thalamic nuclei have been divided into five categories on morphological ground. The anterior nuclei connect the mammillothalamic tract with the gyrus cinguli. The nuclei of the midline, lying along the edge of the third ventricle, are connected with the hypothalamus. The medial nuclei include the medialis dorsalis, which projects to the hypothalamus and prefrontal lobe, centrum medianum (centre median of Luys), and the intralaminar nuclei. The center median and the intralaminar nuclei have no direct connections with the cortex.

The lateral nuclear mass contains the nucleus ventralis anterior which is connected with the basal ganglia, the nucleus ventralis lateralis which connects the superior cerebellar peduncle to the motor areas of the cortex, and the nuclei lateralis dorsalis and lateralis posterior which receive fibers from other thalamic nuclei and are connected with the parietal lobe and the tip of the temporal lobe of the cortex. They are continuous with the pulvinar which is part of the posterior thalamic nuclear complex. The nucleus ventralis posterior, also a part of the lateral nuclear mass, is a relay

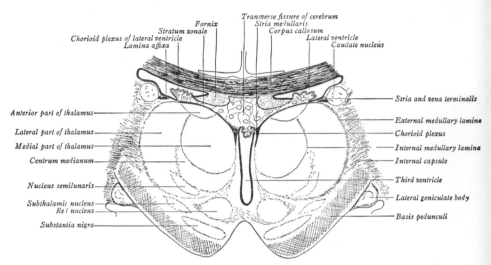

FIG. 15–13.   Diagram of the frontal section through the thalamus and surrounding structures. (From Ranson, S. W., and Clark, S. L., *The Anatomy of the Nervous System*. Philadelphia: W. B. Saunders Company, 1959.)

station for the somesthetic pathways and taste. Its subdivisions and connections are described in the chapter on central somesthetic mechanisms.

The posterior nuclear group include the pulvinar, the medial geniculate body, and the lateral geniculate body. The pulvinar is connected with other thalamic nuclei and has connections with the cortex in the posterior parietal and temporal lobes. The connections of the medial geniculate are described in the chapter on hearing and those of the lateral geniculate in the chapter on vision. It seems a common principle that connections between thalamic nuclei and the cortex run both ways.

There is evidence that several of the thalamic nuclei which do not have specific cortical connections are involved in the regulation of arousal and sleep. They have been termed the "thalamic reticular system," and a description of this system is given in the chapter on arousal and attention (Figure 5–7, Chapter 5).

## The Epithalamus

The epithalamus is an area dorsal and rostral to the superior colliculi in the mesencephalon. It includes the pineal body (not composed of neural elements), the habenular nucleus, stria medullaris, and the posterior commissure. Some of the fibers of the posterior commissure connect together the two superior colliculi. The stria medullaris ends in the habenular nucleus. It arises in the medial olfactory area, subcallosal gyrus, preoptic area, and amygdaloid nuclei. The habenular nucleus is connected with the interpeduncular ganglion in the mesencephalon via the fasciculus retroflexus of Meynert.

# The Telencephalon

## The Basal Ganglia

The cerebral hemispheres consist mainly of a surface layer of gray matter together with a massive substructure of white matter or fibers. However, there are various masses of gray matter within the hemisphere. These are the caudate and putamen (collectively known as the striatum) globus pallidus, the amygdaloid nuclei, and the claustrum (Figure 15–14).

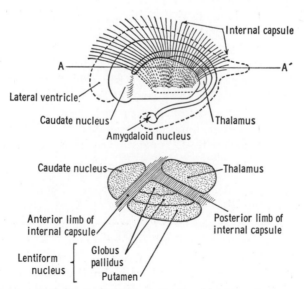

FIG. 15–14. Top: Lateral view of basal ganglia and adjacent structures. Bottom: Horizontal cross section at level AA′ of top diagram. (From Chusid, J. G., and McDonald, J. J., *Correlative Neuroanatomy*, 12th ed. Lange Medical Publications, 1964; after N. B. 1965, *Functional Neuroanatomy*, 5th ed. Lea and Febiger, Everett.)

The caudate nucleus (nucleus caudatus) as its name implies (Latin caudatus—tailed) has a long tail. The head of the caudate bulges into the anterior horn of the lateral ventricle. The tail is U-shaped and curves caudal and ventral and then rostral again on the inferior ventricular horn to end as far rostral as the amygdaloid nucleus (Figure 15 7). The caudate is partly separated from the putamen by the internal capsule, though the two have the same histological structure. The putamen is separated from the globus pallidus (sometimes known as the pallidum) by the internal medullary lamina. (There is a terminological difficulty about these three structures. Together they are known as the corpus striatum. However, the caudate and putamen only are together called the striatum. The globus pallidum and the putamen are together known as the lentiform or lenticular nucleus (because together they are shaped like a lentil; Latin lens—lentil).

Fibers from the striatum pass to the pallidum and thence to the anterior part of the ventral thalamic nucleus as described above.

The claustrum is a thin plate of cell bodies separated by the external capsule (a band of fibers) from the putamen which lies medially, and laterally by another band of fibers from the insula (a part of the cortex).

The amygdaloid body (Greek—amygdaloeides, almond-like) is located in the roof of the inferior ventricular horn and it is continuous with the cortex of the temporal lobe. It is divided into two main parts: the corticomedial and the basolateral, which are further subdivided. The main efferent path of the amygdaloid body is the stria terminalis. This runs to the hypothalamus and preoptic regions. As has been described in detail in the chapter on smell, the amygdaloid body also receives input from the olfactory system. This is why it is often classed as a part of the rhinencephalon, the name for those parts of the telencephalon credited at one time with olfactory function. These parts evolved earlier than the other parts of the telencephalon. The amygdaloid body is also considered to be important in a variety of functions, including emotion, and the regulation of eating, drinking, and sexual behavior.

## The Rhinencephalon

The literal meaning of the term "rhinencephalon" is nose-brain, from the Greek rhis, rhinos, nose, and enkephalos, brain. The main structures comprising the rhinencephalon include the olfactory bulb, and the olfactory tract, which divides into the lateral and medial olfactory striae. Further there is the anterior perforated substance, composed of gray matter extending between the olfactory striae and the optic tract, and also the pyriform area, which includes the lateral olfactory gyrus, the uncus and the anterior portion of the hippocampus (Figure 15–15). The hippocampus (Greek word meaning seahorse) is situated on the floor of the inferior horn of the lateral ventricle. The side which projects into the ventricle is

Longitudinal fissure of cerebrum
Optic nerve
Optic chiasma
Rhinal fissure
Insula
Lateral fissure
Optic tract
Infundibulum
Mammillary body
Cerebral peduncle
Interpeduncular fossa and nucleus
Trigeminal nerve
Abducens nerve
Acoustic nerve { Vestibular n.
Cochlear n.
Glossopharyngeal nerve
Vagus nerve
Hypoglossal nerve
Anterior median fissure

Olfactory bulb
Medial olfactory gyrus
Anterior perforated substance
Lateral olfactory stria
Lateral olfactory gyrus
Diagonal band
Amygdaloid nucleus
Pyriform area
Hippocampal gyrus
Trochlear nerve
Pons
Abducens nerve
Facial nerve
Trapezoid body
Cerebellum
Olive
Chorioid plexus
Accessory nerve
Tractus lateralis minor

FIG. 15–15. Ventral view of the sheep's brain. (From Ranson, S. W., and Clark, S. L., *The Anatomy of the Nervous System*. Philadelphia: W. B. Saunders Company, 1959.)

covered by the alveus, a thin coating of fibers which then continues into the fimbria of the hippocampus which in turn is continuous with the fornix, the chief efferent tract of the hippocampus (Figure 15–16). The hippocampal commissure is a band of fibers connecting together the two fornices close to the crus of the fornix (Latin—crus, leg) a portion of the fornix. The anterior commissure joins the olfactory bulbs and the pyriform areas of the two cerebral hemispheres. A further structure, the analogue of which is proportionately much larger in rat than in man, is the septum. This is a thin-walled structure separating the lateral ventricles, placed between the fornix and the corpus callosum.

Some of the structures of the rhinencephalon form part of the central olfactory pathways (see chapter on taste and smell). Many rhinencephalic structures are considered to be important in the regulation of emotion. The hippocampus is thought to be intrinsically involved in memory functions.

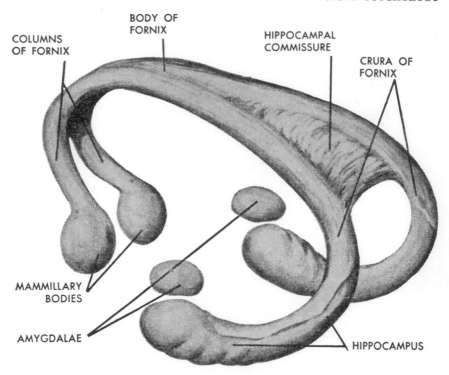

FIG. 15–16. The hippocampus and associated structures. (Crura is the plural of crus.) (From *The CIBA Collection of Medical Illustrations* by Frank H. Netter, M. D. Copyright CIBA.)

## The Cerebral Hemispheres

The exterior of the cerebral hemispheres is covered by a thin mantle of gray matter called cortex. This is composed of layers of cells between which may be seen layers of white matter. In most of the cortex six layers may be seen. There have been various attempts at subdivision of the cortex on various classificatory schemes, such as Brodmann's (Figure 15–17). His divisions of the cortex are the most commonly used and may be regarded as being convenient. As the surface of the cortex has increased in area as one ascends the phylogenetic scale, it has become more and more folded or convoluted. In the rat the surface of the hemispheres is smooth. In man, extensive folding has taken place, presumably to accommodate a larger cortical surface area without a corresponding increase in cranial size. The grooves which have arisen as a result of this folding are called fissures and sulci (Latin—sulcus, furrow). The areas between the sulci are called gyri or convolutions (Greek—guros, round). These form landmarks on the surface of the brain, and have been labeled as indicated in Figures 15–18 and 15–19. However there is some variation in folding from one individual

FIG. 15–17. Areas of the human cerebral cortex each of which possesses a distinctive structure according to Brodmann. A, lateral view; B, medial view. (From Ranson, S. W., and Clark, S. L., *The Anatomy of the Nervous System.* Philadelphia: W. B. Saunders Company, 1959.)

to another. That is why functional localization prior to surgery is often necessary.

The two hemispheres are separated by the longitudinal cerebral fissure. Each hemisphere may be divided into the frontal, parietal, occipital and temporal lobes and the insula (Figure 15–20). The insula lies within the lateral cerebral fissure and so cannot be seen from the surface except by

A.C.G. — Anterior Central Gyrus
A.G. — Angular Gyrus
C.S. — Central Sulcus (Fissure of
          Rolando)
F.P. — Frontal Pole
F.S. — Fissure of Sylvius
I.F.G. — Inferior Frontal Gyrus
I.P.G. — Inferior Parietal Gyrus
I-P.S. — Inter-Parietal Sulcus
I.R. — Island of Reil
I.T.G. — Inferior Temporal
          Gyrus
L.O.G. — Lateral Occipital
          Gyrus
M.F.G. — Middle Frontal
          Gyrus
M.T.G. — Middle Temporal
          Gyrus
M.T.S. — Middle Temporal
          Sulcus
O. — Operculum
O.P. — Occipital Pole
P.C.G. — Posterior Central
          Gyrus
P-C.S. — Pre-Central Sulcus
P.O.C.S. — Post Central Sulcus
S.F.G. — Superior Frontal
          Gyrus
S-M.G. — Supra-Marginal
          Gyrus
S.P.G. — Superior Parietal
          Gyrus
S.T.G. — Superior Temporal
          Gyrus
S.T.S. — Superior Temporal
          Sulcus
T.P. — Temporal Pole

FIG. 15–18.  Lateral aspect of human cerebral hemispheres. The Insula (or Island of Reil) is shown by parting the lips of the lateral cerebral fissure. (From *The CIBA Collection of Medical Illustrations* by Frank H. Netter, M. D. Copyright CIBA.)

FIG. 15–19. The medial surface of the human brain. (Reprinted with permission of the Macmillan Company from *Correlative Anatomy of the Nervous System* by Crosby, Humphrey and Lauer. Copyright, 1962, by the Macmillan Company.)

parting the lips of this fissure (Figure 15–18). The rhinencephalon has already been described (see Figures 15–15 and 15–16).

Going hand in hand with an expansion of the area of the cortex or gray matter on the surface of the cerebral hemispheres as we ascend the phylogenetic scale is an increase in the mass of interconnecting fiber or white matter inside the cerebral hemispheres, streaming either up to or down from the cortex, or interconnecting various portions of the cortex.

One of the largest fiber tracts leading into and out of the cortex is the internal capsule (Figure 15–14). The anterior limb of the internal capsule runs between the caudate and lentiform nuclei. In it run fibers from the lateral nucleus of the thalamus to the frontal lobe. Fibers leaving the frontal lobe run through the anterior limb of the internal capsule to the

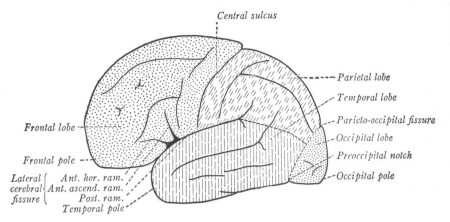

FIG. 15–20. Diagram of the lobes on the lateral aspect of the human cerebral hemisphere. (From Ranson, S. W., and Clark, S. L., *The Anatomy of the Nervous System*. Philadelphia: W. B. Saunders Company, 1959.)

pons. The posterior limb of the internal capsule, dividing the thalamus from the lentiform nucleus (globus pallidus and putamen), consists of fibers running from the thalamus to the cortex (the thalamic radiation) and various efferent tracts from the cortex (Figure 15–10). Such efferent tracts comprise the corticobulbar tract (to the motor nuclei of the cranial nerves in the medulla), the corticospinal tract, the corticorubral tract (to the red nucleus), and the temporopontile tract (from the cortex of the temporal lobe to the pons). As the fibers diverge from the internal capsule to join their various connections in the cortex, the distinctive formation to which this gives rise is called the corona radiata.

The commissures joining together the rhinencephalon have already been described. However, the largest commissure in the nervous system is the corpus callosum which joins together the two cerebral hemispheres. Most of the fibers composing this structure link together symmetrical areas of the two hemispheres.

Not only are there fibers leaving the cortex and arriving at the cortex from other structures, but many join together different parts of the cortex. These are known as association fibers.

# BIBLIOGRAPHY AND AUTHOR INDEX

*The following is a complete list of books and articles, etc., referred to by authors' names in this book. Volume numbers of journals are in boldface and numbers in parentheses refer to pages in this text.*

## A

Ables, M. F., and Benjamin, R. M. Thalamic relay nucleus for taste in albino rat. *J. Neurophysiol.*, 1960, **23**, 376–82. (368)

Ackerly, S. S., and Benton, A. L. Report of case of bilateral frontal defect. In Fulton, J. F. (Ed.), The Frontal Lobes. Baltimore, Md. Williams and Wilkins, 1948, 479–504. (199)

Adametz, J. H., Rate of recovery of functioning in cats with rostral reticular lesions. *J. Neurosurg.*, 1959, **16**, 85–98. (160)

Ades, H. W. Central auditory mechanisms. In American Physiological Society, *Handbook of Physiology, Section 1; Neurophysiology, Vol. I* (Field, J.; Magoun, H. W.; and Hall, V. E. [Eds.]), Baltimore, Md.: Williams & Wilkins Co., 1959. (310)

Ades, H. W., and Felder, R. Acoustic area of monkey (Macaca mulatta). *J. Neurophysiol.*, 1942, **5**, 49–54. (319, 320)

Adey, W. R.; Merrillees, N. C. R.; and Sunderland, S. The entorhinal area: behavioral evoked potential and histological studies of its interrelationships with brain-stem regions. *Brain*, 1956, **79**, 414–39. (208)

Adey, W. R., Sunderland, S., and Dunlop, C. W. The entorhinal area: electrophysiological studies of its interrelations with the rhinencephalic structures and the brainstem. *E.E.G. clin. Neurophysiol.*, 1957, **9**, 309–24. (151)

Adolph, E. F. The internal environment and behavior: III Water content. *Amer. J. Psychiat.*, 1941, **97**, 1365–73. (14)

Adolph, E. F. Thirst and its inhibition in the stomach. *Am. J. Physiol.*, 1950, **161**, 374–86. (25)

Adrian, E. D. Effects of injury on mammalian nerve fibers. *Proc. Roy. Soc. B.* 1930, **106**, 596–618. (230)

Adrian, E. D. Afferent areas in the cerebellum connected with the limbs. *Brain*, 1943, **66**, 289–315. (410)

Adrian, E. D. *The physical background of perception.* Oxford: Clarendon Press. 1947. (168)

Adrian, E. D. The electrical activity of the mammalian olfactory bulb. *EEG clin. Neurophysiol.*, 1950, **2**, 377–88. (377)

Adrian, E. D. Sensory messages and sensation: the response of the olfactory organ to different smells. *Acta. Physiol. Scand.*, 1953, **29**, 5–14. (381)

Adrian, E. D. The action of the mammalian olfactory organ. *J. Laryngol. Otol.*, 1956, **70**, 1–14. (372, 381)

Adrian, E. D.; Cattell, McK.; and Hoagland, H. Sensory discharge in single cutaneous nerve fibers. *Journal Physiol.*, 1931, **72**, 377–91. (243)

Aidar, O.; Geohegan, W. A.; and Ungewitter, L. H. Splanchnic afferent pathways in the central nervous system. *J. Neurophysiol.*, 1952, **15**, 131–38. (283)

Akert, K. Diencephalon. In Sheer, D. E. (Ed.), *Electrical Stimulation of the Brain.* Austin: University of Texas Press, 1961, 288–310. (189, 190, 192)

Akert, K.; Gruesen, R. A.; Woolsey, C. N.; and Meyer, D. R. Klüver-Bucy syndromes in monkeys with neocortical ablations of temporal lobe. *Brain*, 1961, **84**, 480–98. (207)

Akimoto, H.; Yamaguchi, M.; Okabe, K.; Nakagawa, T.; Nakamura, I.; Abe, K.; Torii, H.; and Masahashi, I. On the sleep induced through electrical stimulation of dog thalamus. *Folia psychiat. neurol. Jap.*, 1956, **10**, 117–46. (158, 159, 161)

Albe, D.; Fessard; and L. Kruger. Duality of unit discharges from cat centrum medianum in response to natural and electrical stimulation. *J. Neurophysiol.*, 1962, **25**, 3–20. (274, 285)

Albe, D.; Fessard; and A. Rougeol. Activities gilaterales tardives evognes sur le cortex du chat sous chloralose par stimulation d'une voie somesthetique. *J. Physiol.* (Paris), 1955, **47**, 69–72. (260)

Allen, W. F. Effect of ablating the frontal lobes, hippocampi, and occipito-parieto-temporal (excepting pyriform areas) lobes on positive and negative olfactory conditioned reflexes in dogs. *Am. J. Physiol.*, 1940, **128**, 754–71. (383)

Allen, W. F. Effect of ablating the pyriform-amygdaloid areas and hippocampi on positive and negative conditioned reflexes and on conditioned olfactory differentiation. *Amer. J. Physiol.*, 1941, **132**, 81–92. (383)

Allen, W. F. Results of prefrontal lobectomy on acquired and on acquiring correct conditioned differential responses with auditory, general cutaneous and optic stimuli. *Amer. J. Physiol.*, 1943(a), **139**, 525–31. (383)

Allen, W. F. Distribution of cortical potentials resulting from insufflation of vapors into the nostrils and from stimulation of the olfactory bulbs and the pyriform lobe. *Amer. J. Physiol.*, 1943(b), **139**, 553–55. (382)

Allen, W. F. Effects on partial and complete destruction of the tactile cerebral cortex on correct conditioned differential foreleg responses from cutaneous stimulation. *Am. J. Physiol.*, 1947, **151**, 325–37. (281)

Allen, W. F. Fiber degeneration in Ammon's horn resulting from extirpations of pyriform and other cortical areas and from transections of horn at various levels. *J. Comp. Neurol.*, 1948, **88**, 425–38. (211)

Allers, R., and Halpern, R. Wechselwirkungen gleischzeitiger Erregung Mehrerer Hautsinne. 1. Die Beeinflussung der Tastschwelle durch die Hauttemperatur *Pflüg. Arch. ges. Physiol.*, 1921, **193**, 595–609. (242, 254)

Allison, A. C. The structure of the olfactory bulb and its relationship to the olfactory pathways in the rabbit and the rat. *J. comp. Neurol.*, 1953, **98**, 309–53. (379, 382)

Alpers, B. J. Relation of the hypothalamus to disorders of personality: Report of a case. *A.M.A. Arch. Neurol. Psychiat.*, 1937, **38**, 291–303. (199)

Alrutz, S. Studien auf dem gebiete der temperatursinne. *Skandinav. Arch. Physiol.*, 1900, **10**, 340–52. (257)

Alston, J. H. The spatial condition of the fusion of warmth and cold in heat. *Amer. J. Psychol.*, 1920, **31**, 303–12. (257)

Amassian, V. E. Fiber groups and spinal pathways of cortically represented visceral afferents. *J. Neurophysiol.*, 1951(a), **14**, 445–59. (283)

Amassian, V. E. Cortical representation of visceral afferents. *J. Neurophysiol.*, 1951(b), **14**, 433–44. (283)

Amassian, V. E. Interaction in somatovisceral projection system. *A. Res. Nerv. & Ment. Dis., Proc.*, 1952, **30**, 371–402. (283, 288)

Amassian, V. E., and DeVito, R. V. Unit activity in reticular formation and nearby structures. *J. Neurophysiol.*, 1954, **17**, 575–603. (151)

Amoore, J. E.; Johnston, J. W.; and Rubin, M. The stereochemical theory of odor. *Scientific American*, 1964, **210**, 42–49. (378)

Anand, B. K. Nervous regulation of food intake. *Physiol. Rev.*, 1961, **41**, 677–708. (9, 29)

Anand, B. K., and Brobeck, J. R. Hypothalamic control of food intake in rats and cats. *Yale J. biol. Med.*, 1951, **24**, 123–40. (19, 205)

Anand, B. K., and Brobeck, J. R. Food intake and spontaneous activity of rats with lesions in the amygdaloid nuclei. *J. Neurophysiol.*, 1952, **15**, 421–30. (207, 209)

Anand, B. K. and Dua, S. Feeding responses induced by electrical stimulation of hypothalamus in cat. *Ind. J. med. Research*, 1955, **43**, 113–22. (9, 10)

Anand, B. K., and Dua, S. Stimulation of limbic system of brain in waking animals. *Science*, 1955, **122**, 1139. (197)

Anand, B. K. and Dua, S. Electrical stimulation of the limbic system of brain ('visceral brain') in the waking animals. *Ind. J. med. Res.*, 1956, **44**, 107–19. (193)

Anand, B. K.; Dua, S.; and Shoenberg, K. Hypothalamic control of food intake in cats and monkeys. *J. Physiol.*, 1955, **127**, 143–52. (9)

Andersson, B., and Larsson, B. Influence of local temperature changes in the preoptic area and rostral hypothalamus on the regulation of food and water intake. *Acta. Physiol. Scand.*, 1961, **52**, 75–89. (4)

Andersson, B., and McCann, S. M. Drinking, antidiuresis and milk ejection from electrical stimulation from the hypothalamus of goats. *Acta. Physiol. Scand.*, 1955, **35**, 191–201. (7, 8)

Andersson, B., and McCann, S. M. A further study of polydipsia evoked by hypothalamic stimulation in the goat. *Acta. Physiol. Scand.*, 1955, **33**, 333–46. (7, 8)

Andersson, B., and McCann, S. M. The effect of hypothalamic lesions on the water intake of the dog. *Acta. Physiol. Scand.*, 1956, **35**, 312–20. (8)

Andersson, S. A. Projection of different spinal pathways to the second somatic sensory area in cat. *Acta. Physiol., Scand.*, 1962, **56**, Suppl. 194 1–74. (260, 266, 271, 276, 278, 286)

Araki, T.; Eccles, J. C.; and Ito, M. Correlation of the inhibitory post-synaptic potential of motoneurons with the latency and time course of inhibition of monosynaptic reflex. *J. Physiol.*, 1960, **154**, 354–77. (455, 459)

Araki, T.; Ito, M.; and Oscarson, G. An ionic permeability of the inhibitory post-synaptic membrane of motoneurons. *Nature*, 1961, **189**, 65. (457)

Arduini, A. Enduring potential changes evoked in the cerebral cortex by stimulation of brain stem reticular formation and thalamus. In *Reticular Formation of the Brain*, Jasper, H. H.; Proctor, L. D.; Knighton, R. S.; Noshay, W. C.; and Costello, R. T. (Eds.). Boston: Little Brown and Company, 1958. (103)

Arduini, A., and Arduini, M. G. Effect of drugs and metabolic alterations on brain stem arousal mechanisms. *J. pharmacol. Exper. Therap.*, 1954, **110**, 76–85. (153)

Armstrong, D.; Jepson, J. P.; Keele, C. A.; and Stewart, J. W. Pain-producing substance in human inflammatory exudates and plasma. *J. Physiol.*, 1957, **135**, 350–70. (245)

Aronson, L. R. Hormones and reproductive behavior: Some phylogenetic considerations. In Gorbman, Aubrey. (Ed.), *Comparative Endocrinology*. New York: John Wiley and Sons, Inc., 1958, 98–120. (44)

Arthur, R. P., and Shelly, W. B. Role of proteolytic enzymes in production of

pruritus in man. *J. Invest. Dermat.*, 1955, **25**, 341–46. (253)

Arthur, R. P., and Shelly, W. B. The peripheral mechanism of itch in man. In Wolstenholme, G. E. W., and O'Connor, M. (Eds.), *Ciba Foundation Study Group, Pain and Itch*. London: J. and A. Churchill, 1959, 84–97. (253, 254)

Auleytner, B., and Brutkowski, S. Effects of bilateral prefrontal lobectomy on the classical (type 1) defensive conditioned reflexes and some other responses related to defensive behavior in dogs. *Acta. Biol. Exper.*, 1960, **20**, 243–62. (222)

Austin, V. T., and Steggerda, F. R. Congenital dysfunction of the salivary glands with observations on the physiology of thirst. *Illinois, M. J.*, 1936, **69**, 124–27. (6)

Ax, A. F. The physiological differentiation between fear and anger in humans. *Psychosom. Med.*, 1953, **15**, 433–42. (79)

**B**

Babich, F. R.; Jacobson, A. L.; Bubash, S.; and Jacobson, A. Transfer of a response to naïve rats by injection of ribonucleic acid extracted from trained rats. *Science*, 1965, **149**, 656–57. (91)

Bach, L. M. N., and Magoun, H. W. The vestibular nuclei as an excitatory mechanism for the cord. *J. Neurophysiol.*, 1947, **10**, 331–37. (413)

Baker, P. F.; Hodgkin, A. L.; and Shaw, T. I. Replacement of the protoplasm of a giant nerve fibre with artificial solutions. *Nature*, 1961, **190**, 885–87. (451)

Baldwin, M. Electrical stimulation of the mesial temporal region. In Ramey, E. R., and O'Doherty, D. S. (Eds.), *Electrical Studies on the Unanaesthetised Brain*. New York: Paul B. Hoeber, Inc., 1960, 159–76. (198)

Ball, J. Sex behavior of the rat after removal of the uterus and the vagina. *J. Comp. Psychol.*, 1934, **18**, 419–22. (46)

Ball, J. Male and female mating behavior in prepubertally castrated male rats receiving estrogens. *J. comp. Psychol.*, 1939, **28**, 273–83. (55)

Bard, P. A diencephalic mechanism for the expression of rage with special reference to the sympathetic nervous system. *Am. J. Physiol.*, 1928, **84**, 490–515. (201, 204)

Bard, P. On emotional expression after decortication with some remarks on certain theoretical views, Parts I and II. *Psych. Rev.*, 1934, **41**, 309–29, 424–49. (202, 204)

Bard, P. The effects of denervation of the genitalia on the oestrual behavior of cats. *Amer. J. Physiol.*, 1935, **113**, 5. (46)

Bard, P. The hypothalamus and sexual behavior. *Res. Publ. Assn. nerv. ment. Dis.*, 1940, **20**, 551–79. (52, 53)

Bard, P., and Macht, M. B. The behavior of chronically decerebrate cats. In Wolstenholme, G. E. W., and O'Connor, M. (Eds.), *The Neurological Basis of Behavior*. London: J. & A. Churchill, 1958, 55–75. (202)

Bard, P. and Mountcastle, V. B. Some forebrain mechanisms involved in the expression of rage, with special reference to suppression of angry behavior. In J. F. Fulton (Ed.), *The Frontal Lobes*. Baltimore: Williams and Wilkins, 1948, 362–404. (202, 205, 207, 208, 211)

Bard, P. and Rioch, D. McK. A study of four cats deprived of neocortex and additional portions of the forebrain. *Bull. Johns Hopkins Hosp.*, 1937, **60**, 72–147. (203, 204)

Bare, J. K. The specific hunger for sodium chloride in normal and adrenalectomized white rats. *J. Comp. Physiol. Psychol.*, 1949, **42**, 242–53. (20)

Barker, D. (Ed.), *Symposium on Muscle Receptors*. Hong Kong: Hong Kong University Press, 1962. (393)

Barlow, H. B., and Hill, R. M. Selective sensitivity to direction of movement in ganglion cells of the rabbit retina. *Science*, 1963, **139**, 412–14. (342)

Bartoshuk, L. M.; McBurney, D. H.; and Pfaffmann, C. Taste of sodium chloride solution after adaptation to sodium chloride: implications for the "water taste." *Science*, 1964, **143**, 967–68. (371)

Bash, K. W. An investigation into a possible organic basis for the hunger drive. *J. comp. Psychol.*, 1939, **28**, 109–34. (6)

Batini, C.; Moruzzi, G.; Palestini, M.; Rossi, G. F.; and Zanchetti, A. Persistent patterns of wakefulness in the pretrigeminal midpontine preparation. *Science*, 1958, **127**, 30–32. (153)

Batsel, H. L. Electroencephalographic synchronization and desynchronization in the chronic 'cerveau isolé' in the dog.

*EEG clin. Neurophysiol.*, 1960, **12**, 421–30. (160)

Bauer, H. G. Endocrine and other clinical manifestations of hypothalamic disease. *J. Clin. Endocrinol.*, 1954, **14**, 13–31. (69)

Bauer, J. H., and Cooper, R. M. Effects of posterior cortical lesions on performance of a brightness-discrimination task. *J. comp. physiol. Psychol.*, 1964, **58**, 84–92. (353)

Bazett, H. C. Temperature sense in man. In *Temperature, Its Measurement and Control in Science and Industry*. New York: Reinhard, 1941, 489–501. (244)

Bazett, H. C.; McGlone, B.; Williams, R. G.; and Lufkin, H. M. Sensation. I. Depth, distribution and probable identification in the prepuce of sensory end-organs concerned in sensations of temperature and touch; thermometric conductivity. *A.M.A. Arch. Neurol. Psychiat.*, 1932, **27**, 489–517. (229)

Bazett, H. C., and Penfield, W. G. A study of the Sherrington decerebrate animal in the chronic as well as the acute condition. *Brain*, 1922, **45**, 185–264. (201)

Beach, F. A. The neural basis of innate behavior. I. Effects of cortical lesions upon the maternal behavior pattern in the rat. *J. comp. Psychol.*, 1937, **24**, 393–439. (62)

Beach, F. A. Effects of cortical lesions upon the copulatory behavior of male rats. *J. comp. Psychol.*, 1940, **29**, 193–245. (53)

Beach, F. A. Central nervous mechanisms involved in the reproductive cycle of vertebrates. *Psychol. Bull.*, 1942, **39**, 4, 200–226. (44, 55)

Beach, F. A. *Hormones and Behaviour: a survey of interrelationships between endocrine secretions and patterns of overt response*. New York: Paul B. Hoeber, 1948. (45, 46)

Beach, F. A. Neural and chemical regulation of behavior. In *Biological and Biochemical Bases of Behavior*, Harlow, H. F., and Woolsey, C. N. (Eds.). Madison, Wis.: University of Wisconsin Press, 1958. (57)

Beach, F. A.; Conovitz, M. W.; Steinberg, F.; and Goldstein, A. C. Experimental inhibition and restoration of mating behavior in male rats. *J. Genet. Psychol.*, 1956, 89, 165–81. (57)

Beach, F. A., and Fowler, H. Individual differences in the response of male rats to androgen. *J. comp. physiol. Psychol.*, 1959, **52**, 50–52. (58)

Beach, F. A., and Holz, M. Mating behavior in male rats castrated at various ages and injected with androgen. *J. exp. Zool.*, 1946, **101**, 91–142. (44)

Beach, F. A., and Jaynes, J. Studies of maternal retrieving in rats III. Sensory cues involved in the lactating female's response to her young. *Behaviour*, 1956, **10**, 104–25. (62)

Beach, F. A., and Jordan, L. Sexual exhaustion and recovery in the male rat. *Quart. J. exp. Psychol.*, 1956, **8**, 121–33. (54)

Beach, F. A., and Levinson, G. Effects of androgen on the glans penis and mating behavior of castrated male rats. *J. exp. Zool.*, 1950, **114**, 159–71. (64)

Beach, F. A., and Whalen, R. E. Effects of intromission without ejaculation upon sexual behavior in male rats. *J. comp. physiol. Psychol.*, 1959(a), **52**, 476–81. (54)

Beach, F. A., and Whalen, R. E. Effects of ejaculation on sexual behavior in the male rat. *J. comp. physiol. Psychol.*, 1959(b), **52**, 249–54. (53)

Beach, F. A., and Wilson, J. R. Mating behavior in male rats after removal of the seminal vesicles. *Proc. National Acad. Sci.*, 1963, **49**, 624–26. (46)

Beh, H. C., and Barratt, P. E. H. Discrimination and conditioning during sleep as indicated by the electroencephalogram. *Science*, 1965, **147**, 1470–71. (171)

Behrens, O. V., and Bromer, W. W. Glucagon. *Am. Rev. Vitamins and Hormones*, Academic Press, 1958, 263–301. (26)

Beidler, L. M. Theory of taste stimulation. *J. gen. Physiol.*, 1954, 38(2), 133–39. (359, 362)

Beidler, L. M. Facts and theory on the mechanism of taste and odor perception. In Mitchell, J. H., Jr., *et al.* (Eds.), *Chemistry of Natural Food Flavors.* Quartermaster Research and Engineering Command, 1957, 7–43. (369)

Beidler, L. M. Dynamics of taste cells. In Zotterman, Y. (Ed.), *Olfaction and Taste.* Oxford: Pergamon Press, 1963, 133–38. (361, 365, 369)

Békésy, Georg von. *Experiments in Hearing.* New York: McGraw-Hill, 1960. (297, 302)

Bellows, R. T. Time factors in water drinking dogs. *Amer. J. Physiol.*, 1939, **125**, 87–97. (12, 14, 25)

Benda, C. E. *Developmental Disorders of Mentation and Cerebral Palsies.* New York: Grune and Stratton, 1952. (408)

Bender, M. B. (Ed.). *The Oculomotor System.* New York: Harper and Row, 1964. (434)

Benjamin, R. M. Cortical taste mechanisms studied by 2 different test procedures, *J. comp. physiol. Psychol.*, 1955(a), **48**, 119–22. (368)

Benjamin, R. M. Effect of fluid deprivation on taste deficits following cortical lesions. *J. comp. physiol. Psychol.*, 1955(b), **48**, 502–5. (368)

Benjamin, R. M. Some thalamic and cortical mechanisms of taste. In Zotterman, Y. (Ed.), *Olfaction and Taste.* Oxford: Pergamon Press, 1963, 309–29. (368)

Benjamin, R. M., and Akert, K. Cortical and thalamic areas involved in taste discrimination in the albino rat. *J. comp. Neur.*, 1959, **111**, 231–60. (368)

Bradley, P. B., and Mollica, A. The effect of adrenaline and acetylcholine on single unit activity in the reticular formation of the decerebrate cat. *Arch. itel. Biol.*, 1958, **96**, 168–86. (151)

Brady, J. V. The paleocortex and behavioral motivation. In Harlow, H. F., and Woolsey, C. N. (Eds.), *Biological and Biochemical Bases of Behavior.* Madison: University of Wisconsin Press, 1958, 193–235. (184, 211, 220)

Brady, J. V. Emotional behavior. In American Physiological Society, *Handbook of Physiology, Section 1; Neurophysiology,* Vol. III (Field, J., Magoun, H. W., and Hall, V. E. [Eds.]). Baltimore, Md.: Williams & Wilkins Co., 1960. (184)

Brady, J. V.; Boren, J. J.; Conrad, D.; and Sidman, M. The effect of food and water deprivation upon intracranial self-stimulation. *J. comp. physiol. Psychol.*, 1957, **50**, 134–37. (126)

Brady, J. V., and Nauta, W. J. H. Subcortical mechanisms in emotional behavior: affective changes following septal forebrain lesions in the albino rat. *J. comp. physiol. Psychol.*, 1953, **46**, 339–46. (211, 218)

Brady, J. V., and Nauta, W. J. H. Subcortical mechanisms in emotional behavior: the duration of affective changes following septal and habenular lesions in the albino rat. *J. comp. physiol. Psychol.*, 1955, 48, 412–20. (211)

Brady, J. V., Schreiner, L.; Geller, I.; and Kling, A. Subcortical mechanisms in emotional behavior: the effect of rhinencephalic injury upon the acquisition and retention of a conditioned avoidance response in cats. *J. comp. physiol. Psychol.*, 1954, 47, 179–86. (219, 221)

Brain, R. *Diseases of the Nervous System*, 4th Ed. Oxford: Oxford University Press, 1952. (389)

Brazier, M. A. B. The action of anaesthetics on the nervous system with special reference to the brainstem reticular system. In Delafresnaye, J. F. (Ed.), *Brain Mechanisms and Consciousness.* Springfield, Ill.: Charles C. Thomas, 1954, 163–200. (153)

Benjamin, R. M., and Pfaffmann, C. Cortical localization of taste in albino rat. *J. Neurophysiol.*, 1955, 18, 56–64. (368)

Beritoff, J., and Chichinadze, N. Localization of visual perception in the pigeon. *Bull. Biol. Med. exp. USSR*, 1936, 2, 105–7. (93)

Beritoff, J., and Chichinadze, N. On the localization of cortex processes evoked by visual stimulations. *Trans. Beritov Inst Tiflis*, 1937, 3, 361–74. (93)

Berkun, M. M.; Miller, N. E.; and Kessen, Marion L. Hunger-reducing effects of food by stomach fistula versus food by mouth measured by a consummatory response. *J. comp. physiol. Psychol.*, 1952, **XLV**, 550–55. (17, 25)

Biemond, A. The conduction of pain above the level of the thalamus opticus. *A.M.A. Arch. Neurol. Psychiat.*, 1956, 75, 231–48. (285, 287)

Bilodeau, E. A. *Acquisition of Skill.* New York: Academic Press, 1966. (434)

Bishop, G. H. The organization of cortex with respect to its afferent supply. *Annals., N.Y. Acad., Science.*, 1961, 98, 559–69. (224, 286)

Bishop, P. O., and McLeod, J. G. Nature of potentials associated with synaptic transmission in the lateral geniculate of cats. *J. Neurophysiol.*, 1954, 17, 387–414. (463, 464)

Black, A. H. Heart rate changes during avoidance learning in dogs. *Canad. J. Psychol.*, 1959, 13, 229–42. (182)

Blake, L. The effect of lesions of the superior colliculus on brightness and pattern discrimination in the cat. *J.*

comp. physiol. Psychol.*, 1959, 52, 272–78. (354)

Blum, J. S.; Chow, K. L.; and Pribram, K. H. A behavioral analysis of the organization of the parieto-temporo-preoccipital cortex in the monkey. *J. comp. Neurol.*, 1950, 93, 53–100. (281)

Boman, K. On the mediation of cold pain. *Acta. Physiol. Scandinav.*, 1959, 45, 211–15. (239)

Bond, D.; Randt, C. T.; Bidder, T. G.; and Rowland, V. Posterior septal fornical and anterior thalamic lesions in the cat. *A.M.A. Arch. Neurol., Psychiat.*, 1957, 78, 143–62. (211)

Bonvallet, M.; Dell, P.; and Hiebel, G. Tonus sympathique et activité electrique corticale. *EEG clin. Neurophysiol.*, 1954, 6, 119–44. (64)

Boss, W. R. Hormonal determination of adult characters and sex behavior in herring gulls (Larus argentatus). *J. exper. Zool.*, 1943, 94, 181–203. (44)

Bower, G. H., and Miller, N. E. Rewarding and punishing effects from stimulating the same place in the rat's brain. *J. comp. physiol. Psychol.*, 1958, 51, 669–74. (190)

Bowsher, D. Termination of the central pain pathway in man: the conscious appreciation of pain. *Brain*, 1957, 80, 606–22. (150, 272, 284)

Bowsher, D. The termination of secondary somatosensory neurons within the thalamus of Macaca mulatta: An experimental degeneration study. *J. comp. Neurol.*, 1961, 117, 213–18. (150, 258, 259)

Bradley, P. B., and Elkes, J. The effect of atropine, hyoscyamine, physostigmine and neostigmine on the electrical activity of the brain of the conscious cat. *J. Physiol.*, 1953, 120, 14–15. (147)

Breen, R. A., and McGaugh, J. L. Facilitation of maze learning with post trial injections of picrotoxin. *J. comp. physiol. Psychol.*, 1961, 54, 498–501. (79)

Bremer, F. Physiologie nerveuse de la mastication chez le chat et le lapin centre cortical du goût. *Arch. Inst. Physiol.*, 1923, 21, 308–53. (368)

Bremer, F. L'activite cérébrale au cours du sommeil et de la narcose contribution à l'Etude du mécanisme du sommeil. *Bull., Acad. Roy. Med. Belg.*, 1937, 2, 68–86. (148)

Bremer, F. The neurophysiological problem of sleep. In Delafresnaye, J. F. (Ed.), *Brain Mechanisms and Con-*

*sciousness*. Springfield, Ill.: Charles C. Thomas, 1954, 137–63. (160)

Bremer, F., and Stoupel, N. Facilitation et inhibition des potentiels évoques corticaux dans l'éveil cérébrale. *Arch. int. Physiol.*, 1959, **67**, 240–75. (173)

Bremer, F., and Terzuolo, C. Róle de l'écorce cérébrale dans le processus physiologique du réveil. *Arch. int. Physiol.*, 1952, **60**, 228–31. (150, 151)

Bremer, F., and Terzuolo, C. Nouvelles recherches du le processus physiologique du reveil. *Arch. int. Physiol.*, 1953, **61**, 86–90. (151)

Bremer, F., and Terzuolo, C. Contribution à l'étude des mecanismes physiologiques du maintien de l'activité vigile du cerveau. Interaction de la formation réticulée et de l'écorce cérébrale dans le processus des réveil. *Arch. int. Physiol.*, 1954, **62**, 157–78. (151)

Breternitz, W. Über das Tourtualsche Tauschung. *Z. Sinnesphysiol.*, 1934, **65**, 146–65. (398)

Brierley, J. B., and Beck, E. The effects upon behavior of lesions in the dorsomedial and anterior thalamic nuclei of cat and monkey. In Wolstenholme, G. E. W., and O'Connor, M. (Eds.), *The Neurological Basis of Behavior.* London: J. and A. Churchill, 1958, 90–104. (206)

Broadbent, D. E. The role of auditory localization in attention and memory span. *J. exp. Psychol.*, 1954, **47**, 191–96. (166)

Broadbent, D. E. *Perception and Communication.* London: Pergamon, 1958. (165)

Brobeck, J. R. Food intake as a mechanism of temperature regulation in rats. *Fed., Proc. Amer. physiol. Soc.*, 1948, **7**, 13. (3)

Brobeck, J. R.; Tepperman, J.; and Long, C. N. H. Experimental hypothalamic hyperphagia in the albino rat. *Yale J. biol. Med.*, 1943, **15**, 831–53. (27)

Brogden, W. J. Sensory preconditioning, *J. exp. Psychol.*, 1939, **25**, 323–32. (112)

Bromiley, R. B. and Bard, P. A study of the effect of estrin on the responses to genital stimulation shown by decapitate and decerebrate female cats. *Amer. J. Physiol.*, 1940, **129**, 318–19. (52)

Brookhart, J. M. The cerebellum. In American Physiological Society, *Handbook of Physiology, Section 1; Neurophysiology*, Vol. II (Field, J.; Magoun, H. W.; and Hall, V. E. [Eds.]). Baltimore, Md.: Williams & Wilkins Co., 1960, 1245. (410)

Brookhart, J. M.; Dey, F. L.; and Ranson, S. W. Failure of ovarian hormones to cause mating reactions in spayed guinea pigs with hypothalamic lesions. *Proc. Soc. exper. Biol. and Med.*, 1940, **44**, 61–64. (48)

Brookhart, J. M., and Dey, F. L. Reduction of sexual behavior in male guinea pigs by hypothalamic lesions. *Amer. J. Physiol.*, 1941, **133**, 551–54. (48)

Brookhart, J. M., and Fadiga, E. Potential fields initiated during monosynaptic activation of frog motoneurons. *J. Physiol.*, 1960, **150**, 633–55. (461)

Browder, E. J., and Gallagher, J. P. Dorsal cordotomy for painful phantom limb. *Ann. Surg.*, 1948, **128**, 456–69. (268, 286)

Brown, C. W., and Ghiselli, E. E. Subcortical mechanisms in learning. IV. Olfactory discrimination. *J. comp. Psychol.*, 1938, **26**, 109–20. (383)

Brown, S. and Schäfer, E. A. An investigation into the functions of the occipital and temporal lobes of the monkey's brain. *Phil. Trans. Roy. Soc. Lond. B.*, 1888, **179**, 303–27. (206)

Browne, L. B., and Hodgson, E. S. Electrophysiological studies of arthropod chemoreception. IV. Latency, independence, and specificity of labellar chemoreceptors of the blowfly. *Lucilia, J. Cell comp. Physiol.*, 1962, **59**, 187–202. (361)

Brown-Grant, K.; Harris, G. W.; and Reichlin, S. The effect of emotional and physical stress on thyroid activity in the rabbit. *J. Physiol.*, 1954, **126**, 29–40. (67)

Brust-Carmona, H. C. B., Hernandez-Peon, R. Sensory transmission in the spinal cord during attention and tactile habituation. *Abstr. XXI, Int. Congr. Physiol. Sci.*, 1959, **44**, (171, 172)

Brutkowksi, S. Comparison of classical and instrumental alimentary conditioned reflexes following bilateral prefrontal lobectomies in dogs. *Acta. biol. exper.* 1959, **14**, 291–99. (222)

Brutkowski, S.; Fonberg, E.; and Mempel, E. Angry behavior in dogs following bilateral lesions in the genual portion of the rostral cingulate gyrus. *Acta. biol. exper.*, 1961, **21**, 119–205. (212, 213, 221)

Bullock, T. H. Neuron doctrine and electrophysiology. *Science*, 1959, **129**, 997–1002. (46)

Bullock, T. H., and Hagiwara, S. Intracellular recording from the giant synapse of the squid. *J. gen. Physiol.*, 1956, **40**, 565–77. (457)

Bunn, J. P., and Everett, J. W. Phagocytosis of periodate-treated and virus-coated red blood cells by white blood cells in vitro. *Proc. Soc. exp. Biol. and Med.*, 1957, **96**, 369–371. Block of ovulation by continuous illumination. (70)

Bureš, J., and Burešová, O. The use of Leao's spreading depression in the study of interhemispheric transfer of memory traces. *J. comp. physiol. Psychol.*, 1960, **53**, 558–65. (96, 97)

Bureš, J.; Burešová, O.; and Fifková, E. Interhemispheric transfer of passive avoidance reaction. *J. comp. physiol. Psychol.*, 1964, **57**, 326–30. (197)

Busch, H. F. M. An anatemical analysis of the white matter in the brain stem of the cat. *Thesis, Van Gorcum and Comp. N. V.*, 1961, 116. (259)

Buser, P., and Borenstein, P. Responses somesthesiques, visuelles et auditives, recueillies au niveau du cortex "associatif" suprasylvien chez le chat curarisé non anesthesié. *EEG clin. Neurophysiol.*, 1959, **11**, 285–304. (319)

Bykoff, K. M. In *Russ. Fisiol. Zhurn.*, 1924, **I**, 294–95. (93)

C

Cadwalder, W. B., and Sweet, J. E. Experimental work on the function of the anterolateral column of the spinal cord. *J.A.M.A.*, 1912, **58**, 1490–1893. (268)

Cajal, Ramón Y, S. *Histologie du système nerveux*, Vol. 2. Paris, 1911. (381)

Cajal, Ramón Y, S. *Neuron Theory or Reticular Theory?* M. V. Parkiss and C. A. Fox (Translators). Madrid: Instituto "Ramon y Cajal," 1954. (442)

Cajal, Ramón Y, S. *Histologie du Système Nerveux de l'homme et des Vertebrés*, Vol. 1. Madrid: Consejo Superior de Investigaciones Cientificas, 1955, 839–88. (259)

Caldwell, D. F. Effects of adrenal demedullation on retention of a CAR in the mouse. *J. comp. physiol. Psychol.*, 1962, **55**, 1079–81. (181)

Callaway, E., III; Jones, R. T.; Layne, R. S. Evoked responses and segmental set of schizophrenia. *Arch. gen. Psychiat.*, 1965, **12**, 83–89. (175)

Cannon, W. B. *Bodily Changes in Pain, Hunger, Fear and Rage*, 2nd Ed. New York: Appleton-Century-Crofts, 1929. (179)

Cannon, W. B., and Britton, S. W. Studies on the conditions of activity in endocrine glands, XV: Pseudoaffective medulliadrenal Secretion. *Am. J. Physiol.*, 1925, **72**, 283–94. (201, 202)

Cannon, W. B., and Washburn, A. L. An explanation of hunger. *Amer. J. Physiol.*, 1912, **29**, 441–54. (6)

Carlson, A. J. *The Control of Hunger in Health and Disease.* Chicago: University of Chicago Press, 1916. (4, 5)

Carpenter, C. R. Psychobiological studies of social behavior in Aves, I. The effect of complete and incomplete gonadectomy on the primary sexual activity of the male pigeon. *J. comp. Psychol.*, 1933, **16**, 25–57. (44)

Carpenter, C. R. Psychobiological studies of social behavior in Aves, I. The effect of complete and incomplete gonadectomy on secondary sexual activity, with histological studies. *J. comp. Psychol.*, 1933(a), **16**, 59–96. (44)

Carper, J. W., and Polliard, F. A comparison of the intake of glucose and saccharine solutions under conditions of caloric need. *Amer. J. Psychol.*, 1953, **66**, 479–82. (40, 41)

Carreras, M., and Levitt, M. Microelectrode analysis of the second somatosensory area in the cat. *Fed. Proc.*, 1959, 18–24. (264, 276)

Cawthorne, T.; Dix, M. R.; Hallpike, C. S.; and Hood, J. D. Vestibular function. *Brit. med. Bull.*, 1956, **12**, 131–42. (420)

Cerf, J. A., and Otis, L. S. Heat narcosis and its effect on retention of a learned behavior in the goldfish. *Fed. Proc.*, 1957, **16**, 20–21. (75)

Chamberlain, T. J.; Halich, P.; and Gerard, R. W. Fixation of experience in the rat spinal cord. *J. Neurophysiol.*, 1963, **26**, 662–72. (90)

Chambers, R. M. Effects of intravenous glucose injections on learning, general activity, and hunger drive. *J. comp. physiol. Psychol.*, 1956(a), **49**, 558–64. (143)

Chambers, R. M. Some physiological bases of reinforcing properties of reward injections. *J. comp. physiol. Psychol.*, 1956(b), **69**, 565–68. (143)

Chambers, W. W.; Levitt, M.; Carreras, M.; and Lin, C. N. Central determination of sensory processes. *Science*, 1960, **132**, 1489. (282)

Chang, H. T.; Ruch, T. C.; and Ward, A. A. Topographical representation of muscles in motor cortex of monkeys. *J. Neurophysiol.*, 1947, **10**, 39–56. (430)

Chapman, W. P. Studies of the periamygdaloid area in relation to human behavior. A. *Res. nerv. ment. Dis. Proc.*, 1958, **36**, 258–77. (197, 199)

Chapman, W. P. Depth electrode studies in patients with temporal lobe epilepsy. In Ramcy, E. R., and O'Doherty, D. S. (Eds.), *Electrical Studies on the Unanaesthetised Brain*. New York: Paul B. Hoeber, Inc., 1961, 334–50. (199)

Chapman, W. P.; Rose, A. S.; and Solomon, H. C. Measurements of heat stimulus producing motor withdrawal reaction in patients following frontal lobotomy. A. *Res. nerv. ment. Dis. Proc.*, 1948, **27**, 754–68. (289)

Chapman, W. P.; Schroeder, H. R.; Geyer, G.; Brazier, M. A. B.; Fager, C.; Poppen, J. L.; Solomon, H. C.; and Yakovler, P. I. Physiological evidence concerning importance of the amygdaloid nuclear region in the integration of circulatory function and emotion in man. *Science*, 1954, **120**, 949. (197)

Cherry, C. Two ears—but one world. In Rosenblith, W. A. (Ed.), *Sensory Communication*. Cambridge, Mass.: MIT Press, 1961, 99–1117. (303)

Cherry, E. C. Some experiments on the recognition of speech with one and with two ears. *J. acoust. Soc. Amer.*, 1953, **25**, 975–79. (165)

Chiang, H. M., and Wilson, W. A. Some tests of the diluted-water hypothesis of saline consumption in rats. *J. comp. physiol. Psychol.*, 1963, **56**, 660–65. (124)

Chinn, H. I., and Smith, P. K. Motion sickness. *Pharmacol. Rev.*, 1955, 7, 33–82. (421)

Chow, K. L. Conditions influencing the recovery of visual discriminative habits in monkeys following temporal neocortical ablations. *J. comp. and physiol. Psychol.*, 1952, **45**, 430–37. (82)

Chow, K. L. Lack of behavioral effects following destruction of some thalamic association nuclei in the monkey. *A.M.A. Arch. Neurol. Psychiat.*, 1954, **71**, 762–71. (206)

Chow, K. L. Brain waves and visual discrimination learning in monkey. In Wortis, J. (Ed.), *Recent Advances in Biological Psychiatry*. New York: Grune and Stratton, 1960, 149. (1105)

Chow, K. L. Effect of local electrographic after discharges on visual learning and retention in monkey. *J. Neurophysiol.*, 1961, **24**, 391–400. (102)

Chow, K. L.; Dement, W. C.; and John, E. R. Conditioned electrocorticographic potentials and behavioral avoidance response in cat. *J. Neurophysiol.*, 1957, **20**, 482. (107)

Chow, K. L.; Dcmcnt, W. C.; and Mitchell, S. A., Jr. Effects of lesions of the rostral thalamus on brain waves and behavior in cats. *EEG clin. Neurophysiol.*, 1959, **11**, 107–20. (160)

Chow, K. L., and Obrist, W. D. EEG and behavioral changes on application of Al(OH)$_3$ cream on preoccipital cortex of monkeys. *AMA Arch. Neurol. Psychiat.*, 1954, **72**, 80–87. (101)

Chow, K. L., and Randell, W. Learning and EEG studies of cats with lesions in the reticular formation. Paper read at the first annual meeting of Psychonomics Society, Chicago, 1960. (160)

Chow, K. L., and Survis, J. Retention of overlearned visual habit after temporal cortical ablation in monkey. *AMA Arch. Neurol. Psychiat.*, 1958, **70**, 640–46. (81, 82)

Cizek, L. J. Long-term observations on relationship between food and water ingestion in the dog. *Amer. J. Physiol.*, 1959, **197**, 342–46. (29)

Clark, D.; Hughes, J.; and Gasser, H. S. Afferent function in the group of nerve fibers of slower conduction velocity. *Am. J. Physiol.*, 1935, **23**, 114–69. (244)

Clark, G. Prepubertal castration in the male chimpanzee with some effects of replacement therapy. *Growth*, 1945, **9**, 327–39. (44)

Clark, W. E. Le Gros. The thalamic connections of the temporal lobe of the brain in the monkey. *J. Anat.*, 1936, **70**, 447–64. (319)

Clark, W. E. Le Gros.; Beattie, J.; Riddoch, A.; and Dott, N. M. *The Hypothalamus*. Edinburgh: Oliver and Boyd, 1938. (199)

Cleghorn, T. E., and Darcus, H. D. The sensibility to passive movement of the human elbow joint. *Quart. J. exp. Psychol.*, 1952, **4**, 66–77. (397)

Cohen, B. D.; Brown, G. W.; and Brown, M. L. Avoidance learning motivated by hypothalamic stimulation. *J. exp. Psychol.*, 1957, **53**, 228–83. (189)

Cohen, H. *Lettsomanian Lectures on the Mechanism of Visceral Pain.* T. M. Soc. London., 1944, **64**, 65–99. (288)

Cohen, L. A. Analysis of position sense in human shoulder. *J. Neurophysiol.*, 1958, **21**, 550–62. (398)

Cohen, M. J.; Hagiwara, S.; and Zotterman, Y. The response spectrum of taste fibres in the cat: a single fibre analysis. *Acta. Physiol. Scand.*, 1955, **33**, 316–32. (365)

Cohen, M. J.; Landgren, S.; Strom, L.; and Zotterman, Y. Cortical reception of touch and taste in the cat. *Acta. Physiol. Scand.*, 1957, **40**, 1–50. (368)

Cohen, S. Purification of a nerve-growth promoting protein from the mouse salivary gland and its neuro-cytotoxic antiserum. *Proc. Nat. Acad. Sci.*, 1960, **46**, 302–11. (181)

Cole, K. S., and Curtis, H. J. Electric impedance of the squid giant axon during activity. *J. gen. Physiol.*, 1939, **22**, 649–70. (451)

Collias, N. E. Hormones and behaviors with special reference to birds and the mechanisms of hormone action. In Gordon, E. S. (Ed.), *Symposium on Steroid Hormones.* Madison, Wis.: University of Wisconsin Press, 1950. (43)

Collins, W. E. Effects of mental set upon vestibular nystagmus. *J. exp. Psychol.*, 1962, **63**, 191–97. (420)

Collins, W. F.; Nulsen, F. E.; and Randt, C. T. Relations of peripheral nerve fiber size and sensation in man. *Arch. Neurol.*, 1960, **3**, 381–85. (244)

Coombs, J. S.; Curtis, D. R.; and Eccles, J. C. The interpretation of spike potentials of motor neurons. *J. Physiol.*, 1957, **139**, 198–231. (377, 455)

Coombs, J. S.; Eccles, J. C.; and Fatt, P. The electrical properties of the motoneuron membrane, *J. Physiol.*, 1955, **130**, 291–325. (454, 457)

Coons, E. E.; Levak, Milena; and Miller, N. E. Lateral hypothalamus: Learning of food-seeking response motivated by electrical stimulation. *Science*, 1965, **150**, 1320–21. (9)

Coons, E. E., and Miller, N. E. Conflict versus consolidation of memory traces to explain "retrograde amnesia" produced by ECS. *J. comp. and physiol. Psychol.*, 1960, **53**, 524–31. (77)

Coppock, H. W., and Chambers, R. M. Reinforcement of position preference by automatic intrevenous injections of glucose. *J. comp. Physiol. psychol.*, 1954, **47**, 355. (142)

Corning, W. C., and John, E. R. Effect of ribonuclease on retention of conditioned response in regenerated planarians. *Science*, 1961, **134**, 1363–64. (90)

Cragg, B. G. Centrifugal fibres to the retina and olfactory bulb, and composition of the supraoptic commissures in the rabbit. *Exp. Neurol.*, 1962, **5**, 406–27. (381)

Creed, R. S.; Denny-Brown, D.; Eccles, J. C.; Liddell, E. G. T.; and Sherrington, C. S. *Reflex Activity of the Spinal Cord.* Oxford University Press, 1932. (442)

Crisler, G. Salivation is unnecessary for the establishment of the salivary conditioned reflex induced by morphine. *Amer. J. Physiol.*, 1930, **94**, 553–56. (113)

Critchley, M. *The Parietal Lobes.* Baltimore, Md.: Williams and Wilkins Co. and London: E. Arnold, 1953. (278, 279, 431)

Crocker, E. C., and Henderson, L. F. Analysis and classification of odors. *Amer. Perfum*, 1927, **22**, 325–27. (378)

Cushing, H. *Papers Relating to the Pituitary body, Hypothalamus and Parasympathetic Nervous System.* Springfield, Ill.: Charles C. Thomas, 1932. (199)

### D

Dale, H. H. Pharmacology and nerve endings. *Proc. Roy. Soc.*, 1935, **28**, 319–32. (458)

Dallenbach, K. M. Pain: history and present status. *Amer. J. Psychol.*, 1939, **52**, 331–47. (248)

Darling, F. F. *Bird flocks and the breeding cycle.* London: Cambridge, 1938. (66)

Darrow, D. C., and Yannet, H. The changes in the distribution of body water accompanying increase and decrease in extracellular electrolyte. *J. clin. Investigation*, 1935, **14**, 266–75. (1, 2)

Davidson, J. M., and Sawyer, C. H. Effects of localized intracerebral implantation of oestrogen on reproductive function in the female rabbit. *Acta. Endocrinol.*, 1961, **37**, 385–93. (47, 50, 69)

Davis, C. M. Self-selection of diet by newly weaned infants. *Amer. J. dis. Child.*, 1928, **36**, 651–79. (35)

Davis, Clarence D. The effects of ablations of neocortex on mating maternal behavior and the production of pseudopregnancy in the female rat and on copulatory activity in the male. *Am. J. Physiol.*, 1939, 127, 374. (62)

Davis, H. Peripheral coding of auditory information. In Rosenblith, W. (Ed.), *Sensory Communication.* New York: M.I.T. Press and John Wiley & Sons, Inc., 1961, 119–42. (310)

Davis, R. C.; Garafolo, L.; and Kveim, K. Conditions associated with gastrointestional activity. *J. comp. physiol. Psychol.*, 1959, 52, 466–75. (6)

Davison, C., and Schick, W. Spontaneous pain and other subjective sensory disturbances: clinico-pathologic study. *A.M.A. Arch. Neurol. Psychiat.*, 1935, 34, 1204–37. (285)

Davson, H. (Ed.). *The Eye, Volume 3: Muscular Mechanisms.* New York: Academic Press, 1962. (439)

Dax, E. C., and Radley-Smith, E. J. The early effects of prefrontal leucotomy on disturbed patients with mental illness of long duration. *J. ment. Sc.*, 1943, 89, 182–88. (213)

Déjérine, J., and Roussy, G., Le syndrome thalamique. *Rev. Neurol.*, 1906, 18, 521–32. (284)

Delgado, J. M. R. Cerebral structures involved in transmission and elaboration of noxious stimulation. *J. Neurophysiol.*, 1955, 18, 261–75. (190, 191, 196, 272)

Delgado, J. M. R., and Anand, B. K. Increase of food intake induced by electrical stimulation of the lateral hypothalamus. *Am. J. Physiol.*, 1953, 172, 162–68. (10)

Delgado, J. M. R.; Roberts, W. W.; and Miller, N. E. Learning motivated by electrical stimulation of the brain. *Amer. J. Physiol.*, 1954, 179, 587–93. (114, 186)

Delgado, J. M. R.; Rosvold, H. E.; and Looney, E. Evoked conditioned fear by electrical stimulation of subcortical structures in the monkey brain. *J. comp. physiol. Psychol.*, 1956, 49, 373–80. (190)

Dell, P. C. The recticular formation of the brain. *Henry Ford Hospital International Symposium*, Boston: Little, Brown and Co., 1958, 513–34. (64)

De Lorenzo, A. J. D. Studies on the ultrastructure and histophysiology of cell membranes, nerve fibers and synaptic junctions in chemoreceptors. In *Olfaction and Taste*, Zotterman, Y. (Ed.). Oxford: Pergamon Press, 1963, 5–18. (364)

Dement, W. The occurrence of low voltage fast EEG patterns during behavioral sleep in the cat. *EEG clin. Neurophysiol.*, 1958, 10, 291–96. (162)

de Molina, F. A., and Hunsperger, R. W. Central representation of affective reactions in forebrain and brain stem: electrical stimulation of amygdala, stria terminalis and adjacent structures. *J. Physiol.*, 1959, 145, 251–65. (188, 189, 193, 195, 196, 211)

de Molina, F. A., and Hunsperger, R. W. Organization of subcortical system governing defense and flight reactions in the cat. *J. Physiol.*, 1962, 160, 200–213. (195, 204, 205, 210)

Denny-Brown, R. S.; Eccles, J. C.; Liddell, E. G. T.; and Sherrington, C. S. Reflex Activity of the Spinal Cord. Oxford: Oxford University Press, 1938. (405)

Desmedt, J. G. Neurophysiological mechanisms controlling acoustic input. In Rasmussen, G. L., and Windle, W. F. (Eds.), *Neural Mechanisms of the Auditory and Vestibular System.* Springfield, Ill.: Charles C. Thomas, 1960, 152–64.

Desmedt, J. E. Auditory-evoked potentials from cochlea to cortex as influenced by activation of the efferent olivo-cochlear bundle. *J. acoust. Soc. Amer.*, 1962, 34, 1478–96. (323)

Desmedt, J. E., and Mechelse, K. Corticofugal projections from temporal lobe in cat and their possible role in acoustic discrimination. *J. Physiol. Lond.*, 1953, 147, 17–18. (318)

De Snoo, K. Das trinkende kind im uterus. *Monatschrift J. Gebursh. u. Gynäk.*, 1937, 105, 88. (41, 140)

Dethier, V. G., and Arab, Y. M. Effect of temperature on the contact chemoreceptors of the blowfly. *J. Ins. Physiol.*, 1958, 2, 153–61. (360, 379)

Deuel, H. J., Jr., and Movitt, E. Studies on the comparative nutritive value of fats. III. The effect of flavor on food preference. *J. Nutrition*, 1944, 27, 339–46. (37, 38)

Deutsch, J. A. A new type of behaviour theory. *Brit. J. Psychol.*, 1953, 44, 304–17. (18, 119)

Deutsch, J. A. A machine with insight. *Quart. J. exper. Psychol.*, 1954, 6, 6–11. (116, 119)

Deutsch, J. A. *The Structural Basis of Behavior*. Chicago: University of Chicago Press, 1960. (18, 119)

Deutsch, J. A. Learning and electrical self-stimulation of the brain. *J. theoret. Biol.*, 1963, **4**, 193–214. (126)

Deutsch, J. A. Behavioral measurement of the neural refractory period and its application to intracranial self-stimulation. *J. comp. physiol. Psychol.*, 1964, **58**, 1–9. (130)

Deutsch, J. A. Substrates of Memory and Learning. Dis. of nerv. System. (In press). (87)

Deutsch, J. A., and Blumen, H. L. Counter-injection: A new technique for the analysis of drinking. *Nature*, 1962, **196**, 196–97. (15)

Deutsch, J. A., and Deutsch, D. Attention: Some theoretical considerations. *Psych. Rev.*, 1963, **70**, 80–90. (170)

Deutsch, J. A., and Di Cara, L. Extinction in intracranial self-stimulation as a function of hunger drive. *J. comp. physiol. Psychol.* (In press). (128)

Deutsch, J. A.; Hamburg, M. D.; and Dahl, M. Anticholinesterase-induced amnesia and its temporal aspects. *Science*, 1966, **151**, 221–23. (84)

Deutsch, J. A., and Howarth, C. I. Evocation by fear of a habit previously learned for intracranial electrical stimulation. *Science*, 1962, **136**, 1057–58. (126, 192)

Deutsch, J. A., and Howarth, C. I. Some tests of a theory of intracranial self-stimulation. *Psychological Review*, 1963, **70**, 444–60. (127)

Deutsch, J. A.; Howarth, C. I.; Ball, G. G.; and Deutsch, D. Threshold differentiation of drive and reward in the Olds effect. *Nature*, 1962, **196**, 699–700. (130)

Deutsch, J. A., and Jones, A. D. The water-salt receptor and preference in the rat. *Nature*, 1959, **183**, 1412. (22, 40)

Deutsch, J. A., and Jones, A. D. Diluted water: an explanation of the rat's preference for saline. *J. comp. physiol. Psychol.*, 1960, **53**, 122–27. (22, 40, 142)

Deutsch, J. A., and Mamakos, S. An experimental differentiation between short term and long term memory processes. Paper read to Experimental Psychology Society. Cambridge, 1959. (83)

De Vito, R. V.; Brusa, A.; and Arduini, A. Cerebellar and vestibular influences on Deitersian units. *J. Neurophysiol.*, 1956, **19**, 241–53. (413)

De Vries, H., and Stuiver, M. The absolute sensitivity of the human sense of smell. In *Sensory Communication*, Rosenblith, W. A. (Ed.). New York: John Wiley & Son, 1961, 159–67. (378)

De Wardener, H. E., and Herxheimer, A. The effect of a high water intake on the kidney's abilities to concentrate the urine in man. *J. Physiol.*, 1957, **139**, 53–63. (370)

Dey, F. L.; Fisher, C.; Berry, C. M.; and Ranson, S. W. Disturbances in reproductive functions caused by hypothalamic lesions in female guinea pigs. *Amer. J. Physiol.*, 1940, **129**, 39–46. (48)

Diamant, H.; Funakoshi, M.; Strom, L.; and Zotterman, Y. Electrophysiological studies on human taste nerves. In *Olfaction and Taste*, Zotterman, Y. (Ed.). Oxford: Pergamon press, 1963, 193–203. (363)

Diamond, I. T., and Neff, W. D. Ablation of temporal cortex and discrimination of auditory patterns. *J. Neurophysiol.*, 1957, **20**, 300–15. (322)

Dill, D. B. *Life, heat and altitude*. Cambridge: Harvard University Press, 1938. (2)

Dingman, W., and Sporn, M. B. The incorporation of 8-azaguanine into rat brain RNA and its effect on maze learning of the rat: an inquiry into the biochemical basis of memory. *J. Psychiat. Res.*, 1964, **1**, 1–11. (90)

Dodge, R. Habituation to rotation. *J. exp. Psychol.*, 1923, **6**, 1–34. (419)

Dodt, E. Schmerzimpulse bei temperaturreizen. *Acta. Physiol. Scandinav.*, 1954, **31**, 83–96. (239)

Dodt, E. Discussion of paper by A. Iggo: A single unit analysis of cutaneous receptors with C afferent fibers. In Wolstenholme, G. E. W., and O'Connor (Eds.), *Ciba Foundation Study Group, Pain and Itch, Nervous Mechanisms*. Boston: M. Little, Brown and Co., 1959, 46–59. (239)

Dodt, E., and Zotterman, Y. Mode of action of warm receptors. *Acta. Physiol. Scandinav.*, 1952(a), **26**, 345–57. (236)

Dodt, E., and Zotterman, Y. Discharge of specific cold fibers at high temperatures. (Paradoxical cold.) *Acta. Physiol. Scandinav.*, 1952(b), **26**, 358–65. (257)

Dodwell, P. C. and Bessant, D. E. Learning without swimming in a water maze.

*J. comp. physiol. Psychol.*, 1960, **53**, 422–25. (112)

Dogliotti, M. First surgical sections in man of lemniscus lateralis (pain-temperature path) at brain stem, for treatment of diffused, rebellious pain. *Anesth. et. Analg.*, 1938, **17**, 143–45. (284)

Donovan, B. T., and Van der Werff ten Bosch, J. J. Precocious puberty in rats with hypothalamic lesions. *Nature* (London), 1956, **178**, 745. (69, 70)

Donovan, B. T., and Van der Werff ten Bosch, J. J. Oestrus in winter following hypothalamic lesions in the ferret. *J. Physiol.*, 1956(a), **132**, 57. (70)

Doty, R. W. Functional significance of the topographical aspects of the retinocortical projection. In Jung, R., and Kornhuber, H. (Eds.), *The visual system: Neurophysiology and Psychophysics.* Berlin: Springer-Verlag, 1961. (353)

Doty, R. W.; Beck, E. C.; and Kooi, R. A. Effect of brain stem lesions on conditioned responses in cats. *Exp. Neurol.*, 1959, **1**, 360–85. (160)

Doty, R. W.; Rutledge, L. T., Jr.; and Larsen, R. M. Conditioned reflexes established to electrical stimulation of cat cerebral cortex. *J. Neurophysiol.*, 1956, **19**, 401–15. (114)

Douglas, W. W.; Ritchie, J. M.; and Straub, R. W. The role of non-myelinated fibers in signalling cooling of the skin. *J. Physiol.*, 1960, **150**, 266–83. (230)

Dow, R. S. The electrical activity of the cerebellum and its functional significance. *J. Physiol.*, 1938, **94**, 67–86. (411)

Downman, D. B. B.; Woolsey, C. N.; and Lende, R. A. Auditory areas I, II and Ep: Cochlear representation, afferent paths and interconnections. *Bull. Johns Hopkins Hosp.*, 1960, **105**, 127–46. (318)

Drake, L. G., and McKenzie, K. G. Mesencephalic tractotomy for pain; experience with six cases. *J. Neurosurg.*, 1953, **10**, 457–62. (284)

Dumont, S., and Dell, P. Facilitations spécifiques et non-spécifiques des réponses visuelles corticales. *J. Physiol.* (Paris), 1958, **50**, 261–64. (173)

Duncan, C. P. The retroactive effects of shock on learning. *J. comp. physiol. Psychol.*, 1949, **42**, 32–34. (75)

Durup, G., and Fessard, A. L'electroencephalogramme de l'homme. *L'année Psychol.*, 1935, **36**, 1. (113)

Dusser, J. G. de Barenne. Recherches expérimentales sur les fonctions du système nerveux central faites en particulier sur deux chats, dont le néopallium avait été enlevé. *Arch. néerl. Physiol.*, 1920, **4**, 31–123. (201)

**E**

Ebbecke, U. Uber die temperatur—empfindungen in Ihrer abhangigkeit Von der Hautdurchblutung und Von Den Reflexzentren. *Arch. Ces. Physiol.*, 1917, **169**, 395–462. (244)

Ebner, F. F., and Myers, R. E. Inter- and intra-hemispheric transmission of tactile gnosis in normal and corpus-callosum sectioned monkey. *Fed. Proc.*, 1960, **19**, 292. (95)

Eccles, J. C. *The Neurophysiological Basis of Mind: the Principles of Neurophysiology.* Oxford: Clarendon Press, 1953. (448, 457)

Eccles, J. C. The central action of antidromic impulses in motor nerve fibres. *Pflüg Archiv. ges. Physiol.*, 1955, **260**, 385–95. (461)

Eccles, J. C. *The Physiology of Nerve Cells,* New York: Oxford University Press, 1957. (452, 456, 457, 459, 461)

Eccles, J. C. The effects of use and disuse on synaptic function. In Delafresnaye, P.F, *et al.* (Eds.), *Brain Mechanisms and Learning.* Oxford: Blackwell, 1961, 335–52. (92)

Eccles, J. C. The nature of central inhibition. *Proc. Roy. Soc. B.*, 1961, **153**, 445–76. (452, 456, 459)

Eccles, J. C.; Eccles, R. M.; and Lundberg, A. Types of neurons in and around the intermediate nucleus of the lumbrosacral cord. *J. Physiol.* (London), 1960, **158**, 89–118. (259)

Eccles, J. C.; Eccles, R.; and Magni, I. Central inhibitory action attributable to presynaptic depolarization produced by muscle afferent volleys. *J. Physiol.*, 1961, **15a**, 147–66. (460)

Eccles, J. C.; Fatt, P.; and Landgren, S. The central pathway for the direct inhibitory action of impulses in the largest afferent nerve fibers to muscle. *J. Neurophysiol.*, 1956, **19**, 75–98. (459)

Eccles, J. C.; Magni, I.; and Willis, W. Depolarization of central terminals of group 1 afferent fibres from muscle. *J. Physiol.*, 1962, **160**, 62–93. (460)

Echlin, F., and Propper, N. Sensitization by injury of cutaneous nerve endings in frog. *J. Physiol.*, 1937, **88**, 388–400. (246)

Economo, C. Von. *Die Encephalit is Lethargica.* Vienna: Deuticke, 1918. (160)

Edwards, A. S. The measurement of static ataxia. *Amer. J. Psychol.*, 1942, **55**, 171–88. (429)

Edwards, C., and Ottoson, D. The site of impulse initiation in a nerve cell of a crustacean stretch receptor. *J. Physiol.*, 1958, **143**, 138–48. (377, 462)

Egan, J. P.; Carterette, E. C.; and Thwing, E. J. Some factors affecting multichannel listening. *J. acoust. Soc. Amer.*, 1954, **26**, 774–82. (166)

Egger, M. D., and Flynn, J. P. Effect of electrical stimulation of the amygdala on hypothalamically elicited attack behavior in cats. *J. Neurophysiol.*, 1963, **26**, 705–20. (193)

Eisenman, J.; Landgren, S.; and Novin, D. Functional organisation in the main sensory trigeminal nucleus and in the rostial subdivision of the nucleus of the spinal trigeminal tract in the cat. *Acta. Physiol. Scand.*, Suppl. 214, 1963, **59**, 1–44. (261, 271)

Eist, H., and Seal, U. S. The permeability of the blood-brain barrier and the blood-CSF barrier to $C^{14}$ tagged RNA. *Am. J. Psychiat.*, 1965, **122**, 584–91. (91)

Ek, J.; Jonkees, L. B. W.; and Klijn, J. A. J. On the effect of continuous acceleration. *Acta. Oto-laryngol.*, 1960, **51**, 416–19. (417, 420)

Eldred, E. Posture and locomotion. In American Physiological Society, *Handbook of Physiology, Section 1; Neurophysiology, Vol. II* (Field, J.; Magoun, H. W.; and Hall, V. E. [Eds.]). Baltimore, Md.: Williams & Wilkins Co., 1960, 1067. (429)

Eldred, E.; Granit, R.; and Merton, P. A. Supraspinal control of the muscle spindles and its significance. *J. Physiol.*, 1953, **122**, 498–523. (394)

Elsberg, C. A., and Levy, I. Sense of Smell; New and simple method of quantitative olfactormetry. *Bull. Neurol. Inst. New York*, 1935, **4**, 5–19. (383)

Enomoto, T. F. Unilateral activation of the non-specific thalamic system and bilateral cortical responses. *EEG clin. Neurophysiol.*, 1959, **11**, 219–32. (159)

Enroth, C. Spike frequency and flicker fusion frequency in retinal ganglion cells. *Acta. Physiol. Scand.*, 1953, **29**, 19–21. (350)

Epstein, A. N. Reciprocal changes in feeding behavior produced by intrahypothalamic chemical injections. *Amer. J. Physiol.*, 1960, **199**, 969–74. (27)

Epstein, A. N. Water intake without the act of drinking. *Science*, 1960, **131**, 497–98. (9)

Epstein, A. N., and Stellar, E. The control of salt preference in the adrenalectomized rat. *J. comp. physiol. Psychol.*, 1955, **48**, 167–72. (36, 39, 143)

Eriksen, T. C.; Bleckwenn, W. J.; and Woolsey, C. N. Observations on the postcential gyrus in relation to pain. *Tr. Am. neurol. Ass.*, 1952, **77**, 57–59. (285)

Erulkar, S. D.; Rose, J. E.; and Davies, P. W. Single unit activity in the auditory cortex of the cat. *Bull. Johns Hopkins Hosp.*, 1956, **99**, 55–86. (307, 313)

Ervin, F. R., and Marck, V. H. Physiological observations on the human thalamus. *Trans. Amer. neurol. Assoc.*, 1959, 92–100. (274, 287)

Ervin, F. R., and Marck, V. H. The thalamic organization of pain in man. *Fed. Proc.*, 1961, **20**, 345. (274)

**F**

Falk, J. L., and Titlebaum, L. F. Saline solution preference in the rat: Further demonstrations. *J. comp. physiol. Psychol.*, 1963, **56**, 337–42. (24)

Fangel, C., and Kaada, B. R. Behavioral "attention" and fear induced by cortical stimulation in the cat. *EEG clin. Neurophysiol.*, 1960, **12**, 575–88. (196)

Fantz, R. L. Form preferences in newly hatched chicks. *J. comp. physiol. Psychol.*, 1957, **50**, 422–30. (31)

Fatiga, E., and Brookhardt, J. M. Potential fields initiated during monosynaptic activation of frog motoneurons. *J. Physiol.*, 1960, **150**, 633–56. (461)

Fatt, P., and Katz, B. Spontaneous subthreshold activity at motor nerve endings. *J. Physiol.*, 1952, **117**, 109–28. (459)

Feldman, S. M., and Waller, H. J. Dissociation of electrocortical activation and behavioral arousal. *Nature*, 1962, **196**, 320–22. (147)

Fex, J. Augmentation of cochlear microphonics by stimulation of efferent fibers to cochlea. *Acta. Oto-Laryngol.*, 1959, **50**, 540–41. (324)

Fex, J. Auditory activity in centrifugal and centripetal cochlear fibres in cat. *Acta.*

*Physiol. Scan.*, Suppl., 189, 1962, **55**, 1–68. (324)

Finch, G. Salivary conditioning in atropinized dogs. *Amer. J. Physiol.*, 1938, **124**, 136–41. (113)

Fisher, A. E. Maternal and sexual behavior induced by intracranial chemical stimulation. *Science*, 1956, **124**, 228–29. (47, 49)

Fisher, A. E., and Coury, J. N. Cholinergic tracing of a central neural circuit underlying the thirst drive. *Science*, 1962, **137**, 691–93. (9)

Fishgold, H., and Larry-Bounez, G. C. Réaction l'arrêt et l'éveil dans les lésions du tronc cérébral et des hémispheres. *Rev. Neurol.* (Paris), 1952, **87**, 603–4. (151)

Fishman, I. Y. Single fiber gustatory impulses in rat and hamster. *J. Cell comp. Physiol.*, 1957, **49**, 319–34. (365, 367)

Fitzsimmons, J. T. Drinking by rats depleted of body fluid without increase in osmotic pressure. *J. Physiol.* (London), 1961, **159**, 297–309. (2)

Fjallbrandt, F., and Iggo, A. The effect of histamine, 5-hydroxytryptamine and acetylcholine on cutaneous afferent fibers. *J. Physiol.*, 1961, **156**, 578–90. (240)

Fleishman, E. A. Perception of body position in the absence of visual cues. *J. exp. Psychol.*, 1953, **46**, 261–70. (428)

Flexner, J. B.; Flexner, L. B.; and Stellar, E. Memory in mice as affected by intracerebral puromycin. *Science*, 1963, **141**, 57–59. (83)

Foerster, O. *Die Leitungsbahnen des Schmerzgefühls und die Chirurgische Behandlung der Schmerzzustande*. Berlin: Urban, 1927. (247, 278)

Foerster, O. In *Handbuch der Neurologie*, Vol. 5, Bunke, O. and Foerster, O. (Eds.). Berlin: Springer, 1936. (269, 279, 283)

Foerster, O., and Gagel, O. Die vorder seitenstrang durchschreidung berin neuthen, eire klinische-pathophysiolafische-anatomische grudie. *Ztschr. ges. Neurol. Psychiat.*, 1932, **138**, 1–92. (253, 268, 269)

Fonberg, E., and Delgado, J. M. R. Avoidance and alimentary reactions during amygdaloid stimulation. *J. Neurophysiol.*, 1961, **24**, 651–64. (193)

Frank, K., and Fuortes, M. Presynaptic and postsynaptic inhibition of monosynaptic reflexes. *Fed. Proc.*, 1957, **16**, 390. (459, 460)

Freeman, W., and J. Watts. *Psychosurgery in the Treatment of Mental Disorders and Intractable Pain*. 2nd Ed. Springfield, Ill.: Charles C. Thomas, 1950. (289)

French, G. M., and Harlow, H. F. Locomotor reaction decrement in brain-damaged monkeys. *J. comp. physiol. Psychol.*, 1955, **48**, 496–501. (221)

French, J. D. Brain lesions associated with prolonged unconsciousness. *Arch. neurol. psychiat.*, 1952, **68**, 727–40. (149)

French, J. D.; Amerongen, F. K.; and Magoun, H. W. An activating system in brain stem of monkeys. *Arch. Neurol. Psychiat.*, 1952, **68**, 591–604. (151, 152)

French, J. D.; Hernández-Peón, R.; and Livingston, R. B. Projections from cortex to cephalic brain stem (reticular formation) in monkey. *J. Neurophysiol.*, 1955, **18**, 74–95. (149, 151)

French, J. D., and Magoun, H. W. Effects of chronic lesions in central cephalic brain stem of monkeys. A.M.A. *Arch. Neurol. Psychiat.*, 1952, **68**, 591–604. (149, 159)

French, J. D.; Verzeano, M.; and Magoun, H. W. A neurol basis for the anaesthetic state. A.M.A. *Arch. Neurol. Psychiat.*, 1953, **69**, 519–29. (153)

Fritsch, G. T., and Hitzig, E. Über die elektrische erregbarkeit des grosshirns. *Arch. Anat. Physiol. wiss. Med.* (Leipzig), 1870, **37**, 300–346. (429)

Frommer, G. P. Gustatory afferent responses in the thalamus. In Kare, M. R., and Halpern, B. P. (Eds.), *The Physiological and Behavioral Aspects of Taste*. Chicago: University of Chicago Press, 1961. (368)

Frommer, G. P., and Pfaffmann, C. J. Electrophysiological analysis of gustatory, tongue temperature, and tactile representation in thalamus of albino rat. *The Physiologist*, 1961, **4**, 38. (368)

Fry, G. A. Specification of the direction of regard. (Special Report No. 1, Comm. on Nomenclature and Standards, Amer. Acad. of Optom.). *Amer. J. Optom.*, 1945, **22**, 353–62. (435)

Fry, G. A. Definition and measurement of torsion. (Special Report No. 2, Comm. on Nomenclature and Standards, Amer. Acad. of Optom.). *Amer. J. Optom.*, 1947(a), **24**, No. 7. (435)

Fry, G. A. Definition and measurement of cyclophoria with converged and elevated lines of sight. (Special Report No. 3., Comm. on Nomenclature and Standards, Amer. Acad. Optom.). *Amer. J. Optom.*, 1947(b), **24**, No. 10. (435)

Fulford, B. D., and McCann, S. M. Suppression of adrenal compensatory hypertrophy by hypothalamic lesions. *Proc. Soc. exper. Biol. Med.*, 1955, **90**, 78–80. (71)

Fuller, J. L.; Rosvold, H. E.; and Pribram, K. H. The effect on affective and cognitive behavior in the dog of lesions of the pyriform-amygdala-hippocampal complex. *J. comp. physiol. Psychol.*, 1957, **50**. (89–96)

Fulton, J. F. *Physiology of the Nervous System*. New York: Oxford University Press, 1943. (442)

Fulton, J. F. *Frontal Lobotomy and Affective Behavior*. London: Chapman, 1951. (213)

Fulton, J. F. (Ed.). *A Textbook of Physiology*. 17th Ed. Philadelphia and London: Saunders, 1955. (387)

Fulton, J. F., and Jacobsen, C. F. The functions of the frontal lobes, a comparative study in monkeys, chimpanzees and man. *Abstr. 2nd Int. neurol. Congr.* (London), 1935, 70–71. *Advances mod. Biol.* (Moscow), 1935, 113–23. (213)

Funderburk, W. H., and Case, T. J. The effect of atropine on cortical potentials. *EEG Clin. Neurophysiol.*, 1951, **3**, 213–23. (147)

## G

Gad, J., and Goldschneider, H. Über die summation von Hautreizen. *Ztschr. F. klin. Med. Berl.*, 1892, **20**, 337–73. (248)

Galambos, R. Microelectrode studies on medial geniculate body of cat. III. Response to pure tones. *J. Neurophysiol.*, 1952, **15**, 381–400. (307, 310, 316)

Galambos, R. Suppression of auditory nerve activity by stimulation of efferent fibers to cochlea. *J. Neurophysiol.*, 1956, **19**, 424–37. (323)

Galambos, R. Neural mechanisms in audition. *Laryngoscope*, 1958, **68**, 388–401. (322)

Galambos, R. Studies of the auditory system with implanted electrodes. In Rasmussen, G. L., and Windle, W. F. (Eds.), *Neural Mechanisms of the Auditory and Vestibular Systems*. Springfield, Ill.: C. C. Thomas, 1960. (307, 324)

Galambos, R., and Davis, H. The response of single auditory-nerve fibers to acoustic stimulation. *J. Neurophysiol.*, 1943, **6**, 39–57. (314)

Galambos, R., and Davis, H. Inhibition of activity in single auditory nerve fibers by acoustic stimulation. *J. Neurophysiol.*, 1944, **7**, 287–303. (313)

Galambos, R.; Myers, R. E.; and Sheatz, G. C. Extralemniscal activation of auditory cortex in cats. *Amer. J. Physiol.*, 1961, **200**, 23–28. (306, 322)

Galambos, R.; Rose, J. E.; Bromiley, R. B. Microelectrode studies on medial geniculate body of cat. II. Response to clicks. *J. Neurophysiol.*, 1952, **15**, 359–80. (314)

Galambos, R.; Schwartzkopff, J.; and Rupert, A. Microelectrode study of superior olivary nuclei. *Amer. J. Physiol.*, 1959, **197**, 527–36. (306, 310, 313, 314, 321)

Galambos, R.; Sheatz, G.; and Vernier, V. G. Electrophysiological correlates of a conditioned response in cats. *Science*, 1956, **123**, 376–77. (172)

Gallistel, C. R. Electrical self-stimulation and its theoretical implications. *Psycho. Bull.*, 1964, 23–34. (128)

Ganong, W. F., and Hume, D. M. Absence of stress-induced and "compensatory" adrenal hypertrophy in dogs with hypothalamic lesions. *Endocrinology*, 1954, **55**, 474–83. (71)

Gangloff, H., and Monnier, M. Electrographic aspects of an "arousal" or attention reaction induced in the unanaesthetized rabbit by the presence of a human being. *EEG clin. Neurophysiol.*, 1956, 8, 623–30. (151)

Garcia-Bengochea, F.; Corrigan, R.; Morgane, D. R., Jr.; and Heath, R. G. Studies on the function of the temporal lobes: the section of the fornix. *Tr. Am. neurol. Assoc.*, 1951, **76**, 238–39. (211)

Gardner, E. Physiology of movable joints. *Physiol. Rev.*, 1950, **230**, 127–76. (396)

Gardner, E. D., and Morin, F. Spinal pathways for projection of cutaneous and muscular afferents to the sensory and motor cortex of the monkey (Macacca mulatta). *Am. J. Physiol.*, 1953, **174**, 149–54. (260)

Garten, S. Über die grundlagen unserer orientierung im raum. *Abh. Maths-Phs. Sachs. Akad.*, 1920, **36**, 431–510. (428)

Gasser, H. S. Pain-producing impulses in

peripheral nerves. A. Res. nerv. ment. Dis. Proc., 1942, 23, 44–62. (229)

Gasser, H. S., and Erlanger, J. Role of fiber size in establishment of nerve block by pressure or cocaine. Am. J. Physiol., 1929, 88, 581–91. (243)

Gastaut, H. Correlations entre le système nerveux vegetatif et le système de la vie de relation dans le rhinecephale. J. Physiol. Paris., 1952, 44, 431–70. (59)

Gastaut, H. The brain stem and cerebral electogenesis in relation to consciousness. In Delafresnaye, J. F. (Ed.), Brain Mechanisms and Consciousness. Springfield, Ill.: Charles C. Thomas, 1954, 249–83. (145)

Gastaut, H.; Jus, A.; Jus, L.; Morrell, F.; Storm Van Leeuwen, W.; Dongier, S.; Naquet, R.; Regis, H.; Roger, A.; Bekkering, D.; Kamp, A.; and Werre, J. Etude topographique des reactions electroencephalographiques conditionnées chez l'homme. EEG clin. Neurophysiol., 1957, 9, 1–34. (113)

Gastaut, H.; Morin, G.; and Leseure, N. Étude du comportement des épileptiques psycho-moteurs dans l'intervale de leurs crises. Les troubles de l'activité globale et de la sociabilité. Ann. Méd-Psychol., 1955, 113, 1–27. (199)

Gastaut, H.; Naquet, R.; Vigouroux, R.; and Corriol, J. Provocation de comportements émotionnels divers par stimulation rhinencephalique chez le chat avec électrodes à demeure. Rev. Neurol., 1952, 86, 319–27. (195, 196)

Gault, F. P., and Leaton, R. N. Electrical activity of the olfactory system. EEG clin. Neurophysiol., 1963, 15, 299–304. (105)

Geldard, F. A. The perception of mechanical vibration: III. The frequency function. J. Gen. Psychol., 1940, 22, 281–89. (254, 255, 256)

Geldard, F. A. The Human Senses. New York, London: John Wiley & Sons, Inc., 1953. (254)

Gellhorn, E., and Loofbourrow, G. N. Emotion and Emotional Disorders; a Neurophysiological Study. New York: Harper and Row, 1963. (178)

Gerall, A. A. An attempt to induce precocious sexual behavior in male guinea pigs by injections of testosterone propionate. Endocrinology, 1958, 63, 280–84. (45)

Gernandt, B. Pain conduction in phrenic nerve. Acta. Physiol. Scand., 1946, 12, 255–60. (283)

Gernandt, B. E. Vestibular mechanisms. In American Physiological Society, Handbook of Physiology, Section 1; Neurophysiology, Vol. I (Field, J.; Magoun, H. W.; and Hall, V. E. [Eds.]). Baltimore, Md.: Williams & Wilkins Co., 1959, 549–64. (416)

Gernandt, B., and Zotterman, Y. Intestinal pain: an electrophysiological investigation on mesenteric nerves. Acta. Physiol. Scand., 1946, 12, 56–71. (243, 283)

Gesteland, R. C.; Lettvin, J. Y.; Pitts, W. H.; and Rojas, A. Odor specificities of the frog's olfactory receptors. In Zotterman, Y. (Ed.), Olfaction and Taste, Oxford: Pergamon Press, 1963, 19–34. (372)

Gilman, A. The relation between blood osmotic pressure, fluid distribution and voluntary water intake. Am. J. Physiol., 1937, 120, 323–28. (2)

Gibbs, F. A. Abnormal electrical activity in the temporal regions and its relationship to abnormalities of behavior. Res. Publ. Am. nerv. ment. Dis., 1956, 36, 278–94. (199)

Glees, P. The termination of optic fibres in the lateral geniculate body of the cat. J. Anat., 1941, 75, 434–40. (344)

Glees, P., and Clark, W. E. Le Gros. The termination of optic fibres in the lateral geniculate body of the monkey. J. Anat., 1941, 75, 292–308. (344)

Glees, P.; Cole, J.; Whitty, C. W. M.; and Cairns, H. The effects of lesions in the cingular gyrus and adjacent areas in monkeys. J. Neurol. Neurosurg. Psychiat., 1950, 13, 179–90. (212)

Gleitman, H. Place learning without prior performance. J. comp. physiol. Psychol., 1955, 48, 77–79. (112)

Glickstein, M., and Sperry, R. W. Intermanual somesthetic transfer in split brain rhesus monkey. J. comp. physiol. Psychol., 1960, 53 322–27. (1960)

Gloor, P. Amygdala. In American Physiological Society. Handbook of Physiology, Section I; Neurophysiology, Vol. II. (Field, J.; Magoun, H. W.; and Hall, V. E. [Eds.]). Baltimore, Md.: Williams & Wilkins Co., 1960, 1395–1416. (199, 208)

Goff, G. D. Differential discrimination of frequency of cutaneous mechanical vibration. Doctoral dissertation, University of Virginia, 1959. (255)

Goldberg, J. J.; Diamond, I. T.; and Neff, W. D. Auditory discrimination after ablation of temporal and insular cortex in cat. *Fed. Proc.*, 1957, **16**, 47. (322)

Goldberg, J. J.; Diamond, I. T.; and Neff, W. D. Frequency discrimination after ablation of cortical projection areas of the auditory system. *Fed. Proc. Balt.*, 1958, 17, 55. (321)

Goldberg, M. M., and Neff, W. D. Frequency discrimination after bilateral ablation of cortical auditory areas. *J. Neurophysiol.*, 1961(a), **24**, 119–28. (321)

Goldberg, M. M., and Neff, W. D. Frequency discrimination after bilateral section of the brachium of the inferior colliculus. *J. comp. Neurol.*, 1961(b), **113**, 265–82. (322)

Goldring, S., and O'Leary, J. L. Cortical D. C. changes incident to midline thalamic stimulation. *EEG clin. Neurophysiol.*, 1957, **9**, 577–84. (103)

Goldscheider, A. Untersuchungen uber den muskelsinn. *Arch. Anat. Physiol.*, 1889, Lpz., 369–502. Ministry Supply Trans. No. 20825T. (397)

Goldstein, K. Die lokalisation in der grosshirnrinde. In Bethe et al. (Ed.), *Handb. Norm. Pathol. Physiol.*, Berlin: Springer, 1927, **10**, 600–842. (280)

Goldstein, K. *Aftereffects of Brain Injuries in War*. New York: Grune & Stratton, Inc., 1942. (280)

Goodale, H. D. Feminized male birds. *Genetics*, 1918, **3**, 276–99. (55)

Gordon, G.; Landgren, S.; and Seed, W. A. Responses of single cells in the caudal part of the spinal nucleus of the trigeminal nerve of the cat. *J. Physiol.*, 1960, **193**, 12–13. (271)

Gordon, G.; Landgren, S.; and Seed, W. A. The functional characteristics of single cells in the caudal part of the spinal nucleus of the trigeminal nerve of the cat. *J. Physiol.*, 1961, **158**, 544–59. (260)

Gorska, T., and Jankowska, E. The effects of deafferentation of a limb on instrumental reflexes. In Czechoslovak Academy of Science. *Central and peripheral mechanisms of motor functions* (Proc. Conf. Liblice), Prague, 1963. (395)

Goy, R. W., and Phoenix, C. H. Hypothalamic regulation of female sexual behaviour; establishment of behavioural oestrus in spayed guinea pigs following hypothalamic lesions. *J. Reprod. Fertil.*, 1963, **5**, 23–40. (49)

Graham, C. H., and Hsia, Y. Color defect and color theory. *Science*, 1958, **127**, 675–82. (340)

Graham, C. H., and Kemp, E. H. Brightness discrimination as a function of the duration of the increment in intensity. *J. gen. Physiol*, 1938, **21**, 635. (349)

Granit, R. Centrifugal and antidromic effects on ganglion cells of retina. *J. Neurophysiol.*, 1955, **18**, 388–411. (172)

Granit, R. *Receptors and Sensory Perception*. New Haven: Yale University Press, 1955. (356, 395, 396, 411)

Granit, R. The visual pathway. In Dawson, H. (Ed.), *The Eye*, Vol. 2, New York and London: Academic Press, 1962, 537–763. (330, 331, 337, 356)

Granit, R.; Leksell, L.; and Skoglund, C. R. Fibre interaction in injured or compressed region of nerve. *Brain*, 1944, **67**, 125–40. (247)

Granit, R., and Renkin, B. Net depolarization and discharge rate of motoneurons, as measured by recurrent inhibition. *J. Physiol.*, 1961, **158**, 461–75. (465)

Gray, A. A. On a modification of the Helmholtz theory of hearing. *J. of Anat. Physiol.*, 1900, **34**, 324–50. (302)

Gray, J. The role of peripheral sense organs during locomotion in the vertebrates. In Symp. Soc. Exp. Biol. No. 4. *Physiological Mechanisms in Animal Behaviour*, Cambridge: Cambridge University Press, 1950. (427)

Gray, J. A., and Wedderburn, A. A. I. Grouping strategies with simultaneous stimuli. *Quart. J. exp. Psychol.*, 1960, **12**, 180–84. (167)

Gray, J. A. B. A morphological basis for pre-synaptic inhibition. *Nature*, 1962, **193**, 82. (460)

Graybiel, A.; Clark, B.; and Zarriello, J. J. Observations on human subjects, living in a slow rotation room for periods of two days. *Arch. Neurol.*, 1960, **3**, 55–73. (422)

Graybiel, A., and Hupp, D. I. The oculogyral illusion; a form of apparent motion which may be observed following stimulation of the semicircular canals, *J. aviat. Med.*, 1946, **17**, 3–27. (419)

Green, J. D. Electrical activity in hypothalamus and hippocampus of conscious rabbits. *Anat. Rec.*, 1954, **118**, 304. (49, 51)

Green, J. D. The hippocampus. In American Physiological Society. *Handbook of Physiology, Section 1; Neurophysiology, Vol. II* (Field, J.; Magoun, H. W.; and

Hall, V. E. [Eds.]). Baltimore, Md.: Williams & Wilkins Co., 1960, 1373–90. (211)

Green, J. D., and Adey, W. R. Electrophysiological studies of hippocampal connections and excitability. EEG clin. Neurophysiol., 1956, 8, 245–62. (151)

Green, J. D.; Clemente, C. D.; and de Groot, J. Rhinencephalic lesions and behavior in cats. An analysis of the Kluver-Bucy syndrome with particular reference to normal and abnormal sexual behavior. J. comp. Neurol., 1957(a), 108, 505–45. (208)

Green, J. D.; Clemente, C. D.; and de Groot, J. Experimentally induced epilepsy in the cat with injury of Cornu Ammonis (hippocampus). A.M.A. Arch. Neurol. Psychiat., 1957(b), 78, 259–63. (208)

Green, J. D.; Clemente, C. D.; and de Groot, J. Rhinencephalic lesions and behavior in cats. J. comp. Neurol., 1957, 108, 505–36. (34, 43, 55, 59)

Green, J. R.; Duisberg, R. E. H.; and McGrath, W. B. Focal epilepsy of psychomotor type; preliminary report of observations on effects of surgical therapy. J. Neurosurg., 1951, 8, 157–72. (211)

Greer, M. A. The role of the hypothalamus in the control of thyroid function. J. clin. Endocrinol., 1952, 12, 1259–67. (71)

Greer, M. A. The effect of progesterone on persistent vaginal estrus produced by hypothalamic lesions in the rat. Endocrinology, 1953, 53, 380–90. (70)

Greer, M. A. Suggestive evidence of a primary "drinking center" in hypothalamus of the rat. Proc. Soc. exper. Biol. Med., 1955, 89, 59–62. (8)

Grindley, G. C. The variation of sensory thresholds with the rate of application of the stimulus: 1. The differential threshold for pressure. Brit. J. Psychol., 1936, 27, 86–95. (250)

Groen, J. J. Postnatal changes in vestibular reactions. Acta Oto-laryng., 1963, 56, 390–96. (420)

Groen, J. J., and Jongkees, L. B. W. The threshold of angular acceleration perception. J. Physiol., 1948, 107, 1–7. (417)

Gross, C. G., and Carey, F. M. Transfer of learned response by RNA injection: failure of attempts to replicate. Science, 1965, 150, 1749. (91)

Gross, N. B., and Thurlow, W. R. Micro-

electrode studies of neural auditory activity of cat. II. Medial geniculate body. J. Neurophysiol., 1951, 14, 409–22. (307, 313)

Grossman, M. I.; Cummins, G. M.; and Ivy, A. C. The effect of insulin on food intake after vagotomy and sympathectomy. Amer. J. Physiol., 1947, 149, 100–102. (26)

Grossman, S. P. Eating or drinking elicited by direct adrenergic or cholinergic stimulation of the hypothalamus. Science, 1960, 301–32. (9)

Grossman, S. P. Behavioral effects of chemical stimulation of the ventral amygdala. J. comp. physiol. Psychol., 1964, 57, 29–36. (34)

Grossman, S. P., and Grossman, L. Food and water intake following lesions or electrical stimulation of the amygdala. Amer. J. Physiol., 1963, 205, 761–65. (34)

Grundfest, H. Bioelectric potentials. Ann. Rev. Physiol., 1940, 2, 213–42. (130)

Grüsser, O. J. Rezeptorpotentiale einzelner retinaler Zapfen der Katze. Naturwissenschaften, 1957, 44, 522. (350)

Grüsser, O. J., and Creutzfeldt, O. Eine neurophysiologische Grundlage des Brücke-Bartley-Effectes: Maxima der Impulsfrequenz retinaler und corticaler Neurone bei Flimmerlicht mittlerer Frequenzen. Pflüg. Arch. ges. Physiol., 1957, 263, 668–81. (351)

Grüsser, O. J., and Kapp, H. Reactionen retinaler neurone nach lichtblitzen. II. Doppelblitze mit wechselndem Blitzintervall. Pflüg. Arch. ges. Physiol., 1958, 265, 501–25. (349, 350)

Grüsser, O. J., and Rabelo, C. Reaktionen retinaler neurone nach lichtblitzen. I. Einzelblitze und Blitzruze wechselnder Frequenz. Pflüg. Arch. ges. Physiol., 1958, 265, 501–25. (350)

Guedry, F. E.; Collins, W. E.; and Sheffey, P. L. Perceptual and oculomotor reactions to interacting visual and vestibular stimulation. Percept. Mot. Skills, 1961, 12, 307–24. (419)

Guttman, N. Operant conditioning, extinction, and periodic reinforcement in relation to concentration of sucrose used as reinforcing agent. J. exp. Psychol., 1953, 46, 213–24. (142)

Guttman, N. Equal-reinforcement values for sucrose and glucose solutions compared with equal sweetness values. J. comp. physiol. Psychol., 1954, 47, 358–61. (142)

Guzman-Flores, C.; Buendria, N.; and Lindsley, D. B. Cortical and reticular influences upon evoked responses in dorsal column nuclei. *Fed. Proc.*, 1961, **20**, 330–50. (282)

**H**

Habgood, J. Sensitisation of sensory receptors in the frog's skin. *J. Physiol.*, 1959, **111**, 195–213. (245, 246)

Hagbarth, K. E., and Kerr, D. I. B. Central influences on spinal afferent conduction. *J. Neurophysiol.*, 1954, **17**, 295–307. (172)

Hagen, E.; Knoche, H.; Sinclair, D. C.; and Weddell, G. The role of specialized nerve terminals in cutaneous sensibility. *Proc. Roy. Soc.* (London), 1953, **B141**, 279–87. (227)

Hagstrom, E. C., and Pfaffmann, C. The relative taste effectiveness of different sugars for the rat. *J. comp. physiol. Psychol.*, 1959, **52**, 259–62. (40, 142)

Hahn, H. Die psycho-physischen konstanten und variablen des temperatursinnes. *Z. Sinnesphys.*, 1930, **60**, 198–232. (251)

Hahn, H. *Bertrage zur Reizphysiologie.* Heidelberg: Scherer, 1949. (369)

Haider, M.; Spong, P.; and Lindsley, D. B. Attention, vigilance and cortical evoked potentials in humans. *Science*, 1964, 145–80. (175)

Hain, A. M. The effect of (a) litter size on growth and (b) of estrone administered during lactation (rat). *Quart. J. exp. Physiol.*, 1935, **25**, 303–13. (62)

Hamby, W. B. Reversible central pain. *Trans. Amer. neurol. Assoc.*, 1961, 91–94. (285)

Hammond, P. H.; Merton, P. A.; and Sutton, G. G. Nervous gradation of muscular contraction. *Brit. med. Bull.*, 1956, **12**, 214–18. (396)

Hanbery, J., and Jasper, H. H. Independence of diffuse thalamocortical projection system shown by specific nuclear destruction. *J. Neurophysiol.*, 1953, **16**, 252–71. (57)

Hardy, J. D., and Oppel, T. W. Studies in temperature sensations; stimulation of cold sensation by radiation. *J. clin. Invest.*, 1938, **17**, 771–78. (250)

Hardy, J. D.; Wolff, H. G.; and Goodell, H. Experimental evidence on nature of cutaneous hyperalgesia. *J. clin. Invest.*, 1950, **29**, 115–40. (246)

Hardy, J. D.; Wolff, H. G.; and Goodell, H. *Pain Sensations and Reactions.* Baltimore, Md.: Williams and Wilkins, 1952. (239, 248)

Hardy, R. K. An appetitional theory of sexual motivation. *Psychological Review*, 1964, **71**, 1–18. (56)

Harlow, H. F. Recovery of pattern discrimination in monkeys following unilateral occipital lobectomy. *J. comp. Psychol.*, 1939, **27**, 467–89. (355)

Harlow, H. F. Learning set and error factor theory. In Koch, S., (Ed.), *Psychology: A Study of a Science*, Vol. 2. New York: McGraw-Hill Book Co., 1959. (82)

Harlow, H. F., and Bromer, J. A. Acquisition of new responses during inactivation of the motor premotor and somesthetic cortex in the monkey. *J. gen. Psychol.*, 1942, **26**, 299–313. (114)

Harris, G. W. Electrical stimulation of the hypothalamus and the mechanism of neural control of the adenohypophysis. *J. Physiol.*, 1948, **107**, 418–29. (68, 70)

Harris, G. W. The reticular formation, stress, and endocrine activity, chap. ix. In Jasper, H. H.; Proctor, L. D.; Knighton, R. S.; Noshay, W. C.; and Costello, R. T. (Eds.), *Reticular Formation of the Brain.* Boston: Little, Brown and Co., 1958. (50)

Harris, G. W. Central control of pituitary secretion. In American Physiological Society, *Handbook of Physiology, Section 1; Neurophysiology, Vol. II* (Field, J.; Magoun, H. W.; and Hall, V. E. [Eds.]). Baltimore, Md.: Williams & Wilkins Co., 1960, 1007–38. (67)

Harris, G. W., and Jacobsohn, D. Functional grafts of the anterior pituitary gland. *Proc. Roy Soc.* (London), Ser. B, 1952, **139**, 263–76. (68, 69)

Harris, L. J.; Clay, J.; Hargreaves, F.; and Ward, A. Appetite and choice of diet. The ability of the vitamin B deficient rat to discriminate between diets containing and lacking the vitamin. *Proc. Royal Soc.* (London), Ser. B, 1933, **113**, 161–90. (36)

Hartline, H. K. The receptive field of the optic nerve fibers. *Amer. J. Physiol.*, 1940, **130**, 690–99. (342)

Hartline, H. K. Inhibition of visual receptors by illuminating nearby visual areas in the *Limulus* eye. *Fed. Proc.*, 1949, **8**, 69. (341)

Hartline, H. K., and Ratliff, F. Inhibitory interaction of receptor units in the eye of Limulus. *J. gen. Physiol.*, 1957, **40**, 357–76. (465)

Hartline, H. K., and Ratliff, F. Spatial summation of inhibitory influences in the eye of Limulus and the mutual interaction of receptor units. *J. gen. Physiol.*, 1958, **41**, 1049–66. (465)

Harvey, J. A., and Hunt, H. F. Effect of septal lesions on thirst in the rat as indicated by water consumption and operant responding for water reward. *J. comp. physiol. Psychol.*, 1965, **59**, 49–56. (217, 218)

Harvey, J. A.; Jacobsen, L. E.; and Hunt, H. F. Long-term effects of lesions in the septal forebrain on acquisition and retention of conditioned fear. *Amer. Psychol.*, 1961, **16**, 449. (218)

Harvey, J. A.; Lintz, C. E.; Jacobsen, L. E.; and Hunt, H. F. Effects of lesions in the septal area on conditioned fear and discriminated instrumental punishment in the albino rat. *J. comp. physiol. Psychol.*, 1965, **59**, 37–48. (214, 217, 218)

Hausmann, M. F. The behavior of albino rats in choosing food: II. Differentiation between sugar and saccharin. *J. comp. Psychol.*, 1933, **15**, 419–28. (38)

Hayward, S. C. Modification of sexual behavior of the male albino rat. *J. comp. physiol. Psychol.*, 1957, **50**, 70–73. (57)

Head, H. *Studies in Neurology*. London: Frowde, Hodder & Stoughton, 1920. (224, 247, 269, 271, 275, 280, 285)

Hearst, E., and Whalen, R. E. Facilitating effects of D-amphetamine on discriminated-avoidance performance. *J. comp. physiol. Psychol.*, 1963, **56**, 124–28. (216)

Heath, R. G., and Mickle, W. A. Evaluation of seven years experience with depth electrode studies in human patients. In Ramey, E. R., and O'Doherty, D. S. (Eds.), *Electrical Studies on the Unanaesthetised Brain*. New York: Paul B. Hoeber, Inc., 1960, 214–40. (192, 198)

Heath, R. G.; Monroe, R. R.; and Mickle, W. A. Stimulation of the amygdaloid nucleus in the schizophrenic patient. *Am. J. Psychiat.*, 1955, **111**, 862–63. (198)

Hebb, D. O. *The Organization of Behavior*. New York: John Wiley & Sons, Inc., 1949. (75, 92)

Hécaen, H.; Talairach, J.; David, M.; and Dell, M. B. Coagulations limitées du thalamus dans les algies du syndrome thalamique. Resultats therapeutiques et

physiologiques. *Rev. Neurol.*, 1949, **81**, 917–81. (275, 285)

Hecht, S. Rods, cones and the chemical basis of vision. *Physiol. Rev.*, 1937, **17**, 239–90. (332)

Heinbecker, P.; Bishop, G. H.; and O'Leary, J. L. Pain and touch fibers in peripheral nerves. *Arch. Neurol. Psychiat.*, 1933, **29**, 771–89. (243)

Held, R. Adaptation to rearrangement and visual-spatial after-effects. *Psychol. Beit.*, 1962, **6**, 339–450. (433)

Held, R., and Hein, A. Movement produced stimulation in the development of visually guided behavior. *J. comp. physiol. Psychol.*, 1963, **56**, 872–76. (433)

Helmholtz, H. L. F. *Die Lehre von den Tonempfindungen als Physiologische Grundlage für die Theorie der Musik*, 1st Ed., Brunswick, Germany: Vieweg-Verlag, 1863. (297)

Helmholtz, H. von. *Treatise on Physiological Optics*. Southall: J.P.C., 1925. Translated and edited from the 3rd German edition for the Opt. Soc. Am. (435)

Henning, H. *Der Geruch*, 2d Ed., Leipzig: Barth, 1924. (378)

Hensel, H. Temperaturempfindung und intracutane Wärmebewegung. *Arch Ges. Physiol.*, 1950, **252**, 165–215. (251, 252)

Hensel, H., and Boman K. Afferent impulses in cutaneous sensory nerves in human subjects. *J. Neurophysiol.*, 1960, **23**, 564–78.

Hensel, H.; Iggo, A.; and Witt, I. A quantitative study of sensitive cutaneous thermoreceptors with C afferent fibres. *J. Physiol.*, 1960, **153**, 113–26. (230, 238, 239)

Hensel, H., and Zotterman, Y. Quantitative beziehungen zwischen der entladung einzelner kaltenfasern und der temperatur. *Acta. Physiol., Scand.*, 1951(a), **23**, 291–319. (236, 275)

Hensel, H., and Zotterman, Y. The response of mechanoreceptors to thermal stimulation. *J. Physiol.*, 1951(b), **115**, 16–24. (240)

Hensel, H., and Zotterman, Y. Action potentials of cold fibres and intracutaneous temperature gradient. *J. Neurophysiol.*, 1951(c), **14**, 377–85. (244)

Herberg, L. J. Hunger reduction produced by injecting glucose into the lateral ventricle of the rat. *Nature*, 1960, **187**, 245–46. (4, 26)

Herberg, L. J. Physiological drives investigated by means of injections into the cerebral ventricles of the rat. *Quart. J. exp. Psychol.*, 1962, **14**, 8–14. (8, 26)

Herberg, L. J. Determinants of extinction in electrical self-stimulation. *J. comp. physiol. Psychol.*, 1963, **56**, 686–90. (127)

Hering, E. *Ueber individuelle verschiedenheiten des Farbensinnes*, Lotos, Prague, 1885. (339)

Hernández-Peón, R. Neurophysiological correlates of habituation and other manifestations of plastic inhibition. In Jasper, H. H., and Smirnov, G. D. (Eds.). The Moscow Colloquium on Electroencephalography of Higher Nervous Activity. *EEG clin. Neurophysiol.*, 1960, Suppl. **13**, 101–12. (172, 173)

Hernández-Peón, R.; Alcocer-Cuaron, C.; Lavin, A.; y Santibáñez, G. Regulación centrífuga de la actividad eléctrica del bulbo olfatorio. Primera Reunión científica de Ciencias fisiológieas. Punta del Este, Uruguay, 1957, 192–93. (172)

Hernández-Peón, R., and Brust-Carmona, H. Functional role of subcortical structures in habituation and conditioning. In Delafresnaye, J. F. (Ed.), *Brain Mechanisms and Learning*. Oxford: Blackwell, 1961, 393–408. (173)

Hernández-Peón, R.; Chavez-Ibarra, G.; Morgane, P. J.; and Timo-Iarier, C. Limbic cholinergic pathways involved in sleep and emotional behavior. *Exptl. Neurol.*, 1963, 8, 93–111. (161)

Hernández-Peón, R.; Guzmán-Flores, C.; Alcarez, M.; and Fernández-Guardiola, A. Sensory transmission in visual pathway during "attention" in unanesthetized cats. *Acta. Neurol. Latinoamer.*, 1957, **3**, 1–8. (172)

Hernández-Peón, R.; Guzman-Flores, C.; Alcarez, M.; and Fernandez-Guardiola, A. Habituation in the visual pathway. *Acta. Neurol. Latinoamer.*, 1958, **4**, 121–29. (171)

Hernández-Peón, R., and Hagbarth, K. E. Interaction between afferent and cortically induced reticular responses. *J. Neurophysiol.*, 1955, **18**, 44–55. (150, 151, 172)

Hernández-Peón, R.; Jouvet, M.; and Scherrer, H. Auditory potentials at the cochlear nucleus during acoustic habituation. *Acta. Neurol. Latinoamer.*, 1957, **3**, 114–16. (172)

Hernández-Peón, R., and Scherrer, H. Habituation to acoustic stimuli in cochlear nucleus. *Fed. Proc.*, 1955, **14**, 71. (172)

Hernández-Peón, R.; Scherrer, H.; and Jouvet, M. Modification of electric activity in cochlear nucleus during "attention" in unanaesthetized cats. *Science*, 1956, **123**, 331–32. (171)

Hernández-Peón, R.; Scherrer, H.; and Velasco, M. Central influences on afferent conduction in the somatic and visual pathways. *Acta. Neurol. Latinoamer.*, 1956, **2**, 8–22. (172, 173)

Hervey, G. R. The effects of lesions in the hypothalamus in parabiotic rats. *J. Physiol.*, 1959, **45**, 336–52. (28)

Hess, E. H., and Gogel, W. C. Natural preferences of the chick for objects of different colors. *J. Psychol.*, 1954, **38**, 483–93.

Hess, R., Jr.; Koella, W. P.; and Akert, K. Cortical and subcortical recordings in natural and artifically induced sleep in cats. *EEG clin. Neurophysiol.*, 1953, **5**, 75–90. (158, 161)

Hess, W. R. Stammganglien-Reizversuche, (Verh. Dtsch. physiol. Ges. Sept. 1927), *Ber. ges. Physiol.*, 1928, **42**, 554. (186)

Hess, W. R. Das schlafsyndrom als folge dienzephaler reizung. *Helv. physiol. Acta.*, 1944, **2**, 305–44. (158, 161)

Hess, W. R. *Diencephalon: Autonomic and Extrapyramidal Functions*. New York: Grune and Stratton, 1954. (186)

Hess, W. R. The diencephalic sleep centre. In Delafresnaye, J. F. (Ed.), *Brain Mechanisms and Consciousness*. Springfield, Ill.: Charles C. Thomas, 1954, 117–36. (158, 159, 161)

Hess, W. R. *The Functional Organization of the Diencephalon*. New York: Grune and Stratton, 1957. (186, 188, 192, 426)

Hess, W. R., and Akert, K. Experimental data on the role of hypothalamus in mechanism of emotional behavior. *A.M.A. Arch. Neurol. Psychiat.*, 1955, **73**, 127–29. (189)

Hess, W. R., and Brügger, M. Das subkortikale zentrum der afektiven abwehrreaktion *Helv. physiol. Acta.*, 1943, **1**, 33–52. (161, 186)

Hess, W. R.; Brügger, M.; and Bucher, V. Zur physiologie von hypothalamus area praeoptica und septum, sowie agrenzender balken under stirnhirnvereiche. *Moshv. Psychiat. Neurol.*, 1945, **111**, 17–59. (161, 186)

Hetherington, A. W., and Ranson, S. W.

The spontaneous activity and food intake of rats with hypothalamic lesions. *Amer. J. Physiol.*, 1942, **136**, 609–17. (27)

Higgins, D. C., and Glaser, G. H. Stretch responses during chronic cerebellar ablation. A study of reflex instability. *J. Neurophysiol.*, 1964, **27**, 49–62. (395)

Hilali, S., and Whitfield, I. C. Responses of trapezoid body to acoustic stimulation with pure tones. *J. Physiol.*, 1953, **122**, 158–71. (310)

Hillarp, N. A.; Olivecrona, H.; and Selfverskiold, W. Evidence for the participation of the preoptic area in male mating behavior. *Experientia*, 1954, **10**, 224–25. (49, 59)

Hind, J. E. An electrophysiological determination of tonotopic organization in auditory cortex of cat. *J. Neurophysiol.*, 1953, **16**, 475–89. (317)

Hind, J. E. Unit activity in the auditory cortex. In Rasmussen, G. L., and Windle, W. F. (Eds.), *Neural Mechanisms of the Auditory and Vestibular System.* Springfield, Ill.: Charles C. Thomas, 1960. (317)

Hind, J. E.; Goldberg, J. M.; Greenwood, D. D.; and Rose, J. E. Some discharge characteristics of single neurons in the inferior colliculi of the cat. II. Timing of the discharges and observations on behavioral stimulation. *J. Neurophysiol.*, 1963, **26**, 321–41. (321)

Hirsh, I. J. The relation between localization and intelligibility. *J. acoust. Soc. Amer.*, 1950, **22**, 196–200. (166)

Hodgkin, A. L. The local electric changes associated with repetitive action in a non-medulated axon. *J. Physiol.*, 1948, **107**, 165–81. (465)

Hodgkin, A. L., and Huxley, A. F. A quantitative description of membrane current and its application to conduction and excitation in nerve. *J. Physiol.*, 1952, **417**, 500–544. (451)

Hoebel, B. G., and Teitelbaum, P. Hypothalamic control of feeding and self-stimulation. *Science*, 1962, **135**, 375–76. (27, 126)

Holmes, G. Disturbances of vision by cerebral lesions. *Brit. J. Ophthal.*, 1918, **2**, 353–65. (355)

Holmes, G. Croonian lectures. The clinical symptoms of cerebellar disease and their interpretations. *Lancet*, 1922, **202**, 1177–82, 1231–37. **203**, 59–65, 111–15. (412)

Holt, E. B. *Animal Drive and the Learning Process*. New York: Holt Rinehart & Winston, Inc., 1931. (92)

Horn, G. Electrical activity of the cerebral cortex of the unanesthetized cat during attentive behavior. *Brain*, 1960, **83**, 57–76. (175)

Horridge, G. A. Comparative physiology, integrative action of the nervous system. *Ann. Rev. Physiol.*, 1963, **25**, 523–41. (462)

Horridge, G. A. The electrophysiological approach to learning in isolatable ganglia. *Animal Behavior Supplement*, 1965, **1**, 163–82. (93)

Horvarth, F. H. Effects of basolateral amygdalectomy on three types of avoidance behavior in cats. *J. comp. physiol. Psychol.*, 1963, **56**, 380–89. (220)

Howarth, C. I., and Deutsch, J. A. Drive decay: the cause of fast "extinction" of habits learned for brain stimulation. *Science*, 1962, **137**, 35–36. (123)

Howard, I. P., and Templeton, W. B. *Human Spatial Orientation.* London: John Wiley & Sons, Inc., 1966. (427, 433, 435, 436)

Howarth, C. I., and Ellis, R. The relative intelligibility threshold for one's own name compared with other names. *Quart. J. exp. Psychol.*, 1961, **13**, 236–39. (167)

Hubbard, J. I., and Willis, W. D. Reduction of transmitter output by depolarization. *Nature*, 1962, **193**, 1294–95. (460)

Hubel, D. H. Electro-corticograms in cats during natural sleep. *Arch. ital. Biol.*, 1960, **98**, 171–81. (162)

Hubel, D. H. Single unit activity in lateral geniculate body and optic tract of unrestrained cats. *J. Physiol.*, 1960, **150**, 91–104. (345)

Hubel, D. H.; Henson, C. O.; Rupert, A.; and Galambos, R. Attention units in the auditory cortex. *Science*, 1959, **129**, 1279–80. (169)

Hubel, D. H., and Wiesel, T. N. Integrative action in the cat's lateral geniculate body. *J. Physiol.*, 1961, **160**, 106–54. (344)

Hubel, D. H., and Wiesel, T. N. Receptive fields, binocular interaction and functional architecture in the cat's visual cortex. *J. Physiol.*, 1962, **160**, 106–54. (345, 347)

Hubel, D. H., and Wiesel, T. N. Receptive fields and functional architecture in two nonstriate visual areas (18 and 19) of the cat. *J. Neurophysiol.*, 1965, **28**, 229–89. (345, 347)

Hugelin, A.; Dumont, S.; and Paillas, N. Tympanic muscles and control of auditory input during arousal. *Science*, 1960, **131**, 1371–72. (173)

Hull, C. L. *Essentials of Behavior*, New Haven: Yale University Press, 1951. (6, 12, 137)

Hull, C. L.; Livingston, J. R.; Rouse, R. O.; and Barker, A. N. Time, sham, and esophageal feeding as reinforcements. *J. comp. physiol. Psychol.*, 1951, **44**, 236–45. (18)

Hunsperger, R. W. Ahektreaktionen auf elecktrische reizung in hirnstamm der katze. *Helv. physiol. Acta.*, 1956, **14**, 70–92. (186, 204, 205)

Hunsperger, R. W. Les représentations centrales des réactions affectives dans le cerveau antérieur et dans le tronc cérébral. *Neurochirurgie*, 1959, **5**, 207–33. (188, 190, 192, 197, 205, 207, 208)

Hunt, C. C. On the nature of vibration receptors in the hind limb of the cat. *J. Physiol.*, 1961, **155**, 175–86. (254, 268)

Hunt, C. C., and Kuno, M. Background discharge and evoked responses of spinal interneurons. *J. Physiol.*, 1959, **147**, 364–84. (270)

Hunt, C. C., and McIntyre, A. K. Properties of cutaneous touch receptors in cat. *J. Physiol.*, 1960(a), **153**, 88–98. (226, 234, 241, 268)

Hunt, C. C., and McIntyre, A. K. An analysis of fibre diameter and receptor characteristics of myelinated cutaneous afferent fibers in cat. *J. Physiol.*, 1960(b), **153**, 99–112. (224, 230, 234, 239, 268)

Hunt, H. F. Electro-convulsive shock and learning. *Transactions of the N.Y. Academy of Sciences*, 1965, **27**, 923–45. (77)

Hunt, H. F., and Brady, J. V. Some effects of electro-convulsive shock on a conditioned emotional response ("anxiety"). *J. comp. physiol. Psychol.*, 1951, **44**, 88–98. (77)

Hurvich, L. M., and Jameson, D. An opponent-process theory of color vision. *Psychol. Rev.*, 1957, **64**, 384–404. (339)

Hutt, P. J. Rate of bar pressing as a function of quality and quantity of food reward. *J. comp. physiol. Psychol.*, 1954, **47**, 235–39. (142)

Huxley, H. E. Ultra-structure of striated muscle. *Brit. med. Bull.*, 1956, **12**, 171–73. (387)

Hyde, J., and Gellhorn, E. Influence of deafferentation on stimulation of motor cortex. *Amer. J. Physiol.*, 1949, **156**, 311–16. (394)

Hyden, H., and Egyhazi, E. Nuclear RNA changes of nerve cells during a learning experiment in rats. *Proc. Nat. Acad. Science*, 1962, **48**, 1366–73. (89)

Hyden, H., and Egyhazi, E. Glial RNA Changes during a learning experiment in rats. *Proc. Nat. Acad. Sci.*, 1963, **49**, 618–24. (89)

Hyden, H., and Pigon, A. A cytophysiological study of the functional relationship between oligodendroglial cells and nerve cells of Deiters' nucleus. *J. Neurochem.*, 1960, **6**, 57–72. (89)

## I

Iggo, A. A single unit analysis of cutaneous receptors with C afferent fibres. In Wolstenholme, G. E. W., and O'Connor, M. (Eds.), *Ciba Foundation Study Group. No. 1, Pain and Itch, Nervous Mechanisms*, Boston: Little, Brown and Co., 1959(a), 41–59. (230, 239)

Iggo, A. Cutaneous heat and cold receptors with slowly conducting (C) afferent fibres. *Quart. J. exp. Physiol.*, 1959(b), **44**, 362–70. (239, 240, 246)

Iggo, A. Cutaneous mechanoreceptors with afferent C fibres. *J. Physiol.*, 1960, **192**, 337–53. (230, 234, 239, 266)

Ingram, W. R. Brain stem mechanisms and behavior. *EEG clin. Neurophysiol.*, 1952, **4**, 395–406. (186)

Ingram, W. R.; Barris, R. W.; and Ranson, S. W. Catalepsy: an experimental study. *Arch. Neurol. Psychiat.* (Chicago), 1936, **35**, 1175–97. (204)

Ingvar, D. H. Extraneuronal influences upon the electrical activity of isolated cortex following stimulation of the reticular activating system. *Acta. physiol. Scand.*, 1955, **33**, 169–93. (162)

Ingvar, D. H., and Hunter, J. Influence of visual cortex on light impulses in the brain stem of the unanesthetized cat. *Acta. Physiol. Scand.*, 1955, **33**, 194–218. (356)

Iruichijima, J., and Zotterman, Y. A specificity of afferent cutaneous C fibers in mammals. *Acta. Physiol. Scand.*, 1960, **49**, 267–78. (230, 238, 239)

Irvine, S. R., and Ludvigh, E. Is ocular proprioceptive sense concerned in vision. *A.M.A. Arch. Ophthal.*, 1936, **15**, 1037–49. (399)

Isaacson, R. L.; Douglas, R. J.; and Moore, R. Y. The effect of radical hippocampal ablation on acquisition of avoidance response. *J. Comp. Physiol. Psych.*, 1961, **54**, 625–28. (221)

Ishiko, N., and Loewenstein, W. R. Temperature and charge transfer in a receptor membrane. *Science*, 1960, **132**, 184. (242)

Iwama, K., and Yamamoto, C. Transmission of thalamic somatosensory relay nuclei as modified by electrical stimulation of the cerebral cortex. *Japan, J. Physiol.*, 1961, **11**, 169–82. (282, 286)

**J**

Jansen, J., and Brodal, A. (Eds.). *Aspects of Cerebellar Anatomy.* Oslo: Tanum, 1954.

Jasper, H. H., and Rasmussen, T. Studies of clinical and electrical responses to deep temporal stimulation in man with some considerations of functional anatomy. *A Res. Nerv. Ment. Dis.*, 1958, **36**, 316–34. (197, 198)

Jasper, H.; Ricci, G.; and Doane, B. Microelectrode analysis of cortical cell discharge during avoidance conditioning in the monkey. In Jasper, H. H., and Smirnov, G. D. (Eds.), The Moscow Collogium on EEG and Higher Nervous Activity. *EEG clin. Neurophysiol.*, Suppl. 13, 1960, 137–57. (103, 147)

Jefferson, M. Altered consciousness associated with brain stem lesions. *Brain*, 1952, **75**, 55–67. (149)

Jensen, D. D. Paramecia, planaria and pseudo-learning. *Animal Behaviour Supplement*, 1965, **1**, 9–20. (90)

Jerome, E. A. Olfactory thresholds measured in terms of stimulus pressure and volume. *Arch. Psychol.*, (New York), 1942, **274**, 44. (384)

Jocab, A. Das Kleinhirn. In von Müllendorff (Ed.), *Handbuch der Mikroskopishen Anatomie des Menschen*, Vol. IV. Berlin: Springer, 1928. (407)

John, E. R., and Killam, K. F. Studies of electrical activity of brain during differential conditioning in cats. In Wortis, J. (Ed.), *Recent Advances in Biological Psychiatry.* New York: Grune and Stratton, 1960, 417. (104)

John, E. R.; Leiman, A. C.; and Sachs, E. An exploration of the functional relationship between electroencephalographic potentials and differential inhibition. In *Ann. New York Acad. Sci.*, 1961, **92**, (Pavlovian Conference on Higher Nervous Activity. Kline, N. S. [Ed.]), 1160–82. (105, 106)

Johnson, W. H., and Taylor, M. B. G. Some experiments on the relative affectiveness of various types of accelerations on motion sickness. *Aerosp. Med.*, 1961, **32**, 205–8. (422)

Jones, F. N. A test of the validity of the Elsberg method of olfactometry. *Am. J. Psychol.*, 1953, **66**, 81–85. (384)

Jones, F. N. An olfactometer permitting stimulus specification in molar terms. *Am. J. Psychol.*, 1954, **67**, 147–51. (384)

Jones, F. N. Olfactory absolute thresholds and their implications for the nature of the receptor process. *J. Psychol.*, 1955, **40**, 223–27. (375)

Jones, F. N. An analysis of individual differences in olfactory thresholds. *Am. J. Psychol.*, 1957, **70**, 227–32. (378)

Jones, F. N., and Jones, M. H. Modern theories of olfaction: a critical review. *J. of Psychol.*, 1953, **36**, 207–41. (378)

Jones, M. Second pain: fact or artefact? *Science*, 1956, **124**, 442. (249)

Jouvet, M. Étude neurophysiologique chez l'homme de quelques mécanismes souscorticaux de l'attention. *Psychol. Franc.*, 1957, **2**, 250–56. (171, 174)

Jouvet, M. Recherches sur les mécanismes neurophysiologiques du sommeil et de l'apprentissage negatif. In Delafresnaye, J. F. (Ed.), *Brain Mechanisms and Learning.* Oxford: Blackwell, 1961, 445–81. (164)

Jouvet, M. Telencephalic and rhombencephalic sleep in the cat. In Wolstenholme, G. E. W., and O'Connor, M. (Eds.), *The Nature of Sleep.* London: Churchill, 1961, 188–208. (162)

Jouvet, M. Récherches sur les structures nerveuses et les mécanismes responsibles des differentes phases du sommeil physiologique. *Arch. Ital. Biol.*, 1962, **100**, 125–206. (162)

Judd, D. B. Color perception of deuteranopic and protanopic observers. *J. Res. Nat. Bur. Stand.*, 1948, **41**, 247–71. (340)

Jukes, C. L. Selection of diet in chicks as influenced by vitamins and other factors. *J. comp. Psychol.*, 1938, **26**, 135–56. (37)

Jung, R., and Hassler, R. The extrapyramidal motor system. In American Physiological Society, *Handbook of Physiology, Section 1; Neurophysiology, Vol. II* (Field, J.; Magoun, H. W.; and Hall, V. E. [Eds.]). Baltimore, Md.: Williams & Wilkins Co., 1960. (91, 409)

### K

Kaada, B. R. Somato-motor, autonomic and electrocardiographic responses to electrical stimulation of rhinencephalic and other structures in primate, cat and dog. *Acta. Physiol. Scand.*, 1951, 226, 24, Suppl. 83. (215)

Kaada, B. R.; Anderson, P.; and Jansen, J., Jr. Stimulation of the amygdaloid nuclear complex in unanaesthetised cats. *Neurology*, 1954, 4, 48–64. (193)

Kaada, B. R.; Jansen, J., Jr; and Anderson, P. Stimulation of the hippocampus and medial cortical areas in unanaesthetised cats. *Neurology*, 1953, 3, 844–57. (196, 197)

Kaada, B. R.; Rasmussen, E. W.; and Kveim, O. Effects of hippocampus lesions on maze learning and retention in rats. *Exp. Neurol.*, 1961, 3, 333–55. (220)

Kaada, B. R.; Rasmussen, E. W.; and Kveim, O. Impaired acquisition of passive avoidance behavior by subcallosal septal hypothalamic and insular lesions in rats. *J. comp. physiol. Psychol.*, 1962, 55, 661–70. (218, 221)

Kagan, J. Differential reward value of incomplete and complete sexual behavior. *J. comp. physiol. Psychol.*, 1955, 48, 59–64. (141)

Kagan, J., and Beach, F. A. Effects of early experience on mating behavior in male rats. *J. comp. physiol. Psychol.*, 1953, 46, 204–8. (57)

Kamin, L. J.; Briner, C. J.; and Black, A. H. Conditioned suppression as a monitor of fear of the CS in the course of avoidance training. *J. comp. physiol. Psychol.*, 1963, 56, 497–501. (182)

Karplus, J. P., and A. Kreidl. Gehirn und sympathicus. VIII, (1) zur zentralen Reguliering der loisbeiregungen; (2) Bemerkungen zur Schinerzemp Findlichklit der vegetativen Hypothalamus Zentren, Pflug. *Arch. ges. Physiol.*, 1928, 219, 613–18. (191)

Katsuki, Y. Neural mechanism of auditory sensation in cats, chap. 29. In Rosenblith, W. A. (Ed.), *Sensory Communication*. New York: M.I.T. Press and John Wiley & Sons, 1961, 561–84. (309, 310, 311, 313, 314)

Katsuki, Y.; Suga, N.; and Kanno, Y. Neural mechanism of the peripheral and central auditory system in monkeys. *J. acoust. Soc. Amer.*, 1962, 34, 1396–1410. (309, 310)

Katsuki, Y.; Sumi, T.; Uchiyama, H.; and Watanabe, T. Electric responses of auditory neurons in cat to sound stimulation. *J. Neurophysiol.*, 1958, 21, 569–88. (307, 309, 310, 314, 315, 316)

Katsuki, Y.; Watanabe, T.; and Maruyama, N. Activity of auditory neurons in upper levels of brain of cat. *J. Neurophysiol.*, 1959, 22, 343–59. (310, 314)

Keele, C. A. *Lectures on the Scientific Basis of Medicine*. London: Athlone Press, 1958, 6, 143. (253)

Keidel, W. D. Mechanical frequency discrimination in the cochlea. *International Audiology*, 1962, 1, 37–52. (300)

Keller, A. D. Autonomic discharges elicited by physiological stimuli in midbrain preparations. *Am. J. Physiol.*, 1932, 100, 576–86. (201, 205)

Kellogg, W. N.; Scott, V. B.; Davis, R. C.; and Wolf, I. S. Is movement necessary for learning? *J. comp. Psychol.*, 1940, 37, 99–117. (113)

Kelly, A. H.; Beaton, L. E.; and Magoun, H. W. A midbrain mechanism for faciovocal activity. *J. Neurophysiol.*, 1946, 9, 181–89. (204, 205)

Kendler, H. H. The influence of simultaneous hunger and thirst drives upon the learning of two opposed spatial responses of the white rat. *J. exp. Psychol.*, 1946, 36, 212–20. (117)

Kennard, M. A. Effect of bilateral ablation of cingulate area on behavior of cats. *J. Neurophysiol.*, 1955(a), 18, 159–69. (212)

Kennard, M. A. The cingulate gyrus in relation to consciousness. *J. nerv. ment. Dis.*, 1955(b), 121, 34–39. (212)

Kennedy, G. C. The role of depot fat in the hypothalamic control of food intake in the rat. *Proc. Roy. Soc.*, Ser. B, 1953, 140, 578–92. (3, 4)

Kent, G. C., and Liberman, M. J. Induction of psychic estrus in the hamster with progesterone administered via the lateral brain ventricle. *Endocrin.*, 1959, 45, 29–32. (50)

Kerr, D. I. B. Properties of the olfactory efferent system. *Aust. J. exp. bio. med. Sci.*, 1960, 38, 29–36. (482)

Kerr, D. I. B., and Hagbarth, K. E. An investigation of olfactory centrifugal fiber system. *J. Neurophysiol.*, 1955, 18, 362–74. (382)

Keynes, R. D. The ionic movements during nervous activity. *J. Physiol.*, 1951, 114, 119–50. (452)

Kiang, N. Y-S *An electrophysiological study of cat auditory cortex*. Thesis

(No. 3028), 1955, University of Chicago. (318)

Kiesow, F. Untersuchungen über Temperaturempfindungen. *Philos. St.*, 1895, **11**, 135–45. (226, 240)

Killam, E. K.; Killam, K. F.; and Shaw, T. The effects of psychotherapeutic compounds on central afferent and limbic pathways. *Ann. N.Y. Acad. Sci.*, 1957, **66**, 784–805. (147)

Kim, C. Nest building, general activity and salt preference of rats following hippocampal ablation. *J. comp. physiol. Psychol.*, 1960, **53**, 11–16. (220)

Kimble, D. P. Effects of bilateral hippocampal lesions in rats. *J. comp. physiol. Psychol.*, 1963, **56**, 273–83. (221)

Kimura, D. Effects of selective hippocampal damage on avoidance behavior in the rat. *Canad. J. Psychol.*, 1958, **12**, 213–18. (220)

Kimura, K., and Beidler, L. M. Microelectrode study of taste receptors of rat and hamster. *J. Cell. comp. Physiol.*, 1961, **58**(2), 131–39. (361, 364)

Kinder, E. F. A study of the nest building activity of the albino rat. *J. exp. Zool.*, 1927, **47**, 117–61. (63)

King, F. A. Effects of septal and amygdaloid lesions on emotional behavior and conditioned avoidance responses in the rat. *J. nerv. ment. Dis.*, 1958, **126**, 57–63. (207, 211, 218, 219)

King, F. A., and Meyer, P. M. Effects of amygdaloid lesions upon septal hyperemotionality in the rat. *Science*, 1958, **128**, 655–56. (210)

Klein, M. Uterine distension, ovarian hormones and maternal behavior in rodents. *Ciba Foundation Coloq. Endocrinol.*, 1952, **3**, 84–88. (63)

Klein, M. Aspects biologiques de l'instinct reproducteur dans le comportement des mammifères. In P. P. Grasse (Ed.), *L'Instinct dans le Comportement des Animaux et de L'Homme.* Paris: Masson and Cie, 1956, 287–344. (63)

Kleist, K. *Handbuch der Ärztlichen Erfahrungen in Weltkriege*, Vol. 4. Leipzig: Barth, 1934. (279, 285)

Kling, A., and Hutt, P. J. Effect of hypothalamic lesions on the amygdala syndrome in the cat. *A.M.A. Arch. Neurol. Psychiat.*, 1958, **79**, 511–17. (209)

Kling, A.; Orbach, J.; Schwartz, N. B.; and Towne, J. C. Injury to the limbic system and associated structures in cats (chronic behavioral and physiological effects). *Arch. gen. Psychiat.*, 1960, **3**, 391–420. (211)

Kluver, H. Functional significance of the geniculo-striate system. *Biol. Symp.*, 1942, **7**, 253–99. (353)

Kluver, H., and Bucy, P. C. "Psychic blindness" and other symptoms following bilateral temporal lobectomy in rhesus monkeys. *Am. J. Physiol.*, 1937, **119**, 352–53. (206)

Kluver, H., and Bucy, P. C. An analysis of certain effects of bilateral temporal lobectomy in the rhesus monkey with special reference to "psychic blindness." *J. Psychol.*, 1938, **5**, 33–54. (59, 61)

Kluver, H., and Bucy, P. C. Preliminary analysis of functions of the temporal lobes of monkeys. *Arch. Neurol. Psychiat.*, 1939, **42**, 979–1000. (32)

Kogan, A. B. The manifestation of processes of higher nervous activity in the electrical potentials of the cortex during free behaviour of animals. In Jasper, H. H., and Smirnov, G. D. (Eds.), The Moscow Colloquim on EEG and Higher Nervous Activity. *EEG clin. Neurophysiol.* Suppl. 13, 1960, 51–64. (104, 147)

Kolmer, W. Geschmacksorgan. In Mollendorf, W. V. (Ed.), *Handbuch der Mikroskopischen Anatomie des Menschen III.* Berlin: Springer, 1927. (365)

Knapp, H. D.; Taub, E.; and Berman, A. J. Conditioned responses following deafferentation in the monkey. *Trans. Amer. neurol. Ass.*, 1959, 185–87. (395)

Kohler, I. *Über Aufbau and Wandlingen der Wahrnehmungswelt, insbesondere über "bedingte" Empfindungen.* Wein: Rudolph M. Rohrer, 1951. (441)

Kohn, M. Satiation of hunger from food injected directly into the stomach versus food ingested by mouth. *J. comp. physiol. Psychol.*, 1951, **44**, 412–22. (17, 25)

Koikegami, H.; Fuse, S.; Yokoyama, T.; Watanabe, T.; and Watanabe, M. Contributions to the comparative anatomy of the amygdaloid nuclei of mammals with some experiments of their destruction or stimulation. *Folia Psychiat. et Neurol.* (Japan), 1955, **8**, 336. (34)

Kolbe, H. Die zeitliche Veränderung der Unterschneidsschwelle wahrend der Einwirking eines stetigen Dauerdruckoder Dauerlichtreizes. *Z. Sinnesphysiol.*, 1936, **67**, 53–68. (250)

Koller, G. Der Nestbau der weissen Maus und seine hormonale Auslosung. *Verh. Dtsch. Zool. Ges. Freiburg*, 1952, 160–68. (63)

Koller, G. Hormonale und psychische steuerung beim Nestbau weiser Mause. *Zool. Anz.* (Suppl.), 1956, **19**, (Verh. Detsch. Zool. Ges., 1955), 123–32. (163)

Kolmodin, G. M., and Skoglund, C. R. Analysis of spinal interneurons activated by tactile and nociceptive stimulation. *Acta. Physiol. Scand.*, 1960, **50**, 337–55. (270)

Konorski, J. On the influence of the frontal lobes of the cerebral hemispheres higher nervous activity. In *Problems of the Modern Physiology of the Nervous and Muscle System.* Georgian S.S.R.: Tbilisi Academy of Sciences, 1956. (164)

Kornmüller, A. E.; Lux, H. B.; and Wintrel, R. EEG- Untersuchungen an tieren mit gekrenzten Kreislant. *Naturwissenschaften.*, 1961, **48**, 381–82. (162)

Kosman, M. E., and Gerard, R. W. The effect of adrenaline on a conditioned avoidance response. *J. comp. physiol. Psychol.*, 1955, **48**, 506–8. (181)

Kourilsky, R. Diabetes insipidus. *Proc. Roy. Soc. Med.*, 1950, **43**, 842–44. (8)

Kraft, M. S.; Obrist, W. D.; and Pribram, K. H. The effect of irritative lesions on the striate cortex on learning of visual discriminations in monkeys. *J. comp. physiol. Psychol.*, 1960, **53**, 509–19. (101)

Krakauer, D., and Dallenbach, K. M. Gustatory adaptation to sweet, sour, and bitter. *Amer. J. Psychol.*, 1937, **49**, 469–75. (369)

Kramer, F., and Moskiewicz, G. Beiträge zue Lehre von den Lage-und Bewegungsempfindungen. *Z. Psychol.*, 1901, **25**, 114–15. (398)

Krasne, F. B. General disruption resulting from electrical stimulus of ventromedial hypothalamus. *Science*, 1962, **138**, 822–23. (28)

Kroll, F. W. Schwellenuntersuchungen Bei Läionen der Afferenten Leitungsbahnen. *Ztschr. ges. Neurol. Psychiat.*, 1930, **128**, 751–76. (279)

Kruger, L. Characteristics of the somatic afferent projection to the precentral cortex in the monkey. *Am. J. Physiol.*, 1956, **186**, 475–82. (260)

Kruger, L. Nervous mechanisms. In Wolstenholme, G. E. W., and O'Connor, F. (Eds.), *Ciba Foundation Study Group, Pain and Itch*, No. 1. London: Churchill, 1959, 67. (275)

Kruger, L., and Michel, F. Reinterpreta-

tion of the representation of pain based on physiological excitation of single neurons in the trigeminal sensory complex. *Exp. Neurol.*, 1962, **5**, 157–78. (260)

Kruger, L., and Michel, F. A single neuron analysis of buccal cavity representation in the sensory trigeminal complex of the cat. *Arch. oral Biol.*, 1962(b), **7**, 491–503. (271)

Kruger, L. and Porter, P. A Behavioral Study of the Functions of The Rolandic Cortex in The Monkey. *J. comp. Neurol.*, 1958, **109**, 439–69. (282)

Kruger, L.; Simminoff, R.; and Witkovsky, P. Single neuron analysis of dorsal column nuclei and spinal nucleus of trigeminal in cat. *J. Neurophysiol.*, 1961, **24**, 333–49. (260, 261, 262, 271)

Kryter, K. D., and Ades, H. W. Studies on the function of the higher acoustic nervous centers in the cat. *Am. J. Psychol.*, 1943, **56**, 501–36. (322)

Kuhn, R. Topographical pattern of cutaneous sensibility in the dorsal column nuclei of the cat. *Trans. Amer. neurol. Ass.*, 1949, 227–30. (260)

Kunkle, E. C., and Chapman, W. A. Insensitivity to pain in man. *Proc. Ass. Res. nerv. ment. Dis.*, 1943, **23**, 100–109. (288)

Kuypers, H. G. J. M. *Structure and Function of the Cerebral Cortex.* Amsterdam: Elsevier Publ. Co., 1960(a), 138–43. (282)

Kuypers, H. G. J. M. Central cortical projection to motor and somatosensory cell groups. *Brain*, 1960(b), **83**, 161–84. (282)

Kuypers, H. G. J. M.; Fleming, W. R.; and Farinhott, J. W. Descending projections to spinal motor and sensory cells groups in the monkey: cortex vs. subcortex. *Science*, 1960, **132**, 38–40. (282)

Kuypers, H. G. J. M.; Szwarcbart, M. K.; Mishkin, M.; and Rosvold, H. E. Occipitotemporal corticocortical connections in the rhesus monkey. *Exptl. Neurol.*, 1965, **4**, 245–82. (356)

## L

Landau, W. M., and Bishop, G. H. Pain from dermal, periosteal, and fascial endings and from inflammation; electrophysiological study employing differential nerve blocks. *A.M.A. Arch. Neurol. Psychiat.*, 1953, **69**, 490–504. (247)

Landau, W. M.; Goldstein, R.; and Kleffner, F. R. Congenital aphasia: a clinicopathalogic study. *Neurology*, 1960, **10**, 915–21. (322)

Landgren, S. Convergence of tactile, thermal and gustatory impulses on single cortical cells. *Acta. Physiol. Scand.*, 1957, **40**, 210–21. (368)

Landgren, S. Cortical reception of cold impulses from the tongue of the cat. *Acta. Physiol. Scand.*, 1957, **40**, 202–9. (275)

Landgren, S. The response of thalamic and cortical neurons to electrical and physiological stimulation of the cat's tongue. In Rosenblith, W. A. (Ed.), *Sensory Communication*. New York: M.I.T. Press and John Wiley & Sons, 1961, 437–54. (273, 275)

Langworthy, O. R., and Richter, C. P. Increases in spontaneous activity produced by frontal lobe lesions in cats. *Amer. J. Physiol.*, 1939, **126**, 158–61. (34)

Lanier, L. H.; Carney, H. M.; and Wilson, W. D. Cutaneous innervation; experimental study. *Arch. Neurol. Psychiat.*, 1953, **34**, 1–60. (247)

Larsell, O. *The Cerebellum from Myxinoids to Man*. Minneapolis: University of Minnesota Press, 1960. (410)

Larsson, K. *Conditioning and Sexual Behavior in the Male Albino Rat*. Stockholm: Almquist and Wiksell, 1956. (53, 54)

Lashley, K. S. The accuracy of movement in the absence of excitation from the moving organ. *Amer. J. Physiol.*, 1917, **43**, 169–94. (400)

Lashley, K. S. Studies of cerebral function in learning. V. The retention of motor habits after destruction of the so-called motor area in primates. *A.M.A. Arch. Neurol. Psychiat.*, 1924, **12**, 249–76. (113)

Lashley, K. S. Basic neural mechanisms in behavior. *Psychological Review*, 1930, **37**, 1–24. (113)

Lashley, K. S. The experimental analysis of instinctive behavior. *Psychol. Rev.*, 1938, **45**, 445–71. (46)

Lashley, K. S. The mechanism of vision: XVII. The functioning of small remnants of the visual cortex. *J. comp. Neurol.*, 1939, **70**, 45–67. (355)

Lashley, K. S., and McCarthy, D. A. The survival of the maze habit after cerebellar injuries. *J. comp. Psychol.*, 1926, **6**, 423–33. (113)

Lashley, K. S., and Sperry, R. W. Olfactory discrimination after destruction of the anterior thalamic nuclei. *Amer. J. Physiol.*, 1943, **139**, 446–50. (383)

Latané, B., and Schachter, S. Adrenaline and avoidance learning. *J. comp. physiol. Psychol.*, 1962, **65**, 369–72. (181)

Law, T., and Meagher, W. Hypothalamic lesions and sexual behavior in the female rat. *Science*, 1958, **128**, 1626–27. (49)

Le Beau, J. Anterior cingulectomy in man. *J. Neurosurg.*, 1954, **2**, 268–76. (213)

Leblond, C. P. Nervous and humoral factors in the maternal behavior of the mouse. *J. genet. Psychol.*, 1940, **57**, 327–44. (62)

Lele, P. P., and Wedell, G. The relationship between neurohistology and corneal sensibility. *Brain*, 1956, **79**, 119–52. (227)

Leukel, F. A. A comparison of the effects of ECS and anesthesia on acquisition of the maze habit. *J. comp. physiol. Psychol.*, 1957, **50**, 300–306. (75, 76)

Levi-Montalcini, R., and Booker, B. Excessive growth of the sympathetic ganglia evoked by a protein isolated from mouse salivary glands. *Proc. Nat. Acad. Sci.*, 1960(a), **46**, 373–84. (181)

Levi-Montalcini, R., and Booker, B. Destruction of the sympathetic ganglia in mammals by an antiserum to a nerve-growth protein. *Proc. Nat. Acad. Sci.*, 1960(b), **46**, 384–96. (181)

Levine, J. Studies in the interrelations of central nervous structures in binocular vision: I. The lack of bilateral transfer of visual discriminative habits acquired monocularly by the pigeon. *J. genet. Psychol.*, 1945, **67**, 131–42. (93)

Levine, J. Studies in the interrelations of central nervous structures in binocular vision: II. The conditions under which interocular transfer takes place in the pigeon. *J. genet. Psychol.*, 1945, **67**, 131–42. (93)

Levine, J. Studies in the interrelations of central nervous structures in vision: III. Localization of the memory trace as evidenced by the lack of inter- and intraocular habit transfer in the pigeon. *J. genet. Psychol.*, 1952, **82**, 19–27. (93)

Levine, S., and Soliday, S. An effect of hypothalamic lesions on conditioned avoidance learning. *J. comp. physiol. Psychol.*, 1960, **53**, 497–501. (183, 214)

Levine, S., and Sokiday, S. An effect of adrenal demedullation on the acquisition of a conditioned avoidance response. *J. comp. physiol. Psychol.*, 1962, **55**, 214–19. (181)

Lewis, T. *Pain*. New York: MacMillan Co., 1942. (239, 245, 246)

Leyton, A. S. F., and Sherrington, C. S. Observations on the excitable cortex of the chimpanzee, orangutang, and gorilla. *Quart. J. exp. Physiol.*, 1917, **11**, 135–221. (429)

Liberson, W. T., and Akert, K. Hippocampal seizure states in guinea pigs. *EEG Clin. Neurophysiol.*, 1955, **7**, 211–22. (196)

Lichtenstein, P. E. Studies of anxiety: II. The effects of lobotomy on a feeding inhibition in dogs. *J. comp. physiol. Psychol.*, 1950, **43**, 419–26. (221)

Licklider, J. C. R., and Kryter, R. D. Frequency-localization in the auditory cortex of the monkey. *Fed. Proc.*, 1942, **1**, 51. (320)

Liddell, E. G. T., and Phillips, G. C. Thresholds of cortical representation. *Brain*, 1950, **73**, 125–40. (429)

Lilly, J. C. Learning motivated by subcortical stimulation: The "start" and the "stop" patterns of behavior. *International Symposium on Reticular Formation of the Brain*. Boston: Little, Brown and Co., 1958. (122)

Lindsley, D. B. Emotion. In Stevens, S. S. (Ed.), *Handbook of Experimental Psychology*. New York: John Wiley & Sons, 1951, 473–516. (178)

Lindsley, D. B. Psychological phenomena and the electroencephalogram. *EEG clin. Neurophysiol.*, 1952, **4**, 443–56. (145)

Lindsley, D. B. The reticular system and perceptual discrimination. In Henry Ford Hospital Symposium, *Reticular Formation of the Brain*. Boston: Little, Brown & Co., 1958, 513–34. (173)

Lindsley, D. B. Attention, consciousness, sleep, and wakefulness. In American Physiological Society, *Handbook of Physiology, Section 1; Neurophysiology, Vol. III* (Field, J.; Magoun, H. W.; and Hall, V. E. [Eds.]). Baltimore, Md.: Williams & Wilkins Co., 1960. (155)

Lindsley, D. B.; Schreiner, L. H.; Knowles, W. B.; and Magoun, H. W. Behavioral and EEG changes following chronic brain stem lesions in the cat. *EEG clin. Neurophysiol.*, 1949, **1**, 455–73. (149, 159)

Lippold, O. C. L.; Nicholls, J. G.; and Redfearn, J. W. T. A study of the afferent discharge produced by cooling a mammalian muscle spindle. *J. Physiol.*, 1960, **153**, 218–31. (241)

Lisk, R. D. Diencephalic placement of estradiol and sexual receptivity in the female rat. *Amer. J. Physiol.*, 1962, **203**, 493–96. (50, 69)

Lissman, H. W. Proprioception. In *Physiological Mechanisms in Animal Behavior* (Soc. exp. Biol. Symp. IV). Cambridge: Cambridge University Press, 1950. (393)

Lloyd, D. P. C., and Wilson, V. J. Functional organisations in the terminal segments of the spinal cord with a consideration of central excitatory and inhibitory latencies. *J. gen. Physiol.*, 1959, **43**, 335–45. (458, 459)

Loeffler, J. D. An investigation of auditory responses in insular cortex of cat and dog. Thesis, University of Wisconsin, Madison, 1958. (318)

Loftus, J. P. (Ed.). Symposium on motion sickness with special reference to weightlessness. AMRL-TDR-63-25. Wright-Patterson A.F.B., Ohio, 1963. (421)

Loomis, A. L.; Harvey, E. N.; and Hobart, G. Electrical potentials of the human brain. *J. exp. Psychol.*, 1936, **19**, 249–79. (113)

Loucks, R. B. The experimental delimitation of neural structures essential for learning: the attempt to condition striped muscle responses with faradization of the sigmoid gyri. *J. Psychol.*, 1935, **1**, 5–44. (114)

Loucks, R. B. Studies of neural structures essential for learning II. The conditioning of salivary and striped muscle responses to faradization of cortical sensory elements, and the action of sleep upon such mechanisms. *J. comp. Psychol.*, 1938, **25**, 315–32. (114)

Lowenstein, O. Labyrinth and equilibrium. In *Physiological Mechanisms in Animal Behavior*. Soc. exp. Biol. Symp. IV. Cambridge: Cambridge University Press, 1950. (417)

Lowenstein, O. Peripheral mechanisms of equilibrium. *Brit. med. Bull.*, 1956, **12**, 114–18. (416, 417)

Loewenstein, W. R. Mechanism of nerve impulse initiation in a pressure receptor (Lorenzinian Ampulla). *Nature*, 1960, **188**, 1034–35. (242)

Loewenstein, W. R. Excitation and inactivation in a receptor membrane. *Annals, N.Y. Acad. Sci.*, 1961, **94**, 510–34. (244)

Loewenstein, W. R., and Rathkamp, R. The sites for mechanoelectric conversion in a Pacinian corpuscle. *J. gen. Physiol.*, 1958, **41**, 1245–65. (229)

Lubar, J. F. Effect of medial cortical lesions on the avoidance behavior of the cat. *J. comp. physiol. Psychol.*, 1964, **58**, 38–46. (215, 216, 217)

Lundberg, A., and Oscarsson, O. Three ascending spinal pathways in the dorsal part of the lateral funiculus. *Acta. Physiol. Scand.*, 1961, **51**, 1–16. (259, 271)

Lundberg, A., and Voorhoeve, D. E. Pyramidal activation of interneurons of various spinal reflex arcs in the cat. *Experiontia*, 1961, **17**, 46–7. (461)

**M**

Maclean, P. D. Psychosomatic disease and the "visceral brain." Recent developments bearing on the Papez theory of emotion. *Psychosom. Med.*, 1949, **11**, 338–53. (186)

Maclean, P. D., and Delgado, J. M. R. Electrical and chemical stimulation of fronto-temporal portion of limbic system in the waking animal. *EEG clin. Neurophysiol.*, 1953, **5**, 91–100. (196)

Maclean, P. D. The limbic system ("Visceral Brain") in relation to central grey and reticulum of the brain stem. *Psychosom. Med.*, 1955, **17**, 355–66. (184, 189)

MacLean, P. D.; Dua, S.; and Denniston, R. H. Cerebral localization for scratching and seminal discharge. *A.M.A. Arch. Neurol.*, 1963, **9**, 485–97. (651)

MacLean, P. D., and Ploog, D. W. Cerebral representation of penile erection. *J. Neurophysiol.*, 1962, **25**, 29–55. (51)

MacLeod, J. G. Thalamic representation of splanchnic nerve afferents in the cat. *J. Physiol.*, 1956, **133**, 16. (283, 288)

MacNichol, E. F., Jr. Three-pigment color vision. *Scientific American*, 1964, **211**, 48–56. (331)

Macrae, D. Isolated fear. A temporal lobe aura. *Neurology*, 1954, **4**, 497–505. (199)

Magni, F. R.; Melzak, G.; Moruzzi; and Smith, C. J. Direct pyramidal influences on the dorsal column nuclei. *Arch. Ital. Biol.*, 1959, **97**, 357–77. (282)

Magnus, O., and Lammers, H. J. The amygdaloid complex. Part I. Electrical stimulation of the amygdala and periamygdaloid cortex in the waking cat. *Folia Psychiat. Neerl.*, 1956, **55**, 555–81. (193, 195, 196)

Magnus, R. *Köperstellung.* Berlin: Springer, 1924. (422)

Magnus, R. Some results of studies in the physiology of posture. (The Cameron Prize Lectures.) *Lancet*, **2**, 1926, 531–36, 585–88. (422)

Magoun, H. W. The Waking Brain. 2nd Ed. Springfield, Ill.: Charles C. Thomas, 1963. (148, 150)

Magoun, H. W. The ascending reticular system and wakefulness. In Delafresnaye, J. F. (Ed.), *Brain Mechanisms and Consciousness.* Oxford: Blackwell, 1954, 1–20. (153)

Magoun, H. W.; Atlas, D.; Ingersoll, E. H.; and Ranson, S. W. Associated facial, vocal and respiratory components of emotional expression: an experimental study. *J. Neurol. Psychopath.*, 1937, **17**, 241–55. (186)

Magoun, H. W., and Rhines, R. Spaoticity. In *The Stretch-Reflex and Extrapyramidal Systems.* Springfield, Ill.: C. C. Thomas, 1947. (408)

Maher, B. A.; Elder, S. T.; and Noblin, C. D. A differential investigation of avoidance reduction versus hypermotility following frontal ablation. *J. comp. physiol. Psychol.*, 1962, **55**, 449–54. (221)

Maher, B. A., and McIntire, R. W. The extinction of the CER following frontal ablation. *J. comp. physiol. Psychol.*, 1960, **53**, 549–52. (217, 221)

Makous, W.; Nord, S.; Oakley, B.; and Pfaffmann, C. The gustatory relay in the medulla. In Zotterman, Y. (Ed.), *Olfaction and Taste.* Oxford: Pergamon Press, 1963, 381–93. (367)

Mandler, G. In Brown, R.; Galanter, E.; Hess, E. H.; and Mandler, G. (Eds.), *New Directions in Psychology.* New York: Holt-Rinehart and Winston, 1962, 267–343. (177, 179)

Mann, L. Casuistischer beitrag zur lehre von central entstehenden schmerze. *Berlin Klin. Wochenschr.*, 1892, Bd. 29, 294. (271)

Marañon, G. Contribution a l'étude de l'action émotive de l'adrénaline. *Rev. Franc. D'endocrinol.*, 1924, **2**, 301–25. (179)

Maréchaux, E. W., and Schäfer, K. E. Uber Temperaturempfindungen bei Einwirkung von Temperaturreizen verschiedener Steilheit auf den ganzen Körper. *Arch. Ges. Physiol.*, 1949, **251**, 765–84. (224)

Marriott, F. H. C. Colour Vision: Other Phenomena. In Davson, H. (Ed.), *The Eye.* New York and London: Academic Press, 1962, 273–97. (339)

Marshall, F. H. A. On the change over in the oestrus cycle in animals after transference across the equator, with further observations on the incidence of the breeding seasons and the factors controlling sexual periodicity. *Proc. Roy. Soc. London*, Ser. B, 1937, **122**, 413–28. (66, 67)

Marshall, J. Sensory disturbances in cortical wounds with special reference to pain. *J. Neurol. Neurosurg. Psychiat.*, 1959, **14**, 187–204. (279)

Maruhashi, J.; Mizuguchi, K.; and Tasaki, I. Action currents in single afferent nerve fibres elicited by stimulation of the skin of the toad and the cat. *J. Physiol.*, 1952, **117**, 129–51. (226, 230)

Masserman, J. H. Destruction of the hypothalamus in cats: Effects on activity of the central nervous system and its reaction to sodium amytal. *A.M.A. Arch. Neurol. Psychiat.*, 1938, **39**, 1250–71. (204)

Masserman, J. H. Is the hypothalamus a center of emotion? *Psychosomat. Med.*, 1941, **3**, 3–25. (186, 189)

Masserman, J. H. Behavior and Neurosis. Chicago: University of Chicago Press, 1943. (189, 204)

Masserman, J. H., and Pechtel, C. How brain lesions affect normal and neurotic behavior, An experimental approach. *Am. J. Psychiat.*, 1956, **112**, 865–72. (208)

Maturana, H. R., and Frank, S. Directional movement and horizontal edge detectors in the pigeon retina. *Science*, 1963, **142**, 977–79. (342)

Mayer, J. Glucostatic mechanism of regulation of food intake. *New Engl. med. J.*, 1953, **249**, 13–16. (3, 4)

Mayer, J. Satiety and weight control. *Am. J. clin. Nutrition*, 1957, **5**, 184–85. (4)

Mayer, J., and Marshall, N. B. Specificity of gold thioglucose for ventromedial hypothalamic lesions and hyperphagia. *Nature*, 1956, **178**, 1399–1400. (28)

McBurney, D. H. Magnitude estimation of the taste of sodium chloride after adaptation to sodium chloride. *J. exper. Psychol.* (in press), 1966. (371)

McCann, S. M. Effect of hypothalamic lesions on the adrenal cortical response in the rat. *Amer. J. Physiol.*, 1953, **172**, 265–75. (183)

McCleary, R. A. Taste and post-ingestion factors in specific-hunger behavior. *J. comp. physiol. Psychol.*, 1953, **46**, 411–21. (29)

McCleary, R. A. Type of response as a factor in interocular transfer in the fish. *J. comp. physiol. Psychol.*, 1960, **53**, 549–52. (95, 96)

McCleary, R. A. Response specificity in the behavioral effects of limbic system lesions in the cat. *J. comp. physiol. Psychol.*, 1961, **54**, 605–13. (215, 218)

McCollough, C. Color adoptation of edge detectors in the human visual system. *Science*, 1965, **149**, 1115–16. (348)

McGaugh, J. L. Effects of electroshock stimulation on memory: Amnesia without convulsions. *Science* (in press), 1966. (75)

McGaugh, J. L., and Madsen, M. C. Amnesic and punishing effects of electroconvulsive shock. *Science*, 1964, **144**, 182–83. (77)

McGaugh, J. L.; Westbrook, W.; and Burt, G. Strain differences in the facilitative effects of 5-7-Diphenyl-1-3-Diazamantan 6-ol (1757I.S.) on maze learning. *J. comp. physiol. Psychol.*, 1961, **54**, 502–5. (76, 78)

McNamara, H. T.; Long, T. B.; and Wike, E. L. Learning without response under two conditions of external cues. *J. comp. physiol. Psychol.*, 1956, **49**, 477–80. (112)

Mehler, W. R. In French, J. D., and Porter, R. W. (Eds.), *Recent Contributions of Basic Research & Paraplegia*. Springfield: C. C. Thomas, 1961. (259)

Mehler, W. R.; Feferman, M. E.; and Nauta, W. J. Ascending axon degeneration following anterolateral cordotomy. *Brain*, 1960, **83**, 718–50. (150, 259)

Meikle, T. M., Jr., and Sechzer, J. A. Interocular transfer of brightness discrimination in split-brain cats. *Science*, 1960, **132**, 734–35. (94)

Merton, P. A. Problems of muscular fatigue. *Brit. med. Bull.*, 1956, **12**, 219–21. (391, 392)

Meyers, B., and McCleary, R. A. Interocular transfer of a pattern discrimination in pattern deprived cats. *J. comp. physiol. Psychol.*, 1964, **57**, 16–21. (95)

Michael, R. P. Estrogen-sensitive neurons and sexual behavior in female cats. *Science*, 1962, **136**, 322–23. (50)

Michelson, J. J. Subjective disturbances of the sense of pain from lesions of the cerebral cortex. *A. Res. nerv. ment. Dis. Proc.*, 1943, **23**, 86–99. (285, 287)

Mickle, W. A., and Ades, H. W. A composite sensory projection area in the cerebral cortex of the cat. *Am. J. Physiol.*, 1952, **170**, 682–89. (318)

Miller, N. E. Experiments on motivation. *Science*, 1957, **126**, 1271–78. (7)

Miller, N. E. Learning and performance motivated by direct stimulation of the brain. In Sheer, D. E. (Ed.), *Electrical Stimulation of the Brain.* Austin: University of Texas Press, 1961, 387–97. (191)

Miller, N. E. Chemical coding of behavior in the brain. *Science*, 1965, **148**, 328–38. (9)

Miller, N. E.; Bailey, C. J.; and Stevenson, J. A. F. Decreased "hunger" but increased food intake resulting from hypothalamic lesions. *Science*, 1950, **112**, 256–59. (27)

Miller, N. E., and Kessen, M. L. Is distention of the stomach by a balloon rewarding or punishing? *Am. Psychologist*, 1954, **9**, 430–31. (13, 141)

Miller, N. E.; Sampliner, R. I.; and Woodrow, P. Thirst-reducing effects of water by stomach fistula vs. water by mouth measured by both a consummatory and an instrumental response. *J. comp. physiol. Psychol.*, 1957, **50**, 1–6. (13)

Miller, R. E., and Ogawa, N. The effect of adrenocorticotropic hormone (ACTH) on avoidance conditioning in the adrenalectomized rat. *J. comp. physiol. Psychol.*, 1962, **55**, 211–13. (183)

Milner, B., and Penfield, W. The effect of hippocampal lesions on recent memory. *Trans. Amer. neurol. Assoc.*, 1955, **80**, 42–48. (81)

Minnick, R. S.; Warden, C. J.; and Arieti, S. The effects of sex hormones on the copulatory behavior of senile white rats. *Science*, 1946, **103**, 749–50. (45)

Mirsky, A. F.; Rosvold, H. E.; and Pribram, K. H. Effects of cingulectomy on social behavior in monkeys. *J. Neurophysiol.*, 1957, **20**, 588–601. (212)

Mirsky, I. A.; Miller, R.; and Stein, M. Relation of adrenocortical activity and adaptive behavior. *Psychosom. Med.*, 1953, **15**, 574–88. (183)

Mishkin, M. Visual discrimination performance following partial ablations of the temporal lobe: II. ventral surface v. hippocampus. *J. comp. physiol. Psychol.*, 1954, **47**, 187–93. (207)

Mishkin, M., and Pribram, K. H. Visual discrimination performance following partial ablations of the temporal lobe:

I. ventral v. lateral. *J. comp. physiol. Psychol.*, 1954, **47**, 14–20. (207)

Moncrieff, R. W. *The Chemical Senses.* London: Leonard Hill, 1951. (358, 378)

Moniz, E. Les possibilités de la chirurgie dans la traitement de certaines psychoses. *Lisboa. Med.*, 1936, **13**, 141–51. (213)

Monnier, M. La stimulation electrique du thalamus chez l'homme. *Rev. Neurol.*, 1955, **93**, 267. (267)

Monnier, M.; Koller, T.; and Graber, S. Humoral influences of induced sleep and arousal upon electrical brain activity of animals with crossed circulation. *Exp. Neurol.*, 1963, **8**, 264–77. (162)

Montgomery, M. F. The role of salivary glands in the thirst mechanism. *Amer. J. Physiol.*, 1931(a), **96**, 221–27. (7)

Montgomery, M. F. The influence of atropin and pilocarpin on thirst (voluntary ingestion of water). *Am. J. Physiol.*, 1931(b), **98**, 35–41. (7)

Mook, D. G. Oral and postingestional determinants of the intake of various solutions in rats with esophageal fistulas. *J. comp. physiol. Psychol.*, 1963, **56**, 645, 659. (20)

Moray, N. Attention in dichotic listening: Affective cues and the influence of instructions. *Quart. J. exp. Psychol.*, 1959, **11**, 56–60. (167, 168)

Morin, E. A new spinal pathway for cutaneous impulses. *Am. J. Physiol.*, 1955, **183**, 243–52. (259)

Morison, R. S., and Dempsey, E. W. A study of thalamo-cortical relations. *Am. J. Physiol.*, 1942, **135**, 281–92. (155)

Moritz, A. R., and Henriques, F. C. Studies of thermal injury; relative importance of time and surface temperature in causation of cutaneous burns. *Am. J. Path.*, 1947, **23**, 695–720. (239)

Morrell, F. Interseizure disturbances in focal epilepsy. *Neurology*, 1956, **6**, 327–33. (100, 101)

Morrell, F. In Conditionnement et Reactivité' en Electroencephalographie, Suppl. No. 6, *EEG, clin. Neurophysiol.* Paris: Masson et Cie, 1957. (100, 101, 105)

Morrell, F. Effects of experimental epilepsy on conditioned electrical potentials. *Univ. Minnesota med. Bull.*, 1957, **29**, 82–102. (100, 101)

Morrell, F. An anatomical and physiological analysis of electrocortical conditioning. *Proc. 1st int. Cong. neurol. Sci.* (Brussels), 1957. (100, 101)

Morrell, F. Microelectrode and steady potential shifts suggesting a dendritic locus of closure. In Jasper, H. H., and Smirnov, G. D. (Eds.), The Moscow Colloquium on Electroencephalography of Higher Nervous Activity. EEG clin. Neurophysiol. Suppl. 13, 1960. (103)

Morrell, F. Lasting changes in synaptic organization produced by continuous neuronal bombardment. In Delafresnaye, J. F. (Ed.), Brain Mechanisms and Learning. Oxford: Blackwell, 1961, 375–92. (89, 91, 102)

Morrell, F. Effect of anodal polarization on the firing pattern of single cortical cells. In Kline, N. S. (Ed.), Pavlovian Conference on Higher Nervous Activity. Ann. N.Y. Acad. Sci., 1961, 92, 860–76. (102)

Morrell, F. Electrophysiological contributions to the neural basis of learning. Physiolog. Revs., 1961, 41, 443–94. (105)

Morrell, F.; Barlow, J.; and Brazier, M. A. B. Analysis of conditioned repetitive response by means of the average response computer. In Wortis, J. (Ed.), Recent Advances in Biological Psychiatry, chap. ix. New York: Grune and Stratton, 1960, 123–37. (106)

Morrell, F., and Jasper, H. H. Electroencephalographic studies of the formation of temporary connections in the brain. EEG clin. Neurophysiol., 1956, 8, 201–15. (113)

Moruzzi, G. Synchronizing influences of the brain stem and the inhibitory mechanisms underlying the production of sleep by sensory stimulation. In Jasper, H. H., and Smirnov, G. D. (Eds.). The Moscow Colloquium on Electroencephalography of Higher Nervous Activity. EEG clin. Neurophysiol. Suppl. 13, 1960, 231–56. (161)

Moruzzi, G., and Magoun, H. W. Brain stem reticular formation and activation of the EEG. EEG clin. Neurophysiol., 1949, 1, 455–73. (149, 162)

Mott, F. W. Ascending degeneration resulting from lesions of the spinal cord in monkeys. Brain, 1892, 15, 215–29. (268)

Moulton, D. G. Electrical activity in the olfactory system of rabbits with indwelling electrodes. In Zotterman, Y. (Ed.), Olfaction and Taste. Oxford: Pergamon Press, 1963, 71–84. (381)

Moulton, R.; Spector, W. G.; and Willoughby, D. A. Histamine release and pain production by xanthosine and related compounds. Brit. J. Pharmacol., 1957, 12, 365–70. (253)

Mountcastle, V. B. Modality and topographic properties of single neurons of cat's somatic sensory cortex. J. Neurophysiol., 1957, 20, 208. (276)

Mountcastle, V. B. Some functional properties of the somatic afferent system. In Rosenblith, W. A. (Ed.), Sensory Communication. New York: M.I.T. Press and John Wiley & Sons, 1961, 403–36. (256, 264, 266, 267, 275, 286)

Mountcastle, V. B., and Henneman, E. Pattern of tactile representation in thalamus of cat. J. Neurophysiol., 1949, 12, 85–100. (262)

Mountcastle, V. B., and Henneman, E. The representation of tactile sensibility in the thalamus of the monkey. J. comp. Neurol., 1952, 97, 409–40. (262)

Mountcastle, V. B., and Powell, T. P. S. Neural mechanisms subserving cutaneous sensibility with special reference to the role of afferent inhibition in sensory perception and discrimination. Bull. Johns Hopkins Hosp., 1959, 105, 201–32. (262, 266, 275)

Moushegian, G.; Rupert, A.; and Galambos, R. Microelectrode study of ventral cochlear nuclei of the cat. J. Neurophysiol., 1962, 25, 515–29. (310, 313)

Moushegian, G.; Rupert, A.; Marsh, J. T.; and Galambos, R. Evoked cortical potentials in absence of middle ear muscles. Science, 1961, 133, 582–83. (172, 174)

Mowrer, O. H. Learning theory and personality dynamics. New York: Ronald, 1950. (182)

Moyer, K. E. Effect of adrenalectomy on anxiety motivated behavior. J. genet. Psychol., 1958, 92, 11–16. (183)

Moyer, K. E., and Bunnell, B. N. Effect of exogenous adrenaline on an avoidance response in the rat. J. genet. Psychol., 1958, 92, 11–16. (181)

Moyer, K. E., and Bunnell, B. N. Effect of adrenal demedullation on an avoidance response in the rat. J. comp. physiol. Psychol., 1959, 52, 215–16. (181)

Mozell, M. M., and Pfaffmann, C. The afferent neural process in odor perception. Ann. N.Y. Acad. Sci., 1954, 58, 96–108. (381)

Muller, G. E., and Pilzecker, A. Experimentelle Beitrage zur Lehre vom Gedaechtniss. Z. Psychol. Physiol. Sinnesorg. I, 1900, 1–300. (75)

Murphy, J. P., and Gellhorn, E. Multiplicity of representation versus punctate localization in the motor cortex. Arch. Neurol. Psychiat., 1945, 54, 256–73. (429)

Murphy, J. V., and Miller, R. E. The effect of ACTH on avoidance conditioning in the rat. J. comp. physiol. Psychol., 1955, 48, 47–49. (183)

Myers, R. E. Interocular transfer of pattern discrimination in cats following section of crossed optic fibers. J. comp. physiol. Psychol., 1955, 48, 470–73. (94)

Myers, R. E. Function of corpus callosum in interocular transfer. Brain, 1956, 79, 358–63. (94, 95)

Myers, R. E. Corpus callosum and interhemispheric communication: Enduring memory effects. Fed. Proc. 1957, 16, 92. (94)

Myers, R. E. Localization of function in the corpus callosum. Ann. A. Arch. Neurol., 1959, 1, 74–77. (94)

Myers, R. E., and Henson, C. O. Role of corpus callosum in transfer of tactuokinesthetic learning in chimpanzee. Arch. Neurol., 1960, 3, 404–9. (95)

N

Nachmansohn, D. Chemical and Molecular Basis of Nerve Activity. New York: Academic Press, 1959. (457)

Nafe, J. P., and Wagoner, K. S. The nature of pressure adaptation. J. Gen. Psy., 1941, 25, 323–51. (250)

Nakao, H. Emotional behavior produced by hypothalamic stimulation. Am. J. Physiol., 1958, 194, 411–18. (186, 188, 189, 190)

Naquet, R. Effects of stimulation of rhinencephalon in the waking cat. EEG clin. Neurophysiol. 1954, 6, 711–12. (196)

Naquet, R.; Regis, H.; Fischer-Williams, M.; and Fernandez-Guardiola, A. Variation in the responses evoked by light along the specific pathways. Brain, 1960, 83, 52–56. (174)

Nathan, P. W., and Smith, M. C. Normal mentality associated with a maldeveloped "rhinencephalon." J. Neurol. Neurosurg. Psychiat., 1950, 13, 191–97. (200)

Nauta, W. J. H. Hypothalamic regulation of sleep in rats. An experimental study. J. Neurophysiol., 1946, 9, 285–316. (160)

Neff, W. D. Neural mechanisms of auditory discrimination. In Rosenblith, W. A. (Ed.), Sensory Communication, Cambridge: M.I.T. Press, 1961. (321, 323)

Neff, W. D., and Diamond, I. T. The neural basis of auditory discrimination. In Harlow, H. F., and Woolsey, C. N. (Eds.), Biological and Biochemical Bases of Behavior. Madison: University of Wisconsin Press, 1958, 101–26. (321)

Neff, W. D.; Fisher, J. F.; Diamond, I. T.; and Yela, M. Role of auditory cortex in discrimination requiring localization of sound in space. J. Neurophysiol., 1956, 19, 500–512. (321)

Nelson, D. Do rats select more sodium than they need? Fed. Proc., 1947, 6, 169. (20)

Neuhaus, W. Die Unterschiedung von Duftquantitäten bei Mensch and Hund nach Versuchen mit Buttersäure. Z. Vergl. Physiol., 1955, 37, 234–52. (378)

Niemer, W. T., and Jimenez-Castellanos, J. Cortico-thalamic connexions in the cat as revealed by "physiological neuronography," J. comp. Anat., 1950, 93, 101–23. (356)

Nissen, H. W. Instinct as seen by a psychologist. Psychol. Rev., 1953, 60, 291–94. (57)

Noble, G. K., and Zitrin. Induction of mating behavior in male and female chicks following injections of sex hormones. Endocrinology, 1942, 30, 327–34. (44)

Norsell, U. quoted by Andersson, S. A. Projection of different spinal pathways to the second somatic sensory area in cat. Acta. Physiol. Scand. Suppl. 194, 1962, 1–74. (266)

Novin, D. The relation between electrical conductivity of brain tissue and thirst in the rat. J. comp. physiol. Psychol., 1962, 55, 145–54. (13)

O

Oakley, B., and Pfaffmann, C. Electrophysiologically monitored lesions in the gustatory thalamic relay of the albino rat. J. comp. physiol. Psychol., 1962, 55, 155–60. (368)

Olds, J. Physiological mechanisms of reward. In Jones, M. R. (Ed.), Nebraska Symposium on Motivation. Lincoln: University of Nebraska Press, 1955. (122)

Olds, J. Runway and maze behavior controlled by basomedial forebrain stimulation in the rat. J. comp. physiol. Psy-

*chol.*, 1956, **49**, 507–12. (121, 122, 126)

Olds, J. Self-stimulation of the brain. *Science*, 1958, **127**, 315–24. (121)

Olds, J. Effects of hunger and male sex hormone on self-stimulation of the brain. *J. comp. physiol. Psychol.*, 1958(a), **51**, 320–24. (126)

Olds, J., and Milner, P. Positive reinforcement produced by electrical stimulation of septal area and other regions of rat brain. *J. comp. physiol. Psychol.*, 1954, **47**, 419–27. (115, 119)

Olds, J., and Olds, M. E. Interference and learning in paleocortical systems. In Delafresnaye, J. F. (Ed.), *Brain Mechanisms and Learning*. Oxford: Blackwell, 1961, 153–88. (92)

Orbach, J., and Fantz, R. L. Differential effects of temporal neocortical resections on overtrained and non-overtrained visual habits in monkeys. *J. comp. physiol. Psychol.*, 1958, **51**, 126–29. (81)

Oswald, I.; Taylor, A.; and Treisman, M. Discrimination responses to stimulation during human sleep. *Brain*, 1960, **83**, 440–53. (168)

Ottoson, D. Analysis of the electrical activity of the olfactory epithelium. *Acta. Physiol. Scand. Suppl.*, 122, 1956, **35**, 1–83. (377)

Ottoson, D. Generation and transmission of signals in the olfactory system. In Zotterman, Y., (Ed.), *Olfaction and Taste*. Oxford: Pergamon Press, 1963, 35–44. (377)

**P**

Palestini, M.; Davidovich, A.; and Hernández-Peón, R. Functional significance of centrifugal influences upon the retina. *Acta. neurol. Lat.-Amer.*, 1959, **5**, 113–31. (172)

Palestini, M.; Rossi, G. F.; and Zanchetti, A. An electrophysiological analysis of pontine reticular regions showing different anatomical organization. *Arch. Ital. Biol.* 1957, **95**, 97–109. (151)

Pampiglione, G., and Falconer, M. A. Electrical stimulation of the hippocampus in man. In American Physiological Society, *Handbook of Physiology, Section 1; Neurophysiology, Vol. II* (Field, J.; Magoun, H. W.; and Hall, V. E. [Eds.]). Baltimore, Md.: Williams & Wilkins Co., 1960, 1391–94. (197)

Papez, J. W. A proposed mechanism of emotion. *A.M.A. Arch. Neurol. Psychiat.*, 1937, **38**, 725–43. (184)

Passey, G. E. The perception of the vertical. IV. Adjustment to the vertical with normal and tilted visual frames of reference. *J. exp. Psychol.*, 1950, **40**, 738–45. (428)

Patton, H. D., and Amassian, V. E. Thalamic relay of splanchnic afferent fibers. *Amer. J. Physiol.*, 1951, **167**, 815–16. (283)

Pauker, R. S. The effects of removing seminal vesicles, prostate and testes on the mating behavior of the golden hamster, Cricetus auratus. *J. comp. physiol. Psychol.*, 1948, **41**, 252–57. (46)

Pearlman, C. A.; Sharpless, S. K.; and Jarvik, M. E. Retrograde amnesia produced by anesthetic and convulsant agents. *J. comp. physiol. Psychol.*, 1961, **54**, 109–12. (75, 76, 77, 82)

Pechtel, C.; Masserman, J.; Schreiner, L.; and Levitt, M. Differential effects of lesions of the mediodorsal nuclei of the thalamus on normal and neurotic behavior in the cat. *J. nerv. ment. Dis.*, 1955, **121**, 26–33. (206)

Pechtel, C.; McAvoy, T.; Levitt, M.; King, A.; and Masserman, J. H. The cingulates and behavior. *J. nerv. ment. Dis.*, 1958, **126**, 148–52. (206, 213)

Peiper, A. *Cerebral Function in Infancy and Childhood*. London: Pitman, 1963. (422)

Penfield, W. The cerebral cortex in man. 1. The cerebral cortex and consciousness. *Arch. Neurol. Psychiat.* (Chicago) 1935, **40**, 417–42. (149)

Penfield, W. Mechanisms of voluntary movement. *Brain*, 1954, **77**, 1–17. (168)

Penfield, W. Functional localization in temporal and deep Sylvian areas. *Res. Publ. Ass. Res. nerv. ment. Dis.*, 1958, **36**, 210–26. (197)

Penfield, W. *The Excitable Cortex of Conscious Man*. Liverpool: Liverpool University Press, 1958. (151)

Penfield, W., and Jasper, H. H. Epilepsy and the functional anatomy of the human brain. Boston: Little, Brown and Co., 1959. (197, 198, 262, 278, 283)

Penfield, W., and Rasmussen, T. *The Cerebral Cortex of Man*. New York: Macmillan Co., 1950. (368, 429)

Penny, R. K., and Croshery, J. Instrumental avoidance conditioning of anxious and nonanxious children. *J. comp. physiol. Psychol.*, 1962, **55**, 847–49. (214)

Peretz, E. The effects of lesions of the anterior cingulate cortex on the behavior of the rat. *J. comp. physiol. Psychol.*, 1960, **53**, 540–48. (217)

Perl, E. R. Somatosensory mechanisms. *Ann. Rev. Physiol.*, 1963, 459–89. (191)

Perl, E. R., and Whitlock, D. G. Somatic stimuli exciting spinothalamic projections to thalamic neurons in cat and monkey. *Exp. Neurol.*, 1961, **3**, 256–96. (272, 273, 274, 277, 285)

Perl, E. R.; Whitlock, D. G.; and Gentry, J. R. Cutaneous projection to second-ordel neurons of the dorsal column system. *J. Neurophysiol.*, 1962, **25**, 337–58. (227, 258, 266, 268)

Perry, J. H., and Liebelt, R. D. Extrahypothalamic lesions in goldthioglucose induced obesity in mice. *Anat. Record*, 1959, **133**, 322. (28)

Peters, R. W. Competing messages: The effect of interfering messages upon the reception of primary messages. *USN Sch. Aviat. Med. res. Rep.*, 1954, Project No. NM 001 064.01.27. (167)

Pfaffmann, C. Gustatory afferent impulses. *J. Cell. comp. Physiol.*, 1941, **17**(2), 243–58. (361, 367)

Pfaffmann, C. Gustatory nerve impulses in rat, cat and rabbit. *J. Neurophysiol.*, 1955, **18**, 429–40. (365)

Pfaffmann, C. Taste stimulation and preference behavior. In Zotterman, Y. (Ed.), *Olfaction and Taste*. Oxford: Pergamon Press, 1963, 257–73. (369, 370)

Pfaffmann, C. J.; Erickson, R. P.; Frommer, G. P.; and Halpern, B. P. Gustatory discharges in the rat medulla and thalamus. In Rosenblith, W. A. (Ed.), *Sensory Communication*. New York: Wiley, 1961, 455–74. (367, 368)

Pfalz, R. K. J. Centrifugal inhibition of afferent secondary neurons in the cochlear nucleus by sound. *J. acoust. Soc. Amer.*, 1962, **34**, 1472–77. (323)

The Physiology of Voluntary Muscle. *Brit. med. Bull.*, 1956, **12**, No. 3. (387)

Piéron, H. Vision in intermittent light. In Neff, W. D. (Ed.), *Contributions to Sensory Physiology*. Academic Press, New York and London: 1965, 179–264. (350)

Pilgrim, F. J., and Patton, R. A. Patterns of self-selection of purified dietary components by the rat. *J. comp. physiol. Psychol.*, 1947, **40**, 343–48. (38)

Pirenne, M. H. Visual functions in man.

In Davson, H. (Ed.), *The Eye*. New York and London: Academic Press, 1962, 3–217. (352)

Pliskoff, S. S., and Hawkins, T. D. Test of Deutsch's drive-decay theory of rewarding self-stimulation of the brain. *Science*, 1963, **141**, 823–24. (124, 125)

Plumb, C. S., and Meigs, J. W. Human vibration perception. *Arch. Gen. Psychiat.*, 1961, **4**, 611–14. (256)

Poggio, G. F., and Mountcastle, V. B. A study of the functional contributions of the lemuiscal and spinalthalamic systems to somatic sensibility central nervous mechanisms in pain. *Bull. Johns Hopkins Hospital*, 1960, **106**, 266–316. (259, 262, 272, 273, 277, 285)

Pollock, L. J. A.M.A. *Arch. Neurol. Psychiat.*, 1919, **2**, 667. (248)

Polyak, S. *The Main Afferent Fiber Systems of the Cerebral Cortex in Primates*. Berkeley: University of California Press, 1932. (319, 330)

Polyak, S. *The Retina*. Chicago: University of Chicago Press, 1941. (351)

Polyak, S. In *The Vertebrate Visual System*, Kluver, H. (Ed.). Chicago: University of Chicago Press, 1957. (330)

Pool, J. L. Posterior cordotomy for relief of phantom limb pain. *Ann. Surg.*, 1946, **124**, 386–91. (286)

Pool, J. C. The visceral brain of man. *J. Neurophysiol.*, 1954, **11**, 45–63. (212)

Porter, R. W. Alterations in electrical activity of hypothalamus induced by stress stimuli. *Am. J. Physiol.*, 1952, **169**, 629. (64)

Porter, R. W.; Cavanaugh, E. B.; Critchlow, E. B.; and Sawyer, C. H. Localized changes in electrical activity of the hypothalamus in estrous cats following vaginal stimulation. *Am. J. Physiol.*, 1957, **189**, 145. (51)

Poulton, E. C. Two-channel listening. *J. exp. Psychol.*, 1953, **46**, 91–96. (166)

Pribram, K. H., and Bagshaw, Muriel. Further analysis of the temporal lobe syndrome utilizing fronto-temporal ablations. *J. comp. Neurol.*, 1953, **99**, 347–75. (33, 207)

Pribram, K. H., and Fulton, J. F. An experimental critique of the effects of anterior cingulate ablations in monkey. *Brain*, 1954, **77**, 34–43. (212)

Pribram, K. H. and Kruger, L. Functions of the "olfactory brain." *Ann. N.Y. Acad. Sci.*, 1954, **58**, 109–38. (185)

Pribram, K. H.; Rosner, B. S.; and Rosenblith, W. A. Electrical responses to acoustic clicks in monkey: extent of neocortex activated. *J. Neurophysiol.*, 1954, **17**, 336–44. (319)

Provins, K. A. Sensory factors in the voluntary application of pressure. *Quart. J. exp. Psychol.*, 1957, **9**, 28–33. (398)

Provins, K. A. The effect of peripheral nerve block on the appreciation and execution of finger movements. *J. Physiol.*, 1958, **143**, 55–67.

Purpura, D. P. A neurohumoral mechanism of reticulo-cortical activation. *Am. J. Physiol.*, 1956, **186**, 250–54. (162)

Purpura, D. P. Analysis of axodendritic synaptic organization in immature cerebral cortex. *Ann. N.Y. Acad. Sci.*, 1961, **94**, 604–54. (93)

## Q

Quartermain, D.; Paolino, R. M.; and Miller, N. E. A brief temporal gradient of retrograde amnesia independent of situational change. *Science*, 1965, **149**, 1116–18. (77)

## R

Raab, D. H., and Ades, H. F. Cortical and midbrain mediation of a conditioned discrimination of acoustic intensities. *Am. J. Psychol.*, 1946, **59**, 59–83. (322, 322)

Rabedeau, R. G., and Whalen, R. E. Effects of copulatory experience on mating behavior in the male rat. *J. comp. physiol. Psychol.*, 1959, **52**, 482–84. (58)

Randoin, L.; Causeret, J.; and Gabrel-Szymanski, M. Comportement du jeune rat normal auquel on donne le choix entre de l'eau pure et une solution peu concentrée de chlorure de sodium. *J. Physiol.* (Paris), 1950, **42**, 447–50. (20)

Ranson, S. W. Somnolence caused by hypothalamic lesions in the monkey. *A.M.A. Arch. Neurol. Psychiat.*, 1939, **41**, 1–23. (204)

Ranson, S. W. Functional and clinical significance of hypothalamus. *Quart. Bullet. N. W. Univ. med. School*, 1940, **14**, 137–45. (42)

Ranson, S. W., and Magoun, H. W. Respiratory and pupillary reactions induced by electrical stimulation of the hypothalamus. *A.M.A. Arch. Neurol. Psychiat.*, 1933, **29**, 1179–94. (186)

Rasch, E.; Riesen, A. H.; and Chow, K. L. Altered structure and composition of retinal cells in dark reared cats. *J. Histochem. Cytochem.*, 1959, **7**, 321–22. (91)

Rasmussen, E. W. Experimental homosex-

ual behavior in male albino rats. *Acta. Psychol.*, 1955, **11**, 303–34. (57)

Rasmussen, G. L. The olivary peduncle and other fiber projections of the superior olivary complex. *J. comp. Neurol.*, 1946, **84**, 141–219. (323)

Rasmussen, G. L. Efferent fibers of the cochlear nerve and cochlear nucleus. In Rasmussen, G. L., and Windle, W. F. (Ed.), *Neural Mechanisms of the Auditory and Vestibular Systems.* Springfield, Ill.: C. C. Thomas, 1960. (323)

Ratliff, F. The role of physiological nystagmus in monocular acuity. *J. exp. Psychol.*, 1952, **43**, 163–72. (351, 352)

Reidemeister, C., and Grüsser, O. J. Flimmerlichtuntersuchungen an der Katzenretina I. *Z. Biol.*, 1959, **111**, 241–53; II. *Z. Biol.*, 1959, **111**, 254–70. (350)

Renshaw, B. Influence of discharge of motoneurons upon excitation of neighbouring motoneurons. *J. Neurophysiol.*, 1941, **4**, 167–83. (396)

Reyes, V.; Henry, G. C.; Baird, H.; Wycis, H. T.; and Spiegel, E. A. Localization of centripetal pathways of the human brain by recording of evoked potentials. *Trans. Amer. neurol. Assoc.*, 1951, **76**, 246–48. (191, 272)

Reynolds, R. W. Ventromedial hypothalamic lesions without hyperphagia. *Amer. J. Physiol.*, 1963, **204**, 60–62. (27)

Rheingold, H. I., and Hess, E. H. The chicks preference for some visual properties of water. *J. comp. physiol. Psychol.*, 1957, **50**, 417. (30)

Ricci, G.; Doane, B.; and Jasper, H. H. Microelectrode studies of conditioning: technique and preliminary results. *Excerpta. Med.*, 1957, **4**, 401–15. (104)

Richter, C. P. Mineral appetite of parathyroidectomized rats. *Amer. J. Med. Sci.*, 1939, **198**, 9–16. (35)

Richter, C. P. Total self-regulatory functions in animals and human beings. *The Harvey Lecture Series*, 1942(a), **38**, 63–103. (35, 39)

Richter, C. P. Physiological psychology. *Ann. Rev. Physiol.*, 1942(b), **4**, 561–74. (35)

Richter, C. P., and Hawkes. C. D. The dependence of the carbohydrate, fat, and protein appetite of rats on the various components of the vitamin B complex. *Amer. J. Physiol.*, 1941, **131**, 639–49. (35)

Riesen, A. H. Effects of stimulus deprivation on the development and atrophy of the visual sensory system. *Am. J. Orthopsychiat.* 1960, **30**, 23–36. (91)

Riggs, L. A.; Ratliff, F.; Cornsweet, J. C.; and Cornsweet, T. N. Disappearance of steadily fixated visual test objects. *J. opt. Soc. Amer.*, 1953, **43**, 495–501. (352)

Riley, G. M., and Witschi, E. Comparative effects of light stimulation and administration of gonadotropic hormones on female sparrows. *Endocrinology*, 1938, **23**, 618–24. (66)

Roberts, L. Activation and interference of cortical functions. In Sheer, D. E. (Ed.), *Electrical Stimulation of the Brain*. Austin: University of Texas Press, 1961, 534–36. (197)

Roberts, W. W. Rapid escape learning without avoidance learning motivated by hypothalamic stimulation in cats. *J. comp. physiol. Psychol.*, 1958(a), **51**, 391–99. (186, 190, 192)

Roberts, W. W. Both rewarding and punishing effects from stimulation of posterior hypothalamus of cat with same electrodes at same intensity. *J. comp. physiol. Psychol.*, 1958(b), **51**, 400–407. (190)

Roberts, W. W. Fear-like behavior elicited from dorsomedial thalamus of cat. *J. comp. physiol. Psychol.*, 1962, **55**, 191–97. (187)

Roberts, W. W., and Carey, R. J. Effect of dorsomedial lesions on fear in cats. *J. comp. physiol. Psychol.*, 1963, **56**, 950–58. (219)

Roberts, W. W., and Kiess, H. O. Motivational properties of hypothalamic aggression in cats. *J. comp. physiol. Psychol.*, 1964, **58**, 187–93. (192)

Robinson, S. W., and Mishkin, M. Alimentary responses evoked from forebrain structures in Macaca mulatta. *Science*, 1962, **136**, 260–61. (10)

Root, W. S., and Bard, P. The mediation of feline erection through sympathetic pathways with some remarks on sexual behavior after deafferentation of the genitalia. *Amer. J. Physiol.*, 1947, **151**, 80–90. (46)

Rose, J. E. The cellular structure of the auditory region of the cat. *J. comp. Neurol.*, 1949, **91**, 409–39. (316)

Rose, J. E., and Galambos, R. Microelectrode studies on medial geniculate of the cat. I. Thalamic region activated by click stimuli, *J. Neurophysiol.*, 1952, **15**, 343–57. (306, 319)

Rose, J. E.; Galambos, R.; and Hughes, J. R. Microelectrode studies of the cochlear nuclei of the cat. *Bull. Johns Hopkins Hosp.*, 1959, **104**, 211–51. (314)

Rose, J. E.; Greenwood, O. D.; Goldberg, J. M.; and Hind, J. E. Tonotopical organization, relation of spike-counts to tone intensity, and firing patterns of single elements. *J. Neurophysiol.*, 1963, **26**, 294–320. (310, 315)

Rose, J. E.; Malis, L. I.; Kruger, L.; and Baker, C. P. Effects of heavy, ionizing, monoenergetic particles on the cerebral cortex. *J. comp. Neurol.*, 1960, **115**, 243–55. (93)

Rose, J. F., and Mountcastle, V. B. Touch and kinaesthesis. In American Physiology Society, *Handbook of Physiology, Section 1*; *Neurophysiology, Vol. 1* (Field, J.; Magoun, H. W.; and Hall, V. E. [Eds.]). Baltimore, Md.: Williams & Wilkins Co., 1959, 387–429. (269, 396)

Rose, J. E. and Woolsey, C. N. Structure and relations of limbic cortex and anterior thalamic nuclei in rabbit and cat. *J. comp. Neurol.*, 1948, 279–348. (184)

Rose, J. E. and Woolsey, C. N. The relations of thalamic connections, cellular structure and evocable electrical activity in the auditory region of the cat. *J. comp. Neurol.*, 1949, **91**, 441–66. (319)

Rose, J. E., and Woolsey, C. N. Cortical connections and functional organization of the thalamic auditory system of the cat. In Harlow, H. F., and Woolsey, C. N. (Eds.), *Biological and Biochemical Bases of Behavior*. Madison: University of Wisconsin Press, 1958, 127–50. (316)

Rosenblatt, J., and Aronson, L. R. The decline of sexual behavior in male cats after castration with special reference to the role of prior sexual experience. *Behaviour*, 1958, **12**, 4, 285–338. (44)

Rosenblatt, J., and Aronson, L. R. The influence of experience on the behavioral effects of androgen in prepuberally castrated male cats. *J. animal Behaviour*, 1958(a), G:3, **4**, 171–82. (44)

Rosenthal, S. R. Histamine as possible chemical mediator for cutaneous pain. Dual pain response to histamine. *Proc. Soc. exper. Biol. and Med.*, 1950, **74**, 167–70. (245)

Rosenzweig, M. R. Discrimination of auditory intensities in the cat. *Am. J. Psychol.*, 1946, **59**, 127–36. (322)

Rosenzweig, M. R. Cortical correlates of auditory localization and of related perceptual phenomena. *J. comp. physiol. Psychol.*, 1954, **47**, 269–76. (320)

Rosenzweig, M. R., and Sutton, D. Binaural interaction in lateral lemniscus of cat. *J. Neurophysiol.*, 1958, **21**, 17–23. (321)

Rosenzweig, M. R., and Wyers, E. J. Binaural interaction at the inferior colliculi. *J. comp. physiol. Psychol.*, 1955, **48**, 426–31. (321)

Rosvold, H. E. The effects of electroconvulsive shocks on gestation and maternal behavior. *J. comp. physiol. Psychol.*, 1949, **42**, 118–36. (63)

Rosvold, H. E.; Mirsky, A. F.; and Pribram, K. H. Influence of amygdalectomy on social behavior in monkeys. *J. comp. physiol. Psychol.*, 1954, **47**, 173–78. (207, 208)

Rothfield, L., and Harmon, P. J. On the relation of the hippocampal-fornix system to the control of rage responses in cats. *J. comp. Neurol.*, 1954, **101**, 265–82.

Rothman, H. Zusammenfessender Bericht über den Rothmannschen grosshirnlosen Hund nach klinischer und anatomischer Untersuchung. *Ztchr. ges. Neurol. Psychiat.*, 1923, **87**, 247–313. (201)

Rowan, W. Light and seasonal reproduction in animals. *Biol. Rev.*, 1938, **13**, 374–402. (66)

Ruch, T. C., and Fulton, J. F. Cortical localization of somatic sensibility. The effect of precentral, postcentral and posterior parietal lesions upon the performance of monkeys trained to discriminate weights. *Res. Publ. Ass. nerv. ment. Dis.*, 1935, **15**, 289–330. (28)

Ruch, T. C.; Fulton, J. F.; and German, W. J. Sensory discrimination in monkey, chimpanzee and man after lesions of the parietal lobe. *Arch. Neurol. Psychiat.*, 1938, **39**, 919–37.

Ruch, T. C., and Patton, H. D. The relation of the deep opercular cortex to taste. *Fed. Proc.*, 1946, **5**, 89–90. (368)

Rushton, W. A. H. Peripheral coding in the nervous system. In Rosenblith, W. (Ed.), *Sensory Communication*. Cambridge: M.I.T. Press, 1961. (465)

Rushton, W. A. H. Visual pigments in man. *Sci. Amer.*, 1962, **207**, 120–137. (333, 335, 340)

Rusinov, V. S. An electrophysiological analysis of the connecting function in the cerebral cortex in the presence of a dominant area. *Communs. XIX Intern Physiol. Congr.* (Montreal), 1953. (102)

Russell, I. S., and Ochs, S. One trial interhemispheric transfer of a learning engram. *Science*, 1961, **133**, 1077–78. (96, 99)

Russell, R. W. Brain chemistry and behavior. *Discovery*, 1956, **17**, 314–18. (84)

Russell, W. R., and Nathan, P. W. Traumatic amnesia. *Brain*, 1946, **69**, 280–300. (73)

S

Sano, T. Motor and other responses elicited by electrical stimulation of the cat's temporal lobe. *Folia. Psychiat. Neurol. Jap.*, 1958, **12**, 152–76. (197)

Sato, M. Response of Pacinian corpuscles to sinusoidal vibration. *J. Physiol.*, 1961, **159**, 391–409. (256)

Sawa, M.; Maruyama, N.; Hanai, T.; and Kaji, S. Regulatory influence of amygdaloid nuclei upon the unitary activity in ventromedial nucleus of hypothalamus. *Folia. Psychiat. Neurol. Jap.*, 1959, **13**, 235–56. (210)

Sawa, M.; Veki, V.; Avita, M.; and Harada, T. Preliminary report on the amygdalectomy on the psychotic patients with interpretation of oral-emotional manifestation in schizophrenics. *Folia. Psychiat. Neurol. Jap.*, 1954, **4**, 309–29. (212)

Sawa, M.; Yukiharu, W.; Massaya, A.; and Toshio, H. Preliminary report on the amygdaloidectomy on the psychotic patient, with interpretation of oral-emotional manifestation in schizophrenics. *Folia. Psychial. Neurol. Jap.*, 1954, **7**, 309–29. (6)

Sawyer, C. H. Triggering of the pituitary by the central nervous system. In Bullock, T. H. (Ed.), *Physiological Triggers*. Washington: American Physiological Society, 1957. (49, 69)

Sawyer, C. H. Reproductive behavior. In American Physiological Society, *Handbook of Physiology, Section 1; Neurophysiology, Vol. II* (Field, J.; Magoun, H. W.; and Hall, V. E. [Eds.]). Baltimore, Md.: Williams & Wilkins Co., 1960, 1225–40. (51)

Sawyer, C. H., and Robinson, B. A. Separate hypothalamic areas controlling pituitary gonadotropic function and mating behavior in female cats and rabbits. *J. clin. Endocrinol.*, 1956, **16**, 914. (47, 48, 69)

Schachter, S. Pain, fear and anger in hypertensives and normotensives: a psychophysiologic study. *Psychosom. Med.*, 1957, **19**, 17–29. (179)

Schachter, S., and Singer, J. E. Cognitive, social and physiological determinants of emotional state. *Psychol. Rev.*, 1962, **69**, 379–99. (180)

Schachter, S., and Wheeler, L. Epinephrine, chlorpromazine and amusement. *J. abnorm. soc. Psychol.*, 1962, **65**, 121–28. (180)

Scheibel, M. E., and Scheibel, A. Structural substrates for integrative patterns in the brain stem reticular core. In Jasper, H. H.; Proctor, L. D.; Knighton, R. S.; Roberts, S.; Noshay, W. C.; William, C.; and Costello, R. T. (Eds.), *Reticular Formation of the Brain.* Boston: Little, Brown, & Co., 1958, 31–55. (151)

Scheibel, M. E.; Scheibel, A.; Mollica, A.; and Moruzzi, G. Convergence and interaction of afferent impulses on single units of reticular formation. *J. Neurophysiol.*, 1955, **18**, 309–31. (151)

Schouten, J. F. The perception of subjective tones. *Proc. Koninkl., Ned. Akad. Wetenschap.*, 1938, **41**, 1086–93. (304)

Schreiner, L., and Kling, A. Behavioral changes following rhinencephalic injury in cat. *J. Neurophysiol.*, 1953, **16**, 643–58. (207, 209)

Schreiner, L., and Kling, A. Effects of castration on hypersexual behavior induced by rhinencephalic injury in cat. *Arch. Neurol. Psychiat.*, 1954, **72**, 180–86. (208)

Schreiner, L., and Kling, A. Rhinencephalon and behavior. *Am. J. Physiol.*, 1956, **184**, 486–90. (59, 207)

Schreiner, L.; McRioch, D.; Pechtel, C.; and Masserman, J. H. Behavioral changes following thalamic injury in cat. *J. Neurophysiol.*, 1953, **16**, 234–46. (206)

Schulman, J. L.; Carleton, J. L.; Whitney, G.; and Whitehorn, J. C. Effect of glucagon on food intake and body weight in man. *J. appl. Physiol.*, 1957, **11**, 419–21. (26)

Schulte, A. Transfer und transpositionsversuche mit Monokular Dressierten ⁚ Fischen. *Zeit. f. Vergl. Physiol.*, 1957, **39**, 432–76. (95, 96)

Schwartzbaum, J. S. Changes in reinforcing properties of stimuli following ablation of the amygdaloid complex in monkeys. *J. comp. physiol. Psychol.*, 1960, **53**, 388–95. (209)

Schwartzbaum, J. G., and Ward, H. P. An osmotic factor in the regulation of food intake in the rat. *J. comp. physiol. Psychol.*, 1958, **51**, 555–60. (29)

Scott, E. M. Self-selection of diet. I. Selection of purified components. *J. Nutrition*, 1946, **31**, 397–406. (38, 39)

Scott, E. M., and Quint, E. Self-selection of diet. III. Appetite for B vitamins. *J. Nutrition*, 1946, **32**, 285–91. (37)

Scott, E. M., and Verney, E. L. Self-selection of diet. V. Appetite for carbohydrates. *J. Nutrition*, 1947, **34**, 401–7. (37)

Scott, E. M., and Verney, E. L. Self-selection and diet. VI. The nature of appetites for B vitamins. *J. Nutrition*, 1947, **34**, 471–80. (37)

Scoville, W. B., and Milner, B. Loss of recent memory after bilateral hippocampal lesions. *J. Neurol. Neurosurg. Psychiat.*, 1957, **20**, 11–21. (81)

Sechzer, J. A. Successful interocular transfer of pattern discrimination in "split brain" cats with shock avoidance motivation. *J. comp. physiol. Psychol.*, 1964, **58**, 76–83. (94)

Segundo, J. P.; Arana, R.; and French, J. D. Behavioral arousal by stimulation of the brain in monkey. *J. Neurosurg.*, 1955, **12**, 601–13. (149)

Segundo, J. P.; Naquet; and Buser, P. Effects of cortical stimulation on electrocortical activity in monkey. *J. Neurophysiol.*, 1955, **18**, 236–45. (150)

Selye, H. Stress. *Acta. Inc. Med. Publ.* (Montreal), 1950. (67)

Selye, H. The physiology and pathology of exposure to stress. *Acta. Inc. Med. Publ.* Montreal, 1950. (183)

Semmes, J. S.; Weinstein, S.; Ghent, L.; and Teuber, H. L. *Somatosensory Changes after Penetrating Brain Wounds in Man.* Cambridge, Mass.: Harvard University Press, 1960. (281)

Settlage, P. H. The effect of occipital lesions on visually-guided behavior in the monkey. I. Influence of the lesions on final capacities in a variety of problem situations. *J. comp. Psychol.*, 1939, **27**, 93–131. (355)

Seward, J. P.; Uyeda, A.; and Olds, J. Resistance to extinction following cranial self-stimulation. *J. comp. physiol. Psychol.*, 1959, **52**, 294–99. (120, 126, 128)

Seward, J. P.; Uyeda, A. A.; and Olds, J. Reinforcing effect of brain stimulation on runway performance as a function of interval between trials. *J. comp. physiol. Psychol.*, 1960, **53**, 224–28. (115, 121)

Sharpless, S., and Jasper, H. H. Habituation of the arousal reaction. *Brain*, 1956, **79**, 655–78. (104, 163, 164)

Shealy, C. N., and Peele, T. L. Studies on amygdaloid nucleus of cat. *J. Neurophysiol.*, 1957, **20**, 125–39. (193)

Sheffield, F. D., and Roby, T. B. Reward value of non-nutritive sweet taste. *J. comp. physiol. Psychol.*, 1950, **43**, 471–81. (137)

Sheffield, F. D.; Wulff, J. J.; and Backer, R. Reward value of copulation without sex drive reduction. *J. comp. physiol. Psychol.*, 1951, **44**, 3–8. (140, 143)

Sherrington, C. S. In Schafer, *Text-book of Physiology*, 1900, **2**, 782–883. (52)

Sherrington, C. S. *The Integrative Action of the Nervous System.* New Haven, Conn.: Yale University Press, 1906. (178, 442)

Sherrington, C. *The Integrative Action of the Nervous System.* Cambridge: Cambridge University Press, 1947. (405)

Shuford, E. H., Jr. Relative acceptability of sucrose and glucose solutions in the white rat. Doctoral thesis in psychology, University of Illinois, 1955. (29)

Sidman, M.; Brady, J. V.; Boren, J. J.; Conrad, D. G.; and Schulman, A. Reward schedules and behavior maintained by intracranial self-stimulation. *Science*, 1955, **122**, 830–31. (121, 126)

Siegel, A. C. Deprivation of visual form definition in the ring dove. II. Perceptual motor transfer. *J. comp. physiol. Psychol.*, 1953, **46**, 249–52. (94)

Sinclair, D. C., and Hinshaw, J. R. Sensory changes in procaine nerve block. *Brain*, 1950(a), **73**, 224–43. (249)

Sinclair, D. C., and Hinshaw, J. R. Comparison of sensory dissociation produced by procaine and by limb compression. *Brain*, 1950(b), **73**, 480–98. (249)

Sinclair, D. C., and Hinshaw, J. R. Sensory phenomena in experimental nerve block. *Quart. J. exp. Psych.*, 1951, **3**, 49–72. (249)

Sinclair, D. C.; Weddell, G.; and Zander, E. The relationship of cutaneous sensibility to neurohistology in the human pinna. *J. Anat.*, 1952, **86**, 402–10. (227)

Singer, J. E. Sympathetic activation, drugs and fear. *J. comp. physiol. Psychol.*, 1963, **56**, 612–15. (180)

Singh, S. D. Habit strength and drug effects. *J. comp. physiol. Psychol.*, 1964, **58**, 468–69. (90)

Sjöqvist, O. Studies of pain conduction in the trigeminal nerve. *Acta. Psychiat. Scand.*, Suppl., 1938, **17**, 1–139. (271)

Slocum, J.; Bennett, C. L.; and Pool, J. L.

The role of prefrontal lobe surgery as a means of eradicating intractable anxiety. *Am. J. Psychiat.*, 1959, **116**, 222–28. (199, 213)

Smith, M. P., and Capretta, P. J. Effects of drive level and experience on the reward value of saccharine solution. *J comp. physiol. Psychol.*, 1956, **49**, 553–57. (41, 140)

Smith, Moncrieff, and Duffy, Michael. The effects of intragastric injection of various substances on subsequent barpressing. *J. comp. physiol. Psychol.*, 1955, **48**, 387–91. (17, 25)

Smith, O. A. Stimulation of lateral and medial hypothalamus and food intake in the rat. *Anat. Record*, 1956, **124**, 263–64. (28)

Smith, W. K. The results of ablation of the cingular region of the cerebral cortex. *Fed. Proc.*, 1944, **3**, 42–43. (212, 213)

Snider, R. S. Interrelations of cerebellum and brain stem. *Ass. Res. Nerv. Rent. Dis. Proc.*, 1952, **30**, 267–81. (151)

Sokolov, E. N. Neuronal models and the orienting influence. In Brazier, M. A. B. (Ed.), *Central Nervous System and Behavior.* New York: Josiah Macey, Jr. Foundation, 1960, 187–239. (104)

Sollenberger, R. T., and Hamilton, J. M. The effect of testosterone propionate upon the sexual behavior of castrated male guinea pigs. *J. comp. Psychol.*, 1939, **28**, 81–92. (44)

Solley, C. M. Influence of head tilt, body tilt, and practice on reduction of error in perception of the postural vertical. *J. gen. Psychol.*, 1960, **62**, 69–74. (428)

Solomon, R. L., and Wynne, C. C. Traumatic avoidance learning: the principles of anxiety conservation and partial irreversibility. *Psych. Rev.*, 1954, **61**, 353–85. (182)

Soulairac, A., and Soulairac, M. L. Effects de lésions hypothalamiques sour le comportement sexuel et le tractus genital du rat male. *Ann. Endocr. Par.*, 1956, **17**(6), 731–45.

Spencer, W. A., and Kandel, G. Firing level and prepotentials in hippocampal neurons. *Fed. Proc.*, 1961, **19**, 290. (461)

Sperry, R. W. The problem of central nervous reorganization after nerve regeneration and muscle transposition. *Quart. Rev. Biol.*, 1945, **20**, 311–69.

Sperry, R. W. Corpus callosum and interhemispheric transfer in the monkey

(Macaca mulatta). *Anat. Rec.*, 1958, **131**, 297. (95)

Sperry, R. W. Physiological plasticity and brain circuit theory. In Harlow, H. F., and Woolsey, C. N. (Eds.), *Biological and Biochemical Bases of Behavior.* Madison: University of Wisconsin Press, 1958. (355)

Sperry, R. W. Preservation of high order function in isolated somatic cortex in callosum sectioned cats. *J. Neurophysiol.*, 1959, **22**, 78–87. (95)

Sperry, R. W., and Clark, E. Interocular transfer of visual discrimination habits in a teleost fish. *Physiol. Zool.*, 1949, **22**, 372–78. (95, 96)

Sperry, R. W.; Myers, R. E.; and Schrier, A. M. Perceptual capacity of the isolated visual cortex in the cat. *Quart. J. exper. Psychol.*, 1960, **12**, 65–71. (95)

Sperry, R. W.; Stamm, J. S.; and Miner, N. Relearning tests for interocular transfer following division of optic chiasma and corpus callosum in cats. *J. comp. physiol. Psychol.*, 1956, **49**, 529–33. (94, 95)

Spiegel, E. A.; Kletzkin, M.; and Szekely, E. G. Pain reactions upon stimulation of the tectum mesencephali. *J. Neuropath.*, 1954, **13**, 212–20. (186, 191, 272)

Spiegel, E. A.; Miller, H. R.; and Oppenheimer, M. J. Forebrain and rage reactions. *J. Neurophysiol.*, 1940, **3**, 538–48. (211)

Spiegel, E. A., and Wycis, H. T. Physiological and psychological results of thalamotomy. *Proc. Roy. Soc. Med. Suppl.*, 1949, **42**, 84–93. (191, 206)

Spiegel, E. A., and Wycis, H. T. Stimulation of the brain stem and basal ganglia in man. In Sheer, D. E. (Ed.), *Electrical Stimulation of the Brain.* Austin: University of Texas, 1961, 487–98. (191, 262, 272)

Spiegel, E. A.; Wycis, H. T.; Freed, H.; and Orchnick, C. The central mechanism of the emotions (Experiences with circumscribed thalamic lesions). *Am. J. Psychiat.*, 1951, **108**, 426–32. (206)

Spieth, W.; Curtis, J. F.; and Webster, J. C. Responding to one of two simultaneous messages. *J. acoust. Soc. Amer.*, 1954, **26**, 391–96. (166)

Sprague, D. M. Stimulation of reticular formation in intact unanesthetized and decerebrated cats. *Fed. Proc.*, 1953, **12**, 137. (151)

Sprague, J. M.; Chambers, W. W.; and Stellar, E. Attentive, affective and adap-

tive behavior in the cat. *Science*, 1961, **133**, 165–73. (160)

Stamm, J. S. The functions of the median cerebral cortex in maternal behavior of rats. *J. comp. physiol. Psychol.*, 1955, **48**, 347–56. (62)

Stamm, J. S., and Pribram, K. H. Effects of epileptogenic lesions in frontal cortex on learning and retention in monkeys. *J. Neurophysiol.*, 1960, **23**, 552–63. (101)

Stamm, J. S., and Sperry, R. W. Function of corpus callosum in contralateral transfer of somesthetic discrimination in cats. *J. comp. physiol. Psychol.*, 1957, **50**, 138–43. (95)

Starzl, T. E.; Taylor, C. W.; and Magoun, H. W. Collateral afferent excitation of reticular formation of brain stem. *J. Neurophysiol.*, 1951, **14**, 479–96. (150, 151)

Steggerda, F. R. Observations on the water intake in an adult man with dysfunctioning salivary glands. *Am. J. Physiol.*, 1941, **119**, 409. (7)

Steinhausen, W. Über den Nachweis der Bewegung der Cupola in der intakten Bogengansampulle des Labyrinths bei der natürlichen rotatirischen und calorischen Reizung. *Pflüg. Arch. ges. Physiol.*, 1931, **228**, 322–28. (416)

Stellar, E. The physiology of motivation. *Psychol. Rev.*, 1954, **61**, 5–22. (18)

Stellar, E., and McCleary R. A. Food preferences as a function of the method of measurement. *Amer. Psychologist*, 1952, **7**, 256. (20)

Sterman, M. B., and Clemente, C. D. Forebrain inhibitory mechanisms: Synchronization induced by basal forebrain stimulation. *Exp. Neurol*, 1962(a), **6**, 91–102. (157, 158, 159, 161)

Sterman, M. B., and Clemente, C. D. Forebrain inhibitory mechanisms: Sleep patterns induced by basal forebrain stimulation in the behaving cat. *Exp. Neurol.*, 1962(b), **6**, 103–17. (158)

Stone, C. P. The retention of copulatory ability in male rats following castration. *J. comp. Psychol.*, 1927, **7**, 369–87. (44)

Stone, C. P. Sex drive. In Allen, E. (Ed.), *Sex and Internal Secretions.* Baltimore, Md.: Williams and Wilkins Co., 1939, 1213–62. (45, 62)

Streb, J. M., and Smith, K. Frontal lobotomy and the elimination of conditioned anxiety in the rat. *J. comp. physiol. Psychol.*, 1955, **48**, 126–29. (221)

Strughold, H., and Karbe, M. Vitale Färbung des Auges und experimentelle Untersuchung der gefärbten Nervenelemente. *Ztschr. Biol.*, 1925, **83**, 297–308. (229)

Strumwasser, F., and Rosenthal, S. Prolonged and patterned direct extracellular stimulation of single neurons. *Am. J. Physiol.*, 1960, **198**, 405–13. (103)

Stunkard, A. J.; Van Itallie, T. B.; and Reis, B. B. The mechanism of satiety: effect of glucagon on gastric hunger contractions in man. *Proc. Soc. exper. Biol. Med.*, 1955, **89**, 258–61. (4, 26)

Stunkard, A. J., and Wolff, H. G. Correlation of arteriovenous glucose differences, gastric hunger contractions and the experience of hunger in man. *Fed. Proc.*, 1954, **13**, 147. (26)

Svaetichin, G., and MacNichol, E. F., Jr. Retinal mechanisms for chromatic and achromatic vision. *Ann. N.Y. Acad. Sci.*, 1958, **74**, 404. (336)

Swann, H. G. Function of brain in olfaction: Results of destruction of olfactory and other nervous structures upon discrimination of odors. *J. comp. Neurol.*, 1934, **59**, 175–201. (383)

Swann, H. G. The function of the brain in olfaction; the effects of large cortical lesions on olfactory discrimination. *Amer. J. Physiol.*, 1935, **111**, 257–62. (383)

Sweet, W. H. Trigeminal injection with radiographic control, technique and results. *J. Am. Med. Ass.*, 1950, **142**, 392–96. (269)

Sweet, W. H. Pain. In American Physiological Society, *Handbook of Physiology, Section 1; Neurophysiology, Vol. I* (Field, J.; Magoun, H. W.; and Hall, V. E. [Eds.]). Baltimore, Md.: Williams & Wilkins Co., 1959, 459–502. (191, 268, 269)

T

Takeuchi, A., and Takeuchi, N. Active phase of frog's end-plate potential. *J. Neurophysiol.*, 1960, **22**, 395–411. (457)

Tapp, J. T. Reversible cortical depression and avoidance behavior in the rat. *J. comp. physiol. Psychol.*, 1962, **55**, 306–8. (97)

Tasaki, I. Nerve impulses in individual auditory nerve fibers of guinea pig. *J. Neurophysiol.*, 1954, **17**, 97–122. (310)

Tasaki, I. Hearing. *Annual Rev. Physiol.*, 1957, **19**, 417–38. (309, 313)

Tasaki, I., and Davis, H. Electric responses of individual nerve elements in

cochlear nucleus to sound stimulation (guinea pig). *J. Neurophysiol.*, 1955, **18**, 151–58. (310)

Taub, E. Deafferentation. Paper read to conference on Adaptation. M.I.T., June, 1965. (427)

Tauc, L. Site of origin and propagation of spike in the giant neuron of Aplysia. *J. Gen. Physiol.*, 1962, **45**, 1077–97. (377)

Taylor, J. G. The Behavioural Basis of Perception. New Haven and London: Yale University Press, 1962. (441)

Teitelbaum, P. Sensory control of hypothalamic hyperphagia. *J. comp. physiol. Psychol.*, 1955, **48**, 156–63. (27, 34)

Teitelbaum, P. Random and food-directed activity in hyperphagic and normal rats. *J. comp. physiol. Psychol.*, 1957, **50**, 486–90. (27, 28)

Teitelbaum, P. Disturbances in feeding and drinking behavior after hypothalaic lesions. In *Nebraska Symposium on Motivation*. Lincoln: University of Nebraska Press, 1961. (9, 27)

Teitelbaum, P. Appetite. *Proc. Am. phil. Soc.*, 1964, **108**, 464–72. (5, 28)

Teitelbaum, P., and Epstein, A. N. The lateral hypothalamic syndrome. *Psychol. Rev.*, 1962, **69**, 74–90. (9)

Teitelbaum, H., and Milner, P. Activity changes following partial hippocampal lesions in rats. *J. comp. physiol. Psychol.*, 1963, **56**, 284–89. (220)

Terzian, H., and Dalle Ore, G. Syndrome of Klüver and Bucy reproduced in man by bilateral removal of the temporal lobes. *Neurology*, 1955, **5**, 373–80. (60, 212)

Terzuolo, C. A., and Bullock, T. H. Diverse forms of activity in the somata of spontaneous and integrating ganglion cells. *Arch. Ital. Biol.*, 1958, **96**, 117–34. (458)

Terzuolo, C., and Terzian, H. Cerebellar increase of postural tonus after deafferentation and labyrinthectomy. *J. Neurophysiol.*, 1953, **16**, 551–61. (411)

Teuber, H. L. Perception. In American Physiological Society, *Handbook of Physiology, Section 1: Neurophysiology, Vol. III* (Field, J.; Magoun, H. W.; and Hall, V. E. [Eds.]). Baltimore, Md.: Williams & Wilkins Co., 1960. (353, 354)

Thetford, P. E., and Guedry, F. E., Jr. The postural vertical in unilaterally labyrinthectomized individuals. *U.S. Naval Sch. aviat. Med. Res. Rep.*, 1952,

Proj. No. NM 001 063.01.26 (Jt. Rep. No. 26). (428)

Thomas, G. J., and Slotnick, B. Effects of lesions in the cingulum on maze learning and avoidance conditioning in the rat. *J. comp. physiol. Psychol.*, 1962, **55**, 1085–91. (217)

Thomas, G. J., and Slotnick, B. M. Impairment of avoidance responding by lesions in cingulate cortex in rats depends on food drive. *J. comp. physiol. Psychol.*, 1963, **56**, 959–64. (216, 217)

Thomson, C. W.; McGaugh, J. L.; Smith, C. E.; Hudspeth, W. J.; and Westbrook, W. H. Strain differences in the retroactive effects of electroconvulsive shock on maze learning. *Can. J. Psychol.*, 1961, **15**, 69–74. (75)

Thomson, C. W., and Porter, P. B. Need reduction and primary reinforcement: maze learning by sodium-deprived rats for a subthreshold saline reward. *J. comp. physiol. Psychol.*, 1953, **46**, 281–87. (143)

Thompson, J. C., and Blount, R. F. The age of beginning reactivity of the pituitary-adrenocortical system to stress in the mouse. *Endocrinology*, 1954, **54**, 620–26. (67)

Thompson, J. M.; Woolsey, C. N.; and Talbot, S. A. Visual areas I and II of cerebral cortex of rabbit. *J. Neurophysiol.*, 1950, **13**, 277–88. (345)

Thompson, R. Retention of a brightness discrimination following neocortical damage in the rat. *J. comp. physiol. Psychol.*, 1960, **53**, 212–15. (354)

Thompson, R. Thalamic structures critical for retention of an avoidance conditioned response in rats. *J. comp. physiol. Psychol.*, 1963, **56**, 261–67. (218)

Thompson, R., and Dean, W. A. A further study on the retroactive effects of ECS. *J. comp. physiol. Psychol.*, 1955, **48**, 488–91. (75)

Thompson, R., and Pryer, R. S. The effect of anoxia on the retention of a discrimination habit. *J. comp. physiol. Psychol.*, 1956, **49**, 297–300. (75)

Thompson, R. W. Transfer of avoidance learning between normal and functionally decorticate states. *J. comp. physiol. Psychol.*, 1964, **57**, 321–25. (97)

Thorek, M. Experimental investigation of the role of the Leydig, seminiferous and Sertoli cells and effects of testicular transplantation. *Endocrinology*, 1924, **8**, 61–90. (45)

Thorndike, E. L. Expectation. *Psychol. Rev.*, 1946, **53**, 277–81. (112)

Thunberg, T. Untersuchungen über die bei Einer Einzelnen Momentanen Haut Reizung Aufretenden Zwei Stechenden Empfindungen. *Skand. Arch. Physiol.*, 1902, **12**, 399–442. (248)

Thurlow, W. R.; Gross, N. B.; Kemp, E. H.; and Lowy, K. Microelectrode studies of neural auditory activity of cat. I. Inferior colliculus. *J. Neurophysiol.*, 1951, **14**, 289–304. (307, 313)

Tinbergen, N., and Perdeck, A. C. On the stimulus situation releasing the begging response in the newly hatched herring gull chick (Larus argentatus Pont.). *Behavior*, 1950, **3**, 1–39. (30)

Tinker, M. A. Fixation pause duration in reading. *J. Educ. Res.*, 1951, **44**, 471–79. (437)

Tonndorf, J. Time frequency analysis along the partition of cochlear models: a modified place concept. *J. acoust. Soc. Amer.*, 1962, **34**, 1337–50. (304)

Tow, P. M., and Armstrong, R. W. Anterior cingulectomy in schizophrenia and other psychotic disorders; clinical results. *J. ment. Sc.*, 1954, **100**, 46–61. (213)

Tow, P. M., and Whitty, C. W. M. Personality changes after operations on the cingulate gyrus in man. *J. neurol. Neurosurg. Psychiat.*, 1953, **16**, 186–93. (213)

Towbin, E. J. Gastric distension as a factor in the satiation of thirst in esophagustomized dogs. *Am. J. Physiol.*, 1949, **159**, 533–41. (13, 14)

Travis, R. P., and Sparks, D. L. The influence of unilateral and bilateral spreading depression during learning upon subsequent relearning. *J. comp. physiol. Psychol.*, 1963, **56**, 56–59. (97)

Treisman, A. M. Contexual cues in selective listening. *Quart. J. exp. Psychol.*, 1960, **12**, 242–48. (167)

Trevarthen, C. B. Simultaneous learning of two conflicting problems by split brain monkeys. *Am. Psychol.*, 1960, **15**, 485. (95)

Trincker, D. E. W. The transformation of mechanical stimulus into nervous excitation by the labyrinthine receptors. In *Biological Receptor Mechanisms, Symp. Soc. exp. Biol.*, No. 16. Cambridge: Cambridge University Press, 1962. (417)

Trotter, W. The insulation of the nervous

542                                                    PHYSIOLOGICAL PSYCHOLOGY

system. *Brit. med. J.*, 1926, **2**, 103–7. (247)

Trotter, W., and Davis, H. M. Experimental studies on the innervation of the skin. *J. Physiol.*, 1908–9, **38**, 134–246. (247)

Troxler, J. Über das Verschwinden gegebener gegenstände innerhalb unsers gesichtskreises. *Ophthalmologische Bibliothek*, Vol. 2, 51–53, Himly, K., and Schmidt, J. A. (Eds.). Jena, 1804. (351)

Tsang, Y. C. *Hunger motivation in gastrectomized rats. J. comp. Psychol.*, 1938, **26**, 1–17. (6)

Tunturi, A. R. Further afferent connections to the acoustic cortex of the dog. *Am. J. Physiol.*, 1945, **144**, 389–94. (318)

U

Ursin, H. The effect of amygdaloid lesions on flight and defense behavior in cats. *Exp. Neurol.*, 1965(a), **11**, 64–79. (207)

Ursin, H. Effect of amygdaloid lesions on avoidance behavior and visual discrimination in cats. *Exper. Neurol.*, 1965(b), **11**, 298–317. (220)

Ursin, H., and Kaada, B. R. Functional localization within the amygdaloid complex in the cat. *EEG clin. Neurophysiol.*, 1960, **12**, 1–20. (193, 195)

V

Valenstein, E. S.; Riss, W.; and Young, W. C. Experiential and genetic factors in the organization of sexual behavior in male guinea pigs. *J. comp. physiol. Psychol.*, 1955, **48**, 397–403. (57)

Vanderwolf, C. H. Medial thalamic functions in voluntary behavior. *Canad. J. Psychol.*, 1962, **16**, 318–30. (216, 219)

Vanderwolf, C. H. Improved shuttlebox performance following electroconvulsive shock. *J. comp. physiol. Psychol.*, 1963, **56**, 983–86. (216)

Vanderwolf, C. H. Effect of combined medial thalamic and septal lesions on active-avoidance behavior. *J. comp. physiol. Psychol.*, 1964, **58**, 31–37. (219)

Van Deventer, J. M., and Ratner, S. C. Variables affecting the frequency of response of planaria to light. *J. comp. physiol. Psychol.*, 1964, **57**, 407–11. (90)

Vaughn, E., and Fisher, A. E. Male sexual behavior induced by intracranial electrical stimulation. *Science*, 1962, **137**, 758–60. (51)

Victor, M. Observations on the amnestic syndrome in man and its anatomical basis. In Brazier, M.A.B. (Ed.), *Brain Function II: RNA and Brain Function; Memory and Learning.* Berkeley: University of California Press, 1964. (73)

Vilter, V. Recherches biometriques sur l'organization synaptique de la retine humaine. *C. R. Soc. Biol.* (Paris), 1949, **143**, 830–32. (330)

Vince, M. A. Corrective movements in a control task. *Quart. J. exp. Psychol.*, 1948, **1**, 85–103. (400)

Von Economo, C. *Encephalitis Lethargica.* Translated by K. O. Newman, Oxford, 1931. (198)

Von Euler, C., and Holmgren, B. The role of hypothalamo-hypophysial connexions in thyroid secretion. *J. Physiol.*, 1956, **131**, 137–46. (71)

Von Frey, M. Beiträge sur physiologie des Schmerzsinns. *Math-Phys. Cl.*, Ber. Sächs. Gessellsch. Wiss., Leipzig, 1894, **46**, 283–96. (225)

Von Frey, M. Beiträge zur Sinnesphysiologie des Haut. *Math-Phys. Cl.*, Ber. Sächs. Gessellsch. Wiss., Leipzig, 1895, **47**, 166–84. (226, 257)

Von Frey, M. Zur Physiologie der Druckempfindung. *Arch. Neerl. de Physiol.*, La Haye, 1922, **7**, 142–45. (253)

Von Frey, M., and Goldman, A. Der Zeitliche Verlang der Einstellung bei den Druckempfindungen. *Z. Biol.*, 1915, **65**, 183–202. (250)

Von Frey, M., and Kiesow, F. Ueber die Function der Tast Körperchen. *Z. Psychol.*, 1899, **20**, 126–63. (250)

Von Holst, E., and Mittelstedt, H. Das Reafferenzprinzip. *Naturwiss.*, 1950, **37**, 464–76. (433)

Von Monakow, C. Ueber die localisation vez oblongataherden. *Deutsche Zeitschr. & Nervenheilk*, 1908 s., **36**, 124. (271)

Von Skramlick, E. Psychophysiologie der Tastsinne. *Arch. ges. Psychol.*, 1937, Ergänzungsbd. 4. (250)

Voots, R. J. Periodicity pitch and masking in pathologic ears. *J. acoust. Soc. Am.*, 1962, **34**, 739 (A). (304)

Voronin, L. G., and Sokolov, E. N. Cortical mechanisms of the orienting reflex and its relation to the conditioned reflex. In Jasper, H. H., and Smirnov, G. D. (Eds.), The Moscow Colloquim on EEG and Higher Nervous Activity. *EEG clin. Neurophysiol.* Suppl. 13, 1960, 335–46. (163, 169)

# W

Wagner, H. G.; MacNichol, E. F., Jr.; and Wolbarsht, M. L. The response properties of single ganglion cells in the goldfish retina. *J. Gen. Physiol.*, 1960, 43, 45–62. (337)

Wald, G. The photoreceptor process in vision. In American Physiological Society, *Handbook of Physiology*. Vol. I (Field, J.; Magoun, H. W.; and Hall, V. E. [Eds.]). Baltimore, Md.: Williams & Wilkins Co., 1959. (334, 335)

Walker, A. E. Projection of medial geniculate body to cerebral cortex in macaque monkey. *J. Anat.*, 1937, 71, 319–31. (319)

Walker, A. E. Central representation of pain. *Proc. Res. Nerv. Ment. Dis.*, 1943, 23, 63–85. (272, 284, 285, 286)

Walker, A. E.; Thomson, A. F.; and McQueen, J. D. Behavior and the temporal rhinencephalon in the monkey. *Bull., Johns Hopkins Hosp.* 1953, 93, 65–93. (207)

Wall, P. D. Cord cells responding to touch, damage, and temperature of skin. *J. Neurophysiol.*, 1960, 23, 197–210. (224, 230, 242)

Wall, P. D. Two transmission systems for skin sensations. In Rosenblith, W. (Ed.), *Sensory Communication*. New York: M.I.T. Press and John Wiley & Sons, 1961, 475–96. (268, 270)

Wall, P. D., and Cronly-Dillon. J. Pain, itch and vibration. *A.M.A. Arch. Neurol.*, 1960, 2, 365–75. (270)

Wall., P. D., and Taub, A. Four aspects of trigeminal nucleus and a paradox. *J. Neurophysiol.*, 1962, 25, 110–26. (261, 271)

Walls, G. L. The evolutionary history of eye movement. *Vis. Res.*, 1962, 2, 69–80. (435, 438)

Walsh, R. R. Olfactory bulb potentials evoked by electrical stimulation of the contralateral bulb. *Amer. J. Physiol.*, 1959, 196, 327–29. (382)

Walzl, E. M. Representation of cochlea in cerebral cortex. *Laryngoscope*, 1947, 57, 778–87. (320)

Wangensteen, O. H., and Carlson, A. J. Hunger sensations of a patient after total gastrectomy. *Proc. Soc. Exp. Biol. Med.*, 1931, 28, 545–47. (6)

Ward, A. A. The cingular gyrus: area 24. *J. Neurophysiol.*, 1948, 11, 13–23. (212)

Ward, J. W. The influence of posture on responses elicitable from the cortex cer-ebri of cats. *J. Neurophysiology*, 1938, 1, 463–75. (430)

Ward, J. W. Motor phenomena elicited in the unanaesthetized animal by electrical stimulation of the cerebral cortex. *A Res. Nerv. & Ment. Dis. Proc.*, 1952, 30, 223–37. (430)

Warren, D. C., and Scott, H. M. Influence of light on ovulation in the fowl. *J. Exp. Zool.*, 1936, 74, 137–56. (66)

Warren, R. P., and Aronson, Z. R. Sexual behavior in adult male hamsters castrated-adrenalectomized prior to puberty. *J. comp. physiol. Psychol.*, 1957, 50, 475–80. (44)

Waterhouse, I. K. Effects of prefrontal lobotomy on fear and food responses. *J. comp. physiol. Psychol.*, 1957, 50, 81–88. (222)

Webster, J. C., and Thomson, P. O. Responding to both of two overlapping messages. *J. acoust. Soc. Amer.*, 1954, 26, 396–402. (166)

Weddell, G. The pattern of cutaneous innervation in relation to cutaneous sensibility. *J. Anat.*, 1941, 75, 346–67. (248)

Weddell, G., and Miller, S. Cutaneous Sensibility. *Ann. Rev. Physiol.*, 1962, 24, 199–222. (227, 229)

Weddell, G.; Sinclair, D. C.; and Feindel, W. H. Anatomical basis for alternations in quality of pain sensibility. *J. Neurophysiol.*, 1948, 11, 99–109. (247)

Weil, A. A. Ictal depression and anxiety in temporal lobe disorders. *Amer. J. Psychiat.*, 1956, 113, 149–57. (199)

Weiskrantz, L. Behavioral changes associated with ablation of the amygdaloid complex in monkeys. *J. comp. physiol. Psychol.*, 1956, 49, 381–91. (207, 209, 220)

Weiskrantz, L. Impairment of learning and retention following experimental temporal lesions. In Brazier, M.A.B. (Ed.), *Brain Function II: RNA and Brain Function; Memory and Learning.* Berkeley: University of California Press, 1964. (83)

Weiss, P. Self-differentiation of the basic patterns of co-ordination. *Comp. Psychol. Monogr.*, 1941, 17, 1–96. (432)

Weiss, P. Experimental analysis of co-ordination by the disarrangement of central peripheral relations. In *Physiological Mechanisms in Animal Behavior. Symp. Soc. exp. Biol. No. 4.* Cambridge: Cambridge University Press, 1950. (432)

Weiss, S., and Davis, D. Significance of

afferent impulses from skin in mechanism of visceral pain; skin infiltration as
useful therapeutic measure. *Am. J. M.
Sci.*, 1928, **176**, 517–36. (288)

Weitz, J. Vibratory sensitivity as a function of skin temperature. *J. Exp. Psychol.*, 1941, **28**, 21–36. (254, 256)

Wenzel, B. M. Techniques in olfactometry: a critical review of the last one
hundred years. *Psych. Bull.*, 1948, **45**,
231–47. (383, 384)

Wenzel, B. M. Olfactometric method utilizing natural breathing in an odor-free
"environment." *Science*, 1955, **121**,
802–03. (384)

Westbrook, W. H., and McGaugh, J. L.
Drug facilitation of latent learning, *Psy-
chopharmacologia*, 1964, **5**, 440–46.
(80)

Westheimer, G. Mechanism of saccadic
eye movement. *Arch. Ophthal.*, 1954,
**52**, 710–24. (435)

Westheimer, G., and Mitchell, A. M. Eye
movement responses to convergence
stimuli. *Arch. Ophthal.*, 1956, **55**, 848–
56. (438)

Whalen, R. E. Effects of mounting without intromission and intromission without ejaculation on sexual behavior and
maze learning. *J. comp. physiol. Psychol.*, 1961, **54**, 409–15. (141)

Whalen, R. E. The initiation of mating
in naive female cats. *Anim. Behav.*,
1963, **11**, 461–63. (58)

Wheatley, M. D. The hypothalamus and
affective behavior in cats. *Arch. Neurol.
Psychiat.* Chicago, 1944, **52**, 296–316.
(205, 211)

White, J. C. Autonomic discharges from
stimulation of the hypothalamus in
man. *Res. Publ. An. nerv. ment. Dis.*,
1940, **20**, 854–63. (192)

White, J. C. Sensory innervation of viscera; studies on visceral afferent neurons in man based on neurosurgical
procedures for relief of intractable pain.
*Res. Publ. Ass. nerv. ment. Dis.*, 1943,
**23**, 373–90. (283)

White, J. C., and Sweet, W. H. Pain: its
mechanisms and neurosurgical control.
Springfield: Charles C. Thomas, 1955.
(286)

Whitlock, D. G., and Perl, E. R. Afferent
projections through ventrolateral funiculi to thalamus of cat. *J. Neurophysiol.*, 1959, **22**, 133–48. (262)

Whitlock, D. G., and Perl, E. R. Thalamus projections of spinalthalamic
pathways in monkey. *Exp. Neurol.*,
1961, **3**, 240–55. (259, 262)

Whitty, C. W. M. Effects of anterior
cingulectomy in man. *Proc. Roy. Soc.
Med.*, 1955, **48**, 463–69. (213)

Wiesner, B. P., and Sheard, N. M. *Maternal Behavior in the Rat.* Edinburgh:
Oliver, 1933. (62)

Wikler, A. Pharmacological dissociation
of behavior and EEG sleep patterns in
dogs. *Proc. Soc. exp. Biol. Med.*, 1952,
**79**, 261–65. (147)

Wilkie, D. R. Physiology of voluntary
muscle. *Brit. med. Bull.*, 1956, **12**,
177–88. (391)

Williams, D. The structure of emotions
reflected in epileptic experiences. *Brain*,
1956, **79**, 29–67. (199)

Williams, D. R., and Teitelbaum, P.
Some observations on the starvation resulting from lateral hypothalamic lesions. *J. comp. physiol. Psychol.*, 1959,
**52**, 458–65. (9)

Wilska, A. Eine Methode zu Bestimmung
der Horschwellenamplituden der Trom-
melfells bei verschiedenen Frequenzen.
*Skand. Arch. Physiol.*, 1935, 161–65.
(290)

Wing, M. E. The response of the otolith
organs to tilt. *Acta. oto-laryngol.*, 1963,
**56**, 537–45. (418)

Witschi, E. Seasonal sex characters in
birds and their hormonal control. *Wilson Bull.*, 1935, **47**, 177–88. (62, 67)

Witt, I., and Hensel, H. Afferente Impulse aus der Extremitätenhaut der
Katze bei Thermischer und Mechan-
ischer Reizung. *Pflüg. Arch. ges. Physiol.*, 1959, **268**, 582–96. (240)

Wolf, G. Effect of dorsolateral hypothalamic lesions on sodium appetite elicited by desoxycorticosterone and by
acute hyponatremia. *J. comp. physiol.
Psychol.*, 1964, **58**, 396–402. (25, 39)

Wolff, S., and Hardy, J. D. Studies on
pain. Observations on pain due to local
cooling and on factors involved in the
"cold pressor" effect. *J. Clin. Invest.*,
1941, **20**, 521–33. (239, 289)

Wolff, S., and Wolff, H. G. *Human Gastric Function.* New York: Oxford University Press, 1947. (179)

Wolter, J. R. Über Endigungen Zentrifu-
galer Nervenfasern in der Menschlichen
Netzhaut. V. *Graefes Arch. Opthal.*,
1957, **158**, 524–31. (356)

Wood, C. D. Behavioral changes following discrete lesions of temporal lobe
structures. *Neurology*, 1958, **8**, 215–
220. (193, 207, 208)

Woods, J. W. "Taming" of the wild
Norway rat by rhinencephalic lesions.

*Nature* (London), 1956, **178**, 869. (207)

Woodworth, R. S., and Sherrington, C. S. A pseudo-affective reflex and its spinal path. *J. Physiol.*, 1904, **31**, 234–43. (201)

Woollard, H. H.; Roberts, J. E. H.; and Carmichael, E. A. Inquiry into referred pain. *Lancet*, 1932, **222**, 337–38. (288)

Woolley, D. E.; Rosenzweig, M. R.; Krech, D.; Bennett, E. L.; and Thomas, P. S. Strain and sex differences in threshold and pattern of electroshock convulsions in rats. *Physiologist*, 1960, **3**, 182. (76)

Woolsey, C. N. Organization of cortical auditory system. In: Rosenblith, W. A. (Ed.), *Sensory Communication*, Cambridge: M.I.T. Press, 1961. (317, 318)

Woolsey, C. N., and Walzl, E. M. Topical projection of nerve fibers from local regions of the cochlea to the cerebral cortex of the cat. *Bull. Johns Hopkins Hosp.*, 1942, **71**, 315–44. (316)

Worden, F. G., and Marsh, J. T. Amplitude changes of auditory potentials evoked at cochlear nucleus during acoustic habituation. *EEG clin. Neurophysiol.*, 1963, **15**, 866–81. (174)

Wynne, C. C., and Solomon, R. L. Traumatic avoidance learning: acquisition and extinction in dogs deprived of normal peripheral autonomic function. *Genet. psychol. Monogr.*, 1955, **52**, 241–84. (181)

Wyrwicka, W., and Dobrzecka, C. Relationship between feeding and satiation centers of the hypothalamus. *Science*, 1960, **123**, 805–6. (28)

Wyrwicka, W.; Dobrzecka, C.; and Tarnecki, R. On the instrumental conditioned reaction evoked by electrical stimulation of the hypothalamus. *Science*, 1959, **130**, 336–37. (10)

**Y**

Yamamoto, C., and Iwama, K. Arousal reaction of the olfactory bulb. *Jap. J. Physiol.*, 1961, **11**, 335–45. (382)

Yamamoto, S.; Sugihara, S.; and Kuru, M. Microelectrode studies of sensory afferents in the posterior funiculus of the cat. *Jap. J. Physiol.*, 1956, **6**, 68–85. (265)

Yensen, R. Some factors affecting taste sensitivity in man: II. Depletion of body salt. *Quart. J. exp. Psychol.*, 1959, **11**, 230–38. (370)

Young, P. T. Studies of food preference,

appetite and dietary habit. IX. Palatability versus appetite as determinants of the critical concentrations of sucrose and sodium chloride. *Comp. Psych. Monogr.*, 1949, **19**, (No. 5), 45–74. (20)

Young, P. T., and Greene, J. T. The quantity of food ingested as a measure of relative acceptability. *J. comp. physiol. Psychol.*, 1953, **46**, 288–94. (40)

Young, W. C.; Goy, R. W.; and Phoenix, C. H. Hormones and sexual behavior. *Science*, 1964, **143**, 212–18. (55)

**Z**

Zaus, E. A. Discussion of paper by Austin and Steggerda. *Illinois Med. J.*, 1936, **69**, 127. (7)

Zeman, W., and King, F. A. Tumors of the septum pellucidum and adjacent structures with abnormal affective behavior: An anterior midline structure syndrome. *J. nerv. ment. Dis.*, 1958, **127**, 490–502. (199)

Zigler, M. J., and Holway, A. H. Differential sensitivity as determined by amount of olfactory substance. *J. General Psych.*, 1935, **12**, 372–82. (377)

Zimbardo, P. G. The effects of early avoidance training and rearing conditions upon the sexual behavior of the male rat. *J. comp. physiol. Psychol.*, 1958, **51**, 764–69. (57)

Zotterman, Y. Studies in the peripheral nervous mechanism of pain. *Acta. Med. Scand.*, 1933, **80**, 185–242. (253)

Zotterman, Y. Specific action potentials in the lingual nerve of the cat. *Skand. Arch. Physiol.*, 1936, **75**, 106. (230, 233)

Zotterman, Y. Touch, pain and tickling; an electrophysiological investigation on cutaneous sensory nerves. *J. Physiol.*, 1939, **95**, 1–28. (230, 253)

Zotterman, Y. Species differences in the water taste. *Acta. Physiol. Scand.*, 1956, **37**, 60–70. (19)

Zotterman, Y. Thermal sensations. American Physiological Society, *Handbook of Physiology, Section 1; Neurophysiology, Vol. I* (Field, J.; Magoun, H. W.; and Hall, V. E. [Eds.]). Baltimore, Md.: Williams & Wilkins Co., 1959, 431–58. (230, 245, 252)

Zubek, J. P. Studies on somesthesis. I. Role of the somesthetic cortex in roughness discrimination in the rat. *J. comp. physiol. Psychol.*, 1951, **44**, 339–53. (281)

Zubek, J. P. Studies in somesthesis. II.

Role of somatic sensory areas I and II in roughness discrimination in cat. *J. Neurophysiol.*, 1952, **15**, 401–8. (281)

Zubek, J. P. Studies in somesthesis. IV. Role of somatic areas I and II in tactual "from" discrimination in the rat. *J. comp. physiol. Psychol.*, 1952, **45**, 438–42. (281)

Zwaardemaker, H. *L'odorat*. Paris: Doin, 1925. (378, 383, 385)

# INDEX

*This book has been set in 10 point and 9 point*
*Electra, leaded 2 points. The chapter number is*
*a 30 point Caslon Bold Condensed figure; the*
*chapter title is set in 14 point Caslon No. 3 caps.*
*The size of the type page is 27 by 46½ picas.*